THE
TREDEGAR COMPANY

One of the South Wales Coalfield's 'Big Three'

Lightmoor Press

Lightmoor Press is an imprint of
Black Dwarf Lightmoor Publications Limited
144b Lydney Industrial Estate, Harbour Road
Lydney, Gloucestershire, GL15 4EJ

Printed and bound in Poland by www.lfbookservices.co.uk

THE
TREDEGAR
COMPANY
One of the
South Wales Coalfield's
'Big Three'

Oakdale Colliery, Blackwood

Above & opposite: Two views of Oakdale Colliery.

both Pope/Parkhouse Archive

Leslie M. Shore

General Offices & Pits, Tredegar. 1314.

The Tredegar Offices of the Tredegar Iron & Coal Company were opened not long after 1900 when building construction began. The offices accommodated the colliery operations' senior managers, and the accountancy, commercial, administration, and some technical staff. Coal orders from Great Britain and across the world were received by the commercial section. Railway coal traffic was also organised at the offices. The façade of the building survives to some extent unlike both the railway line and Whitworth Colliery, which can be seen in the background.   *Pope/Parkhouse Archive*

CONTENTS

Tredegar Station of the London & North Western Railway. Coal and passenger traffic made for a busy working day for the station's staff.

In memory of my mother-in-law

Delsie May (née Morgan) Edwards

Rich in kindness and ever generous

Born Blackwood, Gwent 1921
Lived at Wyllie Village for two decades
Died Barrow-in-Furness 2017

Markham Colliery and Valley

Markham Colliery, on the right, perched on the west-facing hillside of Cefn Manmoel, was an initiative of Sir Alfred Markham, a Derbyshire industrialist. He was a notable director in the history of the Tredegar Iron & Coal Company. The colliery's railway traffic was managed by the Great Western Railway. On the left can be seen a section of the Sirhowy Valley line of the London & North Western Railway. In this photograph, Mynydd Bedwellty is the dominant feature of the valley with at its foot, just off centre to the right, the terrace housing of Hollybush.   *Pope/Parkhouse Archive*

INTRODUCTION & ACKNOWLEDGEMENTS

With hindsight, notable events in my life were significant also as preludes to my writing this history of the Tredegar Company and its legacy as part of the National Coal Board. On Saturday, the 18th March 1967, at a St. Patrick Day's dance organised by the New Tredegar branch of the Methodist Association of Youth Clubs, I met Pamela Edwards for the first time. Thus, a New Tredegar, Rhymney Valley, youth met a young woman from Wyllie Village, Sirhowy Valley. On Saturday the 12th August 1972, we married at St. Paul's Church, Grangetown, in Cardiff. My in-laws became Albert John (Jack) and Delsie Edwards. For decades afterwards, in pursuit of my career as a professional mechanical engineer, Pamela and I moved to locations all over Great Britain. The support that the Edwards gave us eased the troubles of house moves, and enhanced life where the Shore family settled. The Edwards's homes, at Gordon Road, Blackwood, and later Elim Way, Pontllanfraith, became bases for us to keep in touch with life in the valleys. However, crucially for writing this history, after March 1967, I became aware of some items of my father-in-law's work as a senior project manager with the National Coal Board. I learnt also that he had links with the Tredegar Iron & Coal Company, and the prized Oakdale Colliery. For thirty years he lived in Wyllie Village.

On the 28th April 2008, Jack Edwards died at Furness General Hospital, Barrow-in-Furness, aged eighty-seven. He had been an inveterate orderly saver of craftsman's tools and materials, household bills and papers, a store of items we viewed as junk, and an incomplete handwritten memoir. Amongst his junk was a cardboard box that contained Tredegar Iron & Coal Company and National Coal Board documents and other such information. Initially I thought that I could use some of the information in the box to write an article about the Tredegar Company for publication in Black Dwarf Lightmoor's *Archive*. Little did I realise in early 2013 that as I foraged around elsewhere in South Wales for other information to write the article that a sequel to my *Peerless Powell Duffryn of the South Wales Coalfield* published in 2012 would be the result.

Once again I owe many people gratitude for the help they gave me that enabled me to produce this work. Regarding assistance with my research, I offer thanks to the following people met in chronological order: Nichola Farr, Libraries Stack & Stock Support Unit, Cardiff Libraries; Stephen Kings, Bargoed Library, and Carol White and Cheryl Taylor, Blackwood Library, Caerphilly County Borough Council; staff at Central Library, Newport City Council; staff at Glamorgan Archives; Howard Humphries, Gwent Archives; Alison Harvey, Special Collections and Archives, Arts and Social Studies Library, Cardiff University; Luisa Money, Ulverston Library, Cumbria County Council; Dr Tony Jukes; Elaine Essery; Professor Philip Hayman; Hilda Kaune and Francis Perry, Institute of Materials, Minerals and Mining; Carol Morgan, Institution of Civil Engineers; Professor John Punter; Rhodri Shore, Llyfrgell Genedlaethol Cymru/The National Library of Wales; Miss Pamela Clark, Royal Archives, Windsor Castle; Dr Bryan Lawton; Dr Michael Bailey; and Brian Davies.

Concerning sourcing illustrations for the work I record my appreciation to: Jon Tallis for the considerable effort and trouble he went to make available to Black Dwarf Lightmoor for copying photographs from A. S. Tallis's album; Mark Barrett, Special Collections and Archives, Arts and Social Studies Library, Cardiff University; Tony Hopkins, Gwent Archives; Ceri Thompson, Curator, Big Pit, National Museum of Wales; the artist Chris Griffin; Philip Hatfield Photography; Oliver Blackmore, Newport Museum and Art Gallery, Newport City Council; Michael McLaren QC; Frances Llewellyn, Bodnant Gardens, National Trust; Sophia Brothers, Science & Society Picture Library; Annette Jones, Tredegar Town Council; Councillor Phillip Prosser, Tredegar History and Archive Society; Clare Turgoose, Tredegar House, National Trust; and Tony Rogers and Tony Hallam.

In March 2013, the late Delsie Edwards, then aged ninety-two, relocated from Pontllanfraith, Sirhowy Valley, to a care home in Dalton-in-Furness. My visits to South Wales became fewer and it became less easy for me to make local 'field' checks. I was fortunate in that Paul Jones of Pontlottyn, who was born at Tredegar, was prepared to carry out such checks for me. Some of my requests were vague, but his resourcefulness yielded helpful answers. I offer Barbara Jones an apology for diverting Paul's attention away from any home priorities.

The contributions made to my work by men who once worked in the coal industry were of course invaluable. My cousin, Clive Shore, the last mechanic raised up Elliot Colliery, put me in contact with Des Caddy, the last manager of Oakdale Colliery. Des Caddy read research drafts of at least the coal mining aspects and gave me constructive comments. James Sorbie, whose management career in the coal mining industry began in Scotland, read my draft of the final chapter and his observations were enlightening. Philip Price of Bargoed responded to queries by sharing with me some of his knowledge both as a miner and as a safety manager in tunnelling. Late in my drafting work, thanks to Ceri Thompson, I received insightful comments about my final chapter from the late Arthur Lewis OBE who once served as colliery manager at Six Bells. The keen help I received from the late Roy Pickford of Abertillery and David Morgan of Oakdale was another special experience. As National Coal Board engineers both men knew my father-in-law.

However, after preparing this history about the Tredegar Company for publication, I must identify five people for especial praise due to the sustained and profound nature of their support. The meticulous Ken Weaver of Barrow-in-Furness from the outset reviewed what I call research drafts, did internet searches, and engaged me in lively discussions that enabled me to clarify some of my thoughts. Professor Trevor Boyns, Cardiff Business School, read the whole of the first draft of a book in chapter form and was timely returning his contributions, which was an extraordinary feat since he was also managing a considerable change in his academic duties. The ever courteous Emyr Evans, Llyfrgell Genedlaethol Cymru/The National Library of Wales, gave me steadfast research support throughout. His organisation of source material for me to read for a week of research at Aberystwyth made for very productive visit. Ian Pope constantly encouraged me during the research and writing stages. Without him giving me access to Black Dwarf Lightmoor's library of photographs the book would have been a meagre set of illustrations due to the cumulative cost of fees charged by many public bodies for use of illustrations in their keeping. Moreover, I believe that Ian's book layout work presents my text in an impressive fashion. However, it is with great sadness that I must record my respect for his late wife, Clare. I will miss her help and good humour as she dealt with the administrative matters associated with my previous publications. Last, having revealed that this book was one result of my romance with Pamela, I reserve for her my greatest thanks. Her support and care was unstinting whilst I selfishly engrossed myself in research and writing.

However, in preparing another work of industrial history I continued to learn that the developing text had to be viewed as a provisional statement. Indeed, there remains the possibility that overlooked in some household is a collection of papers and notes like those once kept by Jack Edwards. Such collections might contain information that can further advance an understanding of the people and affairs of both the Tredegar Company and the National Coal Board in the territory dealt with in what follows. Placing such a thought aside, I hope though that the care taken by people to supply me with authentic information has been accurately represented in the book. As a consequence, the responsibility for factual errors and mistakes rests with me.

Leslie Shore, Ulverston, February 2017

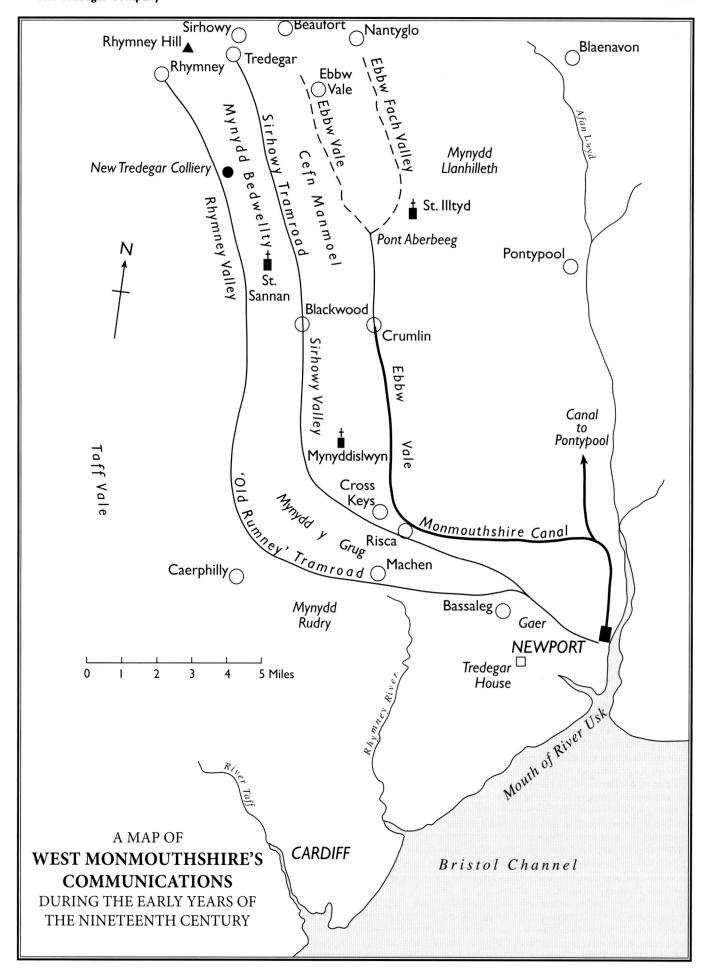

Sirhowy

Rhymney Hill ▲

Rhymney

Tredegar

Beaufort

Nantyglo

Blaenavon

Ebbw Vale

Ebbw Fach Valley

Afan Llwyd

Mynydd Llanhilleth

Mynydd Bedwellty Tramroad

Sirhowy Tramroad

Cefn Manmoel

Ebbw Vale

New Tredegar Colliery ●

† St. Illtyd

Pont Aberbeeg

Pontypool

N

Rhymney Valley

† St. Sannan

Blackwood

Crumlin

Sirhowy Valley

Ebbw Vale

Canal to Pontypool

Taff Vale

† Mynyddislwyn

Cross Keys

Mynydd y Grug

Risca

Machen

Monmouthshire Canal

Caerphilly

'Old Rumney' Tramroad

Mynydd Rudry

Bassaleg

Gaer

NEWPORT □

Tredegar House

Rhymney River

Mouth of River Usk

0 1 2 3 4 5 Miles

River Taff

CARDIFF

A MAP OF
**WEST MONMOUTHSHIRE'S
COMMUNICATIONS**
DURING THE EARLY YEARS OF
THE NINETEENTH CENTURY

Bristol Channel

Chapter One
COAL, MINE and IRON

The elegant Victorian clock tower that adorns the centre of Tredegar recalls wealth earned from making iron and mining coal. The town, a chief one in the old county of Monmouthshire, sits at the head of the Sirhowy Valley where an outcropping swathe of coal and clay ironstone locates a stretch of the northern edge of the South Wales Coalfield. Crucially, this geological feature caused the pioneering of industrial-scale iron making in the locality in 1778 with the inception of the Sirhowy Furnace. The actions of the furnace owners, notable among them being Thomas Atkinson and William Barrow, and the growth of a Monmouthshire canal system served by tramways, launched the Sirhowy Valley's Industrial Revolution.

The pioneers and their successors operated on the Tredegar Estate, which was owned by generations of Morgans who resided at Tredegar House that stands on the outskirts of the city of Newport.[1] In 1800, a partnership, led by Penydarren Ironworks' Samuel Homfray and involving Richard Fothergill and Matthew Monkhouse, leased from Sir Charles Gould Morgan an extensive tract of the Tredegar Estate, which included a northern corner of the Rhymney Valley. As a result, the three partners opened the Tredegar Ironworks south of the Sirhowy Furnace. Coal, limestone and mine – the local term for clay ironstone, fed a greater number of furnaces. Due to the partners' enterprise, people from afar were attracted to the head of the Sirhowy Valley for work. A rapid house building activity followed that founded the town of Tredegar.

Although Tredegar Ironworks opened later than both the ironworks at Dowlais (1759) in the former county of Glamorgan, and Blaenavon (1787) in Monmouthshire, under Samuel Homfray Jnr, it also earned the epithet of being 'Great'. Such a reputation for the Tredegar Ironworks was mainly due to rolling iron rail, beginning around the 1830s, for railway companies. The Railway Age enabled the Tredegar Ironworks together with its Heads of Valleys rivals to become the foremost producers of iron in the world. The South Wales 'Iron Belt' was aptly named.

As an aside to iron making, in 1817 the Tredegar Ironworks began selling 'Tredegar coal' that was shipped from Newport. Then, from the 1840s onwards, merchant shipowners prized the qualities of Tredegar coal as a fuel for steam engine ship propulsion. At sometime during the early decades of the nineteenth century, the business was informally called the Tredegar Company.

At the start of the 1870s, the Tredegar Iron Company's ironworks and coal reserves came under the control of investors who formed the Tredegar Iron and Coal Company. Among the founding directors, the names of Benjamin Whitworth MP and Henry Pochin MP were exalted. Under the general management direction of James Colquhoun, two collieries, Whitworth and Pochin, were sunk, and later the company ventured into steelmaking.

When the twentieth century began, under the chairmanship of Charles McLaren, who became the first Baron Aberconway, the Tredegar Company 'centred' itself upon coal mining. Most of the company's coal was exported to meet a global demand for Welsh steam coal to power merchant ships, and railway locomotives. McLaren Colliery, in Cwm Tysswg, Rhymney Valley, was the first colliery sunk under his chairmanship. Alfred Tallis, the company's general manager of collieries, oversaw the opening of three further deep-mine collieries beginning with Oakdale Colliery, situated at the centre of the length of the Sirhowy Valley, and near the town of Blackwood. An initiative by a director of the company, Sir Arthur Markham MP, led to a mining lease being negotiated to sink Markham Colliery in a gap between the coal workings of Pochin Colliery and Oakdale Colliery. The company's coal output in the first decades of the

twentieth century aided the inexorable rise of the South Wales Coalfield's output to a peak in 1913. The company also built model villages to house workers in the vicinity of McLaren, Oakdale, and Markham collieries.

A gradual weakening in the demand for South Wales coal after the First World War gave way to a marked slump in trade. The slump was due in part to worldwide economic and political forces. However, from the second decade of the twentieth century onwards coal was substituted with diesel oil to power ships. Endemic poor industrial relations further harmed the operation of South Wales coal companies. Nevertheless, in the mid-1920s, the Tredegar Company opened what would be its last colliery, Wyllie, and built an attendant village. However, the 1930s saw mass unemployment, which bred despair not least among communities associated with the Tredegar Iron and Coal Company. By the end of the 1920s, many South Wales people believed that socialism offered the way to a better life.

The 'Bloodless Revolution' of 1945-1950 enabled a Labour Government to transfer the ownership of coal companies to a body of the state, the National Coal Board. The nationalisation of the coal industry made buoyant the hopes of people living in the towns and villages associated with this industry during the 1950s and 1960s. Moreover, during the 1970s, a leap in crude oil prices appeared favourable to coal. However, the nation's regard for a once great industry waned partly due to campaigns of confrontation by the National Union of Miners particularly in the 1980s. Subsequently, the vote of the British electorate swung against Socialist industrial policies.

In the 1980s, local deep-mining ended due to the unprofitable cost of producing coal from the denuded seams of the Sirhowy Valley. The abrupt closure of Oakdale Colliery in 1989 marked the end of two centuries of industrial activity in the valley. Today the landscape serves to connect with that period of history.

Tredegar Estate

The Sirhowy River rises on gently angled slopes of limestone that form Mynydd Llangynidr, from the heights of where can be seen the old counties of Brecon, to the north, and Monmouth in the southern compass. The river's course poured southward from Mynydd Llangynidr to erode the rocks of the Coal Measures.

The town of Tredegar grew up more or less on the 1,000 foot contour, and was set in what has been described as a capacious amphitheatre. The mound-like Rhymney Hill overlooks the town to the west. Rhymney Hill is the northern top of the long broad ridge of Mynydd Bedwellty, which separates the Sirhowy Valley from the Rhymney Valley to the west. The reclining character of the hillside seen eastwards from Tredegar begins to gain bulk and presence as Cefn Manmoel further south. The neighbouring eastern valley, the Ebbw Vale, can be viewed from the summit of Cefn Manmoel. The course of the River Sirhowy ran southward to join the River Ebbw that flows to enter the River Usk south of Newport.

For some period before 1768, in the vicinity of where Tredegar was later built, 'a fine coal cliff' was mined in a manner later termed as 'patching'.[2] The mined land lay in the northern part of the Parish of Bedwellty. The land owners, the Morgan family of Tredegar, lived in a fifteenth century house, Tredegar House, which was surrounded by the vast Tredegar Park.

The Morgans 'claimed descent from the great Welsh princely families but in reality their origins were probably more humble'.[3] By the eighteenth century, the Morgans of Tredegar possibly represented the superior of around ten branches of a family claiming distinguished Welsh roots. The disjointed succession line of the Morgans of Tredegar has relevance for this history.

Following the death of Thomas Morgan of Tredegar in 1699, John Morgan of Machen (born 1672) gained also the Tredegar title. He held to using 'Machen' to distinguish himself from other branches of Morgans, but was also referred to as John Morgan the Merchant of London due to his business activities. In 1706, John Morgan of Machen acquired the Ruperra estate that lay adjacent to the Manor of Machen. He also engaged in industrial ventures, one of which was a forge set in Tredegar Park. His ventures also included an iron smelting furnace at Caerphilly and a forge at Machen. The then small township of Caerphilly stood eight miles westward of Tredegar House in the Rhymney Valley. The hamlet of Machen occupied a gorge carrying the Rhymney River eastward from Caerphilly. The river enters the Bristol Channel two miles east of the centre of the city of Cardiff.

Between 1714 and 1718, under John Morgan of Machen's stewardship, the Edney Gates were erected at Tredegar House. The gates demonstrated the art and skills of Bristol gatesmiths, the brothers William and Simon Edney, for working wrought iron. By the start of the eighteenth century, Bristol was a centre for trade in iron, which included pig iron and bars. Earlier, during the seventeenth century, Bristol merchants were customers for finished iron goods due to there being 'a considerable traffic in pig iron, between the furnaces of the Forest of Dean and the forges of upper Severn and west Midlands'.[4] However, Bristol's trade in iron, during the eighteenth century, stretched way beyond the ironmasters of the River Severn to at least the ironmaking Furness district of Lancashire (now in Cumbria).

John Morgan of Machen had two sons, William and Thomas. Following his death in 1719, his inheritance was shared in a way that also saw William Morgan take the Tredegar title and his brother, Thomas, the Ruperra title. In 1724, William Morgan of Tredegar married Lady Rachel Cavendish, daughter of the 2nd Duke of Devonshire. The following year the social status of the Morgan family was elevated due to William being made a Knight of the Bath.

Sir William Morgan died aged thirty in 1731. Lady Rachel Morgan took charge of the Tredegar Estate. An agent administered her inheritance. The agent's journey on horseback to meet farm tenants at the northern end of the Sirhowy Valley entailed a near forty mile round trip from Tredegar House. An outward course for the journey ran along a mountain ridge on the western side of the Sirhowy Valley. The ridge's northern part is known as Mynydd Bedwellty. Such an outward course, to the valley's head, involved a ten hours' saddle ride. Halfway along the outward course stands the ancient Bedwellty Parish Church of St. Sannan. A nearby farmstead owned by the Tredegar Estate may have been used by the agent for an overnight stay.

The final part of the journey northwards involved riding over a bleak upland, Bedwellty Common, which was prone to poor weather. Clear weather though gave the agent, as Rhymney Hill neared, a chance to be beguiled by the lofty peaks of the Brecon Beacons to the north. He may have also glanced westwards down Cwm Tyssyg, a branch of the Rhymney Valley, that was owned by the Tredegar Estate. The agent would have frowned at the sight of the poor pasture and bog of Cwm Tyssyg since they earned a pittance. A dip was met in the ridge a short ride after seeing Cwm Tyssyg that many locals today call Cefn Golau. The Ordnance Survey names the slope to Rhymney Hill, which is north of the dip, as Cefn Golau – Hill of Light. Nevertheless, the dip served to guide a rider to an easterly descent into the head of the Sirhowy Valley.

The farm tenants at the head of the Sirhowy Valley endured a frugal life, and paid meagre rents to the Tredegar Estate. The estate's principal agent probably delegated the task of rent collection to an assistant. He could then devote time to more valuable matters like keeping abreast of news about the business affairs of other branches of the Morgan family.

In 1757, Thomas Morgan of Ruperra was party to an agreement with Herbert, Viscount Windsor, to enable the working of 'coal, iron ore, limestone, sandstone, and fire-clay' in the Parish of 'Merthir Tidfil' (sic) at the head of the Taff Vale. The agreement led to the establishment, in 1759, of an iron smelting furnace near a brook known as Dowlais. After 1767, with the appointment of John Guest as works manager, the Merthyr Tydfil iron making venture would grow to become the Dowlais Ironworks.[5] Around two decades later, another iron making venture began near to the Dowlais furnaces, Penydarren, which was run by the Homfrays.

Possibly it was the geological knowledge of Abergavenny coal prospectors that saw coal mining start at the head of the Sirhowy Valley. At the outset of the eighteenth century, 'men from Abergavenny' became 'increasingly involved' in the coal trade of Monmouthshire.[6]

In 1768, a map was issued showing coal and iron scourings at the head of the Sirhowy Valley. The map shows that a portion of an agricultural scene had been spoiled for a number of years.[7] An 'old scoury' pond fed ditches that eroded ground to give miners access to mineral seams. Wasted coal and clay ironstone oozed into water ditches that fed the river. Clear stream water from Mynydd Llangynidr met the ditch water and so the River Sirhowy was dyed black. According to John Evans, 'much of the coal was sold locally and in the towns nearby'.[8]

After 1763, the title of the Tredegar Estate was disputed. That year, Lady Rachel Morgan's only bachelor son died. She fought 'unsuccessfully against her brother-in-law, Thomas Morgan [of Ruperra], for nineteen years in the Court of Chancery, to gain the estate for her surviving daughter'.[9] Regardless of the court case, an ironmaking venture was sanctioned by the Tredegar Estate on the east bank of the River Sirhowy opposite the scoured landscape of 1768.

Sirhowy Furnace

In 1778, as a prelude to the venture, a number of partners leased land from the Tredegar Estate. The partners were: Charles Henry Burgh of the town of Monmouth; John Sealy and Bolton Hudson, City of London, grocers and teamen co-partners; William Barrow, City of London, grocer and teaman; and Thomas Atkinson late of South Carolina, North America, and 'now of' Skipton, Yorkshire, a merchant.[10] Maybe crucially it seems that Atkinson 'had been producing iron near Ulverston', then in the county of Lancashire [now Cumbria].[11]

In the eighteenth century ironmaking charcoal-fired furnaces thrived in the Furness district where Ulverston lay. Once coal, as coke, was a proven substitute fuel for charcoal in an iron furnace's charge, some ironmasters moved to the northern outcrop of the South Wales Coalfield. Among the partners, Atkinson and William Barrow took on the practical duties of managing what became known as the Sirhowy Furnace, and 'lived in two small cottages near the Furnace yard'.[12] The furnace lay near the 'confluence of the Nant Melin and the River Sirhowy'.

The Sirhowy Furnace had ready access to mine, later called clay ironstone, that contained maybe around twenty-five per cent iron. One way in which clay ironstone was sourced was by digging through mud left after scouring. The working of 'patches', to get coal and mine, progressed to higher locations on the surrounding hillsides. Subsequently, coal, clay ironstone, and a mineral called 'blackband' was mined by the driving of levels, drift mines as they are sometimes called, into the hillsides.[13] Quarried limestone, for use as a furnace flux, was sourced north of the furnace, which was a cube-like structure, and built from stone picked from the river. 'The yield of iron was about four tons a week at first, but this amount was gradually raised to more than six tons in a couple of years'.[14] Mules were used to transport pig iron made to 'Llanelly [a forge five miles west of Abergavenny], Merthyr, and other destinations'.[15]

Since the area around the furnace was sparsely populated, labour had to be engaged from elsewhere. The Forest of Dean was a recruiting place for furnacemen. However, miners' numbers were 'the majority', and they were mainly south Walians. Arthur Gray-Jones proposed that the owners of the Sirhowy Furnace with Edward Kendall of the neighbouring Beaufort furnace to the east, located at the northern end of the Ebbw Vale, demonstrated 'social responsibilities for their workers'. As

Iron furnace, Whitecliff, Forest of Dean. Operated around the start to the nineteenth century. The design of the orginal Sirhowy Furnace was not unlike that of Whitecliff furnace.   *Ian Pope collection*

'proof' in support of his proposal, he identified that Kendall with Atkinson opened and financed the running of a schoolroom in a building called Capel Waunpound that stood midway between the two furnaces.[16] A literate and numerate workforce was also of benefit to the operation of an industrial operation. Some of the schoolboys as adults, with minds for enquiry into social and political ideas, pondered radical political change.

By the 1790s between forty and fifty workers were employed to operate the Sirhowy Furnace.[17] A rush in building small houses to accommodate migrant workers created Dukestown in the vicinity of the stench, smoke, and dirt expelled from the furnace.

Sir Charles Gould Morgan

In 1792, Charles Gould Morgan took supreme control of the Tredegar Estate due to his marriage to Jane Morgan thirty-four years earlier. She inherited the estate in 1792 from Thomas Morgan of Ruperra. Born in 1726, Charles Gould's success as a lawyer saw him rise to Judge Advocate General, in 1771. He also became the President of the world's first life assurance society, The Equitable Life Assurance Society. In 1792, Charles Gould sought and was 'granted the name and arms of Morgan by Royal licence'. He was later knighted.

Sir Charles Gould Morgan found that the Tredegar Estate was 'seriously encumbered' financially. 'The estate, despite its potential wealth, was beset by a shortage of liquid capital'.[18] Such a financial reckoning for the Tredegar Estate was partly due to the legal cost of nineteen years in the Court of Chancery.

A Bigger Venture

In 1794, the management of the Sirhowy Furnace changed. Richard Fothergill and the Reverend Matthew Monkhouse bought the shares held by Atkinson, who retired, and two other partners. William Barrow remained as a partner. Fothergill and Monkhouse jointly took overall control. Richard Fothergill, also

described as a 'master builder from Clapham in the County of Surrey', had interests in other South Wales ironmaking ventures.[19] Evan Powell claimed that Fothergill was a native of the Forest of Dean, and Oliver Jones proposed that Fothergill may have also had ironmaking interests there.[20] Reverend Matthew Monkhouse, later recognised as being 'Clerk, Sirhowy', according to Evan Powell, hailed from Westmorland, and some unverified search findings suggests that he was born at Lowbridge, north of Kendal, Westmorland, today Cumbria, and was a nephew of Atkinson. Moreover, again not fully affirmed, Fothergill had links with Kendal, and Cumberland. In the eighteenth century, Kendal would have been a centre for some gossip about the adjacent Furness District's ironmaking trade.

Regardless of their past lives, Fothergill and Monkhouse acted to improve the Sirhowy Furnace. The original water wheel for powering the furnace bellows was changed for a larger one. The greater demand for water was met by cutting a channel to tap into the river upstream of the furnace. Coke making was increased. The furnace yield of pig iron grew towards fifteen tons per week. Since a mule could only carry around three hundredweights, pig iron transportation by trains of mules curbed any ideas the partners had for increasing pig iron output.

As the eighteenth century closed the transport of materials and goods in Monmouthshire also saw changes. The opening of the Rassau Tram Road in 1797 enabled Sirhowy Furnace pig iron to be hauled by horse-drawn trams to the Beaufort Furnace at the head of the Ebbw Vale. Perhaps of much greater importance, the Act of 1792 (32 Geo.III c.102) associated with founding the Monmouthshire Canal Company's business caused Fothergill and Monkhouse to speculate about iron markets beyond the Ebbw Vale. The Act led to the opening by 1799 of an Ebbw Vale spur of an emerging Monmouthshire canal system.[21] Crumlin in the Ebbw Vale became the northern terminus of the canal spur for barge traffic with Newport. The Beaufort Furnace, at the head of the Ebbw Vale, was linked by a tramroad to Crumlin for iron product traffic.

Earlier in 1797, William Barrow's finances came under great strain, which forced him to sell his stake in the Sirhowy Furnace. Fothergill became the lead partner in the Sirhowy venture, and was 'convinced' by the need for another furnace. The extra furnace was built and a Boulton and Watt beam engine installed to power the additional blast of air needed for iron smelting. Centuries later Laurence Ince judged that the engine was 'unusual'. The engine's uniqueness may have been due to its dimensions: the beam engine had a piston size of 23¾-inch x 5ft with a 52-inch blowing cylinder. Or maybe its peculiarity was due to other features contained in the following description: 'The steam end of the 18ft beam was connected to an ancillary beam which worked a 20ft flywheel. The blowing cylinder was connected to a 6ft diameter regulator which also received blast from one or more 87-inch x 2ft 3 inch cylinders worked by a 38ft diameter waterwheel'.[22]

The manning of the Sirhowy Furnace was increased to around ninety people. As a two furnace operation, pig iron output increased to over a hundred tons a month, which suggests an annual output at just over 1,200 tons. As a measure for comparison, the pacesetter in Monmouthshire, in the year 1796, was Blaenavon Ironworks, which produced 5,400 tons of pig iron per annum.[23]

Probably foreseeing future growth in the iron trade, Fothergill and Monkhouse envisaged 'a venture even bigger than Sirhowy' by the summer of 1799. A mile or so south of the Sirhowy Furness was an 'ideal site' for creating a sizeable ironworks, Uwchlaw y Coed – wood of the gentleman.[24] However, leases that the partners of the Sirhowy Furnace had entered into several years earlier with the Morgans of Tredegar gave them no power to erect furnaces at Uwchlaw y Coed. John Lloyd has detailed that in the 1700s an attempt by John Mayberry and Thomas Wilkins to set up a Tredegar Forge, possibly in the vicinity of Uwchlaw y Coed, was complicated by legal issues and foundered in, or sometime after, 1778.[25] It is more than likely that John Lloyd's Tredegar Forge was the Tredegar Park venture mentioned earlier.

Nonetheless, in order that the Sirhowy Furnace business could be sustained into the future, Richard Fothergill and Matthew Monkhouse needed to conclude lease re-negotiations with the Tredegar Estate. In 1799, maybe to manage a short-term revenue problem they sub-leased land to Harford, Partridge and Company. Harford, Partridge and Company had acquired the Ebbw Vale Furnace, to the south of Beaufort Furnace, eight years earlier.

The Sirhowy Furnace owners retained an ambition to found a bigger ironworks. Oliver Jones put forward that all they 'needed was someone with enough influence with the Morgans to negotiate for them and enough money to help them build the ironworks. For good reasons their choice fell on Samuel Homfray'.[26] Samuel Homfray seemed to be the ideal envoy for conducting business with the Tredegar Estate. The Merthyr Tydfil ironmaster had married a widowed daughter of Sir Charles Gould Morgan, in 1793. According to M. J. Dowden, the son-in-law of Sir Charles Gould Morgan was also on the lookout for an ironworks investment opportunity in Monmouthshire.[27] His brother, Jeremiah, had led the way east from the head of the Taff Vale to open Ebbw Vale Ironworks in 1789.

By at least around the time of his marriage, Samuel Homfray was the managing partner of the Penydarren Ironworks. In 1796, the partnership that owned the ironwork comprised Samuel Homfray and his two brothers, Jeremiah and John, William Forman and Henry Forman. The Forman family 'had extensive business interests in London including participation in the ordnance trade'.[28] The Formans were destined to become a 'notable' source of capital finance for enabling the growth of the iron industry in the South Wales Coalfield.[29]

Samuel Homfray may have had another motive for opening an ironworks in Monmouthshire. According to M. J. Dowden, Penydarren Ironworks was in a 'weak position compared to those of the giant Cyfarthfa and Dowlais works' due to a number of circumstances. 'Given these circumstances it was essential for Samuel Homfray to break into the increasingly lucrative Monmouthshire valleys on advantageous terms'.[30]

Fothergill and Monkhouse's idea for an ironworks venture at Uwchlaw y Coed was also timely in another respect. The Tredegar Estate's financial woes could be eased by encouraging the development of industrial ventures on its property. Mutual interests coincided in an agreement.

A Lease for an Industrial Venture

In London on the 20th March 1800 a 'Heads of Sir Charles Morgan's Lease' was signed. 'The Lease from Sir Charles Morgan Bart to Samuel Homfrey, Richard Fothergill, and Matthew Monkhouse' was signed by Charles Morgan, Charles Morgan, Samuel Homfrey.[31] The first Charles Morgan signature was Sir Charles Gould Morgan of Tredegar and the second one was his son's, who linked his name to 'Ruperra'. Specified was: 'Samuel Homfrey on behalf of himself and Richard Fothergill, and Matthew Monkhouse agrees to take this lease'. Such wording put the Penydarren ironmaster in command of a Monmouthshire ironworks development.

The Lease granted the partners, Homfray, Fothergill, and Monkhouse, termed the 'Takers', a list of rights. The first right was to 'coal and mines' by working 'clay, sand, stone, slate, firestones etc.' under Bedwellty Common, Cwm Tyssyg, a southern area of Mynydd Llangattock, an area east of the Sirhowy River that included a part of Mynydd Manmoel, which belonged to the Abercarne (sic) Manor. John Lloyd found in another, but undeclared, source that 'the Minerals under Bedwellty Common are stated to 1,000 acres, under the Valley of Cwm Tyssock (sic) 500, and under the lands in the Parish of Machen and Risca [Mynydd Manmoel part of the Abercarne Manor], 1,500 acres'.[32]

The partners were further allowed to exploit other natural resources. 'Inclosed Lands, and of two pieces opposite the adjoining Sirhowy River – Subject to the existing Leases [regarding Sirhowy Furnace] – The tenants of all which paying their existing Rents to the Takers, who are to pay a net rent £300

per annum for the first 5 years and £500 per annum afterwards for the *Term of 99 years* [writer's italics]…' 'Timber to be had from the Tredegar Estates (sic) as required provided it is ready for felling on paying a fair price for the same'. Thus 'Pitt (sic) Timber' was made available for at least mining use. The partners were further given 'liberty' to use all water that they could collect. The partners could also draw water from the course of the Sirhowy River draining the estate to a point one mile south of where the river joined the River Ebbw.

The lease also outlined the envisaged ironmaking business. The Takers were granted 'liberty to erect any Forges or Works on' the banks of the River Sirhowy. Homfray, Fothergill, and Monkhouse were committed to 'expend on the Premises in Erecting Works' £10,000. Offered tentatively to give an idea of the scale of the investment, in 1798 the Dowlais Ironworks was valued at £61,000.[33]

The lease further gave the Takers 'liberty to make a Tram or other road down the Sirhowy valley to join the [Monmouthshire] Canal for erecting Warehouses there paying reasonable damages for the land'. Although such a means of land communication was essential, maybe an early sign of cooperation between Morgan-Homfray is represented in the lease's clause regarding sea transport: 'The Takers to make use of Mr Morgans Wharfs at Newport for all Articles and Things they may have occasion to bring down' the valley tram road 'for shipping and to send all the Iron by his Vessels to Bristol which they have occasion to send there, Mr Morgan engaging to charge no more than the Customary and then times price for the Wharfage and Freighting'. John Lloyd noted that Sir Charles Gould Morgan and his son, Charles Morgan of Ruperra, jointly owned the wharfs, but the son 'was then engaged in a shipping business at Newport'.[34]

Crucially though, the signed Heads of Sir Charles Morgan's Lease enabled Samuel Homfray, Richard Fothergill, and Matthew Monkhouse to build an ironworks at the head of the Sirhowy Valley. In 'deference' to Sir Charles Morgan the 'Tredegar Iron Works' came into being, which became more familiarly written as the 'Tredegar Ironworks', and known locally as 'the works'.[35] However, the year 1800 was a bad time to start an ironmaking venture.

South Wales Iron workers were dismissed from work due to a slump in demand for iron and so they and their dependents faced poverty. Desperate men among them took lawless action. Troops of soldiers were deployed across the South Wales 'iron belt' to reassert law and order. Regardless, Homfray, Fothergill, and Monkhouse planned for the future midst such commotion.

A task taken by Homfray was arranging the ways and means for transporting Tredegar Ironworks' products to Newport.[36] Homfray began to plan the building of a tramroad down the Sirhowy Valley, and onwards as directly as was practical to the Tredegar Wharfs, Pillgwenlly, Newport.[37] Such a way meant that the Ebbw Vale spur of the Monmouthshire Canal was bypassed.

Samuel Homfray was a 'determined, pugnacious figure' according to one opinion. Regarding the movement of iron products from Merthyr Tydfil to Cardiff, Homfray had earlier led opposition against the near exclusive control of the running of the Glamorgan Canal, opened in 1794, by Richard Crawshay of Cyfarthfa Ironworks, Merthyr Tydfil. 'A Bill was brought forward for a competitive tramroad to run between Cardiff, Merthyr and the adjacent ironworks. The Bill was withdrawn under the pressure from the Crawshays, working through the [Glamorgan] Canal Company'. Yet, 'despite this setback the road was built'. The tramroad in Glamorgan was due to Homfray's 'skilful exploitation of a legal loophole'.[38]

Moving Iron and Coal

The Penydarren ironmaster negotiated with the Monmouthshire Canal Company to test the feasibility of transporting Tredegar Ironworks' product via the Ebbw Vale branch of the canal. An outcome was that he entered into an agreement with the canal company on the 18th December 1800, so that:

On, or before the 25th December 1801, [the canal company] would make a good and sufficient tramroad, according to the plans of Benjamin Outram, of Butterly, in the County of Derby, Engineer, from the Tredegar Iron Works, to join their Canal near Risca Church, with all convenient turnouts, and if required, to construct a double rail.

Such a tramroad should be made of convenient width for Carts to pass by the side, and the road to be open to the public on payments of the same tolls as are taken in the Newport District of Turnpike Roads; Provisions as to reimburse Homfray and Co. the money expended by them.

Samuel Homfray and Partners consequently became 'bound' to send 'all Iron, Coal, etc., from their works by that line'. The Monmouthshire Canal Company applied the following charges:

That the through Tonnage rate per ton from the Works to the Wharf at Newport should be 3s. per ton for all iron, and 2s. per ton for all coal, and for timber and other goods 3s. per ton, the whole distance being reckoned to be 24 miles. For shorter distances proportional tonnage [rates] to be charged. Tonnage for coal to be at the long weight, each Ton consisting of 21 Hundred of 120 lbs. and of iron of 20 cwts., of 120 lbs., with the usual allowance of 30 lbs. for Breakages.[39]

The agreement included some terms of value to the ironworks' partners. Payment charges were delayed until the works began to trade. The canal operator 'undertook to make the whole length of tramroad from the Tredegar Works to the junction with the canal at Risca'.[40] The canal company agreed to 'keep the Tramroad in good repair and the Canal well supplied with water, and in times of frost to keep the navigation open by means of ice boats'.

Homfray and his 'Co-partners' and the Monmouthshire Canal Company became committed to doing 'their utmost to secure the passing of an Act of Parliament [for] carrying the terms of such an Agreement into effect'.[41] In 1802, the Monmouthshire Canal Navigation Act (42 Geo. III c.115) was passed. This Act enabled the 'construction of a tramway, from the [canal company's] canal dock at Newport via [nearby] Bassaleg towards Risca, where at the appropriately named Nine Mile Point, it would join up with the Sirhowy tramroad from the Tredegar works'. Furthermore, 'of the stretch from Newport to Nine Mile Point, one mile of the track, which was to pass through Tredegar Park and thereafter known as the Park Mile, was to be constructed and maintained by the landowner, Sir Charles [Gould] Morgan, who was empowered to charge the same rate of tolls for this stretch as that charged by the canal and tram companies'.[42]

In 1993 M. J. Dowden observed concerning the 1802 Monmouthshire Canal Navigation Act: 'The Tredegar interest had succeeded in securing an excellent position in Monmouthshire, and the new [Tredegar] iron works seemed poised to challenge the established plants at Ebbw Vale and Blaenavon'.[43] Vital also had been the consent of the Duke of Beaufort to enable limestone quarried near Trevil in 'the parish of Llangynider (sic), in the County of Brecon', to be transported by tramway to the Tredegar Ironworks. Thus, with Duke of Beaufort limestone, mine and coal from the Tredegar Estate, the Tredegar Ironworks had natural resources fit for an iron furnace's charge. Homfray, Fothergill, and Monkhouse were set ready to embark together upon a commercial adventure into the iron trade of the world.

However, M. J. Dowden has contended that the agreement of December 1800, 'was but the first round in a protracted contest between the Morgan-Homfray connection and the canal Company'. Years earlier, although the Morgans of Tredegar had subscribed £5,200 to back the formation of the Monmouthshire Canal Company, the sum was insufficient to take control of the venture. The Harfords, ironmasters of Melingriffiths and Ebbw Vale, through investing £10,200 in the canal company, took the commanding role. Indeed, M. J. Dowden judged that the 'Harfords, like Crawshay in Glamorgan, sought to use the canal company to advantage, in collusion with other heavy-investing

industrialists, such as Thomas Hill of Blaenavon'. Another goal for the Harfords and Thomas Hill, of the Blaenavon Ironworks, was to 'control access to the sea through the Canal Company'. Sometime before the 25th December 1801, the canal company 'threatened to use compulsory purchase granted to them under the Act of 1792 unless Sir Charles [Gould Morgan] undertook to construct wharfs and warehouses on his land, at his own expense'. Thus, 'the relations' between the Tredegar Estate and the canal company became 'somewhat strained'.[44]

Speculatively, the Harfords and Thomas Hill and Blaenavon may have also united to make the Tredegar Ironworks' entry into the iron market difficult. The Ebbw Vale and Blaenavon works dominated iron production in the Monmouthshire valleys at the time.

Parliament and Chancery

Although motives can be a matter of conjecture, the canal company sought 'legal means to redress the balance of advantage' that they thought favoured the Tredegar Estate. 'The weakest link in the Morgan-Homfray connection was the original 1800 agreement granting the Bedwellty lands, minerals and water for 99 years'. The law at the time deemed that 'the granting of leases for longer than twenty-one years or the opening of new mines constituted voluntary waste, a form of fraud upon a power, which involved an unauthorised act altering the character of the land'. The canal company 'sought to exploit the weakness to the full, embroiling its rivals in parliamentary and Chancery proceedings' especially following the passing of the 1802 Monmouthshire Canal Navigation Act.[45]

The canal company's actions 'forced' Sir Charles Gould Morgan to seek an Act of Parliament 'to extend his powers'. His private Parliamentary Bill 'sought power to grant leases of estates devised by the will of John Morgan Esq. and to enable Charles Morgan to charge the estates of which he was tenant for life in possession with the amount laid out on wharfs and other improvements'.[46] During the Bill's passage an amendment was tabled 'purporting to prove that the minerals of the Bedwellty tract had been worked in the lifetime of John Morgan, and that great advantage would arise from the power to grant a long lease'. Samuel Homfray 'attended to support this amendment, swearing that he was willing to take a 99 years lease of this land [as defined in the 1800 agreement] at £552 and to lay out £40,000 in erecting the works'.[47]

However, 'the unconditional passing of the Bill was prevented by the extraordinary intervention of the Lord Chancellor, Lord Eldon. He insisted that both the power of leasing and the charging of the estates with the sum expended on wharfs should be made subject to the approval of the Court of Chancery'. As M. J. Dowden commented, the 'spoiling tactics of the Monmouthshire Canal Company seemed to be taking effect'.[48] Yet, the case in Chancery ended in 1803 with 'a partial success for Tredegar'. Sir Charles Gould Morgan was 'empowered to raise £5,297 from the settled estate to cover the cost of building wharfs and warehouses'.[49]

Regardless, the Court ruled that Sir Charles Gould Morgan had exceeded his 'powers as tenant for life in possession'. 'As far as textbook law and judicial decision were concerned a lease for 99 years was impossible'. Moreover, a lease of twenty-one years was 'not sufficient … to gain an adequate return on £40,000 investment' in a Tredegar Ironworks. The 'evidently good relations between Morgan and Homfray' fortunately 'provided a way out' of the difficulties met in Chancery, although 'albeit one of dubious legal standing' according to Dowden. Although in a 'literal sense' the terms of the 'ruling were adhered to', an agreement was reached between Homfray and his in-laws that 'the 21 year lease would be successfully renewed up to the full term of 99 years'. In spite of casting doubt upon the legal soundness of such an agreement, M. J. Dowden concluded that the outcome was 'clearly satisfactory for the Tredegar Alliance', Sir Charles Morgan of Tredegar and Samuel Homfray.[50]

Despite the Tredegar alliance suffering 'considerable inconvenience' partly due to the scheming Monmouthshire Canal Company, the construction of the Tredegar Ironworks progressed as parliamentary and legal matters ran their course. Furthermore, if Homfray's vow of investing £40,000 in the Tredegar Ironworks became a fact, the Ebbw Vale and Blaenavon ironworks were set to face a formidable rival competing for a share of the iron market.

Tredegar Ironworks

At an early stage in the development of the Tredegar Ironworks, William Thompson and William Forman, associates of Homfray's at Penydarren Ironworks, were added to the Tredegar Ironworks' partnership. Moreover, the Tredegar Ironworks and Sirhowy Furnace became an integrated business. Matthew Monkhouse managed the Sirhowy Furnace whilst Richard Fothergill took charge of the Tredegar Ironworks.

Regarding overseeing the technical design of the new works, Samuel Homfray's agent was the Cornish born engineer Richard Trevithick. Homfray's faith in Trevithick's talent as an engineer was revealed publically a number of years later. The ironmaster wagered that Trevithick could apply steam locomotion to tramroad haulage. On the 21st February 1804, a steam locomotive designed by Trevithick hauled a cargo of iron and seventy men along a Merthyr Vale tramroad. The sequel was a technical revolution: railway locomotion. The Cornishman's visits to Tredegar Ironworks also furthered Homfray's interests.

The Tredegar Ironworks began its operation with two furnaces. In 1801, furnace combustion used air delivered from a Boulton Watt 40-inch x 8ft beam blowing engine. The blowing engine was also coupled to a 52ft diameter waterwheel that also operated hammers and turned rolls. The iron make tapped from Tredegar Ironworks' furnaces made real a part of the founders' vision.

Circa 1803, a Richard Trevithick vertical-cylinder engine, made at Penydarren, was installed at Tredegar to drive puddle rolls. The Trevithick engine at Tredegar proved to be a robust piece of engineering since it was used until 1856.[51]

The investment in puddling and rolling mills at Tredegar Ironworks in 1807 allowed bar-iron to be produced. Also by that year, pig iron production was 'running at four thousand tons annually'. 'Dust and grime settled everywhere but were cheerfully accepted as signs of the awaited prosperity'. Waste, as shale tips, began to grow around the northern end of the valley.[52]

A sequel to the 1802 Monmouthshire Canal Navigation Act was the formation of the Sirhowy Tram Road Company with Homfray, Watkin Homfrey, Rowland Fothergill and William Henry Forman as directors.[53] The Sirhowy Tram Road, linking Tredegar Ironworks to Newport, began the movement of horse-drawn cargoes of iron product in 1805.

The following year saw the death of Sir Charles Gould Morgan and his successor, also Sir Charles Morgan (1760-1846), became chairman of the Sirhowy Tram Road Company and the Tredegar Wharf Company. 'The Official seal of the Sirhowy Tram Road Company included as its symbols a train of loaded trams, a bunch of workmen's tools, the north and south compass points, the motto 'Perseverance' and the date 1802. Oliver Jones reflected that 'both the motto and the compass points' came 'from Homfray's earlier days at Penydarren'. The trials that Sir Charles Gould Morgan and Homfray had experienced, from 1800 to 1803, to enable industrial development to progress on the Tredegar Estate, had also called for perseverance.

In 1834, the Sirhowy Tram Road won praise from T. G. Cummings. 'The great Sirhowy Tram Road is a double road part of the way ... [the width] of the road is 4ft 2 inch ... the sleepers are stout blocks of stone'. The tram road 'extends from Pillgwenlly, near Newport, to the Sirhowy and Tredegar Iron Works, a distance of twenty-four miles, whence it continued to Trefil lime works' to the north of Sirhowy Furnace. The total expense for the tramroad was '£74,000 or about £3,000 per mile'. People of the then rural parts of the Sirhowy Valley gasped with astonishment on first seeing teams of four, or five, horses drawing fifteen wagons. Each wagon carried between forty and fifty hundredweights of goods. The sweat on the brow, or terror in the face of the man keeping the tram-trains under control, may have caused either anxiety or some amusement among bystanders.

The regularity of the noise due to braking and 'spragging' of the tram-trains served as a gauge of the demand for iron. The call for iron, during the early years of the Sirhowy Tram Road, was largely due to the military and naval needs of the Napoleonic Wars 1803-1815.[54] The year after the battle of Waterloo in 1815, the pig iron production of the Tredegar Ironworks was 7,499 tons, which was nearly twenty per cent less than the previous year's output, 9,225 tons.[55]

In 1816, due to the 'depressed state of the iron trade', Tredegar Ironworks 'gave 'notice to workmen, that a further reduction in the price of their work must take place'. The workmen were 'driven almost to despair by this intelligence; they concluded that nothing but misery awaited them; and came to the desperate resolution, that it was better to seek redress by tumultuously assembling than to work'. The workers first marched to Merthyr Tydfil and afterwards around the ironworks of Monmouthshire, attracting other workers dissatisfied with their wages to join their protest. One response by Government to the marching of upwards 12,000 workmen was to send military troops

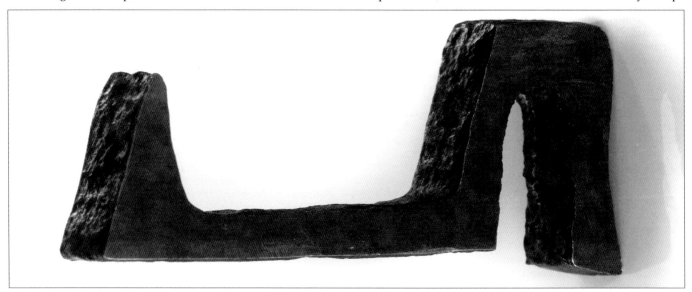

A section through a combined tramroad and edge rail obtained from a Merthyr Vale tram road uncovered whilst removing a coal tip.

A. J. Edwards Collection

into the valleys to secure civil order.[56] However, a meeting at Bassaleg, near Newport, between workers representatives and magistrates, none of which were ironmasters, led to the ironmasters withdrawing their notices.[57]

Nevertheless, the year 1817 marked the start of a new business activity for the Tredegar Ironworks. Up until that year coal raised from the Tredegar Estate was used by the works and for local household fuel. In that year 'a contract was signed for "Tredegar coal" to be delivered to Newport'. 'The first delivery was made by train of twelve specially constructed trams, two horse teams conveying the trams to Newport over the Tredegar (sic) tramway'.[58] More than likely the coal was sold for household fuel. Coal from the Mynyddislwyn seam, sourced in the Sirhowy Valley around the then village of Blackwood, sold well in the household market.

Fothergill versus Harfords

Around the time that the Napoleonic Wars ended, Fothergill and Monkhouse became anxious about the future of Sirhowy Furnace. The forty year lease for the Sirhowy Furnace in 1778, agreed with Charles Henry Burgh, expired in 1817. But a number of years before 1817, Harford, Partridge and Company of Ebbw Vale acquired ownership of the Sirhowy property. During the middle of 1817, Harfords offered Richard Fothergill lease terms, which at an annual rental of £2,500 was greater than the mere £134 rent agreed with Charles Henry Burgh.[59] 'Early leases of the second half of the eighteenth century … show that the landlords had no real idea of the true value of their mineral holdings'.[60] Thus Harfords' offer would have been judged a fair one by Richard Fothergill's South Wales ironmaster peers, but Fothergill rejected the offer.

After the lease ended, Richard Fothergill defied moves by the Hartfords to take ownership of the Sirhowy Furnace property. Ultimately Fothergill surrendered, but beforehand he wrecked the Sirhowy operation. Tram rails were ripped up so disconnecting the operation from the Tredegar Ironworks. All portable plant and machinery were removed from Sirhowy. Fothergill eventually had to pay the Harfords' £6,000 bill for such defiance.

Richard Fothergill's pique was compounded. The Sirhowy Ironworks operation was repaired, and later developed. Sirhowy pig iron was transported to the Hartford, Partridge & Company works for puddling and rolling. The Sirhowy Furnace became a servant of the iron industry in the Ebbw Vale.

Samuel Homfray Junior

In 1818, Tredegar Ironwork's future was entrusted to Samuel Homfray Junior, aged twenty-three, the son of the man that had made his mark as the Penydarren ironmaster. He settled into living at 'Bedwellty House' as the first occupant. The sturdily built house stood south-west of the ironworks. The house was purposefully built for the resident partner of the works. After 1818, a ring of trees and parkland flourished as the surrounds for Bedwellty House. At home, the Homfray family were isolated from a landscape that due to the expansion of industrial development had become ravaged.

The initial call from the Tredegar Ironworks for coal and mine caused the driving of levels. All the levels were opened before Samuel Homfray Jnr took office according to Oliver Jones's list:[61]

Year	Level Name
1800	Cwm Rhos
1800	Bryn Oer
1801	Jack Edwards's
1802	Yard
1806	Hard
1809	Shop
1810	Forge (driven adjacent to the furnaces)
1812	Tramroad

It can only be speculated that on joining the Tredegar Ironworks that Samuel Homfray Jnr dealt with matters arising

Samuel Homfray Junior (1795-1882)
Oil on canvas portrait painted in 1882 at Glen Usk, Caerleon, where he had retired to after living at Bedwellty House, Tredegar. Edward Henry Corbould (1815-1905) was the artist.
Reproduced with permission of Newport Museum & Art Gallery

from Sirhowy Furnace's change of ownership. The end to the two Sirhowy Valley's ironworks functioning as an integrated business caused some disorder. That the Tredegar Ironworks tapped into a new catchment of water, Bryn Bach Pond, around the time of his appointment, may have been viewed by Homfray as a good greeting.

However, pig iron output figures for the first four to five years of his office suggests that no major additional investments were made in plant and equipment at the Tredegar Ironworks. Market growth prospects may have been viewed as insufficient for ironworks expansion. For the year Samuel Homfray Jnr took charge, output was 8,258 tons of pig iron. The five blast furnaces of Tredegar had yielded 10,350 tons the year before, 1817. Although the works' output fell to 7,140 tons in 1819, the annual outputs varied around 9,000 tons for the next three years.[62]

A Fledgling town

Nevertheless, by the 1820s, the Monmouthshire valleys were 'established …. as a major centre of iron making' in the world.[63] Rival ironworks to Tredegar, in addition to Ebbw Vale and Nantyglo, like works at Abersychan, Blaina, and Rhymney (Bute), also attracted itinerant labour. Some of these nomadic workers settled down to reside in houses adjoining the Tredegar Ironworks. At an isolated site of graves on Cefn Golau, a headstone dated to 1848 refers to the buried person as a native of 'the Tredegar Iron Works'. For convenience, the name of Tredegar is used hereafter for the township.

The 'first big outbreak of' fever hit Tredegar in 1813. 'Poor drinking water, lack of sewers,' was not seen to be contributory causes. 'Warm weather was generally blamed for the fever'. Then, from the autumn of the year 1832 until the spring of the following year, a cholera epidemic spread around Tredegar. In the year 1848

Bedwellty House, Tredegar. Home to Samuel Homfray Junior from 1818 to 1853 as the resident partner at Tredegar Ironworks.   *Phil Hayman*

another outbreak of cholera hit Tredegar.[64] The Cefn Golau graves mentioned above were for victims of cholera despite disinfectant being used. The cure, a supply of clean water and sanitation, was probably engineered due to the 1848 Public Health Act.

Around the time of Samuel Homfray Junior's appointment a fledgling town had taken form with the Tredegar Ironworks as its centre. By the 1820s, there stood, flanking the western-side of the ironworks, 250 Tredegar works owned houses, and owner-occupied properties comprising twenty shops and thirty-two other buildings. A notion that the eventual town was 'planned according to specific principles' has been mooted.[65]

Oliver Jones has described in detail the fledgling town, which is summarised next.[66] Housing built for employees of the Tredegar Ironworks was small in size, of cheap construction, and poorly furnished. Water for drinking and washing was drawn from streams. Regarding public health, there was no sanitation. At least the occupants of company houses enjoyed the comfort of warmth at home due to a free supply of coal once a fortnight.

The Company Shop was the district's chief purveyor of household food and goods. Opened in 1800 by the Tredegar Ironworks, the Company Shop traded using a kind of the truck system. Workers were paid tokens instead of money. The tokens were exchanged for food and goods at the Company Shop. Oliver Jones held that the truck system 'became a means of out-and-out exploitation much resented by the workers'. The first truck shop of the district was opened in 1778 in Sirhowy by Atkinson and associates, and expanded further by Fothergill and Monkhouse.

'Escape' from what today would be viewed as the basic 'conditions of early Tredegar', according to Oliver Jones, was available at either 'the inn or the chapel'. The inns were 'well patronised' not only for drinking beer, but for seeing travelling entertainers. 'Inn life' though 'could be exceptionally rowdy at weekends when fights and quarrels were more likely to occur'. The singing of a chapel's congregation, on the other hand, lifted the spirit in a much more sober way. The founding of Siloh, the district's first chapel, occurred in 1806. Afterwards more chapels were built at Tredegar. A small Roman Catholic Church was erected in the locality in the 1820s. Anglicans worshipped at the Bedwellty church of St. Sannan until the year 1831 when St. George's Church was built to the north of the Tredegar Ironworks.

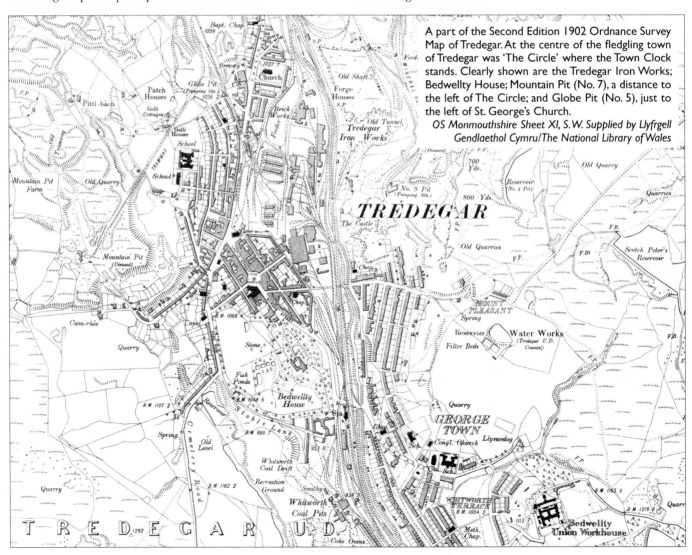

A part of the Second Edition 1902 Ordnance Survey Map of Tredegar. At the centre of the fledgling town of Tredegar was 'The Circle' where the Town Clock stands. Clearly shown are the Tredegar Iron Works; Bedwellty House; Mountain Pit (No. 7), a distance to the left of The Circle; and Globe Pit (No. 5), just to the left of St. George's Church.
OS Monmouthshire Sheet XI, S.W. Supplied by Llyfrgell Gendlaethol Cymru/The National Library of Wales

Early Nineteenth Century cholera victims' grave stones found to the south of Cefn Golau Cemetery. In the background to the left are the upper reaches of Cwm Tysswg.   *Author*

A desire for elementary education among the local population would take decades to be partly satisfied. The chapels taught basic literacy so that the Bible could be read. In 1811, there were at least four privately run schools in the town for the teaching of reading, writing and arithmetic. In 1837, the Tredegar Ironworks 'decided to promote' a scheme 'to provide the children of the workmen of the town with education at a reasonable cost.' A 'school was opened at the Town Hall in 1837, twopence a week being taken from the father's wages for each child over six years of age and not yet at work. The money was deducted whether the child went to school or not'. Oliver Jones noted that although 'the management of the school was supposed to be in the hands of a committee composed of Company officials and workmen's representatives' the 'real power lay with the Company'. Nevertheless, he acknowledged that 'the scheme registered a big advance in educational effort'. 'The Town Hall school functioned from 1837 to 1876, but in 1871 it passed under the authority of the newly constituted School Board set up under the Act of 1870 which made the elementary education compulsory for all children'.

Yet, it was the search for work that brought people to the head of the Sirhowy Valley. 'The census of 1801 gave the numbers living in the Parish of Bedwellty as 619'.[67] 'The population [of the town of Tredegar] had reached the figure of eight thousand by 1833 and by 1840 – Sirhowy included – it was nearly ten thousand'.[68] The growth in employment was also a stimulus for conflict between ironmasters and workers.

Scotch Cattle

The early period of Samuel Homfray Junior's tenure of office saw his sway over employed workers challenged. In 1822, a rumour spread around the 'iron belt' of South Wales that the ironmasters 'intended' to force a reduction in wages in anticipation of a fall in business. The rumour proved true. Workers went on strike, and rioting broke out across the 'iron belt'. However, Oliver Jones later judged that the 'memory of 1822 became as bitter as 1816 had been sweet'.[69] Some workers, as a response to 'the pain of defeat', joined the Scotch Cattle.

The historian Gwyn A. Williams identified that 'in the 1820s the colliers of Monmouthshire organized their first unions and their Scotch Cattle resistance groups'.[70] The Scotch Cattle was a secret society. In 1903, Charles Wilkins related that 'the 'Scotch Cattle were bands of men enrolled privately in most of the ironworks towns, with the object first of restricting the output of minerals, and thereby keeping up prices of iron and the wages of miners', and proposed that:

Every herd of Scotch Cattle had a bull as leader, selected for his strength and violence. The band of say, Merthyr, was directed to punish a delinquent at Tredegar; one at Tredegar

to visit Hirwaun. Each man was armed, face blackened, and the skin and horns of a cow worn, and with great bellowings, they would assail a house smash the furniture, and burn down the premises. Mercy was rarely exercised….[71]

The counsel of Samuel Homfray Junior's father may have been invaluable during troubled times. However, his father died in 1822. Regarding halting the activities of the Scotch Cattle, Samuel Homfray Jnr seems to have been thwarted.

In 1834, six miles south of Bedwellty House, just to the north of Argoed, a hamlet, operated Havodrynyscoed Colliery, a level. The occupiers of six houses associated with the level were subjected to a 'diabolical attack' by a gang of men. 'Disguised in their working clothes, and with blackened faces, came bellowing about, having fire arms and pickaxes'. Four days earlier, a notice left at the mouth of the level where Thomas Thomas worked demanded that 'the master to discharge some of the workmen in one week or the "Skotch (sic) Bull" is coming'. The houses were 'very much injured; five were attacked and the furniture destroyed in three of them, and the windows of the other two'. Joan, the wife of Thomas Thomas was shot by gun fire. As she lay on the floor, with wounds bleeding from which she later died, the invaders continued to smash furniture. Fleeing the Thomas's house, the men then visited Argoed where they entered Edward Morgan's house. He was attacked with a mandrel that hit his left knee to leave a bloody wound an inch and a half deep. The gang fled again, and escaped arrest. Samuel Homfray Jnr, a 'most active, intelligent, and indefatigable magistrate', examined 'the affair'. *The Glamorgan, Monmouth & Brecon Gazette* plea was for Mr Homfray to 'make the results of his enquires known to the Home Office'.[72] But suppression of the Scotch Cattle was impaired by fear among intimidated workers.

Charles Wilkins claimed that the formidable Scotch Cattle caused cavalry to be stationed at Tredegar. Apparently arrested ringleaders were taken before the magistrates at Pontypool, and sentenced to various terms of imprisonment.[73] Oliver Jones writing many decades later was forthright in condemning the 'excesses to which the Scotch Cattle resorted'.[74] He further recognised that in the 1820s outlawed trade union activities became items of business in a local lodge of a social society, the Oddfellows. Nevertheless, during the 1820s, the behaviour of the Scotch Cattle did not distract Samuel Homfray Jnr from furthering Tredegar Ironworks business.

Pit Sinkings

As the partner in residence, Samuel Homfray Jnr made decisions about pit sinkings. A primary task for him was to weigh up what coal and mine was needed for the ironworks. Oliver Jones offered the following list of early pit sinkings for the Tredegar Ironworks:[75]

Year	Pit Name or Number
1806	Duke Pit
1818	Bryn Bach; later known as No. 1
1821	Evan Davies's Pit (No. 2)
1826	Ash Tree Pit; also known as Pwll Mary Isaac
1830	Water Wheel Pit
1830	Brigg's Pit; later No. 4
1832	Doctor's Pit; later No. 6
1834	Quick Pit; No. 3
1834	Ty Trist[76]

Predating Samuel Homfray Junior's time as resident partner, the Duke Pit seems to have been the district's only pit sinking. The depth of the sinking was thirty-five yards, which without an explanation, Charles Wilkins later stated was a 'great event'.[77] The diameter of the pit's shaft was later reported to have been eight feet.[78] However, Oliver Jones further noted: 'there was another small iron-mine pit about seventy yards to the south of No. 12, but the date of the sinking is not known'.

From around 1828 onwards until 1841 the Tredegar Ironworks' mining agent, Theophilus Jones, and maybe a successor, oversaw pit sinkings. The district's sinking activity promoted the reputation of a local 'master sinker', Edward James. Edward James's name once prefixed Sirhowy Ironworks' First Class Pit. 'With his sons, he sunk a number of the Sirhowy [Ironworks] pits including No. 9. The Tredegar Ironworks also employed his services starting with Bryn Bach Pit.[79]

As a general remark, up until around the mid-1830s, coal mining mainly served the operational needs of the Tredegar Ironworks. Between the years 1823 and 1839, as the following table shows, blast furnace capacity of the works remained constant at five.[80]

Year	Owner	Built	in Blast
1805	S. Homfray	2	2
1810	Fothergill	4	4
1823	(not known)	5	-
1825	Homfray & Co.	5	5
1830	(unclear)	5	not known
1839	Thompson & Co.	5	5

The work's pig iron output in 1817 was 10,350 tons, which seems to have been near the maximum output then attainable with installed plant and facilities. In 1828, with the addition of another blast furnace by 1823, and seemingly a high demand for iron product, pig iron output leapt to 14,341 tons in 1828.[81] During the 1820s, William Aubrey served as the Tredegar Ironworks' engineer but in 1827 he died after being 'thrown from his horse' riding on Waunpound.[82]

Introducing Railway Locomotion

In 1828, Samuel Homfray Jnr appointed Thomas Ellis, aged twenty-three year, as engineer-in-charge of the Tredegar Works. A duty for Ellis was to manage, among others, his father, also named Thomas Ellis. As an aid to distinguishing them, hereafter Thomas Ellis senior and Thomas Ellis junior are respectively father and son. Thomas Ellis senior was born at Wellington, Shropshire. In 1800, after being apprenticed to Messrs Botsfields, Thomas Ellis senior moved to work at Penydarren. He was subsequently assigned to the Tredegar Ironworks. Thus, his son, Thomas Ellis junior, was born at Tredegar in 1805, and served his apprenticeship at Tredegar Ironworks under his father. After completing his apprenticeship, Thomas Ellis junior became chief engineer at Thomas Hill's Garnddyrys Works, Blaenavon. Some overture from Homfray brought Ellis junior back to the Tredegar Ironworks as engineer-in-charge.

Around the start of December 1828, the Tredegar ironmaster instructed Thomas Ellis senior, acting engineer-charge, and Theophilus Jones, mining agent, to assess the merits of stream locomotives built by George and Robert Stephenson. Homfray had 'heard of the wonderful "travelling steam engines" at Newcastle which were reducing the cost of haulage by 50 per cent'.[83]

Inspired by Richard Trevithick's engineering of a steam locomotive in South Wales and other pioneering locomotives, George Stephenson developed one for the haulage of wagons at Killingworth Colliery. *Blucher*, his first locomotive, operated in 1814. However, maybe of greater significance for the Monmouthshire men was that the year of their visit coincided with the development by Robert Stephenson & Company of a locomotive called the *Lancashire Witch*. The locomotive was later judged to be 'far in advance of any contemporary'.[84]

On the 10th December 1828, the Tredegar Ironworks' representatives visited the colliery after a six day horse-drawn coach journey. At the colliery they met men in the van of the commercialisation of steam locomotion, George Stephenson, Robert Stephenson, Nicholas Wood, and Mr Fenwick.[85] Ellis and Jones left Killington Colliery briefed about locomotives. Robert Stephenson also gave them a letter of introduction to T. L. Gooch, Railway Office, Liverpool. Ellis and Jones inspected a 'tunnel and other works' at Liverpool.

A report by Ellis and Jones caused Samuel Homfray Jnr to place an order with the Stephensons to supply the Tredegar Ironworks with a locomotive. An entry in Robert Stephenson & Co. works ledger records for the 18th July 1829, stated: 'The Tredegar Iron Co., Abergavenny – For one Locomotive Engine Complete delivered at their wharf at Pillgwenlly as per agreement - £550.0.0 – One Strong Box hooped with iron - £1.18.0 [making a total of] £551.18.0'. The Company's Engine Record Book further noted a 'retrospective entry for Works Number 15: 9 inch x [unstated cylinders] – wheels 3ft 6 inch diameter with 'one tube' – [sold to] Humfrays (sic). Tredegar'.[86] The locomotive was later referred to as *Humphrey's Engine, Wales B*. Around 1828 Stephenson's locomotive drawings carried reference letters A, B, C and D that indicated variants in design based upon the *Lancashire Witch*.[87]

Thomas Ellis junior probably supervised at Tredegar the mechanical adjustments needed to bring the delivered locomotive into working order for a first run down the Sirhowy Valley. According to the *Monmouthshire Merlin* of the 26th December 1839, the Tredegar Iron Company was 'confidently' expected 'to start a locomotive engine the day' of Sir Charles Morgan's Cattle Show, held at Court-y-Bella Farm on the 11th December.[88] Humphrey's Engine would then haul a cargo of iron to Newport. Despite heavy rainfall, some people who attended the cattle show left it to witness the run of the locomotive. The spectators gathered in vain.

The Stephenson engine departed Tredegar Works early in the morning 'but unfortunately, at one of the crossings in the tram-road, which was not long enough for the steam-carriage, the wheels got out of the tram-plates, which caused the detention of some hours; and coming through Tredegar Park, the chimney was carried away by a branch of a tree hanging over the tram-road, and in consequence of these accidents did not arrive at Newport till evening'.

According to C. W. Ellis, the hazard posed by tree branches was anticipated by his ancestor. Before the day of the show, Thomas Ellis junior ordered workers to fell branches that hung across the tramroad. However, 'the men got as far as Bassaleg and then went "on the spree", so when Stephenson's "Flyer" came, the driver of course thought that the men were in Newport, instead of which they were in the pub'.[89]

Regardless, the *Monmouthshire Merlin* report mentioned that the chimney was repaired next day and notably added: 'we saw the engine at work; she went at the rate of ten miles and hour, having nothing attached to her then but the carriage with a reservoir of water'. In 1866, Alexander Basset, who served as agent to the Tredegar Estate, seems to have used the newspaper's report to acknowledge that the show day run was 'the first journey made with the Stephenson engine from Tredegar Iron Works to Newport'.[90] The 1839 report also described the locomotive:

> The engine is very neat and compact—the carriage consists of six wheels, on which is the boiler and machinery; behind which the engineer stands to work it—there is also a carriage attached carrying the coke to supply the above as required. The engine is about eight horsepower, and brought 53 tons of iron, besides its own weight, making altogether 80 tons at the rate of six miles an hour, with much ease, and without forcing the engine'.

The foregoing recollects the introduction of commercial steam locomotion to Monmouthshire. The *Monmouthshire Merlin* appraised that 'it is generally believed the engine will answer the purpose intended, and that horses will soon be put out of request'. C. W. Ellis claimed that the steam engine's performance 'was twice as fast as the tram horses could go and with double the amount they could take'.

The Stephenson locomotive was re-named *Britannia* by Samuel Homfray Jnr. In 1830, the *Monmouthshire Merlin* referred to the locomotive as a 'steam-tug'.[91] However, of crucial importance, the arrival of steam locomotion in the Sirhowy Valley was a cue for the Tredegar ironmaster to ponder: what business prospects did a fledgling railway industry offer an ironworks?

Thomas Ellis junior did some locomotive engineering. He faced setbacks, which can dog a new technology. On the 14th October 1830, a Tredegar Iron Company fireman, Thomas Jones, aged twenty-five years, was 'severely scalded and bruised by the bursting of a locomotive boiler' in the parish of Bedwellty. Jones died shortly afterwards.[92] Later that year, according to Oliver Jones, Homfray read an anonymous letter 'calling' on him 'to get rid of the [locomotive] monster'.

Ellis, though, applied himself to designing a Tredegar built locomotive, named *St. David*, which began operation in 1832. *St. David* 'differed from its prototype to the extent that it had its smoke stack rising from the top of the boiler instead of curving up from the front'. Such a design copied Stephenson designed locomotives *Northumbrian* and *Planet* introduced in 1830. Thus it seems that the 1828 meeting fostered a cooperative relationship between the Tredegar works and the Stephensons. Indeed, Thomas Ellis junior 'never failed to acknowledge the [Stephenson] source' of influence in his locomotive designs. The *St. David* 'had a long eventful career; it was stripped down and completely remodelled in 1848 again to Ellis's design and then continued working until the 1880s when it was finally put aside'.[93]

In 1830s and 40s, seven further locomotives, named *Tredegar, Charlotte, Jane, Lord Rodney, Lady Sail, Prince Albert, Fanny and Charlotte*, were built at Tredegar for work on the Sirhowy Tramroad. 'Also two small locomotives for the narrow [gauge] coal route, and then in 1852-3 the *Bedwellty*'.[94]

In April 1843, one of the Tredegar Company's locomotives, the *Vulcan*, halted at Blackwood for its crew to take 'refreshment' at The George Hotel. Whilst in the hotel the crew heard an explosion and witnessed window frames being wrecked, but may have been unaware that 'a part of the [hotel's] roof was carried away'. 'The men, in rushing out discovered that it was the engine on the line that had exploded'. It was clear to view that pieces of the fractured locomotive boiler had killed two

men, a Mr Davies, Buttery Hatch, Rhymney Valley, and Philip Williams, a Blackwood tradesman. 'Two other persons were afterwards discovered in a field near the railway having been struck by pieces of the engine'. It was deemed 'impossible' for the two persons to 'recover' from the injuries received. 'Great damage' was also done 'to several houses near the spot'. The cost of property loss, engine included, was estimated to be at least £1,000. The explosion was 'reported to have resulted from the engine-driver neglecting to open the valve, after shutting off the steam, when getting off the engine'.[95]

An analysis offered in 1843 by James Brown, Cwm Celyn and Blaina Iron Works, of 'cost of locomotive power', based upon 1842 data, revealed that the respected Stockton & Darlington Railway's costs were nearly thirteen per cent greater than the Tredegar Company's' Sirhowy Valley line.[96] Brown's analysis suggests that the Tredegar Company could bear the cost of the explosion's bill.

Although Blackwood's public, horrified by the explosion, probably scorned steam locomotion, the company's technical ability had won plaudits. James Brown also wrote that the company had 'disadvantages to contend against, such as little contemplated by the general class of railway engineers, and as far as my judgment and experience go, I frankly acknowledge that I am surprised at their having succeeded to the extent they have done against all these peculiar disadvantages'. Other words of his reveal that he admired the merits of the locomotive engines and engineers in the employ of the Tredegar Iron Company.

Thomas Ellis junior also nurtured some relationship with one of his apprentices, Daniel Gooch. Wilkins claimed that the father of the Gooch household was 'a reduced gentleman who came from the North of England with the Homfrays, as an accountant'.[97] He also referred to an 'entry in a book in the keeping of the Ellis family' that 'Daniel Gooch: Entered the [Tredegar] works 1832; left 1834'. Moreover, 'young Daniel drifted into the pattern shop at the ironworks'.[98] Thus, in heat of the Tredegar works' foundry, the formation of an illustrious Great Western Railway man, Sir Daniel Gooch (1816-1889), began.

Thomas Ellis junior on the footplate of *St. David*. Date unknown.

Pope/Parkhouse Archive

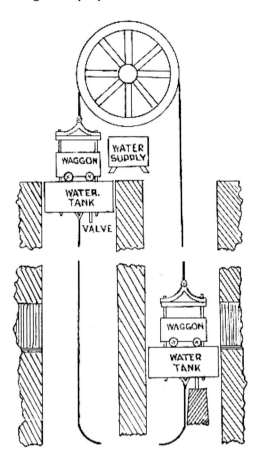

Introduction of balance-winding

Concerning the Tredegar Iron Company and its coal mining operation, in March 1830 the *Monmouthshire Merlin* noted the inception of another technical development:

It was worthy of remark that while steam is being thus employed to convey from place to place the treasures of this mountainous district from their native beds, it is getting into disuse by the application of a new invention of what are called balance-pits. The simplicity of this invention is its greatest recommendation. A shaft is sunk of an oval form, and across the centre at its top, a little above the mouth of it runs a cast iron tank, supplied with water from a reservoir near. By the contrivance of wheels and chains a platform is suspended, upon which the carriage to be lowered is placed. Underneath this is fixed a box or bucket to hold water, let into from a valve in the tank. By the weight of the water the empty carriage descends the shaft on one side, and a loaded one is brought up on the other.[99]

Evan Davies's Pit was chosen for the company's introduction, in 1829, of balance-winding.[100] As a general rule, capstan devices turned by tethered horses were in 1830 the common means for winding coal or mine. Thus the *Monmouthshire Merlin* article invaluably identifies a notable change in colliery engineering

Balance-winding headgear – Brynpwllog or Rogers Pit, from near Rhymney. The Tredegar Ironworks introduced balance-winding at Evan Davies' Pit in 1829. The Brynpwllog or Rogers Pit winder is preserved at Big Pit, National Museum of Wales. *Author*

undertaken by the Tredegar Company. Moreover, the mining agent would have delegated engineering aspects to Thomas Ellis junior to manage. Ellis would have overseen the design and assembly of the cast-iron structure erected over a pit's shaft upon which was assembled the winder's mechanical components. According to a local historian, Evan Powell (1839-1891), the deepest balance-winding pit in the South Wales Coalfield, sunk in 1841, was the district's Mountain Pit. He also claimed that Mountain Pit set a world record 'for one day's coal raising for pits of its kind', but the associated figure was not found.[101] Thomas Ellis junior was entitled to boast that the operational achievement was due to his work. However, he might not have liked being trumped by the work of the Ebbw Vale Company's engineer. Steam winding was introduced to the district at the Sirhowy Ironworks' Engine Pit before 1840.[102]

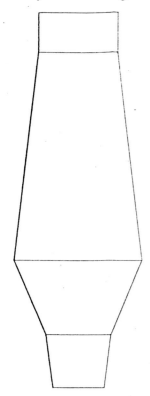

Vertical Section through a Tredegar Ironworks Blast Furnace in 1855. The lowest truncated cone section of a blast furnace was called the hearth. The shape and size of a furnace had a bearing upon pig iron smelting power. Tuyeres penetrating the circular, in plan, wall of the hearth allowed 'blast' air entry for combustion of the coke in the furnace charge stacked above the hearth. The truncated section above the hearth was known as the boshe, which directed melted materials downwards. In this Tredegar blast furnace the boshe's angle was 69 degrees. The full height of the furnace and hearth were respectively 42ft, and 6ft. The maximum diameter of the furnace was 15ft. In 1855 the weekly make of pig iron from such a furnace was 110 tons.

William Truran, The Iron Manufacture of Great Britain *(1855)*

Ironmaking Developments

In 1835, at Tredegar Ironworks, 'the attempt was first made, during a heavy demand for rails, for which Tredegar had a good repute, to introduce hot blast'.[103] The benefit of using hot blast was that less coal was used for smelting pig iron. James Beaumont Neilson had only proved the practical application of his hot blast invention at the Clyde Ironworks, Glasgow in 1832.[104] At Tredegar, the 'early efforts [with hot blast] failed, yet eventually success attended the management and the gratifying average was brought about of 80 tons per furnace weekly'.[105] The Tredegar Ironworks was the pioneer user of hot blast in South Wales.

According to Wilkins, in 1838 the Tredegar Ironworks' managers were 'on their mettle, and the construction of machinery, more sheds, &c., went on apace, and the neighbouring works of Sirhowy were equally on alert'.[106] Although in 1838 saw the 'virtual collapse' of British railway building, South Wales ironworks were 'partly cushioned by accelerating exports' of rail.[107]

Thomas Ellis junior also introduced at Tredegar a system of reversing for blooming rolls for making iron rail. Around 1860, William Menelaus of Dowlais Ironworks, reflected: 'For some time it worked well, and answered the purpose for which it was intended; but the wear and tear was considerable, and eventually it was abandoned'.[108] Menelaus's comment suggests that he had taken notice of Ellis's work when he designed the Goat Mill, Dowlais, completed in 1859, which was a major technical milestone. The Dowlais man, valued Ellis's work in the context

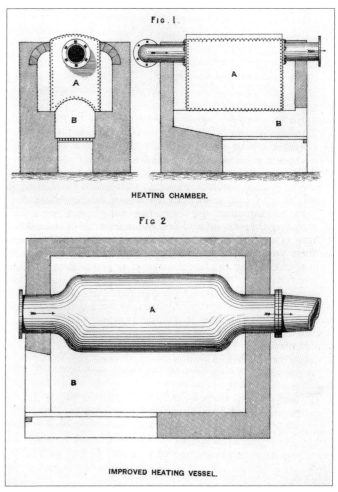

Neilston's Hot Blast Stove. Figure 1 shows the first design Neilston's applied at Clyde Iron Works, near Glasgow, in 1829, to heat air prior to feeding tuyeres in a blast furnace's hearth. Made of wrought iron, the pioneering design needed much maintenance. Fig. 2 shows a cast iron design development. Subsequent design modifications and developments led to the adoption of hot blast with the Tredegar Ironworks being the pioneer user in the South Wales Coalfield.

Proceedings, SWIE: 1882-3, Vol. XVII

of what he described as being the 'great [technical] exertions … to improve machinery for rolling' of rail.

Working at the ironworks involved a ten hour day's shift that began at 5.30 a.m.[109] Every one employed at the works inhaled fumes of smoke and sulphur. During the years 1838, 1839, and 1840 Tredegar ironworkers were fully employed. The works' pig iron production output tonnage for the respective years were 15,526, 14,861, and 15,288.[110] Yet, some ironworkers during this period of years possessed reserves of energy to actively support a campaign seeking radical political change.

Chartists[111]

During the 1830s a national movement gathered pace to achieve 'six points of the People's Charter' that included winning electoral rights for ordinary people.[112] On the cusp of 1839 around ten Monmouthshire Chartist lodges met to nurture worker support for the movement. Lodge meetings were held at Tredegar and Blackwood.[113]

In April 1839, Homfray received intelligence that a Chartist rally was to be held in Tredegar on the 1st May. He with other magistrates served notices to close the town's public houses on May Day. A Chartist 'procession' through the town' occurred and the ironmaster watched it in the company of other magistrates. He also 'distinguished himself' by 'going round the beer-shops several times during the day to see that the order of the magistrates was not infringed'.[114] Later in May, a Chartist gathering occurred in a field at Blackwood. The gathering's speeches, some in Welsh, were listened to by Samuel Homfray Jnr and two other magistrates. 'The tone' of the speakers was deemed to have been 'much subdued'.[115]

The processions and gatherings were a prelude to insurrection. In November 1839, cohorts of Tredegar ironworkers and Sirhowy Valley miners joined other cohorts of mainly Monmouthshire workers and marched on Newport. A riot was put down. On the cusp of 1840, the government convened a Special Commission at Monmouth to try the arrested Chartists that included leaders like Zephaniah Williams (1795-1872). Williams, born near Argoed, had earlier served as an agent of the Sirhowy Ironworks. Homfray was a member of the Commission's twenty-three man Grand Jury. The Chartist leaders lost their trials and were exiled to Van Diemen's Island (today Tasmania), but years later received pardons.[116]

'In the years after' the Chartists marched on Newport 'there were frequent references to 'bad feeling in South Wales, and a few signs of renewed interest in revolutionary politics'.[117] Moreover, 'there was a tendency in the early 1840s to regard every form of worker action as Chartist-inspired or revolutionary'.[118] Oliver Jones observed: 'After the debacle at Newport, Chartism never recovered its former strength though as a force it was by no means spent'. 'With the exception of annual parliaments all the principles of the Charter are now on the Statute Book'. He also promoted a thought: 'It is well that we sometimes remind ourselves of the part played by Tredegar and Sirhowy in the long struggle for democracy'.[119] People lower down the Sirhowy Valley can equally lay claim to the meaning implied in his thought.

Chartist Statue, Chartist Bridge, Blackwood. In 1839, some workers employed at Tredegar Ironworks and Sirhowy Valley colliers joined with other South Wales and Monmouthshire workers and marched on Newport. The march was part of a Chartist campaign for Parliamentary reform such as winning voting rights for ordinary people. The statue honours the memory of the march.   *Author*

Beginnings

Concerning the development of industry, Oliver Jones concluded his historical study by observing that 'by the 1840s the early days of Sirhowy and Tredegar were over. The Industrial Revolution had done its work'. He acknowledged that 'yet to come' were 'bigger Iron Works and the bigger collieries'.[120] The beginnings of that future arose from investment decisions made by Samuel Homfray Jnr and partners during the period when local Chartist power grew to its crest. Tredegar Ironworks pit sinkings, with the exceptions of the years 1830 and 1834, had been singular events spread over three decades before 1838. However, from 1838 until 1841, as the following table shows, the pattern became two pit sinkings a year:[121]

Year	Pit Name or Number
1838	Steven Charle's Pit; No. 8
1838	Yard Pit; No. 10. In the Top Yard near Yard Level
1839	No. 9. (Not to be confused with Sirhowy No. 9)
1839	Evan Evan's Pit; No. 11. South of No. 8
1840	Globe Pit; No. 5
1840	David Jervis's Pit; No. 12. South of No. 11
1841	Mountain Pit; No. 7
1841	Upper Ty Trist.

Moreover, as the next table reveals, by 1841 the potential pig iron making capacity of the ironworks was increased due to two extra blast furnaces:[122]

Year	Owner	Built	in Blast
1839	Thompson & Co.	5	5
1841	Thompson & Co.	7	6
1843	Joint Stock	7	6
1847	Tredegar Iron Co.	7	7

Thus from 1841, there was the prospect of a call for coal as coke to charge seven blast furnaces. Pits had to be sunk to replace exhausted level and pit workings. Yet, investing in a two year pit sinking pattern after 1838 suggests that the owners of the Tredegar Ironworks had other markets in mind for local coal.

Steam Coal

Significantly, after 1838, with the realisation of the imagination of the engineer Isambard Kingdom Brunel (1806-1859), a new niche market was created for 'Tredegar coal'. Prior to 1838, Brunel proposed to the Great Western Railway Company the idea of building a steam ship to operate a Bristol-New York route. The substitution of steam power for sail to propel ocean-going ships had yet to be proved. Brunel was enabled to take on the challenge, and designed the paddle steamer *Great Western*, which had an estimated 'burden of 1,400 tons'.[123] The ship's structure was built of oak with iron stiffening. Any tender from Brunel to the Tredegar Ironworks for the supply of iron stiffening would more than likely have been declined.

'Tredegar coal' was though chosen by Brunel to stoke the boilers of the *Great Western* so that steam raised powered the Maudslay, Sons & Field marine engine that drove the ship's paddles. 'Six hundred tons of [Tredegar] coal was the general quantity taken on board' of the ship that made her maiden voyage in 1838. The price paid by the Great Western Steam Ship Company for ship coal at Bristol in 1841 was 11s. 6d. per ton.[124] In 1840, a newspaper advertisement broadcasted that Tredegar coal exclusively powered the *Great Western*.[125]

Then in 1841, Captain Hosken, who skippered the *Great Western* on eighteen voyages, told a House of Commons committee meeting that 'Tredegar coal' was 'advantageous for steaming' because 'he had never lost one hour of time, he had always proceeded, at the time appointed, to sea and had uniformly arrived, without any stoppage in the channel [Bristol Channel?], under every variety of weather and circumstances, night and day'. For comparison purposes, the captain had 'tried [coal from] Liverpool, Scotch, Pictou, Sidney, and Newcastle, and

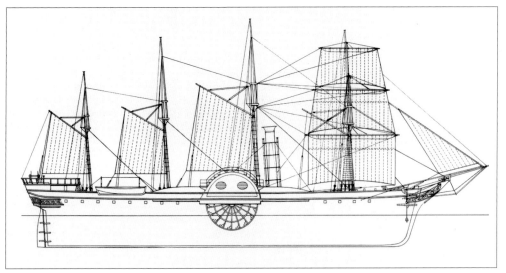

Paddle Steamer *Great Western*. An 1837 side elevation drawing of Isambard Kingdom Brunel's pioneering sea-going steam ship. Powered by Tredegar coal.
Courtesy of Science Museum/ Science & Society Picture Library

the coal in America; and with the exception of Anthracite and another coal in America, which we can only use when going very slow, we use one-fifth less Tredegar than any other'. Moreover, regarding a practical aspect of stoking, he revealed that 'we find a difference in cleaning our fires with the Tredegar coals; we never clean our fires before the fifth day, and sometimes it is seven or eight days; but with every other description of coals we are obliged to clean every three or four days, thereby causing a great deal of waste as well as injury to the fire bars'.[126] Captain Hosken's testimony not only roused further interest in Tredegar coal, but helped promote the link between the Monmouthshire part of the South Wales Coalfield and the term 'steam coal'.

As early as 1821, when the Royal Navy ordered its 'first of class' steam paddle-driven ship, the Admiralty took an interest in the qualities of coal for raising steam. In 1844, the Tredegar Company was invited by the Admiralty to tender for the supply of coal to power steam ships.[127]

However, much more propitiously for the Tredegar Iron Company, around the cusp of the 1840s, a Monmouthshire coalowner, Thomas Powell of the Gaer, Newport, met a County Durham mining engineer, John Nixon. The engineer had registered that the South Wales Coalfield possessed coal with

qualities ideal for powering marine steam propulsion. Powell had just opened a colliery near Aberaman, south of the town of Aberdare. Powell accepted Nixon's offer to act as an agent to introduce Aberaman Colliery coal to France. Between the years 1840 and 1843, the County Durham man proved to River Loire steamship operators the value of Powell's Aberaman coal. He thus enabled a breakthrough for the South Wales Coalfield: entry into the coal market of France. But much more notably, Nixon's French success was the start of the South Wales Coalfield gaining a global reputation as the prime source for fuel to power steam ships.[128]

Admiralty coal-steam raising trials between the years 1848 and 1851 further endorsed the superior merits of Welsh steam coal. Coals trialled were supplied from at least the coalfields of Durham and Northumberland, termed 'Newcastle Coal', Scotland and South Wales. The trials resulted in the Admiralty listing steam coals mined in an area of Glamorgan, with Aberaman as a useful reference location, as the fuel to fire the boilers of Her Majesty's ships.

Over a period from the 1st April 1858 to the 23rd March 1871, Tredegar coal was trialled fifteen times by the Admiralty.[129] The Admiralty's hand-written trial results for Tredegar coal were found impossible to decipher. However, in 1858, the owner of

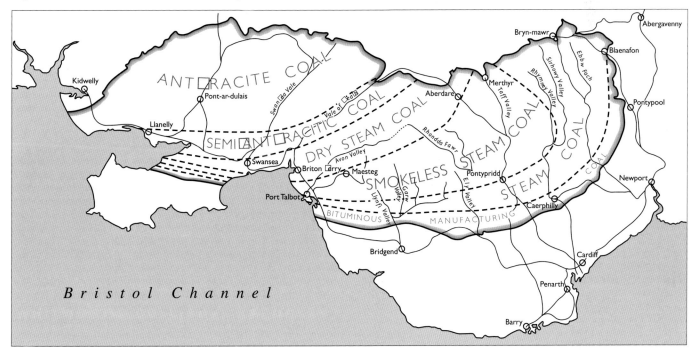

South Wales Coalfield and its varieties of coal. Used by the coal industry of South Wales at the start of twentieth century.

Newport Docks at opening in 1842. The dock's access involved foresight since it was sized in anticipation of steam ships that were much larger than sailing ships.

Reproduced with permission of Newport Museum & Art Gallery

collieries producing Tredegar coal was invited to tender for a contract to supply 'steam vessel coal' by the Admiralty's Royal Dock Yard, Pembroke.[130] The invitation to tender also included Aberaman Merthyr and Ebbw Vale coals whose trial results were published in 1857.[131]

Although Ebbw Vale coal needed more stoking and gave off more smoke than the Admiralty's highest ranked coals such as Aberaman Merthyr,[132] merchant ship owners were gifted by the trials further grounds for using Monmouthshire steam coal to power their ships. The evaporative power of Ebbw Vale coal was only 5% less than Aberaman Merthyr coal. The income of a merchant ship owner was determined by the weight of cargo transported by sea. A steam ship carrying coal as fuel meant that the owner lost some related weight in cargo, and so forfeited income. Bunkering a steam ship with Monmouthshire steam coal offered the prospect of carrying at least 15% more weight in cargo than a ship powered by Newcastle coal.

Moreover, and notable, due in part to knowledge gained from the Admiralty trials, coals of the South Wales Coalfield were found to 'change profoundly in character and with considerable regularity as they are traced across the coalfield'.[133] A map that illustrated the types of coal found in the coalfield was in common use at the start of the twentieth century.[134] The coal types were classified on the map as zones: manufacturing, steam, smokeless steam, dry steam, semi-anthracitic, and anthracite. Although the boundaries between each zone can be viewed as arbitrary, an area of the 'steam' zone lay under the Sirhowy Valley due to coal seams in a group of strata comprising the top of 'Lower Coal Measures' and the lower part of 'Upper Coal Measures'. The remarks made by Captain Hosken in 1841 about Tredegar coal heralded the 'steam' coal zone.

Great Western also had a profound effect upon Mr Cubitt's engineering plans for Newport docks. In January 1839, the Newport Dock Company held a meeting about 'adapting the entrance lock from the river into the Basin, for the admission of steam ships' whilst catering for 'enlarged dimensions of modern vessels'. Present at the meeting was Samuel Homfray Jnr who seconded a resolution: 'That it is desirable that the dock be constructed upon a scale to admit vessels of the dimensions of

the Great Western steamer'. The resolution was accepted with some provisos.[135] Newport Docks opened for trade on the 10th October 1842, to capitalise partly upon the promise of greater shipments of steam coal from Monmouthshire.

However, around 1845, the market distribution of Tredegar coal, and other differences, annoyed Charles Morgan of Tredegar (1792-1875), the grandson of Sir Charles Gould Morgan, later 1st Baron Tredegar. The Tredegar Iron Company sent steam coal by rail to other ports as well as Newport. Charles Morgan inherited the Tredegar Estate in 1846 after the death of his father, another Charles Morgan of Tredegar born in 1760. In the late 1840s, Charles Morgan of Tredegar took legal action to contest the company's practice of sending coal to any port, and also, dealt with later, importing iron ore. He 'maintained that under their lease, the Tredegar Company had no power to import ore from abroad or send coal elsewhere other than to Newport'. On the 13th March 1848, Mr W. N. James of Lincoln's Inn held that 'the company could import foreign ores and send coal away [to other ports]'.[136] The shipment of iron rail by the company appears never to have become a matter of dispute with the landowner.

Retirement of Samuel Homfray Junior[137]

On the 26th August 1853, 150 people gathered for a dinner at Tredegar Town Hall to mark Samuel Homfray Junior's retirement 'from the management of the Tredegar Works'. The resident partner had overseen a business that had flourished. 'The 1830s, '40s and '50s were the heyday for Welsh rail'.[138] The steady growth in blast furnaces capacity at the works offers a simple measure of his response to the market created by the Railway Age.

Another factor that had a bearing upon the development of the Tredegar Iron Company's fortunes is proposed. Samuel Homfray Jnr possessed a mind that could embrace the business risk posed by the early adoption of technical invention. His appointment in 1828 of Thomas Ellis junior as engineer-in-charge of the Tredegar Works had profound effects. Steam locomotion was pioneered in Monmouthshire. The raising of coal using balance-winding was also, seemingly, introduced into the county in the Tredegar district. The decisions Homfray made to sink two pits a year between 1838 until 1841, further proved key to Tredegar coal seizing commercial opportunities presented by the advent of steam ship propulsion. In supporting a motion at an 1839 meeting of the Newport Dock Company he also enabled the new dock to be engineered to take steam ships. The Tredegar Iron Company's business gained from the application of engineers' ideas.

In an effusive speech, the chairman of the Tredegar Town Hall dinner, Thomas Brown, asserted that the ironmaster was 'a man of no ordinary character'. As a magistrate 'no man could be more upright or anxious to do even-handed justice'. Regarding 'political strife', which 'came among them occasionally', 'Mr Homfray over came all obstacles' in 'those contests' and brought 'forth feelings of great respect'. He claimed that the ironmaster's 'acts of charity were so unbounded: the widows and orphans, the old and decrepit were all recipients of his kindness'. William Jones, a master smith, spoke for Tredegar Ironworks workers. He paid tribute to a 'worthy master'. 'Mr Homfray' was 'honest and upright'. 'He had never appealed to him in vain, nor had any other workman, but if their demands were reasonable their application was at once granted. During the unfortunate times when strikes occurred, Mr Homfray was foremost to settle them, and had on all occasions succeeded to the satisfaction of the workmen and the tradesmen'.

Nevertheless, perhaps key to appreciating Samuel Homfray Junior's stature as a partner lies in the reasons for the variety of names used for the ironworks business. The name Tredegar Iron Company was entered in the Robert Stephenson & Co. works ledger and sustained use of the name was found thereafter. Yet, during the period he served as resident partner, the business was also cited as: Samuel Homfray and Company, Thompson & Company, Thompson, Forman & Company, and Tredegar Ironworks Company. No explanation was found for such diversity in names for the business. Nevertheless, S. Homfray Esq. was recognised in Monmouthshire for 'possessing great and varied ability in business' and to have 'applied that talent, as to promote the well-being of the industrious classes'.[139]

For retirement, he removed from Bedwellty House to live at Glen Usk near Caerleon, Monmouthshire. The move ensured 'the Morgan-Homfray connection' remained convivial. The relationship was constant and 'operated on a number of levels'. 'Strong' family links were sustained.[140] The Tredegar ironmaster was 'a frequent guest at the house of his cousin Charles'.[141] In the 1840s Homfray served as the election agent for Octavius Morgan,[142] 'supporting his Protectionist stance through political crisis of Peel's ministry', and gave 'considerable encouragement to the Morgans in their [commercial] schemes'.[143]

However, reflecting upon the thirty-five years he had resided at Bedwellty House, 'from which he had been absent only a short period', Samuel Homfray Junior claimed that he had 'endeavoured to foster' the town of Tredegar 'and make it such as it now stands in the county of Monmouth'.[144]

NOTES

1 In 1934, J. H. Thomas, of the Tredegar Minerals Estate Office, Cardiff, produced a short historical account of the 'Tredegar Mineral Estate'. His account identifies Morgan of Tredegar minerals property dispersed around the counties of Glamorgan and Brecon as well as Monmouthshire. An edition of J. H. Thomas's account was saved from destruction and kept at Tredegar Library. William Smith produced and published a facsimile of J. H. Thomas's account.

2 John Evans, 'Early Industrial Development', in *The Gwent County History, Vol. 3, The Making of Monmouthshire, 1736-1780*, ed. Madeleine Gray and Prys Morgan. (University of Wales Press, 2009), pp.372-4.

3 David Freeman, *Tredegar House*. (Newport Borough Council, 1989). p.3.

4 Arthur Raistrick, *Dynasty of Iron Founders*. (Sessions Book Trust, 1989). p.18.

5 Edgar Jones, *A History of GKN Volume One: Innovation & Enterprise 1759-1918*. (Macmillan, 1987), p.5 and p. 11.

6 John Evans, 'Early Industrial Development', op. cit., p.372.

7 John Evans, 'Early Industrial Development', op. cit., p.373, shows a part of the map. Llyfrgell Genedlaethol Cymru/National Library of Wales, Tredegar map, Vol. 4, map LV.

8 John Evans, *op. cit.*, p.372 & p.373.

9 David Freeman, op. cit., p.7.

10 John Lloyd, *Early History of the Old South Wales Iron Works 1760-1840*. (1906), p.145.

11 Arthur Gray-Jones, *A History of Ebbw Vale*. (Gwent Count Council, 1970), p.46.

12 Oliver Jones, *The Early Days of Sirhowy and Tredegar*. (Tredegar Historical Society, 1969), p.31.

13 'Black Band' is a 'coaly' 'clay ironstone containing sufficient carbonaceous matter to allow calcining [roasting] without the extra fuel'. H. M. Hudspeth and D. W. Phillips, *Coal Measure Rocks: Part 1 – Classification, Nomenclature and Relative Strengths*. (HMSO, 1937), p.18. However, according to William Truran, not until about 1830 did ironmasters 'extensively' use this 'peculiar ore' for smelting. William Truran, *The Iron Manufacture of Great Britain*. (1855), footnote, p.8.

14 Oliver Jones, op. cit., p.30.

15 Charles Wilkins, *The History of the Iron, Steel, Tinplate and other Trades of Wales*. (1903), p.175.

16 Arthur Gray-Jones, op. cit., pp.47-48.

17 Oliver Jones, op. cit., p.31.

18 M. J. Dowden, 'Land and Industry: Sir Charles Morgan, Samuel Homfray and the Tredegar Lease of 1800', *Cylchgrawn Llyfrgell The National Library of Wales Journal*, Vol. XXVII (1993), pp.27-28.

19 Oliver Jones, op. cit., p.33.

20 Evan Powell, *History of Tredegar*.(1884), p.19.

21 Trevor Boyns, 'Communications and Commerce', in *The Gwent County History, Vol. 4, Industrial Monmouthshire, 1870-1914*, ed. Chris Williams, Ralph A. Griffiths, and Sian Rhiannon Williams. (University of Wales Press, 2011), p.57.

22 Laurence Ince, *The South Wales Iron Industry 1750-1885*. (Ferric, 1993), p.109.

23 Jeremy K. Knight, *Blaenavon Ironworks*. (Cadw, Revised edition 1992), p.8.

24 Oliver Jones, op. cit., pp.35-38.

25 For a full account of Mayberry and Wilkin's attempt to set up a Tredegar Forge see John Lloyd, op. cit., pp.136-139.

26 Oliver Jones, op. cit., p.37.

27 M. J. Dowden, op. cit., p.28.

28 Laurence Ince, op. cit., p.57.

29 Michael Atkinson and Colin Baber, *The Growth and Decline of the South Wales Iron Industry 1760-1880*. (University of Wales, 1987), p.51. The Hartfords and Bacon families were also identified as 'notable' sources of capital finance.

30 M. J. Dowden, op. cit., p.28.

31 'Heads of Sir Charles Morgan's 20th March, 1800'. Ref: 266 Maybery, Llyfrgell Genedlaethol Cymru National Library of Wales.

32 John Lloyd, op. cit., pp.143-144.

33 Edgar Jones, op. cit., p.13.

34 John Lloyd, op. cit., p.142.

35 Oliver Jones, op. cit., p.38.

36 M. J. Dowden, op. cit., pp.24-26.

37 M. J. Dowden, op. cit., p.29.

38 M. J. Dowden, op. cit., pp.24-26.

39 John Lloyd, op. cit., p.143.

40 John Lloyd, op. cit., p.142.

41 John Lloyd, op. cit., p.143.

42 Trevor Boyns, op. cit., p.58.

43 M. J. Dowden, op. cit., p.30.

44 M. J. Dowden, op. cit., p.26.

45 M. J. Dowden, op. cit., p.30.

46 M. J. Dowden, op. cit., p.31.

47 House of Lords Records Office, Proceedings at Committees on Private Bills and Other Matters, Session 1801/2 as referenced by M. J. Dowden, op. cit., p.32.

48 M. J. Dowden, op. cit., p.32.

49 M. J. Dowden, op. cit., p.34.

50 M. J. Dowden, op. cit., p.34.

51 Laurence Ince, op. cit. p.135.

52 Oliver Jones, op. cit., p.44. The materials that comprised the shale tips were not detailed.

53 William Smith, *The History of the Tredegar Mineral Estate*. (Park Mile, 2013), p.11.

54   Michael Atkinson and Colin Baber, *op. cit*, p.7; from J. M. Winter (ed.), *War and Economic Development*. (Cambridge, 1975), pp. 91-103.

55   John Lloyd, op. cit., p.144. Lloyd sourced Tredegar Works' annual output figures from: Scrivenor's *Iron Trade*, p.126 – 1802-1830, and: Scrivenor's *Iron Trade*, p.294 –1831-1840.

56   'Monmouthshire', *The Morning Chronicle*, 26 Oct 1816.

57   Oliver Jones, op. cit., p.77-78.

58   'Some South Wales Collieries: No. 2 The Tredegar Iron and Coal Company Limited', *The Welsh Coalfields*, reprinted from 'The Syren and Shipping' (1906) [hereafter WCF: TI&C], p.45.

59   Regarding the rent for 1778 see Table 6, Michael Atkinson and Colin Baber, op. cit., p.23. The data for the table was taken from John Lloyd, op. cit..

60   Michael Atkinson and Colin Baber, op. cit., p.23.

61   Oliver Jones, op. cit., p.49.

62   John Lloyd, op. cit., p.144.

63   Michael Atkinson and Colin Baber, op. cit, p.8.

64   Oliver Jones, op. cit., p.41.

65   John B. Hilling, 'The Development of Tredegar 1800-1820', *Gwent Local History*, Journal of the Gwent Local History Council, No.94 (2003), p.58.

66   Oliver Jones, op. cit., pp.60-79.

67   Oliver Jones, op. cit., p.22.

68   Oliver Jones, op. cit., p.72.

69   Oliver Jones, op. cit., p.78-79.

70   Gwyn A. Williams, *When Was Wales*? (Penguin, 1985), p.172.

71   Charles Wilkins, op. cit., p.178.

72   'Sanguinary Outrage by Scotch Cattle', *The Glamorgan, Monmouth & Brecon Gazette*, 1 Nov 1834, p.3.

73   Charles Wilkins, op. cit., p.179.

74   Oliver Jones, op. cit., p.79.

75   Table of pit sinkings. Oliver Jones, op. cit., p.50.

76   OS Ref No. SO 147077.

77   Charles Wilkins, op. cit., p.179.

78   WCF: TI&C, p.45.

79   Oliver Jones, op. cit., p.57.

80   Philip Riden and John G. Owen, *British Blast Furnace Statistics*. (Merton Press, 1995), p.28.

81   John Lloyd, op. cit., p.144.

82   Letter, C. W. Ellis to *Monmouthshire Evening Post*, 23 Feb 1912.

83   Letter, C. W. Ellis, op. cit., 23 Feb 1912.

84   J. G. H. Warren, *A Century of Locomotive Building by Robert Stephenson & Co. 1823-1923*. (1923, reprint 1970). pp.140-149.

85   C. W. Ellis's letter detailed that his ancestor met Robert Stephenson, and Robert Stephenson Junior. Robert Stephenson's marriage produced no children. George Stephenson was active as an engineer and became the first president of the Institution of Mechanical Engineers for the years 1847-48, and was succeeded as president by his son, Robert, who died in 1859.

86   Information courtesy of Dr Michael Bailey, extracted from the works records of Robert Stephenson & Co., The National Railway Museum Archives, York.

87   J. G. H. Warren, op. cit., pp.152-158.

88   Also reported was that the locomotive had to stop twice during its twenty-four mile journey from the Tredegar Works to Newport so as to replenish the water 'reservoir', which took 'about three quarter [of] an hour each time'. 'Newport', *Monmouthshire Merlin* (hereafter MM), 26 Dec 1829, p.3.

89   Letter, C. W. Ellis, op. cit.

90   A. Basset, 'The Port of Newport and the Coal Field', *Proceedings, South Wales Institute of Engineers* [hereafter SWIE], Vol.V (1866), pp.147-8.

91   According to the newspaper article, the 'steam-tug', had been successfully run 'twelve months' earlier. 'Latest Intelligence - Steam Carriages', MM, 27 March 1830, p.3.

92   'Inquests taken before William Brewer, Esq. Coroner', MM, 23 Oct 1830, p.3.

93   Oliver Jones, op. cit., p.54.

94   Letter, C. W. Ellis, op. cit.

95   'Railway Accident', *The Welshman*, 5 May 1843, p.3.

96   'Newport and Nantyglo Railway', MM, 29 Apr 1843, p.4.

97   Charles Wilkins, op. cit., p.182.

98   Charles Wilkins, op. cit., p.182.

99   'Latest Intelligence - Steam Carriages', MM, 27 March 1830, p.3.

100 Oliver Jones, op. cit., p.50.

101 Oliver Jones, op. cit., p.50.

102 Oliver Jones, op. cit., p.57.

103 Charles Wilkins, op. cit., p.180.

104 See James Colquhoun, 'On Hot Blast Stoves', SWIE, Vol.XIII (1882-1883). Colquhoun, general manager Tredegar Iron & Coal Company,

kept an original drawing of Neilson's 'stove' pipe from which 'sprung the many varieties that have been erected in all parts of the country', see p.472.

105 Charles Wilkins, op. cit., p.180.

106 Charles Wilkins, op. cit., p.181.

107 J. C. Carr and W. Taplin, *History of the British Steel Industry*. (Basil Blackwell, 1962), p.7.

108 William Menelaus, 'On Rolling Heavy Iron Rail', SWIE, Vol.II (1860-61), p.82.

109 'District Intelligence', *Western Mail* [hereafter WM], 13 March 1873, p.4.

110 John Lloyd, op. cit., p.144.

111 Oliver Jones, op. cit., pp.82-83.

112 The six points were: a vote for every man aged 21 and over; voting by ballot; the abolition of property qualification for MPs; payment of MPs; equal number of electors per constituency; and annual Parliaments.

113 David J. V. Jones, *The Last Rising: The Newport Chartist Insurrection of 1839*. (University of Wales Press, paperback 1986), p.65.

114 'Chartist Meeting at Tredegar', MM, 4 May 1839, p.3.

115 'Chartist Meeting at Blackwood', MM, 25 May 1839, p.3.

116 David J. V. Jones, op. cit., pp.186-198.

117 David J. V. Jones, op. cit., p.219.

118 David J. V. Jones, op. cit., p.224.

119 Oliver Jones, op. cit., p.109.

120 Oliver Jones, op. cit., p.109.

121 Oliver Jones, op. cit., p.50.

122 Philip Riden and John G. Owen, op. cit., p.28.

123 'West-India-Packet Station', *The British Mercury*, 18 Sept 1841. The *Great Western* was 'about 16½ feet even keel'. 'She drew from 12 feet 9 inches to 14 feet' on the 'return voyage' [to Avon].

124 'West-India-Packet Station', op. cit., 18 Sept 1841.

125 'To the Editor of *Monmouthshire Merlin*, Steam Coals, Tredegar Ironworks, near Newport, Monmouthshire', *Hampshire Telegraph and Sussex Chronicle*, 9 March 1840, p.3. The advertisement included a letter by Christopher Claxton, managing director, Great Western Steam Ship Company.

126 'Royal Mail Steam Packet Station', MM, 25 Sept 1841, p.3.

127 J. H. Morris and L. J. Williams, *The South Wales Coal Industry 1841-1871*. (University of Wales Press, 1958), p.29.

128 Leslie M. Shore, *Peerless Powell Duffryn of the South Wales Coalfield*. (Lightmoor, 2011), p.17.

129 An entry from the Admiralty coal returns summary of Welsh Coals (Steam) at Admiralty Dock Yards from 1st April 1858 to 23 March 1871. Coalowners Association, Llyfrgell Genedlaethol Cymru / National Library of Wales (LLGC/NLW Location L2/4/2 (iv).

130 'Contract for Steam Vessel Coals', *Pembrokeshire Herald and General Advertiser*, 7 May 1858, p.3. In 1860, the Royal Dock Yard, Pembroke, required that the coal be 'handpicked or properly screened and made free from small coal', and be 'fresh raised'. *Pembrokeshire Herald and General Advertiser*, 3 Aug 1860, p.3

131 Mr Cox, 'On the Combustion of Coal', SWIE, Vol.1 (1857), table, p.222.

132 J. H. Morris and L. J. Williams, op. cit., p.35.

133 Regardless, even in 1944 it remained vital for a review of British coal to observe: 'When comparing South Wales coals with coals from other coalfields, certain factors should be noted. For instance, the free-burning coals of South Wales have, compared with the free-burning coals of elsewhere, a much lower percentage of volatile matter, a much lower percentage of inherent moisture, less hydrogen and a considerably greater calorific value on the dry ash-free basis'. *The Efficient Use of Fuel*. (HMSO, 1944), p.10.

134 See Hugh Bramwell, 'The Economics of the South Wales Coalfield', SWIE, Vol. XXXVI (1920), Plate II.

135 'Newport Dock Company', MM, 19 Jan 1839, p.3.

136 William Smith op. cit., p.13.

137 'Homfray Testimonial', *The Cardiff and Merthyr Guardian Glamorgan Monmouth Gazette*, 10 Sept 1853, p.4.

138 J. C. Carr and W. Taplin, op. cit., p.7.

139 'Testimonial to S. Homfray Esq', MM, 19 Aug 1853, p.4.

141 M. J. Dowden, op. cit., p.36.

142 Tredegar Park MSS, 406-452, Llyfrgell Genedlaethol Cymru / National Library of Wales.

142 Charles Octavius Swinnerton Morgan (1803-88) became MP for the county of Monmouth 1841-74. He was 1st Lord Tredegar's brother. He was also a noted antiquary.

143 M. J. Dowden, op. cit., p.36.

144 'Homfray Testimonial', *The Cardiff and Merthyr Guardian Glamorgan Monmouth Gazette*, 10 Sept 1853, p.4.

Chapter Two
OWNERSHIP CHANGES

The community of Tredegar was a legacy of industrial enterprise that had enabled the Tredegar Ironworks to grow under Samuel Homfray Junior's management. People were attracted to the town for employment due to mining and the ironworks. The 1851 census counted 12,171 people living at Tredegar. By that year, the town's population was 'overwhelmingly composed of migrants or sons and daughters of migrants' attracted there for work.[1] In 'terms of population origin, language and culture the town was overwhelmingly Welsh. Already, however, this Welshness was being diluted by local concentrations of English and Irish migrants for whom English became the *lingua franca*'.[2]

In 1850, a London newspaper reporter visited Tredegar, which he thought was a 'town of rising importance'. However, he observed that 'many of the houses – and the lodging houses more particularly – are sadly overcrowded; indeed house accommodation should be extended – a subject well deserving the attention of the Tredegar Iron Company'. He learnt that 'some improvements have, since the advent of the cholera, been made in the sanitary conditions of the town by draining and cleansing, but much remains to be done before the town can be said to be well drained and lighted'. He witnessed though 'water sold from a barrel drawn by a horse in the streets – a bell used to inform its inhabitants that the necessity of life was near'. As some explanation for the water selling enterprise, he suggested that local wells had run dry due to the 'ground having been freely undermined in every direction for minerals'. Oddly, he noted that there 'were no beer-houses in Tredegar', which suggests that he did not roam around the town like Samuel Homfray Junior had done on May Day 1839.

The reporter further recorded that 'there was 'no "truck" – or at all events no violation of the right of the workmen to go to what ever market they please with their incomes'. As a Londoner, he probably accepted as the norm that shopkeepers flourished. Remarkably as early as the 1820s, when the Company Shop had a stronger hold on workers' purchases of household food and goods, owner-occupied shops traded.[3] Oliver Jones, over a century later, judged that the Company Shop was 'never allowed to become a tyranny in Sirhowy and Tredegar that it became in other places'.[4]

Concerning local worker wage rates and hours of working, the reporter reckoned that they were on a par with Merthyr Tydfil's. He was also told that a weekly pension was paid by the Tredegar Iron Company to their 'steady workmen' grown old and being 'past labour'.[5]

A year later the reporter could have written an article about a Tredegar attempt to bring its coal mining industry to the attention of the British public. A fifteen ton monolith of coal 'was hewn by John Jones' from the company's Yard Level with the 'aim of exhibiting it at the Great Exhibition' of 1851 at Crystal Palace. Alas 'probably the most famous "lump" of coal ever cut in Monmouthshire' did not make the journey to the exhibition.[6] Instead, the monolith of coal was placed in the grounds of Bedwellty House as a statement about Tredegar's importance as a mining town.

In the year 1854, Richard Powell Davis took on the management of Tredegar Ironworks. Since time had to elapse before he made his mark upon the running of the works, its output for a number of years after his appointment spoke for Samuel Homfray Junior's tenure of control. By 1855, the Tredegar works could operate eight blast furnaces and the weekly make of pig iron per furnace was 110 tons. For the year 1855, the works produced 45,760 tons of pig iron.[7] Thus, the works had grown five-and-a half fold in terms of output under Homfray. Regarding a Monmouthshire

The 15-ton monolith of coal shown is kept in the grounds of Bedwellty House, Tredegar. The monolith was cut at the Yard Level and is a tribute to the skill and methods used by collier John Jones. The Tredegar Company's intention was to show it at the 1851 Great Exhibition, Crystal Palace, Hyde Park, London.

Philip Hayman

ironworks' pig iron output league, in 1855 the works held fourth place. Top of the league was Rhymney (Bute) at 58,500 tons, the runner-up was Abersychan at 55,920 tons, and placed third was Nantyglo at 49,920 tons.[8]

By 1854, use of the 'furnace' label for Sirhowy was redundant. In 1844, the Harfords lost control of the Sirhowy and Ebbw Vale ironworks due to the 'misfortunes of their banking partner' to a six man partnership, which included Thomas Brown and was led by Abraham Darby.[9] At Sirhowy pig iron was made for the Ebbw Vale Ironworks up until around 1883 whilst coke was made there until 1905. Nevertheless, in 1855, the yield of iron from the five furnace Sirhowy Ironworks was 33,800 tons of iron.[10] Thus that year, the combined iron output of the two ironworks at the head of the Sirhowy Valley was 89,560 tons of iron.[11]

Tredegar Town Clock[12]

Arguably the erection of the Tredegar Town Clock in the late 1850s was not only a show of local self-esteem but announced that the iron industry flourished in the town. Mrs Mary Elizabeth Davis, the wife of the manager of the Tredegar Ironworks, was the prime mover for such a landmark. The cue for Mrs Davis actions might have been the notion of a clock tower for the Palace of Westminster mooted around the same time. Her husband offered to pay 80 per cent of the cost estimated for a town clock as long as she raised the balance. Although she died in the middle of 1857, the well of support she nurtured in the town for a clock tower idea was strong.

The town clock's foundation was laid in 1858. The Newport iron foundry of Charles Jordan cast the component parts of the

Tredegar Town Clock.   *Author*

seventy-two feet high tower. Although the exact date when the clock began to operate as a timepiece is not known, its contemporary was the Clock Tower of the Houses of Parliament. 'Big Ben', the great bell of the Houses of Parliament's Clock Tower was cast in 1858.[13] Nevertheless, in 1969, Oliver Jones wrote: 'The Town Clock can claim its own line of beauty – that of sturdy craftsmanship of a bygone age'. The descendants of John Jones and fellow Yard Level miners might be amused to read a suggestion that the Town Clock's design was influenced by art featured in the iron exhibits shown at the 1851 Great Exhibition[14]

The Town Clock did not necessarily win credit for introducing to the head of the Sirhowy Valley a local reference for the time of the day. The ironworks' 'hooter' sounded when its workers could take breakfast, dinner, and teatime.[15] Yet, the Town Clock may be considered to be a memorial to the men and boys who lost their lives working for the Tredegar Iron Company.

During the years 1851 to 1855, twenty-two fatalities occurred at the company's mine workings, and there were five explosions. During this period, attempts by Herbert Francis Mackworth, Her Majesty's (here after HM) Inspector of Mines, to prosecute Tredegar's ironmasters for inadequacies in mining practices failed. As outlined by G. W. J. Lowering: 'It was the owners of the collieries attached to the ironworks that Mackworth had the greatest difficulty. Not only did they form a majority on the Bedwellty bench, but he estimated that nearly one-half of the accidents that year [in Monmouthshire] had occurred in pits belonging to them'.[16] Such information suggests that the Tredegar Company did not tolerate any interference in the way it conducted mining.

Bedwellty Pits

The sinking of Bedwellty Pits for the company began in 1853 on roughly the 850 feet contour of the western hillside of the Sirhowy Valley, and two miles south of Bedwellty House.[17] The colliery involved greater investment than previous local mining ventures. Samuel Homfray Jnr and partners allocated a part of their wealth earned from the iron rail boom years to sink and engineer the colliery. The Tredegar Iron Company partners might have wondered if they were taking a gamble on a trade predicated upon the demand for steam coal to power merchant ships.

Perhaps the partners drew comfort from Thomas Powell's activities in the Rhymney Valley. From the site of Bedwellty Pits, a leap of a mile and a half south-west, over the highest point of Bedwellty Common, Twyn yr Hyddon – hill of the stag, sinking had begun at Powell's New Tredegar Colliery. In 1851, Temple Robert Stroud (1828-1908) initiated the sinking of Powell's colliery.[18] In October 1857, the desired seam of steam coal was found at 315 yards.[19] That Thomas Powell, a driven coal owner, persisted for years at New Tredegar Colliery to find steam coal was a sign that he judged that the return on his investment would eventually be profitable.

Thomas Ellis junior may have initiated the engineering of Bedwellty Pits. He ended twenty-five years of service with the Tredegar Company in 1854.[20] Years later, in 1861, 'Welsh workmen' carried him in a chair around the Great Western Railway's Swindon Works 'in celebration' of having produced 'the first newly rolled rail' from the work's rolling mill.[21] He was succeeded at Tredegar by Edwin Richards.

Edwin Richards's father was engineer and general manager of Rhymney Ironworks up until he died in 1839.[22] At Tredegar, nepotism played some part in Richards's immediate appointment of an assistant, his younger brother, Edward Windsor (1831-1921). E. Windsor Richards's formation as an engineer occurred at Rhymney Ironworks, and he was destined to become one of the 'outstanding engineers in the steel industry'.[23]

Seemingly though, the task of engineering Bedwellty Pits was delegated to Thomas Ellis (the younger), a son of Thomas Ellis junior. Thomas Ellis the younger was responsible for erecting the colliery's steam winding engines.[24] The colliery's shaft diameters were of 'large dimensions', one shaft being 16 feet

Bedwellty Pits in 1865. Sunk in 1853 to mine steam coal from the Elled seam and the Big Vein found respectively at depths of 210 and 250 yards.
The Illustrated London News

diameter and the other 11 feet. By 1865, the colliery's 'downcast' shaft bottomed out at around 255 yards. The downcast shaft cut through the Elled seam at 210 yards, the Big Vein at 250 yards, and a little deeper the Yard Vein. The other shaft was sunk to the Elled seam, and made the 'upcast'.[25] The colliery, it was claimed in 1865, featured 'ventilation of superior description' due to using a furnace at the foot of the upcast. Moreover, by 1865, the colliery had been linked underground to Ty Trist Colliery 'so that the means of ventilation and of escape are most abundant'.[26] Hewn from the Elled seam and Big Vein was steam coal. By the 1940s, when a far more rigorous classification of coals prevailed, the ideal use for the seams' coal was coking.[27]

The distribution of Tredegar Company goods, iron rail and coal, was also set for improvement. In 1859, Parliamentary powers were 'sought to change the name of the Sirhowy Tram Road Company to the Sirhowy Railway Company and to maintain and work it as a railway'.[28] An 1860 Act of Parliament not only enabled the desired change in company name but instigated the construction of a standard gauge railway line around 1863.[29] Sydney W. Yockney (1813-1893) was the engineer responsible for building the railway. He was an original member of the Great Western and South Wales Railway staff, and later in his career became the engineer and general manager of the London & North Western Railway (L&NWR).[30]

Other rail traffic options became available to the Tredegar Company. In 1862, the L&NWR took over the Merthyr, Tredegar, and Abergavenny Railway Company made financially weak trying to build a railway across the Heads of the Valleys. The takeover was a sign of a 'battle … between three of the largest companies in the country, the GWR, the L&NWR and the Midland Railway to gain a share' of business arising from the expansion of commercial opportunities in the valleys of South

Wales and Monmouthshire.[31] In acquiring the Heads of Valleys line, the L&NWR was placed cheek by jowl with the pulse of the coal and iron industries at the head of the Sirhowy Valley.

In June 1862, a four man partnership controlled the Tredegar Iron Company. Samuel Homfray Jnr and his uncle, Reverend Watkin Homfray, each held a sixth of the company's shares. The other shareholders were: Richard Fothergill, and William Henry Forman. For unknown purposes, Samuel Homfray Jnr used his shares as security to borrow from the company £19,073 1s. 3d.[32] No information was found to confirm if, or not, Homfray repaid the loan. Nevertheless, a few years later a company colliery manager faced a law court's bail charge, and would have been grateful that it was partly covered due to the generosity of the former ironmaster.

Rules and Regulations

In 1865, the Tredegar Iron Company issued Rules and Regulations for collieries and mine works to all its officials and workers. An 1855 Act of Parliament had ordered all coal owners to 'observe' a set of 'General Rules', seven in number, and to further provide 'Special Rules for Each Coal Mine'.[33] One of the 'General Rules' concerned underground ventilation The 1855 Act also commanded a coal owner to inform 'Persons employed' about the General and Special Rules by having them 'painted on a Board or Printed on paper'.[34] However, just five years later, the 1855 Act of Parliament was superseded by the 1860 Regulation and Inspection of Mines Act that contained more provisions and was much more exacting. Regarding 'General Rules', fifteen were listed of which an important addition was controls for the use of safety lamps.[35]

No earlier document by the Tredegar Iron Company concerning 'Rules and Regulations' was found than one issued

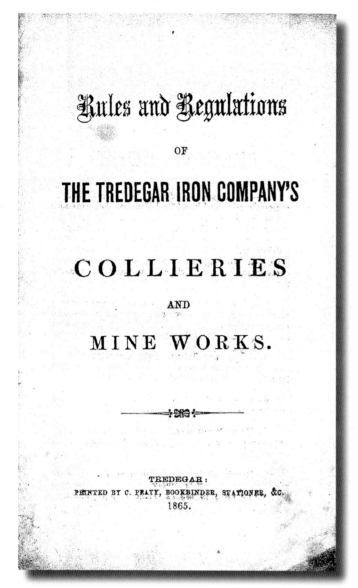

Rules and Regulations

OF

THE TREDEGAR IRON COMPANY'S

COLLIERIES

AND

MINE WORKS.

TREDEGAR:
PRINTED BY C. PRATT, BOOKBINDER, STATIONER, &C.
1865.

A facsimile of the cover page of a copy in the keeping of the Cardiff City Libraries Stacks.

by the company in 1865.[36] Likely to confuse, the document's 'Special Rules' are a verbatim copy of the 'General Rules' in the 1860 Act whilst the document's 'General Rules' meant 'Special Rules' under the Act.

The following selective outline of the company's 1865 Rules and Regulations gives some idea about the safety standards the company was aspiring to achieve. The opening section of the Rules and Regulations detailed fifteen 'Special Rules' but only a couple are given next. The first Special Rule required that 'an adequate amount of Ventilation shall be constantly produced in Coal Mines or Collieries and Ironstone Mines, to dilute and render harmless noxious gases'. The noxious gas was methane, but more commonly known as fire-damp. The third Special Rule dealt with the use of safety lamps. 'When ever Safety Lamps are required to be used, they shall first be examined and securely locked by a Person or Persons duly authorized for this purpose'.

The company's 1865 'General Rules' were to be 'observed by all persons in the management of, or employed in or about the Coal or Ironstone Mine'. The first 'General Rule' placed upon the colliery manager the onus for the 'charge and direction of the Mine and Works, and of all persons employed in or about the same'. He was given full power 'to carry out whatsoever may be necessary for safety, and for rendering effective the General and Special Rules'. He was accountable for employing 'competent Agents to superintend the mine and Workmen', and directed to

see that the foregoing employees 'clearly' understood and were 'attentive to their respective duties'. He was responsible for laying-out the 'Ventilation of the Mine so as to answer the first Special Rule'. Moreover, he had to 'take especial care that the General Rules' were 'attended to'. The colliery manager chose the form of lighting used underground. Where he judged that the use of candle light underground was unsafe, his duty was to sanction the use of locked safety lamps.

The duty of 'Engineers' was specified next in the company's General Rules. The Works' Engineer was charged with appointing 'competent persons' to 'superintend [colliery] machinery, to see that is proper and efficient, and it is kept in repair, and tested when necessary'. The 'Engineer' was expected to check and test winding machinery, 'ropes and chains and their fastenings' of a carriage [cage], before men were allowed to descend a mine's shaft. The Work's Engineer was further accountable for the maintenance of boiler plant and equipment.

The 'Engineer', put in sole charge of operating the prime colliery engine, appears to have been the forerunner of the winding-engine man. At a Tredegar Iron Company colliery or mine, no other person other than the Engineer was allowed in 'the [winding] engine house'. The 'Engineer' was expected to 'attend' also to 'all safety valves, steam gauges, and water gauges'.

The General Rules detailed the work of both 'Banksman' and 'Hitcher'. The Banksman was ordered to 'make the signals, and have control of the men at the shaft top [pit bank]'. A task for the Banksman was to 'prevent' alcoholic drink, and 'persons not sober from descending the shaft'. At the foot of a shaft, the Hitcher was responsible for signals to the Banksman regarding cage movement. The Banksman and Hitcher were expected to limit cage use to no more than eight men. The safe storage of coal, tools, and materials aboard a cage was another duty for the two officials.

The company's General Rules used the terms Underlooker or Gaffer for the post that was more commonly known in the South Wales Coalfield as Overman, which is used hereafter. The duties of the two foremost underground officials, the Overman and the Fireman, were prescribed in the General Rules. 'In the absence of the Manager', the Overman was granted 'full power and authority over all other persons employed underground'. Reporting directly to the Overman were the Hitcher and the Fireman. The Overman and the Fireman were expected to 'obey and enforce the Rules, and not suffer a breach of any without reporting to the Manager'. The Banksman was also accountable to the Overman for any tasks that affected underground work.

Maybe the three chief safety duties for the Overman were keeping 'full and effectual ventilation' of mine workings, seeing that underground 'roads [were] kept in a safe state', and to 'suspend operations attended with unusual risk'. Both the Overman and Fireman were expected to act to remove 'all accumulations of fire-damp' encountered.

The Fireman had two chief safety duties. First, to test 'carefully with a safety lamp, the whole of the workings, to ascertain whether the roof [was] safe and they are free from fire-damp, so as to caution any workman against entering any portion of the Mine, which may be in an improper condition'. Last, 'The Fireman shall examine the edges of every old working, rubbish place, fall in the roof, and return air-courses'.

Colliery workers had to observe ten 'General Rules', which are not fully detailed next. Workmen were obligated to obey colliery officials' directions. Every worker was held 'responsible for the safety of his working place, and in every place where several men are at work'. The Overman chose one worker 'to take charge of [a group of workers], and be more specifically responsible for, the safety of the working place'. A taboo for workers was leaving a 'lighted candle, nor any other light in any part of the Mine' when ending work. Workmen were further expected to observe rules concerning safety lamp use. 'Neglect of the Rules', or disobedience of officials, would lead to a workman being 'sent out of the Mine with a view to the investigation of the case, and the punishment of the offender'.

The degree of illiteracy among colliery workers hindered the application of the company's Rules and Regulations. At Bedwellty Pits, for example, some primitive selection test for underground jobs was used. Boys were allowed underground at ten years of age if they could read and write. Yet, illiterate boys of twelve years of age could be tasked to open and close underground ventilation doors.[37] In time, some of the boys became the next generation of colliers. However, it was the colliery manager who was charged under one of the 'General Rules' to 'take care that the Workmen' were 'acquainted with the Rules, causing them to be read over when desirable'.

Portrayed in words by the Tredegar Iron Company in its 1865 Rules and Regulations for collieries and mine works was managerial authoritarianism. The document spoke for an age where the management of workers was based upon a master and servant relationship. So maybe the age ought to be condemned for the tenor of the document. Or, from another perspective, the company, unless it had not issued General and Special Rules 'painted on a Board or Printed on paper' before, ought to be commended for meeting the 1860 Regulation and Inspection of Mines Act. The workers may have carped about the autocratic controls they were subjected to, but the virtuous intention of Rules and Regulations was to improve the safety of their dangerous occupation. Nonetheless, the company's 1865 Rules and Regulations set officials and workers a safety standard to meet. The likely penalties, in the event of anyone neglecting or wilfully violating the Rules and Regulations, upon a 'summary conviction' in a court of law, were fines or imprisonment.

'Colliery Explosion at Tredegar'

By June 1865, the Bedwellty Pits had been in operation for nearly two decades. Employed 'ordinarily' at Bedwellty Pits, in 1865 were between 200 and 300 workers.[38] However, the colliery had been 'idle for eighteen months' previous to, at the latest, May 1865.[39]

The colliery's manager was William Bevan. Born and bred at Tredegar, he had been employed for twenty years as an underground agent.[40] He had managed Bedwellty Pits for sixteen years. The duration of his time spent managing the colliery suggests he supervised its sinking beginning in 1849, which is earlier than the year of 1853 commonly found.[41]

According to a Tredegar collier, Mr J. Hutton, Bevan applied 'regular study to secure the protection of the underground workman; that could be proved; and if they searched the iron district, from Pontypool to Aberdare, as the saying was, they could not find a place better managed for air than the Tredegar Works …. they could go down at Bedwellty and pass through to Brynbach, and that showed there was plenty air from one end of the works to the other'. Moreover, he saluted William Bevan for his 'carefulness', 'diligence', and that 'there never was a more civil man to his workman'.[42] Such praise of a colliery manager appears not to accord with a man empowered by the state to act as an autocrat. The exercise of autocracy by a manager risked making him unpopular among officials. Moreover, loose gossip by embittered officials, overheard by colliery workers, fostered more antipathy towards the manager. The fear of losing his job, maybe, cautioned a colliery worker from criticising an official to his face, or sharing rude views about a colliery manager with an official.

Nevertheless, the Bedwellty Pits' manager was said to have set an example during the 1860 Black Vein Colliery, Risca, explosion that killed 146 men. David Davies, an overman at another company colliery, speaking in Welsh, stated that Bevan 'worked hard at Risca, while others appointed to go down with him neglected their duty'.[43] Late on Friday the 16th June 1865, William Bevan rushed to Bedwellty Pits to tackle an identical crisis, which became national news.

In early July 1865, the *Illustrated London News* reported the deaths of twenty-six men and boys due to an explosion of gas at Bedwellty Pits. The time and date of the explosion was between ten and eleven in the evening. The *Illustrated London News* item detailed that:

It seems that, on the morning of the explosion the "fireman" as he is called, whose duty is to see that the mine is free of inflammable vapours, went down as usual to examine the working places, and discovered gas in a cross-heading in the back workings, where a man named David Jones and his son worked. The accumulation of gas was by no means large, but the fireman thought it advisable to put the danger signal up. The colliery was worked entirely by naked lights, but if gas were discovered in any place safety-lamps would be provided for the men in the immediate neighbourhood.[44]

According to the *Illustrated London News*, father and son were issued safety lamps when they 'went down [the pit] on the day of the explosion'. The newspaper also related that David Jones and his son, John, of ten years of age, did not check for gas, and 'that, the gas getting too strong, fire was communicated from the lamp, and the explosion followed; and about half-past ten a sudden rumbling noise was heard by men at the top of the pit, and it was discovered that the gas had fired'. Since father and his son were killed by the explosion, the cause of the explosion cited by the *Illustrated London News* involved speculation. Furthermore, the newspaper did not mention that the head of the Sirhowy Valley had a history of miners being killed by underground explosions.

However, the London journalist's report made plain several harrowing aspects of the Bedwellty Pits explosion. 'Fortunately, the effect of the explosion did not reach the bottom of the shaft …. Gangs were immediately formed for the purpose [of rescue], and it was discovered that the gas had fired in the "back workings". Forty-six men and boys were working in this section of the colliery and by the dint of extraordinary exertion on the part of the exploring parties a good many were got out…'

The *Monmouthshire Merlin* gave further details about the Bedwellty Pits' explosion. 'The damage to the colliery is very small; one or two days work will suffice to set it to rights. The pestilent blast apparently was confined to a small area, and sped with the rapidity of lightning'. 'It may be mentioned that one boy, as if struck by a door, had received a violent blow on the head so severe, indeed, that the skull was laid open, and the brains protruded'.[45]

The *Illustrated London News* report disclosed that the colliery's 'back workings' lacked a sufficient flow of air. The use of furnace ventilation, like that at Bedwellty Pits, was common practice in the South Wales Coalfield. Although by around the middle of the 1800s the South Wales Coalfield colliery owners led the pioneering of mechanical ventilation in Britain, doubts prevailed about using complicated machinery. Thus, an appraisal that Bedwellty Pit's ventilation was of a 'superior description' was accepted as true by opponents of mechanical ventilation.

Nevertheless, the humane consciences of colliery manager and officials would have been troubled by the gruesome effect of the 1865 Bedwellty Pits' explosion. Wound up from underground was 'body after body'. The bodies 'landed on the [pit] bank' while news of the explosion spread. 'Hundreds' of Tredegar people 'gathered around the top of the pit. Mothers were seen in tears for sons, wives for their husbands, children for their fathers, and fathers deploring the loss of sons upon whom their old-age they depended for support'.[46]

The depth of grief felt in Tredegar after the June 1865 explosion at Bedwellty Pits is possibly beyond comprehension today. A list of the dead due to an explosion a century and a half ago could also be viewed as a futile gesture since the bond of kith and kin directly with the event may have perished. Yet, an obligation of a history about the Tredegar district is to recall the names and known details about men and boys who lost their lives on the 16th June 1865:[47]

Name	Living	Status
William Allen	Unknown	married, wife and family
David Beynon	Georgetown	25 years, single
George Carter	Cinder Tips	50, married, wife and one child
William Carter	do.	16 years, son of the above
Thomas James	Georgetown	30, wife and two children
Richard Jenkins	Cinder Tips	40, married, wife and family

Phillip Jenkins	do.	14 years, son of the above
Daniel Jones	Ebbw Vale	35, married, wife
David Jones	Georgetown	40, married, wife and four children
John Jones	do.	10 years, son of the above
John Jones	do.	34, single
Lewis Lewis	do.	40, married, wife, five children
Thomas Lewis	New Tips	13 years
Morgan Meredith	Cinder Tips	21, single
Thomas Meredith	do.	50, married one child-girl
Edwin Morgan	Market Street	10 years
Thomas Morgan	do.	14 years, brother of above
David Price	Georgetown	21, single
David Rees	High Street	30, single
Thomas Richards	Transport Row	19, single
Thomas Steed	Abode unknown	22, single
William Steed	do.	40, married, wife, no children
Thomas Thomas	Cinder Tips	30, married, wife and three children
Edward Watkins	New Tips	19, single
Charles Wedlock	New Tips	30, single
Thomas Williams	Mount Street	21, single

Also severely injured were two New Tip's men, Francis Thomas and John Lewis. Slightly injured was Lewis Williams of Lower Farm.

Adjourned Inquiry[48]

On the 13th July 1865, at the Greyhound Inn, Tredegar, an adjourned inquiry into the deaths at Bedwellty Pits assembled. The Coroner was W. H. Brewer. Two Newport solicitors, H. J. Davies and Mr Justice, acted for the company. William Bevan's legal representative, a Mr James, 'watched the proceedings'. A HM Inspector of Mines, Lionel Brough, was present.

William Bevan was the main witness called by the Coroner for cross-examination. The colliery manager told the inquiry that he went 'down the pit very often'. He recalled that the 'pit was all right' during his last underground inspection, which occurred a week before the 16th June, explosion. However, 'a little gas was found in the face of Roberts' heading' that could have been dealt with by repairing loose brattice door so that air could circulate. Nevertheless, soon afterwards, he told the colliery's overman, John Reynolds, to 'drive' the heading on as fast as he could'.

Collier Richard Jenkins was given the task to drive the heading. The colliery manager related that he met Richard Jenkins on the colliery surface on Wednesday the 13th June, and learnt that collier David Jones had 'taken down the door at cross hole in Roberts' heading'. Bevan asked Jenkins to 'tell John Jehu, the fireman, to have the door put up as soon as possible'. The collier replied that 'Jehu said he could not clear it till Saturday night'.

Bevan then narrated that on the afternoon of Thursday the 14th June he 'made it his business to go to the head of the pit' to ask John Jehu about the extent of underground gas and the status of the door. The fireman told the manager that 'it would not been safe' to put up the door 'until Saturday night'. In response to a question of the Coroner's, about the manager refraining from investigating the state of gas underground on the Wednesday the 13th June, Bevan stated: 'I thought there could not possibly be any danger. There were 8,000 or 9,000 feet of air passing per minute'. Adding that his reason for going to the pit head was not the gas, but to 'have the heading gone on with directly'. Regarding the state of gas underground at the time, he put the onus upon both the fireman and the overman to advise him, which he claimed they did not.

Nonetheless, at the inquiry, the colliery manager acknowledged that it had 'been proved there was danger' at Bedwellty Pits. He remarked: 'I think that David Jones's boy fired the gas. Had I

Funeral cortège at Tredegar for some of the twenty-six colliers killed in the 1865 explosion at Bedwellty Pits. The background includes the Tredegar Ironworks that then operated nine blast furnaces compared with the two when it was founded in 1800. *The Illustrated London News*

thought there had been a danger, I should have ordered all the men out of that part of the pit. I cannot account for the Jones's boy going into that place – it would only be conjecture'.

He followed his allegation about the action of the ten year old John Jones with an utterance about some of the duties of a colliery manager and overman. Regarding the employment of underground workers, he stated that the overman 'puts on all men without consulting me'. He also stated that it was the overman's duty to judge if the gas underground was a danger to life or not.

William Bevan's utterance was a cue for the HM Inspector of Mines to draw the Coroner's attention to the first 'Special' rule of the 1860 Regulation and Inspection of Mines Act. The reading of the rule gave the Coroner grounds to conclude: 'The manager is the responsible man for the management of the pit'.

During further cross-examination, William Bevan held that 'the overman did not report the gas to me'. He also confessed to not knowing about a small explosion at the colliery prior to the 16th June, which was mentioned at the inquiry. He then repeated that on the fateful Friday he 'did not apprehend danger'. His proceeded to describe the underground lighting practices of the colliery:

The pit is worked with naked lights, it is not sufficiently dangerous for lamps. We never give lamps to work by except they are locked. Those are my orders. A great number of men carry their own lamps that are not locked, and have done so for 20 years. It would be a hard case for us to stop them from taking their own lamps.

Regarding the actions of David Jones and his son, the manager attested that the father used a lamp. However, 'his boy had a naked light, and Jones himself *worked* [as emphasised by the *Monmouthshire Merlin*] with a naked light'.

William Bevan was subsequently questioned by the HM Inspector of Mines, who cited case examples of small quantities of gas detected underground to test the colliery manager's response. In summary: the colliery manager was adamant that with 'all that air' at Roberts' heading he did not 'apprehend there was any danger', and saw no need to go underground. On ending his cross-examination Lionel Brough declared: 'Mr Bevan has not done himself justice as to the quantity of air'. The colliery manager responded: 'the boy Jones must have gone into the cross hole and crawled in eight or ten yards. He could not have reached to have fired the gas with a naked light'.

The witness that followed the manager of Bedwellty Pits at the inquiry was the HM Inspector of Mines. He 'never had occasion to find fault with the quantity of air' at the colliery, which he had often visited. He was thus of the opinion:

That the catastrophe is by no means attributable to want of power or of proper area underground to produce a safe and adequate amount of ventilation. The gas that fired was that which was lying in the upper part of Roberts' cross heading, and the explosion occurred either at the intersection of the upper main cross hole, or at the mouth of the little cross hole, a few yards westwards thereof – most likely at the latter.

Later in his testimony, Lionel Brough stated 'that the third General rule [of the 1860 Regulation and Inspection of Mines Act] was disobeyed on that morning; it demands that "whenever safety lamps are required to be used, they shall first be examined and securely locked". Had it been done that morning David Jones and his boy would not have been able to fire the gas, and so would have escaped and with them of course, the other 24 persons now dead'. He was further of the opinion that 'Jones or his boy fired the gas'. Although he judged that the colliery was not one where it was needed in 'general' to use locked lamps for underground work, he repeated: 'That the lives of so many people should be in the hands of a man and a mere child is greatly to be deplored'.

Mr James, William Bevan's legal representative afterwards cross-examined Lionel Brough, and also the Coroner. The defence lawyer's questions included ones to test the HM Inspector of Mines's understanding of the 'rules'. In summary, Brough and the Coroner held to their positions regarding the interpretation of the rules. Mr James contending finally that 'it was simply a question of whether Mr Bevan had been guilty of an error of judgment or not' regarding the use of lamps. "I grant that Bevan made a mistake," the Coroner said.

The inquiry's jury deliberated for nearly two hours before giving a verdict that 'astounded' the manager of Bedwellty Pits. "Gross neglect of Mr Bevan in not seeing himself to the [brattice] door being replaced, and the men turned out at the pit for so doing; not having done so was the cause of the explosion and death of David Jones and twenty-five others."

Twelve members of the sixteen man jury voted for the verdict. Three members of the jury wanted an 'Accidental Verdict'. Nevertheless, the Coroner declared that the result was 'equivalent to a verdict of Manslaughter against Mr Bevan'. The colliery manager was committed for trial at the Monmouthshire Assizes. Samuel Homfray Jnr and C. [L?] A. Homfray paid a two-thirds share of William Bevan's bail, which cost £300.

Protest[49]

During the nineteenth century religious and temperance movements 'swept Wales'. As a result of a 'temperance surge in Tredegar in 1859 some seven thousand signed the pledge'. It was in 1862 that Tredegar's New Temperance Hotel began to trade and was followed by the opening of a Temperance Hall.[50] On the 20th July 1865, 2,000 people gathered at the hall for an evening meeting to protest against the manslaughter verdict reached at the Bedwellty Pits' inquiry. 'All classes were represented in the assembly – clergy, professional men, tradesmen, and miners', with among them Mr Reed, the general manager of the Tredegar Iron Works Company. The meeting's chairman was 'Mr Harrhy (manager of the Bank)'. The object of the meeting, put by the chairman, and greeted with cheers, was 'to express sympathy with Mr Bevan in the position he was placed by the late verdict, and which he did not believe was agreed by the inhabitants in generally'.

The conduct of the meeting was generally orderly. Speeches given in praise of William Bevan prompted the tabling of a number of resolutions. If a composite resolution had evolved during the meeting it might have stated 'regret at the verdict against one of their townsmen … who especially merited goodwill of all right thinking men'; that the meeting was 'of the opinion that the verdict given …is not in accordance with the evidence adduced' at the inquiry; and that the jury had 'dealt with greater harshness than the circumstances of the case necessitated'.

Criticism about the backgrounds of some members of the inquiry's jury was an aspect of the meeting. A contention by Isaac Rees, flannel manufacturer, incited 'slight confusion'. "I beg to differ from the feeling of the meeting! You had a jury of influential men –," said Isaac Rees. He battled to continue, but his words were broken by angry cries, "Turn him out."

After three cheers were raised to salute William Bevan, the meeting ended at ten o'clock.

The Trial[51]

The trial of William Bevan, before Justice Barron Channel, occurred during August 1865 at the Shirehall, Monmouth. The Monmouthshire Assizes' grand jury of twenty-two men, 'a body of gentleman of intelligence and experience', included Samuel Homfray Jnr and L. Augustus Homfray. William Bevan was charged with 'feloniously killing and slaying David Jones, at the New Pits Colliery (sic), at Tredegar'. A witness at the trial was HM Inspector of Mines Lionel Brough. An account was given in court of the June explosion that killed twenty-six colliers. 'Shortly before the court rose on the first day' the jury 'returned' no 'true bill' against the defendant.

The jury's statement was construed by the prosecution counsel, Mr Powell QC, to mean that 'Mr Bevan was not guilty of any culpable negligence, and that the deceased colliers died from other circumstances'. The judge agreed with the prosecutor's interpretation. The judge proceeded to state that the deaths were 'due to two circumstances—the one owing to taking down the [brattice] door, which materially interfered with the ventilation and the other by men descending the pit with unlocked lamps, with neither of which circumstances was the manager immediately connected'. He then directed the jury to give a not guilty verdict, which they returned. However, William Bevan's trials had not ended.

Regina v.
Samuel Homfray, William Henry Foreman, and Rowland Foreman

An action taken by Lionel Brough, HM Inspector of Mines for the South-Western District, led to summonses being issued against the Tredegar Iron Company. The case, Regina v. Samuel Homfray, William Henry Foreman, and Rowland Foreman was heard before magistrates, J. Davies and F. Levick Jnr, at Tredegar Petty Sessions over a 'protracted' period, autumn 1865 to winter 1866.

The first charge against the defendants was 'that being owners of a certain colliery in Bedwellty they did not cause an adequate amount of ventilation to be constantly produced in such colliery, to dilute and render harmless certain noxious gases to such an extent that the working places, working places and travelling roads, were not in a fit state for working therein.'[52] A 'great deal of evidence' was submitted. The magistrates dismissed the charge.[53]

The second summons was that the 'defendants had not properly fenced off a place in actual course of working and extension, so as to prevent access thereto Bedwellty Pits'. This charge was also dismissed.[54] The trial ended in February 1866 with the prosecution failing to make a case for the third and final summons, the use of unlocked safety lamps at the colliery.[55]

Provisions in the 1860 Regulation and Inspection of Mines Act had enabled Lionel Brough to bring charges against the colliery's owners.[56] A part of his motive may have to publicly shame Samuel Homfray Jnr et al. During the trial the defence counsel took issue with the inspector for letters he had written to William Bevan prior to the Bedwellty Pits' explosion. 'They knew such letters as these would create a great prejudice among the mass of men, as if we were killing people by wholesale in this colliery ….; and they put in these beggarly things written by the inspector in his armchair at Clifton [Bristol]'.[57] The proprietors though were not called to testify before the magistrates. Maybe Lionel Brough can at least be credited for persisting with the pursuit of prosecutions following the 1865 disaster at Bedwellty Pits. His district for mines inspection comprised Devonshire, Gloucestershire, Monmouthshire and Somerset.

The main witnesses called for cross-examination were the colliery's manager, overman (John Reynolds), and a number of workers.[58] Wise colliery officials, who for nine months after the explosion suffered stress due to the legal process, became much more safety conscious. In November 1868, William Bevan, by then the company's mineral agent, died aged just forty-three.[59]

Uncertain times

In 1869, the following survey of plant, pits, drifts, and employment figures indicates that the Tredegar Company's operation remained vibrant:

Blast Engines, one of 600 Horsepower	4
Blast Furnaces	9
Puddling Furnace with refineries	8
Mill Furnaces	36
Trains of rolls working puddling bars	4
Sets of roll for blooming	9
Sets of rolls for finishing	4
Men and boys employed	4,800
Women employed	450
Horses	280
Locomotives	6
Pits, and levels	32
(producing coal and ironstone) [60]	

The survey suggests that the company remained a capable manufacturer of iron products like rail. Yet, by the end of the 1860s, local and external factors may have given rise to doubt among some of the Tredegar Iron Company's partners about the future for such a business.

Up until around the 1840s, the cost of mining local clay ironstone was low, 'but the major portion of the ironstone was obtained by distinct underground workings in hard ground, underneath the coal seams and generally in pins or layers a few inches in thickness'. J. H. Thomas further noted that the following veins were worked at Tredegar:

Soap Vein	3 inches thick
Black Vein	6 inches thick
Spotted Vein	6 inches thick
Red Vein	9 inches thick in three layers
Blue Vein	6 inches
Big Vein	9 inches in three layers [61]

Nevertheless, by the 1850s, Heads of the Valleys ironmasters like the Tredegar Company imported much more iron ore than in the past. Furness District and Cumberland (now Cumbria) ores, in particular, had been proved by Heads of the Valleys ironworks to make iron at a relatively cheaper cost than clay ironstone. A primary factor was that the iron content of South Wales clay ironstone was inferior to ore mined in north-west England. Clay ironstone's iron content ranged between 8% and 40%. The haematite iron ores sourced from the Furness District and Cumberland averaged 60% metal content. Another factor was that once the decades of easy access to bands of Tredegar clay ironstone ended, deeper mining caused the material's cost to rise. Furthermore, the iron content in deeper-mined clay ironstone was found to be even less than that previously sourced.

The Heads of the Valleys ironworks demand for Furness and Cumberland ores partly caused the price of haematite iron ores to rise. Another contributory cost factor was a growing demand for haematite iron ore since it was vital for flawless operation of the novel Bessemer steel making process. Nevertheless, the ironmasters of South Wales knew that pig iron smelted using haematite iron ores was better suited to the rolling of rail than pig iron made from clay ironstone. The future for mining clay ironstone at the head of the Sirhowy Valley looked bleak.

The period of years from 1870 to 1872 saw a boom in ironmaking. However, the year 1871 began with a brief strike by miners across some parts of the South Wales Coalfield, which included those of the Tredegar district. The miners demanded higher wages. Following a miners' conference in May 1871, a longer strike closed the collieries of the Rhondda and Aberdare (Cynon) Valleys, but the Tredegar collieries appeared to operate as usual.[62]

At the Tredegar Ironworks, in June 1871, the 'old' Company Shop was put to new use. The building was 'fitted up in capital style as offices wherein to conduct book keeping in connection with the works', and so accountancy clerks became 'sufficiently distant [from the works] to escape some of the smoke and sulphur'.[63] The clerks relocated from offices at the centre of the works.

There was no change in the conditions of work for the miners of the Tredegar district. In July 1871, at Tyley's Pit, which does not appear to be have been run by the Tredegar Iron Company, an explosion caused the 'top' to come down on seven miners 'whilst timbers were being fixed'. A horse was 'roasted alive' and some days later, one of the miners, William Naish, died. The miners at Tyley's Pit used candle light underground.[64] Weeks later a collier named William Ephraim was killed at the Tredegar Ironworks' Ash Tree Pit.[65]

The Tredegar Company, though, took legal action against some colliery employees not following its Rules and Regulations for mining work. In September 1871, a 'furnaceman' at Bedwellty

Pits, James O'Neale, served two months in jail for the 'stoppage of ventilation'.[66] Then in October 1871, William Morris, in charge of the pumping engine at Ty Trist Colliery, was fined five shillings for a rise in the level of water that damaged walling.[67] The company proclaimed that the penalties 'ought to have a salutary effect on all persons holding responsible positions in collieries'.

In 1871, the population of Tredegar, which also included people in living in remote hamlets like Manmoel, was put at 12,389. A newspaper report of that year describes changes taking place in the town concerning the provision of public utilities. Charles Street, Tredegar, was plumbed with piped gas and water supplies. The supply of the 'liquid gem' ended the carrying of water in pitchers from a well.[68]

The year though, with the benefit of hindsight, saw a notable event, the birth of the Tredegar Health and Education Fund for Tredegar Iron Company workers.[69] A part of the aim of the fund was to provide a means for covering the cost of workers' medical bills. Workers' subscriptions, based upon a share of their wages, grew a fund of money for the inauguration of the envisaged scheme that is described more fully below.

The evolution of the management of the Tredegar Company for the period merits prior attention. An uneasy relationship developed between Sir Charles Morgan and the Tredegar Company, which the Tredegar Estate referred to as Forman and Company. In 1868, the tenor of the landlord-industrial tenant relationship altered after Samuel Homfray Jnr sold his stake in the Tredegar Company to the Forthergill and Forman families.[70] Although the Morgan-Homfray alliance continued, it may not have served as a means for mediation between landlord and industrial tenant.

Sir Charles Morgan's advisors complained to him about a number of issues, and lodged allegations about lax management at the Tredegar industrial enterprise.[71] The import of 'foreign' ores, as mentioned earlier, had upset Charles Morgan of Tredegar, and he still had cause to grouse that the Tredegar Company was neglecting 'the development of native ore'. By 1867 the company raised about half the quantity of clay ironstone it had done in 1857. Regardless, one serious complaint he heard from his advisors was that the 'coal burned to produce a ton of iron was expensive compared with other works in the country, in fact being double what it ought to have been, and that it was being wasted'. Such a complaint suggests that Sir Charles Morgan's advisors had detailed knowledge of the iron industry.

The landowner was further told that at Tredegar Ironworks 'no proper plans of the iron and coal workings were being kept'; and 'it was impossible to find how much coal and iron had been extracted'. Forman and Company appeared to have rebuffed an approach by Morgan's advisors for such information. 'Certain figures were, however, obtained in connection with a report covering the years 1866 to 1871 inclusive, which shows that the average raisings of coal were 464,527 tons whilst the ironstone amounted to 67,445 tons per annum during the same period'.[72]

Maybe of greater significance, the probing by, or on behalf of, the Tredegar Estate revealed that Forman and Company had doubts about the future of Tredegar Ironworks as a business. According to J. H. Thomas: 'It appears from [Tredegar Estate] correspondence that the company were desirous of disposing of their lease as they were not agreeable to spending any further money in developing and improving the ironworks'. In circa 1871, as a reaction to Forman and Company's intentions, Sir Charles Morgan turned to a county Durham born industrialist, George Elliot, with a sound background in coal mining for help.[73]

George Elliot (1815-1893) possibly came to Sir Charles Morgan's notice around 1864. That year Elliot led an acquisition by a group of investors of the steam coal collieries owned by the sons of the late Thomas Powell of the Gaer, Newport, to form the Powell Duffryn Steam Coal Company.[74] An asset of Powell Duffryn (PD) was New Tredegar Colliery whose steam coal reserves were owned by the Tredegar Estate. Maybe of importance to Sir Charles Morgan, the formation of Powell Duffryn had shown that Sir George Elliot, he was made a baronet in 1874, was adept at winning investor support for his business projects.

Indeed, a 'view to [Elliot] buying the ironworks' was what the Tredegar Estate wanted. The services of Alexander Basset, who might have still been the estate's agent, were called upon by the County Durham industrialist to value the assets of the Tredegar Iron Company. According to J. H. Thomas, Bassett estimated a 'total value of the undertaking at £522,930, but nothing transpired'.[75] Although J. H. Thomas's subsequent account of this period can be shown to be less than coherent, his portrayal of the Tredegar Ironworks being beset by inertia cannot be ignored.[76] Neither could the ironworks' owner neglect the ever active world of industrial relations.

Early in November 1872, union leaders, pressed by colliers and ironworkers in parts of the South Wales 'iron belt', demanded that ironmasters raise their wages by 10 per cent by the end of the month. The ironmasters rejected the demand due to the trade outlook. Instead, the ironmasters, seemingly united as a body, gave notice of a ten per cent fall in wages in order that their operations could continue to earn a profit. The planned wage cut incensed the ironmasters' workers across South Wales, and a strike was called for the New Year.

On Friday the 1st January 1873, men at Tredegar pits brought all the horses up from underground, and the iron workers began to put out furnace fires. No hooter sounded at Tredegar Ironworks on the following Monday. By Tuesday the 5th January, 1,888 'underground' men of Tredegar, Sirhowy, and Ebbw Vale were reported as being 'affected by the strike'. Although the workers received wages on the eve of the strike, tenants of company houses had money deducted as usual for rent, but the supply of free coal ceased. An intense darkness fell on Tredegar on Wednesday night.[77] By the 1st February, soup kitchens catered for the 'half famished community' of Tredegar.[78] A settlement agreed between the Brogden-run Llynvi, Tondu, & Ogmore Coal & Iron Company and its workers presaged the end of the South Wales Coalfield strike. During March, some Tredegar's colliers and ironworkers began work despite no local settlement.

Although the 1873 strike collapsed partly due to local agreements between companies and workers' representatives, a trade union development troubled South Wales' coal owners and ironmasters. Prior to 1873, the ironmasters were inclined to act independently regarding industrial relation affairs. Some coal owners, on the other hand, were united through being members of the South Wales Steam Collieries Association. However, both groups of employers became alarmed by the activities of a trade union with ambitions to become a force in Great Britain, the Amalgamated Association of Miners (AAM). The union's head office was in Manchester.

Tredegar was a recruiting ground for the AAM. By 1873, the union's Tredegar branch appeared organised complete with elected leaders, Ebenezer Howell, Titus Davies, John Cavill, James James, and John Lewis. In March 1873, the union's president, Mr Halliday, spoke at Tredegar's Temperance Hall. He urged the many colliers present in the hall to 'go to the company, and say they were ready to accept Dowlais's terms'.[79] Halliday's tactic, maybe due to thinking that South Wales ironmasters were selfish, involved divide and rule. However, as a move to forestall a threat to their power from the AAM, the ironmasters with coal business interests and coal owners forged an alliance. In July 1873 the Monmouthshire and the South Wales Collieries Association was founded with Richard Fothergill as its first president.

Earlier in March that year, the image of Tredegar was tarnished at the Monmouthshire Assizes. Justice Quain observed that as a proportion of all criminal cases brought to trial at the court, Tredegar's share was by far the highest. He attributed some of the cause of the cases to overcrowded housing, and called upon the Tredegar Company 'to remove the disgrace which had fallen upon' the town.[80]

Nevertheless, with Tredegar workers humbled by the 1873 strike, the 1865 Bedwellty Pits' explosion not forgotten, and Justice Quain's judgment a stain upon Tredegar's reputation, a momentous change in the ownership of the Tredegar Iron Company occurred.

Tredegar Iron & Coal Company

In the year 1873 a Memorandum and Articles was signed that founded the Tredegar Iron and Coal Company. Forty-six company shareholders had agreed to subscribe capital so that the company could acquire the Tredegar Company's assets. The Tredegar Iron & Coal Company was registered on the 26th March 1873, with a nominal capital of £1¼ million divided into 20,000 'A' shares of £50 each and 10,000 'B' shares of £25 each. The official record of the registration indicates that seven signatories took 8,900 shares.[81]

According to the company's fifty year history the first board of directors comprised: Sir Issac Lowthian Bell, Sidney Carr Glyn, William Menelaus, William Newmarch, Henry Davis Pochin, Benjamin Whitworth, and Edward Williams.[82] George Thomas Clark (1809-1898) seems also to have been a founding director.[83] As a group, the founding directors were revered in the company's history as 'names … famous in the industrial life of the country'.[84] Indeed, this was true. Sir Issac Lowthian Bell (1816-1904), senior partner Bell Brothers, Middlesbrough, was the 'patriarchal figure of the late Victorian iron industry'.[85] The engineer William Menelaus (1818-1883), gifted with foresight, was head of the Dowlais Company. He possessed a rounded appreciation of the iron, steel, and coal industries.

Born in 1824, Henry Davis Pochin's background was as a 'successful industrial chemist from Manchester who invested his profits in iron, coal, and engineering'.[86] Regarding public life, Pochin was elected mayor of Salford for the years 1855 and 1856, and as a Liberal Member of Parliament served the Stafford constituency between the years 1868-69. He 'belonged to the group of advanced Liberals which included Cobden, Bright, and Fawcett'.[87]

Henry Davis Pochin (1824-1895)
A founder director of the Tredegar Iron and Coal Company who served as chairman for one year, 1893. 'The Chemist' was painted by Walter Ouless RA in 1875.   *Courtesy of McLaren Family Archive*

Benjamin Whitworth (1815-1893) was a Manchester businessman who later served as the last Member of Parliament for an Irish constituency, Drogheda. Maybe a statement made by Benjamin Whitworth in 1867 anticipated him taking an increasing shareholder interest in companies like Tredegar Iron and Coal: 'Coal will always give a fair return for the whole capital invested [in the business], and anything you get from the iron will be an addition in the shape of a bonus.'[88] Whitworth and Pochin were also Bolckow, Vaughan & Company shareholder-directors. Moreover, Edward Williams (1826-1886), who began his industrial career at Dowlais Ironworks, became a lifelong friend of Menelaus, was the general manager of Bolckow, Vaughan & Company's ironworks based at Middlesbrough.

The industrialists as directors of the Tredegar Company were joined by two men with contacts in banking. 'The growth of banking and credit system since the 1850s and the establishment of limited liability under the 1862 Companies Act had facilitated the supply of money for new industrial development'.[89] Sidney Carr Glyn (1835-1916) had family ties with a private bank, Glyn, Mills, and Company. William Newmarch (1820-1882) had risen from humble circumstances to become chief officer of Glyn, Mills, and Company at forty years of age. Glyn, Mills, and Company financed railway construction work around the world.

The name of the company, Tredegar Iron & Coal Company, clearly expressed its purpose. The company was set up to earn financial returns from making iron and mining coal. Almost coincidentally, the Newport-Abercarn Black Vein Company was formed to sink in 1873, south of Crumlin in the Ebbw Vale, Celynen Colliery. The investors in the Newport-Abercarn Black Vein Steam Coal Company may have been persuaded to part with their money due to predictions that future company share dividends would be at least twenty per cent per annum.[90] No such forecast about future dividends was found concerning the start of the Tredegar Iron & Coal Company. Nevertheless, in risking a part of their personal wealth on a Tredegar venture, Sir Issac Lowthian Bell *et al.* desired financial gain over some period of time.

Regarding the directors' assessment of the Tredegar Iron & Coal Company's coal annual output, in 1873 it was 596,925 tons. For comparison: the coal outputs achieved by other South Wales Coalfield companies like Ebbw Vale, Powell Duffryn, Blaenavon Iron Company, and Dowlais in the year 1873 were respectively 1,020,000 tons, 1,000,000 tons, 915,613 tons and 800,000 tons.[91] Compared with the output from such companies', and all things being equal, the Tredegar Company appeared to offer growth prospects as a coal company. Moreover, the annual ironmaking output at Tredegar was around that when Samuel Homfray Jnr retired from running the works.

Just before the month of March ended, members of the 'new company' were seen visiting the works to value its assets.[92] Days later terms, not specified, were reached between the new company and its colliery workers so ending the year's industrial relations troubles.[93]

The directors of the Tredegar Iron & Coal Company also made two crucial management appointments. Edmund Petley became the company's secretary and one of his first tasks involved setting up his base, a London Office.[94] Around September 1873, the company appointed the forty year old James Colquhoun as general manager of collieries and the works. James Colquhoun was born on the 12th August 1833, at Tollcross, near Glasgow. His birthplace lay just to the north of the Clyde Ironworks, where he completed his apprenticeship.[95] He was recruited by the Tredegar Company from the Llynvi, Tondu, & Ogmore Coal & Iron Company.

A gathering of Llynvi Tondu, & Ogmore Coal & Iron Company 'agents and workers' took place at Maesteg to bid farewell to James Colquhoun. He received much praise at the gathering that included one tribute about his 'acts of kindness'. In his speech, he declared that he had striven to attain 'mutual confidence in the relationship of master and servant'. The use of the terms 'master' and 'servant' were part of the vernacular of managers, but workers would have smarted at being called 'servants'. Nevertheless, James Colquhoun's quest for goodness in manager-worker relationships was conveyed from the Maesteg gathering, via the coal industry's press, to Tredegar. 'His desire and aim was that all men might trust and depend upon his word'.[96]

Such a high-minded assertion, made in the aftermath of the 1873 strike, may have rung true with agents and workers of Llynvi, Tondu & Ogmore Coal & Iron Company, but when it was read in Tredegar it prompted some scepticism. James Colquhoun, though, was probably wise to the likelihood that in Tredegar he would be greeted with suspicion. But as a symbol of his power, he worked in an office that lay within Bedwellty House.

Workers' Health Care

Matters brought to James Colquhoun's attention upon taking up his post as general manager included the Tredegar Health and Education Fund. The protagonists of the fund had probably already met, or expected to meet, prejudice within the private-based, business oriented, medical profession about entering into a contractual arrangement with a workers' managed medical scheme. The involvement of the most senior manager of the Tredegar Iron & Coal Company in the scheme stood to aid bridging any credibility gap with the medical profession.

An approach by the protagonists of the medical scheme to James Colquhoun proved successful. Arguably a less obliging and unimaginative general manager would have been hostile to such a scheme, and it probably would have suffered a major setback. Conceivably it was Colquhoun's advice that led by around October 1873 to the drafting of a 'Memorandum of an Agreement' that set the course for fulfilment of the protagonists' aims. He most certainly arranged for the draft agreement to be scrutinized by the company's lawyer, which probably enhanced the terms of the 'Memorandum of an Agreement' made on the 1st December 1873, between the trustees, James Colquhoun;

John Lloyd, a Tredegar collier; and Benjamin Jarman, a Tredegar ironworker; and George Arthur Brown, described as being a 'Tredegar Surgeon and Apothecary'.[97]

The Memorandum of an Agreement registers that the aim of the trustees was the 'maintenance of health education for all workmen and employees, including their wives and children employed at the Tredegar Iron and Coal Works'. Furthermore, the 'paid' trustees were 'appointed to manage' specified arrangements, and 'stipulations for providing the necessary medical attendance as may be necessary for carrying out the said arrangements'.

The 'paid George Arthur Brown' was expected 'to provide all such Medical Attendance and Medicine as may be necessary and requisite for all the workmen, their wives, and children, including Managers, Agents, and all other employees at [Tredegar] Iron and Coal Works … at such sum, and upon such terms' that were detailed. His income as a surgeon and apothecary was set by a 'rate of payment of one penny and three farthings per Pound sterling' per weekly wage earned by 'all men, women and others employed at the said Tredegar Iron and Coal Works'.

In the absence of company employment figures for 1873, the figures given earlier for 1869 are used to reckon the weekly

A portion of the Memorandum of an Agreement', signed in 1873, that created a worker organised health scheme due to cooperation with the Tredegar Iron & Coal Company.

Courtesy of Gwent Archives, D.3246.221

income raised for the Tredegar medical service at its outset. In 1869, the company's ironworks and collieries' operation employed 4,800 men, women and boys. Thus, if only 4,000 men and women subscribed to the scheme, an estimated weekly income of around £20, otherwise £1,000 per annum, was allotted to George Arthur Brown to provide the service defined above. In the event of 'any reduction in the present wages' taking 'place then an additional sum in the pound beyond the sum' given above '(upon the earnings of the said workmen and other persons employed at the said Tredegar Iron and Coal Works) shall be made and paid to the said George Arthur Brown' with a ceiling rate per week set at five pence per pound.

The agreement burdened George Arthur Brown with the costs associated with two further aspects. He was expected to pay for a stock check of 'Drugs and other Medicines' held at his surgery 'seven days' after he signed the December agreement. He was further required to pay the trustees 'Seventy Pounds per annum for the dwelling house, surgery, garden and other premises, and fields now occupied by him at Tredegar'. The agreement was 'considered' to have come into 'force from the first day of October 1873. Six calendar months notice of termination in writing was required of either party to the other.

The 1873 Memorandum of an Agreement between the trustees and George Arthur Brown was a notable milestone in the history of medical provision for at least Monmouthshire industrial workers. An archival check did not identify an earlier scheme. Moreover, the agreement proved to be a sound base for sustaining a medical service for the employees of the Tredegar Iron & Coal Company. For many decades afterwards, the scheme retained the services of a series of medical people.

Around New Year 1911, after forty-two years service, Dr George Brown died in post as chief medical officer of the Tredegar Workmen's Medical Aid Scheme, as it was then called.[98] By the end of February 1911, forty-seven applications for the post he had held were received by the administrators of the scheme. Two suitable candidates emerged from the selection process, Dr Brown, the son of Dr George Brown, and Dr Davies. A ballot of the scheme's members made the final choice. Although on the 25th February alleged voting irregularities were reported regarding the members' ballot, the press announced on the 4th March that Dr Edwin Thomas Harries Davies MD, MS, LRCP, FRCS had been appointed chief medical officer. Dr Davies, a native of Carmarthenshire, trained at St. Mary's Hospital, London, resigned from a position at the London Temperance Hospital to take up the post at Tredegar at a salary of £750 per annum. *The Merthyr Express* applauded the appointment: 'Tredegar is fortunate in securing a gentleman of such distinction'.[99]

In 1914, surviving records identify John Addison Wilson as being the first dentist contracted by the scheme.[100]

In 1915, Dr Davies pioneered motorised doctor calls in the Tredegar District.[101] He was authorised by the trustees of the Tredegar Workmen's Medical Aid Scheme to buy 'at his own cost an Argyll Motor car 15 h.p. 4-cylinder standard touring model' and 'employ and pay a chauffeur'. Showing some consideration maybe, the Trustees covenanted 'to pay £8 6s. 8d. to the Doctor' seemingly to cover the cost of car use on medical business.

The subscribers to the Tredegar Health and Education Fund acquired a great sense of ownership for the medical scheme. However, once the scheme was established, some workers began to resent the company's involvement. However, wise counsel offered by a company general manager who was a committed trustee of the Fund was no doubt valued by some of the trustees who represented the workers' interests.

The Company's Plans

However, in 1873, people newly employed by the Tredegar Iron & Coal Company – as printed on the company's letter head – asked themselves: what would the future bring? Had the founding directors of the company been attracted to taking over Homfray's industrial legacy to grow a much more powerful entity, or to make a quick profit, and then sell it on to other investors?

The actions of James Colquhoun offered some clues about the Tredegar Company's future. The Scot was a mechanical engineer steeped in iron industry knowledge and experience. He was not a qualified mining engineer. However, employment with the Llynvi, Tondu, & Ogmore Coal & Iron Company had given him an appreciation of the South Wales coal industry. The degree of autonomy the directors of the Tredegar Company gave him to act as the company's general manager of collieries and the works is unknown. Among the directors there were some men with an inclination for hands-on involvement in both the operational and strategic aspects of companies. Nevertheless, it can be surmised, that with the founding of the company and some process of engagement between the directors and James Colquhoun, a plan for action emerged.

Planning in 1873 involved speculation about the futures of the iron and coal trades. Possibly the greatest strategic dilemma that confronted the directors was whether, or not, the Tredegar ironworks had a future as a producer of steel. A company director, Edward Williams, had been to the fore in 1869 at the 'first of numerous discussions' on 'steel versus iron'.[102] The stance he took in 1869 was 'that though ingot rails were much more enduring than piled rails, their widespread use must be prohibited by cost until the phosphoric ores were available for steelmaking'. Regarding his outlook for that year, Bolckow, Vaughan's general manager was 'satisfied that we can make very good iron rails from the iron of the Cleveland district'. He was not alone in the British iron industry at casting dispersion's upon Britain's infant steel industry.

Due to the high cost of Furness and Cumberland haematite iron ore, some British pioneer steel makers sought low phosphoric iron ores from elsewhere at home and abroad to make sound Bessemer steel. From the 1850s some South Wales ironmasters opened and developed haematite mining at Llantrisant and on Exmoor.[103] The Forest of Dean was another source of haematite ore.[104] Nevertheless, by July 1873, one worry for Welsh ironmasters was the expense of having to 'rely upon a supply of foreign iron ores than had formerly been the case'. Ores were being shipped from Spain and South America to Tredegar.[105] Perhaps the iron and steel dilemma, and the expense of iron ore, caused the directors to procrastinate over entering steel making. The directors of the Tredegar Company quickly gave James Colquhoun approval to progress colliery developments.

Whitworth Pits

Early in April 1875, just over a quarter of a mile south of Bedwellty House and to the north of Ty Trist Colliery, a ceremony occurred that announced a new colliery.[106] Edward Williams of Middlesbrough cut turf at two adjacent locations to mark where two pit shafts were to be sunk for the company.[107] James Colquhoun held a high regard for Edward Williams. After the death in 1886 of the general manager of Bolckow, Vaughan Colquhoun offered an eulogy: 'He had known him for a great many years, as a man of great practical ability, who was thoroughly acquainted with all the details of the manufacture of steel and iron, and when great difficulties presented themselves, Mr Williams' advice was frequently sought, which he would give in the frankest way possible'.[108] Another tribute, which preceded Colquhoun's, recognized Williams as a 'generous-hearted man, straightforward in all his conduct'. A director of the Tredegar Iron & Coal Company with such a character was likely to be a rich source of constructive help for Colquhoun.

Although Edward Williams led the turf cutting ceremony, the colliery was named after a fellow director, Benjamin Whitworth who had been elected company chairman. One of the colliery's shafts was sunk to the Bwdwllog seam that was useful for coking. Two hundred coke ovens were later erected adjacent to the colliery. The name of the seam appears to have been borrowed from the Blaenavon district where it was known as the Bydylog seam, which was a bituminous coal having properties comparable with Durham coal. Later, once a correlation of coal seams in the Tredegar district was established, the Bwdwllog was

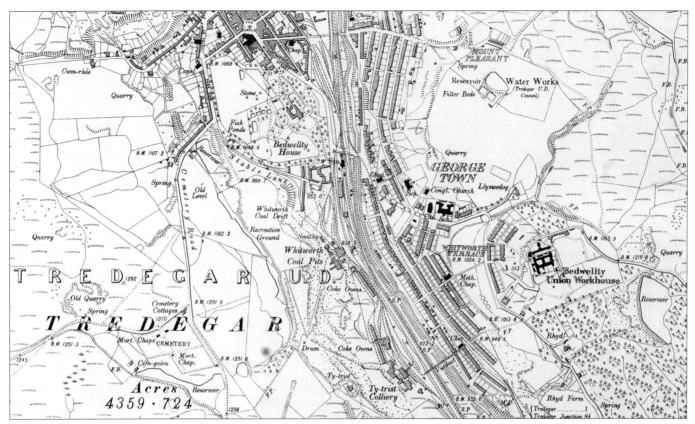

A part of the Second Edition 1902 Ordnance Survey Map of Tredegar. Whitworth Pits and Ty Trist collieries - seen at centre. Rhyd (Hall), home to the general manager of collieries of the Tredegar Iron & Coal Company, is to the right of Ty Trist as are the Reservoir partly built using colliery waste from Ty Trist Colliery, see later, and Bedwellty Union Workhouse. Cefn Golau Cemetry is to the left of Ty Trist.

OS Monmouthshire Sheet XI, S.W. Supplied by Llyfrgell Gendlaethol Cymru/The National Library of Wales

Whitworth Number 1 and 2 Pits. The first colliery opened by the Tredegar Iron & Coal Company. Sunk in 1875. Total manning, above and below ground, at the colliery peaked at around 800 during the years 1911 and 1912.

Pope/Parkhouse Archive

recognised as the Yard seam. The plan for the other shaft was to work the Old Coal seam. However, and vitally, the Bwdwllog seam and the Old Coal seam were sources of steam coal.[109]

Coal was first raised from the Whitworth Pits in 1876.[110] In 1880, the colliery comprised two winding shafts, a 'daylight engine plane drift', and was 'fitted out in the best of style'. The surface arrangements included 'two pairs of winding engines; one pair large pair of hauling engines; one small hauling engine; coal screening …' In 1880, Whitworth Pits raised 1,200 tons of coal per day.[111]

Tribulations & Developments

If the expansion of the coal mining activity was fully supported by the directors of the company, those who were new to the South Wales Coalfield may have felt much unease about ironmaking. 'By 1875 the replacement of iron rails by steel was well underway in Britain'.[112] Furthermore, the Government's Board of Trade, a year later, issued information that heralded the possible death of the Tredegar Ironworks: 'that of rail exports [from Britain] totalling 365,000 tons only 190,000 tons were of iron compared with the 897,000 tons of rails – virtually all iron – exported in 1870'. Such a slump in business for the Heads of the Valleys ironworks, and an uncertain market for coal, pushed coal owners in particular to take actions to stem financial losses.

An Amalgamated Association of Miners' campaign in 1874 for wage rises for colliery workers ran counter to the needs of coal owners. In 1874 coal owners' incomes fell due to a slump in the coal trade. The union sought wage rises for its members across the coalfields of England as well as South Wales. On the 31st December 1874, members of the Monmouthshire and the South Wales Collieries Association, which included Tredegar Iron & Coal Company, announced that from the 1st January 1875, a worker wage reduction of 10% would be imposed. The conflicting stances of the coal owners and the union caused, depending upon viewpoints, either a lock-out or a strike. The Monmouthshire and the South Wales Collieries Association classed it as a 'strike and lock-out'.

Events at Tredegar, reported on the 2nd February 1875, depict a lock-out. Tredegar colliers 'went to the various pits this morning with a view to follow their daily avocations, but locks and bars were against them, and they returned home'.[113] However, although the ironworks' operation of rail and puddling mills continued, it was foreseen that rolling work would end 'in a week or ten days' due to coal supplies being exhausted. Moreover, starved of fuel, the furnaces' fires would be extinguished, and so 'will be felt the stern reality which stares everyone in the face'. Such a picture of a coal owner lock-out was commonplace across the South Wales Coalfield.

Mark Warne and David Powell were the 'Old Tredegar' delegates at an AAM conference held in April 1875.[114] The attitude of the fledgling Monmouthshire and the South Wales Collieries Association was steadfast. Union delegates also appeared firm in opposing some of the coal owners' demands that had to be met before a return to work was sanctioned.

Regarding the South Wales Coalfield, members of the AAM held out for five months, until July 1875, before capitulating.[115] Union members and their families were reduced to poverty and starvation. The agreement that ended the 1875 strike or lock-out brought about the introduction of a wage-to-coal market price regulator mechanism called the Sliding Scale. Such a mechanism was for coal owners a much desired means for controlling wage costs.

The Monmouthshire and the South Wales Collieries Association also arranged for its members to subscribe to a contingency fund, which became known as the strike fund. Subscriptions raised £300,000 for the contingency fund from which coal companies were recompensed for financial losses incurred due to a colliery workers' strike. However, in 1875, or 1876, news of the bankruptcy of the Amalgamated Association of Miners would have delighted coal owners, but inflamed rancour among many South Wales Coalfield workers.

Alexandra Docks, Newport

On the 10th April 1875, the Alexandra Docks, Newport, was opened with much pomp.[116] Both William Menelaus and James Colquhoun, representing respectively the Dowlais Company and the 'Tredegar Iron Works', were among a host of guests at the event. The dock, conceived of by a past president of the Institution of Civil Engineers, John Robinson McLean, was designed and planned by engineer-in-chief James Abernethy, and constructed by Messrs Griffiths and Thomas.

Earlier, much of Monmouthshire's coal and iron was shipped from Newport by either Usk River jetties or the town's first dock situated to the north of Alexandra Docks. Newport's first dock grew in two stages.[117] Sir Charles Morgan (1760-1846) encouraged the founding of the town's dock on the Pillgwenlly area of the Tredegar Estate. As a result, the opening of a dock basin and improved access to the River Usk in 1842, due in part to Samuel Homfray Junior's support, defined the first stage of growth. Sir Charles Morgan of Tredegar (1792-1875) supported the second stage of the dock's expansion. In 1859, he became the first Baron Tredegar, the year after the dock's second stage of growth ended. In March, 1858, the basin had a total 'floating area of 11½ acres'.

The shipment tonnages from Newport's first dock, for selected years, 'may not be uninteresting':

Year	Dock Shipments (Tons)	
	Coal	Iron
1843	32,572	12,033
1858	180,711	61,872
1874	490,835	131,914[118]

In 1864, a company was formed with the aim of opening at Newport the Alexandra Docks as an addition to the first dock. Among the directors of the Alexandra Docks company were Lord Tredegar, and a partner in the Tredegar Iron Company, William Forman. By 1866, just over 164 acres were secured by the company for the purposes of wharfage, sidings, warehouses etc, and another ninety-three acres for the 'deposit of [ship] ballast'.[119] Measures were also put in hand so that two railway branch lines, one to link with the Great Western Railway and another to join with other Monmouthshire railways systems, were made ready to serve the new docks. The floating area of the opened Alexandra Docks covered nearly twenty-nine acres that is two-and-a-half times the size of Newport's first dock, which was thereafter called the Old Docks, or Town Docks.

The *Monmouthshire Merlin* wrote that the Alexandra Docks' acreage 'was no mean space for a town like Newport, where floating accommodation was concerned'. Adding: 'We venture to say that … Newport came to the front with a liberality and a spirit which would not have exceeded by any port of similar size and importance in the kingdom'.[120] It seems that the key factor taken into account to plan the size of the Alexandra Docks in 1864 was an estimate made of the unworked coal in the Monmouthshire valleys.[121] Alexander Basset made the estimate, which he put at 2,000 million tons. His estimate was used as evidence in the Parliamentary process that ended with an Act that authorised the construction of Alexandra Docks. Following the opening of the new Newport docks, the directors of the Alexandra Docks felt some anxiety about whether, or not, the coal companies of the Monmouthshire valleys would invest in new coal production.

There were newspaper concerns about a 'dark and forbidding background' at the time of the dock opening. The 1875 strike or lock-out of workers at South Wales and Monmouthshire collieries was into its third month. The *Monmouthshire Merlin* perceived the view of an 'intelligent foreigner' to Newport. On 'seeing the unbounded signs of rejoicing which have prevailed', the foreigner would have had 'some difficulty in realising the fact that "war to the knife and knife to the hilt" was, as between Capital and Labour, the order of the day, and that the district generally was passing through

Tredegar Iron & Coal Company's Locomotives.

Paul Jackson collection

Ty Trist Colliery. Opened by Tredegar Ironworks in 1834. In the foreground on the left are shown a part of the colliery's coking ovens. Photograph was taken circa 1905.

Pope/Parkhouse Archive

Ty-Tryst Colliery. Tredegar - 18

In 1947, Ty Trist Colliery was one of the British coalfields' oldest operational collieries. The colliery's operational longevity was partly due to the Tredegar Iron & Coal Company closing adjacent collieries, Whitworth and Bedwellty Pits, so as to manage the working of the Tredegar Estate coal resources at the northern end of the Sirhowy Valley from one location. The North Pit, headgear on the left of three, saw steam winding commissioned in 1869 while also in the same year pumping equipment was installed at the centre pit. Steam winding replaced water-balance winding at the colliery.

Pope/Parkhouse Archive

a terrible and exampled period of industrial depression'.[122] The directors of the Alexandra Docks Company hoped that such industrial gloom was a temporary situation.[123]

Indeed, during 1875, the Tredegar Company's general manager oversaw a number of further colliery developments.[124] Mountain Pit's water-balance winding was scrapped for the introduction of steam engine winding and 'other improvements'. 'The objectionable occupation of the streets by tramways' was rectified in Tredegar by constructing a new system of railways. With respect to a community health issue, the company recognised that there was 'much room for sanitary improvements in Tredegar'.

Ty Trist Colliery[125]

At Ty Trist Colliery, the southern neighbour of Whitworth Pits, the erection of coke ovens began sometime around 1875. In 1869, seventy-five coke ovens were operated at Bedwellty Pits. The Tredegar Iron & Coal Company generally adopted the 'Ty Trist' spelling, which will be generally used hereafter for the colliery's name, but the variant 'Ty Tryst' occurs in some reference sources. The colliery, opened in 1834, was named after a farmhouse that once stood on the valley's western hillside above the pit's site. As Tŷ Tristwch, the farmhouse's name meant 'house of sorrow or sadness'. Oliver Jones appeared sceptical about local folklore's explanations for such a 'sombre name'. Evan Powell, writing in 1884, thought it pleasing to relate that the farmhouse was once the 'home of a hobgoblin' called 'Bwca Trwyn' ['bogey snout' perhaps] that milked 'every cow in the locality'.[126] Powell claimed that Ty Trist was once an 'extensive farm' for corn and hay.

A newspaper article in 1869 grants a picture of Ty Trist Colliery, and also Bedwellty Pits, at the time of the formation of the Tredegar Iron & Coal Company. At Ty Trist three pits existed. In 1869, one pit used water balance-winding to raise coal from the Yard Seam at 100 yards and the Big Vein at an unknown depth. At the Middle pit, a 16-inch beam engine worked a pump's rod by a connecting rod and T-bob to lift water to the surface for, seemingly, piping to Bedwellty Pits for steam raising. However, by the year's end, erected at the Ty Trist's North pit were a new winding engine and a headgear of angle iron, cross-braced. The engine featured two 25-inch diameter cylinders, 4ft stroke, and drove: one 10ft diameter drum, direct acting that wound coal from the Yard Seam and another 10ft drum to raise coal from the Old Coal seam at 200 yards depth. With the engine in operation, water balance-winding at the colliery later became obsolescent. At Ty Trist the daily coal output, before the new winding engine was operated, was 350 tons. Based upon a 300 day working year, a disputable assumption since, for example, miners were not employed when coal orders were scarce, the colliery could produce 105,000 tons of coal per annum.

As a contrast, 550 tons of coal per day was the rate raised in 1869 at Bedwellty Pits. Thus by applying the above assumption, the colliery yielded 165,000 tons a year. No manning figures were given for either colliery. The colliery's upcast winding engine though comprised two 25-inch diameter horizontal cylinders, 4ft stroke, used 9ft rope rolls to wind from the Yard seam at 230 yards. The colliery's downcast engine had one 28-inch diameter horizontal cylinder, 6ft stroke, and raised coal from the Yard seam and the Elled seam at 202 yards. Of interest, a comparison between the depths of the Yard seam at Ty Trist and Bedwellty Pits offers a rough idea of the dip in the rock strata. The collieries stood a mile apart, and over that distance, south from Ty Trist, the slope of the strata fell circa 145 yards.

A strong claim can be made that a furnace ventilated foul air from underground at Ty Trist in 1869. One furnace, 8 foot wide, was stoked with 50 tons of coal a week to ventilate Bedwellty Pits. The total volume of air distributed underground at Bedwellty Pits was 72,950 cubic feet a minute, which offers a convenient reference datum for later. The Tredegar Iron Company retained furnace ventilation after the 1865 Bedwellty Pits' disaster whilst, during the next four years, there was a 'considerable' trend towards machines for ventilation in the South Wales Coalfield.[127]

A mechanical ventilator was operated at Bedwellty Pits' neighbouring colliery in the Rhymney Valley, New Tredegar.

A comparative appraisal of the way in which the Tredegar Iron Works Company worked coal at the time was difficult to make due to a lack of related South Wales Coalfield information. However, Longwall was utilised to work the Yard seam in at least at Bedwellty Pits, but Pillar-and-Stall was also used at the colliery. That twenty-six horses were employed at Bedwellty Pits to move trams underground suggests that the company made wide spread use of horse power for such purposes. However, an underground haulage engine dragged trams a distance of 1,200 yards to move Yard seam coal at Ty Trist. A tram at Bedwellty Pits was made of iron, described as 'close-bodied', carried one ton of coal, and rolled along wrought iron tram plates due to 14 inch diameter tram-wheels.

Undoubtedly, in 1869, the Tredegar Iron Company's 1865 Rules and Regulations remained in force. Thus, the use of naked lights underground by its miners was not discouraged. With the benefit of hindsight, working using naked lights was a reckless act. Yet, the practice around the cusp of the 1870s was a norm of the mining industry. For example, in 1870, in a speech, Mr T. Halliday, leader of the AAM said: 'We [AAM] want ventilation provided in every part of the mine where a miner ought to go. Every pit should be so ventilated that the miner could work in safety with a naked light'.[128] His speech contained no call for the mandatory issue of safety lamps to miners by coal companies. Indeed, his speech contained no reference to safety lamps at all. Regardless, after 1873, the onus for setting safety standards passed to the Tredegar Iron & Coal Company. The colliery manager continued to be the person held legally accountable for fulfilling the standards.

Concerning the form of the colliery assets acquired in 1873, the 1869 newspaper article gave a sketch. Water balance-winding operated at eleven pits of the Tredegar Iron Company. The company operated twenty-two pits and levels to access coal or mine. Around 2,000 tons of mine was mined each week. About half of the coal produced was used to make iron at the works with the balance sent to Newport. The total amount of coal wound each day was 1,650 tons. Again using the above assumption for a working year of operation, the coal mine workings in total could produce 495,000 tons, which tallies with the 464,575 tons average mentioned much earlier. However, of some significance, in 1869 the combined coal outputs of Bedwellty Pits and Ty Trist was a fifty-five per cent share of the Tredegar Iron Company's total production. The Tredegar Iron & Coal Company also inherited a despoiled landscape at the head of the Sirhowy Valley.

Regardless, despite the risk to nature, one of the company's quests was to harvest more steam coal. The company's addition of 1,200 tons of coal a day at Whitworth Pits suggested that it was in a hurry to grow its coal interests. Sometime before 1876, the company committed itself to explore for coal at a location to the south of Tredegar. Such a venture involved mining coal, if found, at a greater depth than any coal company had done before in the Sirhowy Valley. Did such a venture signal that the ambition of the directors was to shape a 'Great' coal company?

NOTES

1   John B. Hilling, 'The Migration of People into Tredegar during the Nineteenth Century', *Gwent Local History*, Journal of the Gwent Local History Council, No.100 (2005), p.24. As an example, in 1851, Thomas Shore (1832-1901) married Ann Pritchard (1832-1908) in Rhymney. The Writer's great-great grandparents were from Bath, Somerset, and Tredegar respectively. In 1841 Ann Pritchard's father, Rees, was a Tredegar boot and shoe maker, and may have made some of the boots that local ironworkers and miners wore for marching as Chartists on Newport in 1839. Thomas and Ann Shore moved to live in Tredegar before 1860 when their son, Rees, was born in the town. Letter, Iestyn Jones to Writer, 10 Dec 2014.

2   John B. Hilling, op. cit., p.37.

3   Oliver Jones, op. cit., p.60.

4   Oliver Jones, op. cit., p.68.

5   'Labour and the Poor', *The Morning Chronicle*, 29 April 1850.

6   Bill Jones, 'The Coal Industry', in *The Gwent County History*, Vol.4, op. cit., p.90.

7   William Truran, *The Iron Manufacture of Great Britain*. (1855), p.172.

8   William Truran, op. cit., p.172.

9   The other partners were: Alfred Darby, H. Dickenson, F. Tothill, and J. Robinson in addition Arthur Gray-Jones, op. cit., p.86.

10 William Truran, op. cit., p.172.

11 William Truran, op. cit., p.172.

12 Main source for story of the Town Clock, Oliver Jones, op. cit., pp.118-124.

13 'Big Ben' was named after Sir Benjamin Hall MP, Parliament's First Commissioner of Works. His father, also Benjamin Hall, owned the first ironworks at Rhymney by 1810, and died in 1817. His son inherited his estate, was knighted, and later made a Baron taking the title of Lord Llanover.

14 A floor of the Coalbrookdale Museum of Iron gives a perspective on the effect that the 1851 Great Exhibition had upon the design of iron goods.

15 'The Great Strike in South Wales', WM, 6 Jan 1873.

16 G. W. J. Lowering, 'Herbert Francis Mackworth and the Coal Industry in Monmouthshire', *Gwent Local History*, Journal of the Gwent Local History Council, No.80 (1996).

17 OS Ref No. SO 154060.

18 Email, Brian Stroud to Black Dwarf Lightmoor, 12 Oct 2012.

19 William Smith, op. cit., p.31.

20 Letter, C. W. Ellis to *Monmouthshire Evening Post*, 23 Feb 1912.

21 From an undated April 1861 edition of *Swindon Advertiser*. Alan S. Peck, *The Great Western at Swindon Works*. (Oxford Publishing, 1983), p.48.

22 Charles Wilkins, op. cit., p.201.

23 Edgar Jones, op. cit., p.320. E. Windsor Richards, as general manager of Bocklow, Vaughan, & Co., Middlesbrough, enabled Sidney Gilchrist Thomas to prove his Basic steelmaking invention as a production process. He served as president of the Institution of Mechanical Engineers (1896-97).

24 Letter, C. W. Ellis to *Monmouthshire Evening Post*, 23 Feb 1912. Thomas Ellis Number 3 later left the employment of the Tredegar Company to erect a large mill at Penydarren. He ended his working life as engineer and colliery manager of Wingfield Colliery, which stood in the vicinity of where the town of Bargoed grew in the Rhymney Valley.

25 'Colliery Explosion', MM, 24 July 1865, p.3.

26 'The Tredegar Colliery Explosion-Termination of the Inquest', MM, 24 July 1865, p.8.

27 According to a 1942 classification, Bedwellty Pits' coal ranked as Bituminous II: volatiles 22-30 %, carbon was in the range from 88.0 to 91.0%, hydrogen 4.8–5.3%, and calorific value 15,500 to 15,800 Btu [British Thermal Unit] /lb. Data from the *South Wales Coalfield (Including Pembrokeshire) Regional Survey Report*. (HMSO, 1946), [hereafter: SWC-RegRpt], pp. 20-21. In 1944, Durham coal was classified as Bituminous Group IV: volatiles 37-25 %, carbon was in the range from 84 to 89%, hydrogen 4.5–5.5%, and calorific value 15,030 to 15,660 Btu/lb. *The Efficient Use of Fuel*. (HMSO, 1944), pp.8-9.

28 William Smith, op. cit., p.11.

29 Trevor Boyns, 'Communications and Commerce', op. cit., p.64.

30 'Death of Mr S. H. Yockney', *South Wales Daily News*, 30 Dec 1893, p.6.

31 Trevor Boyns, 'Communications and Commerce', op. cit., p.65.

32 Len Burland, 'Homfray: An Industrial Dynasty', *Gwent Local History*, Journal of the Gwent Local History Council, No.101 (2006), pp.20-22.

33 Regarding 'General Rules' the other main ones were: fencing around shafts, use of signalling from pit bottom to the surface, and that steam boilers be fitted with gauges for steam pressure etc. *Inspection of Coal Mines in Great Britain Act* [14th August 1855], C A P CVIII, p.878.

34 1855 *Inspection of Coal Mines in Great Britain Act*, p.879.

35 *An Act for the Regulation and Inspection of Mines* [28th August 1860], C A P CLI, p.1393 regarding safety lamp controls.

36 *Rules and Regulations of The Tredegar Iron Company's Collieries and Mine Works*. (1865). Cardiff City Libraries Stacks.

37 'Colliery explosion at Tredegar', MM, 15 July 1865, p.8.

38 'Colliery Explosion at Tredegar', MM, 22 July 1865, p.5.

39 'The Tredegar Colliery Explosion – Termination of the Inquest', MM, 15 July 1865, p.8.

40 'Colliery Explosion near Tredegar', MM, 24 June 1865, p.3.

41 'The Tredegar Colliery Explosion', MM, 15 July 1865, p.8.

42 'Bedwellty Colliery Explosion', MM, 22 July 1865, p.5.

43 'Bedwellty Colliery Explosion', MM, 22 July 1865, p.5.

44 'The Colliery Explosion at Tredegar', *Illustrated London News*, 1 July 1865, pp.628-30.

45 'Colliery Explosion near Tredegar', MM, 24 June 1865, p.3.

46 'The Colliery Explosion at Tredegar', *Illustrated London News*, 1 July 1865, pp.628-30.

47 'Colliery Explosion near Tredegar', MM, 24 June 1865, p.3.

48 'The Tredegar Colliery Explosion – Termination of the Inquest', MM, 15 July 1865, p.8.

49 'The Tredegar Colliery Explosion – Termination of the Inquest', MM, 15 July 1865, p.8.

50 Brian Glover, *Prince of Ales*. (Alan Sutton, 1993), p.27.

51 'Monmouthshire Summer Assizes', MM, 12 August 1865, p.2.

52 'The Late Explosion at Tredegar', *Merthyr Telegraph and General Advertiser for the Iron Districts of South Wales*, 14 Oct 1865, p.4.

53 'Tredegar – The Late Explosion', *Cardiff Times*, 27 Oct 1865, p.6.

54 'The Tredegar Explosion', *Merthyr Telegraph and General Advertiser for the Iron Districts of South Wales*, 11 Nov 1865, p.4.

55 'Local Intelligence' and 'Tredegar Special Sessions', *Merthyr Telegraph and General Advertiser for the Iron Districts of South Wales*, respectively 11 Oct 1865, p.4 and 3 March 1866, p.3

56 *An Act for the Regulation and Inspection of Mines* [28th August 1860], C A P CLI, para.

57 'District Intelligence- Tredegar, Adjourned Special Session', MM, 28 Oct 1865, p.6.

58 'District Intelligence- Tredegar, Adjourned Special Session', MM, 28 Oct 1865, p.6.

59 'Death of Mr William Bevan, Mineral Agent', *Merthyr Telegraph and General Advertiser for the Iron Districts of South Wales*, 5 Dec 1868, p.4. Steps were afterwards taken to erect a memorial tablet at St. George's Church. 'Memorial to the Late William Bevan', MM, 5 June 1869, p.3.

60 William Smith, op. cit., p.12.

61 William Smith, op. cit., pp.8-9.

62 'The Miners' Conference and the Colliers of South Wales', WM, 8 May 1871.

63 'District Intelligence', WM, 8 June 1871.

64 'District Intelligence', WM, 8 June 1871.

65 'District Intelligence', WM, 1 August 1871.

66 'District Intelligence', WM, 8 Sept 1871.

67 'District Intelligence', WM, 26 Oct 1871.

68 'District Intelligence', WM, 21 Nov 1871.

69 Rayner Rosser, *Collieries of the Sirhowy Valley*. (Old Bakehouse Publications, 1996), p.104. She credits Mrs Norah Childs, for fifty years Secretary to the Medical Aid Society, for providing her with 'an extensive handwritten history of the Society', see p.119.

70 A Newport Libraries briefing note, 'Tredegar Ironworks' (2013).

71 William Smith, op. cit., pp.12-13.

72 William Smith, op. cit., p.13.

73 Leslie M. Shore, op. cit., pp.27-28.

74 Leslie M. Shore, op. cit., pp.28-29.

75 William Smith, op. cit., p.14.

76 Furthermore, J. H. Thomas's presentation of the period circa 1871 to 1881 does not make plain that in 1873 the Tredegar Iron and Coal Company was formed to acquire the Tredegar ironworks and coal properties. Nevertheless, the Writer's point ought not to be taken as criticism of Thomas's work. Researchers can only empathise with his remark that 'it was not always an easy matter to follow events in their sequence on account of some missing documents'; William Smith, op. cit., p.6.

77 'The Great Strike in South Wales', WM, 6 Jan 1873.

78 'The Great Strike in South Wales', WM, 1 Feb 1873.

79 'The Great Strike in South Wales', WM, 13 March 1873.

80   'Monmouthshire Assizes', WM, 29 March 1873.
81   (House of Commons) Parliamentary Papers, Session 1874, Paper 24, vol. LXII, folio 500.
82   *The Tredegar Iron and Coal Company Limited 1873-1923*, hereafter TICC, p.1. Gwent Archives, Misc Mss 1147.
83   WCF: TI&C, op. cit, p.45. G. T. Clark was one of the foremost industrialists of South Wales during Victorian times; see Brian Ll. James ed., *G. T. Clark: Scholar Ironmaster in the Victorian Age*. (University of Wales Press, 1998). Clark, as a trustee of the Dowlais Iron Works, oversaw the performance of the company's general manager, William Menelaus.
84   TICC, op. cit., p.1.
85   J. C. Carr and W. Taplin, op. cit., p.13.
86   J. C. Carr and W. Taplin, op. cit., p.86.
87   'Lady Aberconway', *The Times*, 5 Jan 1933, p.12.
88   *Annual General Meeting Report*, Bolckow, Vaughan & Company. (1867), p.16.
89   J. C. Carr and W. Taplin, op. cit., p.37.
90   *The Colliery Guardian* [hereafter TCG], 'Monmouthshire & South Wales', Vol.XXV, 30 May 1873, p.655. The Newport-Abercarn Black Vein Company's registered nominal capital of £150,000 'befitted a new, speculative venture; that of the Tredegar Iron & Coal Company was £1¼ million, recognising that it was largely taking over existing assets', Comment Prof. Trevor Boyns to Writer, 31 Aug 2015.
91   Trevor Boyns, 'Growth in the Coal Industry: the Cases of Powell Duffryn and the Ocean Coal Company', ed. Colin Baber and L. J. Williams, *Modern South Wales: Essays in Economic History*. (University of Wales Press, 1986), table 2, p.155, Source: W. G. Dalziel, Records of the Several Coal Owner's Association of South Wales, 1864 to 1895, and Llyfrgell Genedlaethol Cymru / National Library of Wales Coalowners' Association records. Annual Summary for 1914-15.
92   'District Intelligence', WM, 1 April 1873.
93   'District Intelligence', WM, 3 April 1873.
94   'Tredegar Iron and Coal Company, Limited', *The Sheffield & Rotherham Independent*, 20 June 1895, p.7.
95   'Obituary', *The Journal of the Iron and Steel Institute*, Vol. XLV, (1894), p.390.
96   TCG, 'Monmouthshire & South Wales', Vol.XXVI, 1 Aug 1873, p.145.
97   Gwent Archives, D.3246.221.
98   *The Merthyr Express* [hereafter ME], 11 Feb 1911.
99   ME, 4 March 1911.
100 Gwent Archives, D.3246.226.
101 Gwent Archives, D.3246.229 and D.3246.2210.
102 J. C. Carr and W. Taplin, op. cit., p.30.
103 See M. Atkinson and T. Boyns, 'Haematite Mining in Glamorgan in the Nineteenth Century', *Glamorgan Historian*, Vol.12 (1981), pp. 108-122.
104 See R. A. Gayer and J. T. G. Stead, 'The Forest of Dean Coal and Iron-Ore Fields' in *Geological Excursions in South Wales & the Forest of Dean*, Edited by Douglas A. Basset & Michael G. Bassett. (Geologists' Association South Wales Group, 1971), p.24, pp.28-29
105 TCG, 'Monmouthshire & South Wales', Vol. XXVI, 11 July 1873, p.39.
106 OS Ref No. SO 144080 approximately. Today where Tredegar Comprehensive School stands.
107 'District Intelligence', WM, 9 April 1875.
108 'Death of the late Mr Edward Williams', SWIE, Vol.XV (1886-87), p.5.
109 The properties of the Bwdwllog and Old Coal seams were the same as that given for Bedwellty Pits see earlier note.
110 TICC, op. cit., p.2.
111 Charles Wilkins, op. cit., p.170.
112 J. C. Carr and W. Taplin, op. cit., p.95.
113 'District Intelligence', WM, 2 Feb 1875.
114 'Amalgamated Association of Miners' half-yearly conference', WM, 7 April 1873.
115 *Centenary Review*, WM, 1 May 1969, p.12.
116 Leslie M. Shore, op. cit., pp.37-38.
117 A. Bassett, 'The Port of Newport and the Coal Field', op. cit., p.150.
118 'Opening of the Alexandra Docks', MM, 16 April 1875, p.2.
119 Bassett, 'The Port of Newport and the Coal Field', op. cit., p.157.
120 'Opening of the Alexandra Docks', MM, 16 April 1875, p.2.
121 A. Bassett, 'The Port of Newport and the Coal Field', op. cit., p.160.
122 'Opening of the Alexandra Docks', MM, 16 April 1875, p.2.
123 Sir George Elliot, as a director of both the Powell Duffryn Steam Coal Company and Alexandra Docks Company, was open about his frustration about the lock-out in the South Wales Coalfield. In a speech of his during the dock's opening he reproached the South Wales Collieries Association's stance, and advocated arbitration. 'Opening of the Alexandra Docks', MM, 16 April 1875, p.5. Covered also in Leslie M. Shore, op. cit., p.38.
124 'District Intelligence', WM, 9 April 1875.
125 Regarding Tredegar Company colliery technical details, 'Coal Mining in Monmouthshire', WM, 20 Nov 1869, p.6. Located at OS Ref. SO 147076
126 Evan Powell, op. cit., p.11
127 'On the Prevention of Colliery Accidents', WM, 7 Aug 1869, p.2
128 'Important Conference of the Amalgamated Association of Miners at Pontypridd', WM, 26 Nov 1870, p.3.

A postcard view entitled 'Bedwellty Pits Nr Tredegar' shows a pair of Tredegar wagons. The colliery itself is off to the right.   *Pope/Parkhouse Archive*

Pochin Colliery, Near Tredegar. 1890. (1)

Pochin Colliery. A turf cutting ceremony by Laura Pochin, later Lady Aberconway, in May 1874, marked the opening of the second steam coal colliery by Tredegar Iron & Coal Company. There are some interesting buildings concerned with the loading of coal under which are a variety of Tredegar Company wagons, some with lettering on the sweep (curved) and some straight. At this date there appears to be only a single Just visible are the lines of the L&NWR's Sirhowy Branch which ran between the colliery and its spoil heaps from which the photograph was taken. The bridge on timber supports takes the tubs full of waste from the colliery over the L&NWR lines to the waste heaps.

Pope/Parkhouse Archive

Chapter Three
COAL and STEEL

In May 1876, Miss Laura Pochin 'cut the first sod of pits' that she christened 'Pochin'.[1] She would have delivered a 'neat and pointed speech'.[2] The naming of the colliery fêted the surname of another director of the Tredegar Iron & Coal Company. Henry Davis Pochin and his family may have been charmed by the company's gesture.

The site of the Pochin sinking, on the 800 foot contour of the western side of the Sirhowy Valley, lay nearly three miles south of Tredegar's Town Clock. Today, the western surroundings of the site might be viewed as the bleakest part of the valley. A thin escarpment of Pennant sandstone follows approximately the line of the 1,300ft contour at the top of a steep hillside, Darren Ddu (Black Hill). 'Darren' was the name used by the Tredegar Estate for its property upon which Pochin Colliery was sunk. The escarpment marks the transition from hillside to the plateau of Mynydd Bedwellty. Perched on Darren Ddu is a feature known locally as the 'rocking stone', which although a misnomer does provide a giddy seat to view the valley below.

Laura Elizabeth Pochin, aged twenty-two, may have found the stark hillside scenery of Darren Ddu like a part of Wales she may have been familiar with. Two years earlier, her father purchased the 2,000 acre Bodnant estate, Denbighshire. The estate lay on the eastern side of the River Conway with an outlook westward to the wild hills of the Carneddau. Although her industrialist father had already widened his interests into farming, developing the Bodnant estate saw him begin a new vocation, gardening. He employed Mr E. Milner of Norwood as his landscape gardener.

In early 1877, Henry Davis Pochin convened a 'public dinner' on the Bodnant estate. The chairman of the event, the estate agent, declared it was the intention of 'Mr Pochin' to make the Bodnant estate a 'model estate in North Wales'.

The body of the event's audience comprised the tenants of the Bodnant estate. The tenants heard its owner recall that he had been a 'working man' all his life and felt 'no worse for it'. 'I have risen early and stayed up late to study'. His field of study was chemistry, and he had applied the science with equal dedication. Due to resolve, astuteness in commercial ventures, some luck, he became a successful industrialist, and so reaped wealth.

At the 'public dinner', Pochin also revealed that he was a ship owner and shipbuilder, but gave no hint of being a coal owner. Or did he? He reflected: 'I remember well what a marvellous achievement it was thought to be when steamers were built to run between Holyhead and Dublin, that only consumed 12 pounds of coal per hour'. However, in 1877, 'we can construct steamers that will consume 2 pounds of coal per hour'.[3] Such a trend to more efficient steam engines for powering ships was information of considerable importance to a coal owner.

Although Pochin stated in his speech an aim to make agriculture more efficient, he tried to dispel any tenant's preconception that he was a mean spirited industrialist. He offered the thought: 'Whether we live in a large or small house, or whether we are rich or poor, one unfailing source of happiness is within reach of all, even of the lowest capacity, and that is the boundless field of nature, where you may find gems on every hand, and in every hedge row, and no man can monopolise these'. Perhaps more relevant to the needs of most of his audience, Pochin announced that another of his aims was to improve the tenants' cottages.

Regarding the start to his development of the Bodnant estate, '100 artisans' were employed to remodel and extend Bodnant House, and fifty men grafted as gardeners. By the end of the first two years of Pochin's ownership visitors to the estate would have viewed a 'handsome mansion' and some sixty acres of 'flower gardens, walks, lakes, lawns, and pleasure grounds'.

A portion of Henry Davis Pochin's wealth had also been invested in South Wales with the founding of the Tredegar Iron & Coal Company. If he had been present with his daughter in May 1876, at the turf cutting ceremony below Darren Ddu, he might have been struck by the sylvan beauty of spring enlivening the eastern side of the colliery site. Woodland covered the west-facing hillside of Cefn Manmoel. Pochin might have also learnt that primitive industrialists had earlier used Cefn Manmoel's resource of timber to fuel a charcoal furnace on a site near a farmstead to the south-east of the colliery sinking. The remains of the furnace were viewed in 1831 by Eddil Gwent, who wrote an early local history of Tredegar, Hanes Tredegar. The furnace was dated to 1738 by Eddil Gwent whilst Evan Powell proposed the early 1600s. For a period around 1738, some Bretons ran the furnace. A plea of Eddil Gwent's was that the name of the farmstead be perpetuated, which it has been: Pont Gwaith yr Haern – The Bridge Iron Works.[4]

Pochin Colliery

After Miss Pochin took her leave from the colliery site, the noise of work returned to near Pont Gwaith yr Haern after a century of rural peace. Beith Brothers began to sink two shafts; one eighteen feet in diameter with the other shaft sixteen feet in diameter.

As the Pochin sinkings proceeded, the company coped with a number of travails. Production output dipped at the ironworks during the first months of 1878 due to a lack of orders. In March 1878, an order was received, but it was only sufficient to keep the ironwork's rolling mills going for about a month.[5] The steam coal trade was in a 'fair' state, but the sale of house coal was considered to be 'sluggish'.

During February 1878, the colliers at Bedwellty Pits went on strike 'over the manner' in which the 'work of the screens was being carried on'.[6] The strike continued into the month of April partly because some of its supposedly idle colliers were working at Abercarn Colliery. The Tredegar Iron & Coal Company responded by ordering some of the men employed at its other collieries to 'take the place of the men on strike'. The company also threatened, 'in the case of a refusal of the order', that all its collieries would be closed.[7] The strike ended soon afterwards.

Sinking at Pochin Colliery though met 'heavy feeders of water'. Cameron pumps were 'put in, and in this way delay was avoided'.[8] Yet, as the company longed for the new colliery to come into operation it drew some comfort from the ironworks' fortunes. 'Matters go on swimmingly at these prosperous and successful works', reported The Colliery Guardian in April 1881.[9]

No doubt no pun was intended with the word used to describe a lively ironworks whilst water was being pumped out of the Pochin sinkings. At the start of July 1881, the British coal industry learnt that the Elled seam, 'the finest house coal known', was 'pierced' at Pochin. Moreover, the company's ironworkers were described as being 'as brisk as bees, [with] the only draw back being the wage rate'. With regard to the company's colliery workers: 'The men seem to work contentedly, strikes are sins of the past'.[10] Perhaps like the arrival of a high pressure weather system, an optimistic mood appeared to have settled upon the Tredegar district. Such a mood may have lingered. Later that month, the company announced that at 340 yards below the surface at Pochin Colliery the steam coal seam, the Big Vein, had been found.[11] Although the Big Vein was six feet thick 'at the top of the valley', at Pochin it was three feet thick but of 'good quality'.[12]

Although in August 1881 it was reported that 1,000 tons of coal had been raised at Pochin Colliery, not until the September did Beith Brothers end their 'arduous labours'. The sinkers left two shafts each bottoming out at around 385 yards.[13] The thicknesses of the coal seams found at Pochin Colliery below the Big Vein in order found during sinking were: Yard Coal, three feet; ¾ Seam, four feet; Polka, four feet; Rhas Las, three feet; Meadow Vein, six feet six inches; and Old Coal, six feet.[14]

Regarding the engineering of Pochin Colliery, the Tredegar Company took some noteworthy technical actions. A large compound steam pumping engine was installed half way down a shaft to extract water from undergound. Moreover, a further hydraulic pumping engine 'was arranged' to raise water from feeders entering at higher levels of a shaft.[15] The investment in pumping was recognition that the southern dip in the strata of the Sirhowy Valley served as a drain for the abundant rain that fell on at least Mynydd Llangynidr.

An 1884 newspaper's illustration of the colliery shows sturdy wooden headgears. Wooden headgears were generally used for sinking. However, it seemed odd that a company making iron rail had not utilised such a product in the structural design of the headgears.[16] Installed further at Pochin were two large winding engines 'capable of raising one thousand tons of coal a day from each pit'. Regarding ventilation, a large Guibal ventilating fan was installed. The No.1 shaft was the upcast. Coal screens were erected, as were surface buildings usually associated a colliery.

Although a 'good' new road was constructed to allow a flow of traffic to service some of the needs of an operational colliery, railway transport was vital to its operation.[17] The colliery's workers were recruited from a wide area. Workers drawn from the Tredegar and Blackwood districts used a L&NWR passenger service to travel to and from a colliery halt. In July 1876, the L&NWR had 'snatched from under the noses of its rivals the Sirhowy (Railway) route to Newport'.[18] Thus, the traffic and passenger inspector for the Sirhowy Railway of ten years, Mr R. Davies of Tredegar, 'transferred' his services to the L&NWR. He had been responsible for making 'the arrangements for the first passenger train from Sirhowy to Newport', which in 1865 comprised first, second, and third classes for travel.[19] A railway passenger's journey in 1865 from Sirhowy Station, which lay about half-a-mile north of Tredegar Town Clock, to Newport Station, a distance of around twenty-two miles, took one and a half hours. A train ride of around five miles from Blackwood Station to a halt at Pochin Colliery took around twenty-two minutes.[20]

A number of the colliery's workers, particularly those who lived at two hamlets, Troedrhiwgwair to the north of the colliery and Hollybush to its south, walked to work. Troedrhiwgwair and Hollybush each stood just over a mile from the colliery.

For the year 1884, the company worked Pochin Colliery as a single shift operation. That year, on Saturday the 8th November around 330 men worked a shift at the colliery. A number of these workers had travelled to the pit from Rhymney Valley locations such as near Maesycmmer and Fleur-de-Lys. One of the workers from around Maesycmmer, named only as 'Scotty' in a newspaper report, had once been a 'farm servant at Place [Plas Bedwellty?] farm'. Another worker, John Jones, who lived at the Bryn near Maesycwmmer, was employed because of his skill in horsemanship since he was known as 'Shon yr Haulier'. A worker living at Fleur-de-Lys would have walked over a hill to Blackwood Station, a distance of nearly two miles, to catch a train at a very early hour of the day for a ten hour shift underground at Pochin Colliery. Tough, fit, and determined colliers dwelt in at least Monmouthshire during the late nineteenth century.

Thomas H. M. Stratton was more than likely the Pochin Colliery's first manager serving from sometime before 1881. He was reported in 1884 as being responsible for 'opening out' the colliery. He was a certified colliery manager. An 1872 Act of Parliament deemed that every coal mine be placed under the charge of a certificated manager. The 1872 Act also required that the Home Secretary be told about all mining accidents,

Getting to Work 1: The Pochin colliers train composed of twenty 6- and 4-wheeled carriages hauled by a L&NWR locomotive.

Pope/Parkhouse Archive

Getting to Work 2: Before a day's work, or in this case a night's work, could commence the men had to collect their lamps from the lamp room. This is being done at the windows which are numbered, probably according to the men's lamp check numbers. *Pope/Parkhouse Archive*

Getting to Work 3: Finally the descent could commence. The men on the cage formed a 'bond' and it was usual that if you were on the first bond down you were also the first back up. Note the gates above the cage at either end, these were lifted out of the way when the cage came up.

Pope/Parkhouse Archive

Blast Furnaces at Tredegar Iron and Steel Works. Several of the blast furnaces are visible here, together with their associated stoves and, to the right, the blowing engine house. A number of the Tredegar Iron & Coal Co's railway wagons can also been seen. In the right foreground are a number of low four-wheeled bolster wagons with dumb buffers, when a pair were coupled together as seen here they could be used for carrying rail. Between the two sets is a wagon numbered 826 which may have been allocated to carrying coke having been built by the Cardiff Rolling Stock Co. in May 1893. Behind these wagons are two lettered up for Tredegar Smokeless Steam Coal which appear to be freshly painted grey with white lettering. To their left is another variation on the lettering with TREDEGAR at the top and SMOKELESS STEAM COAL below; all have 'CARDIFF' on the side door.

Pope/Parkhouse Archive

give directions with regard to Coroners' inquests into deaths from mining accidents, and prescribe a regime of penalties for offences against the Act.[21] Whilst a certified manager had taken charge of beginning to harvest coal from Pochin Colliery, the company's directors were pursuing crucial negotiations with the Tredegar Estate.

During the period of years from 1877 to 1881 the Tredegar Iron & Coal Company held meetings with the Tredegar Estate to try to extend the twenty-one years lease for the ironworks and coal mining property. The outcome was that the company was granted a lease term of fifty years on the 25th March 1877, after giving the Tredegar Estate a number of concessions.[22]

One concession of the company's was to sell the Darren property of forty-six acres upon which Pochin Colliery was built to the forty-three year old Godfrey Charles Morgan, hereafter identified as 2nd Lord Tredegar. J. H. Thomas believed that the purchase price agreed was £8,000. His explanation for the Tredegar Estate's purchase of the Darren property seems somewhat obscure. He wrote that the acquisition of the property was to 'prevent the company from working the Tredegar Estate minerals and also foreign properties by pits other than those already established on the Tredegar Estate'. Perhaps the Tredegar Estate gained some advantage with regard to positioning itself for future negotiations involving the development of its coal mining property. Nevertheless, regarding the Darren property, the Tredegar Estate was set to earn a further income from the Tredegar Iron & Coal Company. For fifty years, the rent income was set at £139 per annum with a wayleave 'on all coal worked … calculated at 7d. per ton of 2,520 lbs'.

The Tredegar Estate's apparent bid for some control over the company's development seems much clearer in terms of the ironworks and coal property with the exception of that covered by the Darren agreement. The Tredegar Company was 'covenanted to spend £50,000 in reconstructing the works', and to pay a 'dead rent of £3,000 and 7d. per ton royalties on coal above 36,000 tons per annum'. However, with the benefit of hindsight, entering into such a covenant around the year 1880 was a risky commitment for the company.

Tredegar Steel

Consensus exists among historians that the year 1880 marked the death in South Wales of its ironmaking industry. During the '1870s Welsh iron rail [output] fell from 534,000 tons in 1869 to less than 100,000 tons in 1877', the 'historic works' of Heads of the Valleys like Tredegar had to put up a 'strenuous fight' to survive.[23] Not all of the blast furnaces of South Wales cooled down to be razed. Some blast furnaces became servants of making steel.

The commercial 'turning point' in Britain for the use of Sir Henry Bessemer's eponymous iron into steel conversion process occurred in 1875.[24] Pioneering commercial bulk steel production began at both Ebbw Vale and Dowlais around 1862 and 1865 respectively. Rhymney entered the steel making age in 1877.[25] So, as the 1880s dawned, Tredegar people were spectators at night of the sight of the surrounding hills becoming silhouettes due to illuminations caused by 'blowed' Bessemer converters at Ebbw Vale and Rhymney. The puffs of steam of the *Britannia* had given the people of the Sirhowy Valley a gentle introduction to a new technology. The lucent way in which the steel revolution showed itself first at the head of the Sirhowy Valley was much more alarming. The Tredegar Ironworks' seventy-two puddling furnaces lay on the brink of obsolescence.[26] Some iron workers at the Tredegar works felt unease about the security of their employment. By the mid-1880s, the Welsh wrought iron industry 'limped to its death'.[27]

The future of the Tredegar Ironworks hinged upon the investment policy of the Tredegar Iron & Coal Company. Investing in steel plant at Tredegar involved 'neutralising' a number of business risks. Around 1878, Richard Laybourne, concerning the Bessemer plant erected at Rhymney, wrote: 'Seeing that all the ores used in the manufacture of steel are imported, it becomes a nice question as to the best site for steelworks in this district; some parties contending that they should be at the port of import, and thus save the railway freight upon the ores, and also the cost of carrying the rails to the port of shipment'.[28] Laybourne also warned of a likely rise in labour costs since 'dearer' skilled Bessemer converter operators would need to be employed.

In March 1878, a coal industry journal reported that the Tredegar Company was contemplating investment in a 'large and extensive steelworks'.[29] In 1880, as a prelude, the company commissioned a 'fourth' new blast furnace having a size that dwarfed the earlier ones.[30] In 1881, the Tredegar Ironworks comprised eight blast furnaces, with only five in operation, and five rolling mills.[31] An aim for the design of the 'whole plant and machinery' for the Tredegar 'Steel Works' was to 'economise labour to the utmost possible extent'.[32] In October 1881, James Colquhoun met representatives of Messr Davy and Sons of Sheffield to discuss the supply to the Tredegar Company of at least rolling mill plant.[33]

Steelmaking plant installation got underway at Tredegar in 1882. The Tredegar Bessemer shops were designed to produce 3,000 tons of steel per week. The design led to two ten-ton Bessemer converters being sited opposite each other. Each converter was served by a casting pit. In 1882, a finished pit was 'forty feet in diameter and furnished with three ingot cranes'. The converters were 'situated very conveniently to the blast furnaces, and the ladle containing the molten metal [pig iron] is raised by a hydraulic hoist placed in the centre of the pits'. A small stationary engine powered the transfer of pig iron by ladle from the furnaces to a converter.

A Bessemer converter, having a shape like a tulip, faced skyward during a 'blow' of pig iron, after which it drooped to unload molten steel, before being re-charged with molten pig iron. A worm and wheel arrangement, hydraulically powered, controlled a converter's motion. Air for the 'blow' at $25lb/in^2$ was injected from a box at the base of a converter.

A substance called speigeleisen was used to control steel make quality. In 1856, steel making attempts by the Ebbw Vale Iron Company were marred by flawed material. The company approached the metallurgist Robert Forester Mushet of Coleford in the Forest of Dean to find a cure. Mushet's experiments developed a special alloy of iron, manganese and carbon, which he called 'triple compound'. The Ebbw Vale Company trialled his triple compound, and in September 1856 rolled a flawless double-headed steel rail. Mushet's triple compound prompted other rival metallurgical cures, which as a group were called speigeleisen. At Tredegar, cupolas moved by hydraulic lifts fed speigeleisen, a German term, to the converters.

At Tredegar, the operation of the cranes and Bessemer converters was controlled from a location known in the industry as a 'pulpit'. Through giving instructions to a team of other skilled men, an able operator directed from the pulpit the making of a stock of steel for rolling. Ingots filled with Bessemer steel in the casting pits were moved to the rolls by crane.

The rich tacit knowledge of rolling iron at Tredegar was a boon for introducing the working of steel. The first step, for fashioning an ingot of steel fit for a line of rolls to form a rail, was known as cogging. Tredegar's cogging mill engines were described in 1883 as being horizontal 'reversing engines, with overhung cylinders, each 40-inch diameter and five feet stroke; they are fitted with balanced side valves, worked through reversing links of the Allan type, by eccentrics fitted to separate shafts, and driven by drag links from the main cranks'. The reversing was 'effected by a steam cylinder, fitted with suitable controlling gear'. The cranks were made of cast steel with the crank shaft of 'best wrought scrap iron'. The spur gearing had a ratio of 'about' 2 to 1. 'The total weight of the cogging engines was about 140 tons'. All the 'starting handles' were 'brought to an elevated platform erected over the centre of the engine, so that the man in charge' had 'complete view both of the engine and of the rolls'. The product of cogging was called a 'Bloom'.

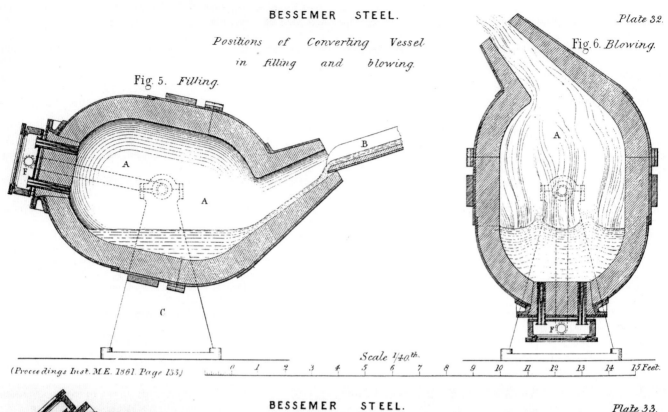

BESSEMER STEEL.

Positions of Converting Vessel in filling and blowing.

Fig. 5. *Filling.*

Fig. 6. *Blowing.*

Plate 32.

Scale 1/40.th.

(*Proceedings Inst. M.E. 1861. Page 133.*)

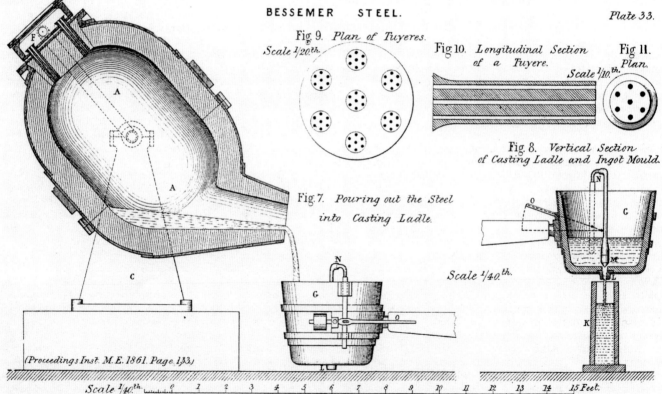

BESSEMER STEEL.

Plate 33.

Fig 9. *Plan of Tuyeres.*
Scale 1/20.th.

Fig 10. *Longitudinal Section of a Tuyere.*
Scale 1/10.th.

Fig 11. *Plan.*

Fig. 8. *Vertical Section of Casting Ladle and Ingot Mould.*

Fig. 7. *Pouring out the Steel into Casting Ladle.*

Scale 1/40.th.

(*Proceedings Inst. M.E. 1861. Page 133.*)

Scale 1/40.th.

Bessemer Converter Operation. Steelmaking, using the Bessemer Conveter process, officially began at Tredegar in 1883. Diagrams from Barraclough, K. C. *Steelmaking* 1850-1900. (The Institute of Metals, 1990), pp.62-65.   *Provided courtesy of the Institute of Materials, Minerals, & Mining*

Precise control of the sizing of the finished iron product was engineered into the design of Tredegar's rolling operation. 'The live rollers, worked by a small engine' were 'placed before and behind the rolls', which were two high, and the ingots bloomed down to 7-inch square. Moreover, a 'system of live rollers was laid in a direct line from the last groove of the cogging to the first groove of the roughing rolls'. 'At about a forty feet distance from cogging stood the bloom shears to cut blooms to 'any desired length'.

For blooms chosen for rolling into rail, 'a switch' guided them 'straight to the roughing rolls of the finishing mill'. A steam traverser acted to link the rolled item issuing from the roughing rolls to the finishing mill. The finishing mill engines were horizontal reversing having cylinders 48-inch diameter and 4ft 6 inch stroke.

Rail clearing the finishing mill was carried by live rollers to the saw. 'Each length [of rail] when sawn' was passed on to a 'cantering machine', after which a skid, 'worked by a rope' carried forwarded the rail into a cooling tank. Machines for doing straightening, drilling, 'ending', and punching were 'conveniently placed' to 'facilitate the finishing of the rails'.

As a result of capital investment in plant and equipment Tredegar had entered the steel rail making age. But how did the company's steal making capacity compare with neighbouring rivals? By 1879, the Rhymney Iron Company operated two off seven ton capacity Bessemer converters.[34] The plant at Rhymney was 'constructed and guaranteed to make 500 tons of steel per week'. But 'in one week as much as 1,127 tons of steel was made'. As a result, after six months of making steel at Rhymney, the company's directors declared to shareholders that the plant was 'capable of turning out about 1,000 tons of steel ingots per week'.[35] In 1880, the Ebbw Vale Steel, Iron & Coal Company 'possessed six converters, four of which had a capacity of eight tons and two a capacity of ten tons'.[36] The Ebbw Vale Company also disclosed that such Bessemer converter plant 'had an aggregate steel ingot productive capacity of 1,000 tons per week'. Thus, based upon the foregoing figures, the Tredegar works was capable of producing more steel than at least the Rhymney works.

The Tredegar Bessemer converter plant design prediction of 3,000 tons of steel per week could be misread, and so mislead people. The Ebbw Vale works' aggregate weekly output figure gave a better guide to what in practice could be expected from operating Bessemer converter plant at the time. Moreover, based upon a comparison of Bessemer converter capacities between the two works, it appeared that Ebbw Vale had a greater output potential than Tredegar. Nevertheless, with regard to the reason for the Tredegar Company's investment in steel rolling plant, it was designed to be 'able to produce 60,000 to 70,000 tons per annum' of Bessemer steel rails.

Company officials and 'a goodly number of townspeople' watched the first steel ingot being rolled at the Tredegar steelworks in late August 1882.[37] However, 2nd Lord Tredegar formally opened the steelworks on the 8th May 1883. Under the 'conductorship of Mr Colquhoun', he 'witnessed the complete process'. A luncheon was held afterwards at the Town Hall chaired by Benjamin Whitworth. The local landowner's speech at the luncheon began by teasing Henry Pochin about his wish 'to leave as soon as possible'. He warned him that 'he never spoke under an hour and three-quarters'. However, after a few more brief witty remarks and words of thanks, Lord Tredegar offered a toast: 'Prosperity to the Company and the New Works. 'James Colquhoun's address mentioned that a 'very hard fight [was] going on in the manufacture of iron between all the nations of the earth, and between the Americans, the French, and the Belgians in particular'.[38]

Death, Poor Trade, and a Riot

At the time, 2,000 people were employed at the Tredegar works including 500 to 600 women who 'perform work equally as hard as that done by the men and boys'.[39] In June 1883, Thomas Griffith, a labourer, became the Bessemer Steelworks' first fatality due to being 'entangled' and 'crushed' in a lift mechanism. He left a widow and five children.[40]

By December, trade at the works was 'not so brisk as to constrain the men to believe that all fears of another reduction of wages being proposed may be dismissed'. Workmen had accepted an earlier reduction in wages. However, due to the apparent 'amenable' nature of the workforce, it was 'not thought probable that there will be anything approaching to a prolonged dispute'.[41]

With the advent of steelmaking, one class of worker at Tredegar faced a bleak future, the puddler. Truran registered in the 1850s that the make of puddling was dependent upon the skill of the puddler, quality of iron operated on, and the general character of the coal'.[42] The puddler's craft faced death at Tredegar with the introduction of steel making.

The birth of Bessemer steel making at Tredegar may also be linked to local anti-Irish riots that occurred in 1882. Extensive damage to property occurred in a number of the streets of the town. A unit of soldiers was drafted to the town to restore law and order. At the time, many reasons were proclaimed about the cause of the riots from the effects of drunkenness to a vendetta against a racial minority viewed as likely to take the low paid jobs created to support steelmaking.[43] Gloomy fallacies may also have prevailed within the Tredegar district about the income rewards for, and skills needed, to work as a Bessemer operator. Steel making at Tredegar seems not to have enjoyed an auspicious start from the perspective of ordinary people.

A Business Duet

Nevertheless, and notable, in 1882 the Tredegar Company caught up with its Monmouthshire rivals, Rhymney Iron Company and Ebbw Vale Steel, Iron & Coal Company, to begin a new kind of business duet, steel and coal. Although making iron was basic to the duet, blast furnace operation was only a means to a business end.

Nonetheless: what were the intentions of the Tredegar Iron & Coal Company, Rhymney Iron Company and Ebbw Vale Steel, Iron & Coal Company in around 1880 with respect to the steam coal business? In the absence of figures that discern coal used for iron smelting from the coal 'exported' for steam raising purposes, only an interim answer to the question is offered through reference to the collieries sunk after 1850. The Tredegar Iron & Coal Company and its predecessor sank Bedwellty Pits, Whitworth Pits, and Pochin Colliery between circa 1850 and 1882. Over the same period, the Rhymney Iron Company sank only New Duffryn Colliery, in 1867, and the Ebbw Vale Steel, Iron & Coal Company just Wain (sic) [later known as Waun] Lwyd Colliery in 1875.[44] This comparison of sinkings suggests that the Tredegar Company was keener to obtain business from supplying fuel to the steam raising market than its Monmouthshire rivals. Moreover, the company's sinkings for steam coal surpassed that of the Rhymney Valley operation of Powell Duffryn Steam Coal Company, which acquired Thomas Powell's New Tredegar Colliery in 1864. Following taking ownership of New Tredegar Colliery, Powell Duffryn, whose business was solely coal, sank no new collieries in the Rhymney Valley until 1883 when Elliot West Colliery was sunk. Thus, arguably, around 1880 any developments by the Tredegar Iron & Coal Company of its coal business merited watching by the coal owners of the South Wales Coalfield.

Death of Samuel Homfray Junior

Samuel Homfray Junior, who had established the Tredegar Ironworks as a 'Great' works, which was Sir Henry Bessemer's description, died on the 16th November 1882, at eighty-six years of age. He was buried at St. Basil Church, Bassaleg, where monuments of the Morgans of Tredegar House are prominent. It was his service as Mayor of Newport between November 1854 and November 1855 that may have prompted the brief note about him in the Monmouthshire press: 'In business, municipal, and social life his name was a "household word", and his death will create a chasm which cannot be filled'.[45] Moreover, a spokesman at a December 1882 meeting of Newport Town Council said that Homfray 'was liberality itself and kindness itself'.[46] Such praise does not accord with a lingering perception that South Wales' ironmasters of the nineteenth century acted with ruthlessness.

Endless-Rope Haulage

As the general manager of the Tredegar Iron & Coal Company, one of James Colquhoun's duties was to improve methods of working to lower the unit cost of both steel and coal production. The invention of the Bessemer process, driven by an aim to make cheaper malleable iron, caused a revolution in terms of the mechanisation of the major heavy industry of South Wales, iron and steel. In comparison, technical advances in the coal industry tended to progress gradually.

In the late 1870s, James Colquhoun was given licence by the directors to invest in the mechanisation of handling of coal and related materials. At the time there were three principal types of mechanical material handling systems for him to consider. First, there was a system known as 'Main-and-tail rope'. This system involved hauling full trams filled with material one way ('outbye') on the 'main rope' whilst a lighter in construction 'tail' rope pulled empty trams in the opposite direction ('inbye'). At the 'inbye station' the tail rope was exchanged mechanically for the main rope. One winding drum was always in gear, while the other ran loose on its shaft letting out a rope as needed. Trams were pulled along a single line of rails. The speed of travel of a tram was about 10 miles per hour. 'Main-and-tail' was the general system adopted in South Wales, but no information was found to be able to gauge how widely used such a system was in the South Wales Coalfield, or particularly the Tredegar Company, during the late 1870s.[47]

Another option for the Tredegar Company's general manager to study was classed as a 'Number 1 endless-rope system'.

This system was in reality a modification of the main-and-tail system, and worked at a similar speed. James Colquhoun did not have to travel far from Tredegar to form a judgment about a Number 1 endless-rope system in use. Around the cusp of the 1880s, the Cymmer Colliery and Rhymney Iron Works Company were among the pioneering users of the Number 1 endless-rope system in the South Wales Coalfield.[48] The Rhymney Company initiated the operation of the Number 1 endless-rope system at three locations, Lower Level, the Clay Level, and Terrace Pit. Colquhoun obtained associated 'particulars through the kindness of Mr [David?] Evans, General Manager, Rhymney Iron Works'. The Tredegar Company promptly followed the Rhymney Company and installed a No.1 endless-rope system for haulage at Whitworth No. 2 Pit.[49]

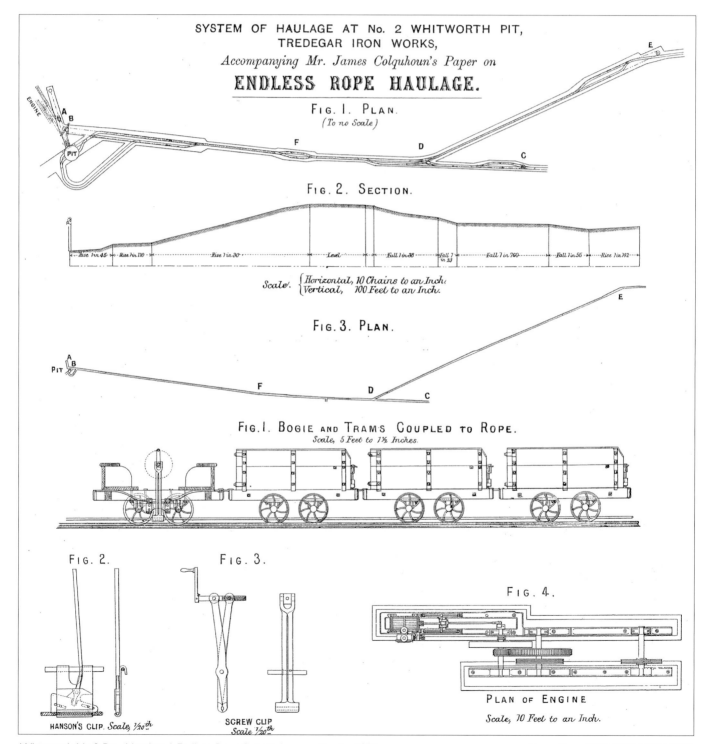

SYSTEM OF HAULAGE AT No. 2 WHITWORTH PIT, TREDEGAR IRON WORKS,

Accompanying Mr. James Colquhoun's Paper on

ENDLESS ROPE HAULAGE.

Fig. 1. Plan. (To no Scale)

Fig. 2. Section.

Scale: Horizontal, 10 Chains to an Inch. Vertical, 100 Feet to an Inch.

Fig. 3. Plan.

Fig. 1. Bogie and Trams Coupled to Rope. Scale, 5 Feet to 1½ Inches.

Fig. 2.   Fig. 3.

Hanson's Clip. Scale 1/20th

Screw Clip. Scale 1/20th

Fig. 4.

Plan of Engine. Scale, 10 Feet to an Inch.

Whitworth No.2 Pit - Number 1 Endless-Rope System. In operation by 1882.

Proceedings, SWIE: 1882-83, Vol. XVIII

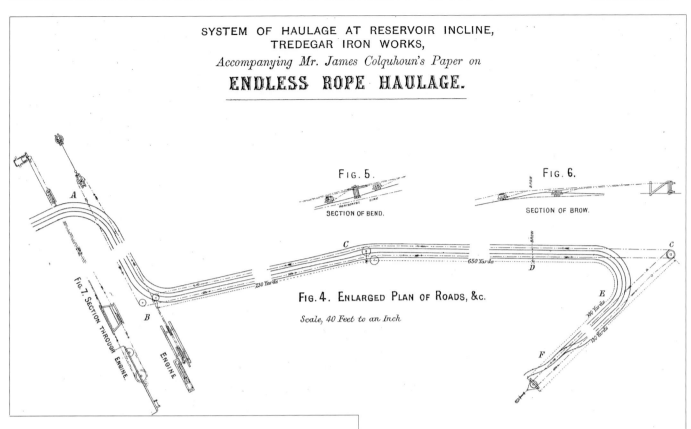

SYSTEM OF HAULAGE AT RESERVOIR INCLINE,
TREDEGAR IRON WORKS,
Accompanying Mr. James Colquhoun's Paper on

ENDLESS ROPE HAULAGE.

FIG. 5.

SECTION OF BEND.

FIG. 6.

SECTION OF BROW.

FIG. 4. ENLARGED PLAN OF ROADS, &c.

Scale, 40 Feet to an Inch

FIG. 7. SECTION THROUGH ENGINE.

ENGINE.

In late 1882, James Colquhoun offered an observation: 'As nearly all the shallow coal has been worked out in this District [not defined, but probably the Tredegar District], and the winnings are deep, it is of the highest importance that the best system of haulage should be adopted in order to cheapen the cost of production'. He further registered that 'various local circumstances determine the system that will prove the cheapest and most effective'.[50]

Also around 1880, James Colquhoun trialled the 'No. 2 endless-rope system', the third principal type of material handling system then available. Although 'extensively used in the Midland Counties', the Reservoir Incline, Tredegar, became the site for the first installation of a No. 2 endless-rope system in the South Wales Coalfield. Thus, Colquhoun's 1882 paper to the South Wales Institute of Engineers, 'Endless-Rope Haulage' had significance for the South Wales Coalfield.

The remit for the Reservoir Incline project was to move 'rubbish from several pits and also from the coal washing machine' up an incline to deposit 'the same along the embankment of the Water Works Reservoir in order to strengthen it'.[51] An important differentiating design feature of a Number 2 endless-rope system was a double line of rails for tram haulage. The rubbish was loaded into trams at Ty Trist pits a short distance northward from a haulage engine. The endless-rope system was powered by a steam powered haulage engine having a 16-inch diameter cylinder, and a 3 feet stroke. The engine's output was geared 1 to 5 so as to drive two grooved rope driving-guiding pulleys; one 7 ft, and the other 6ft in diameter. The distance from the winding engine to the brow of the Reservoir incline was 890 yards. The incline's gradient was 'irregular and almost extremely steep, the average rise …. to [the] brow being 1 in 6, the total rise being over 300 feet'.

The 'Reservoir Incline' system's rope moved at an average speed of 1½ miles per hour. A line of hanging chain slings, each chain separated from another by a distance of eighty yards, were attached to the moving rope. A tram moving from the Ty Trist rubbish loading point rolled down a short ramp of rail to the system's haulage engine. Upon arriving at the haulage engine, a loaded tram was fastened to a chain by the engineman for it to begin an ascent up the incline. 'The full, or up-line', had 'safety points at distances of 80 yards to prevent the loaded trams

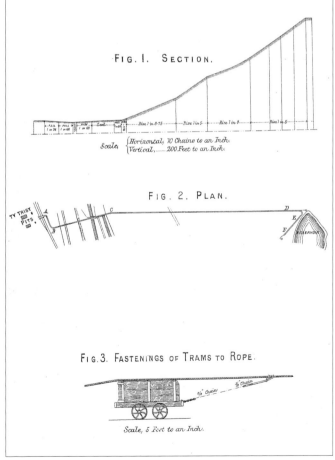

FIG. 1. SECTION.

Scale: { Horizontal, 10 Chains to an Inch. Vertical, …… 200 Feet to an Inch.

FIG. 2. PLAN.

FIG. 3. FASTENINGS OF TRAMS TO ROPE.

Scale, 5 Feet to an Inch.

Reservoir Incline - Number 2 Endless-Rope System. Operated between Ty Trist Colliery and a reservoir situated on Cefn Manmoel identified earlier on a map. Operated by 1882, and was the first Number 2 Endless-Rope System used in the South Wales Coalfield.

Proceedings, SWIE: 1882-83, Vol. XVIII

running wild should any mishap occur'. Just beyond the brow of the incline, an attendant unhitched a loaded tram. The tram then ran along a 'permanent' way, first to a station where rubbish was dumped, and then moved to the attendant for tying on to the hanging chain. An empty tram then descended the incline. Girls were employed 'for taking out the full and returning the empty trams'. One girl was employed at the Ty Trist loading station with another at the reservoir refuse dumping station.

Operating the system at an average speed 1½ miles per hour, 300 tons of rubbish per day was regularly moved up the Reservoir Incline. The number of trams in use at one time was limited to thirty. However, Colquhoun had some grounds for believing that if the rope moved at two miles per hour, 500 tons of rubbish a day would be transported.

A comparison of system running costs further helped coal owners make haulage system choices. The cost per ton per mile for the Reservoir Incline system, when moving 300 tons per day, was reckoned to be 1.333d., which compared favourably with an average figure sourced by James Colquhoun of 2.993d.[52] If 500 tons of refuse was moved per day, the cost per ton mile would fall to 1.184d. Regarding the Whitworth No. 1 system, the total cost per ton per mile was 2.70d.

Mr Hort. Huxham, the Secretary of the South Wales Institute of Engineers, made a rigorous analysis of Colquhoun's costs. Regarding the No. 2 Endless-Rope system, Huxham concluded that the Reservoir Incline system, from an operation cost perspective, had proved 'very successful'.[53]

Regarding wider adoption of the system, James Colquhoun was certain that the No. 2 Endless-Rope system 'could not be applied to the haulage of coal trams as loaded in South Wales as the rope being carried on top of trams would crush the large coal'.[54] Trams used in the South Wales Coalfield were greater in size than elsewhere since they were 'thought to be better adapted to working steam coal seams'. He acknowledged that 'various local circumstances determine the system that will prove cheapest and most effective'.[55] Mr David Evans [Rhymney Iron Works?] held that the No. 2 Endless-Rope system was 'not adapted for use on undulating roads … in which case the tail-rope system of haulage answered much better and worked well'.[56] However, he judged that the 'slow rate of speed of the Endless Rope System was in itself conducive to safety'.[57]

James Colquhoun's paper prompted some grumbling about the wear and tear of ropes. Mr R. W. Southern 'doubted' whether the "life" of ropes 'would on average last two years'.[58] However, this was later contested by Hort. Huxham who had learnt from 'an engineer of considerable experience' that ropes used in an endless-rope system operated at a Nottinghamshire colliery had seen out 'some five years' of operation.[59] Indeed, a couple of years later, James Colquhoun reported that the rope on the Reservoir Incline had 'been working between four and five years'.[60]

Mining engineer members of the South Wales Institute of Engineers were naturally curious to know if the Endless-Rope system was useful for underground coal haulage. Richard Bedlington thought that 'the reason why the Endless-Rope system had not been used to any extent was owing chiefly to the difficulty and cost of maintaining a double roadway, in consequence of the weak nature of the roofs of the coal seams with which they had to contend'.[61] Hort. Huxham judged that since the collieries of South Wales were 'working large volumes of coal, which had to be hauled from several branching roadways that were extending yearly in length, the Tail-Rope system would be found more generally useful and more economical than any other system'. However, Whitworth Colliery, as an example, was to feature both 'main-and-tail rope', and 'endless-rope' systems for underground haulage.

Nonetheless, between the years 1880 and 1885, saw an advance in the mechanisation of materials haulage in the South Wales Coalfield with the Tredegar Company as a leader. The issues of the wear and tear of engines, ropes, pulleys, sheaves, trams, and so on would become perennial. However, regarding coal and rubbish haulage underground, the day had not arrived when a mechanical system made redundant the use of horses to pull trams. Until that day arrived, the death of a pit horse would be lamented by at least a coal owner.

A View of Industrial South Wales

In the late-Eighties the Tredegar Iron & Coal Company survived as a piece of the industrial South Wales jigsaw. Concerning this period, in 1884 James Colquhoun presented a survey of industrial South Wales.[62] 'It is almost superfluous to state that South Wales enjoys a peculiar importance as regards the superiority and extent of its coalfields, the manufacture of its iron, steel and tinplates'. 'Coal is the backbone of South Wales, and being the second largest producer in the kingdom, it is a matter of pre-eminent importance that those entrusted with the management of collieries should apply themselves assiduously to keep pace with the newest discoveries that are found most suitable for each peculiar locality of colliery'. Complacency was ever a threat to a business's survival. The collieries of the South Wales Coalfield produced 22,817,378 tons and 24,975,433 tons of coal respectively in the years 1882 and 1883. Only the total output of the northern-eastern coalfields of England, Durham and Northumberland, surpassed that of the South Wales Coalfield in Great Britain during those years.

James Colquhoun, though, was uneasy about the state of the iron and steel industry of South Wales. 'An almost unprecedented depression exists in the steel rail industry, and considering the enormous power of production, there appears to be no immediate prospect of a demand sufficient to keep the works [of South Wales] fully employed'. Moreover, the effect of metallurgical change upon the rail market had yet to be fully comprehended. 'The life of a steel rail has not yet been definitely determined, but unquestionably there will be much fewer renewals required than with iron,' he predicted.

Perhaps the general manager of the Tredegar Company reassured its directors by advising them about possible new markets for steel rail. His claim was: 'There are vast tracts of country unprovided with railways –in India, China and elsewhere – which will no doubt, as civilisation advances, and the importance of railway communication becomes appreciated, create a further demand'. Moreover, he hoped British railway engineers would adopt the German practice of laying steel sleepers. Nevertheless he drew some comfort from knowing that South Wales still held 'a prominent position in the manufacture of steel rails, having made 410,676 tons in 1883, out of a total make in the United Kingdom of 1,097,174 tons'.

Pivotal to lowering the cost of steel production, James Colquhoun argued that it was essential for companies to incur 'a large expenditure in remodelling … blast furnace plant, to reduce the cost of pig iron'. Concerning the competitiveness of the South Wales industry, he judged that 'the results will compare favourably, both as regards the consumption of fuel and the produce per furnace, with any district of the United Kingdom'. He highlighted that 'not very many years ago 100 tons per furnace was considered a large output, but now 600 to 700 tons is not considered extraordinary working. This has been accomplished by increasing the height and section of furnace, in raising the temperature of the blast from 1,000 to 1,500 deg. Fahrenheit, by improved iron and brick stoves, and by other improvements'. Regarding the total production of pig iron in the United Kingdom in 1883, the figure was 8,490,224 tons. Cleveland stood first on the tonnage output list of British districts making pig iron, Scotland was second, whilst South Wales ranked third by producing 887,259 tons.

James Colquhoun, familiar with the development of shipbuilding on Clydeside, appeared puzzled by South Wales' minor place in such an industry. South Wales had seen 'great progress in mining and metallurgy; but in shipbuilding anything that can be said is of a disappointing character'. Chepstow he identified as the most important shipbuilding location in South Wales, but launched there from 1879 to 1883 was just a total of 12,796 tons weight in ships. In 1883, the gross tonnage of ships 'built in iron and steel' in the United Kingdom was 1,012,735. He speculated: 'if shipbuilding could be made a financial success [in South Wales], it would not only help the industrial establishment of the hills, but bring a large increment of prosperity to the principal ports of the channel'. Thus he was keen to 'discover a reason why' shipbuilding had not 'received greater attention from the enterprising people who are concerned in the prosperity of South Wales'.

The significant role of skilled labour in shipbuilding was one aspect that James Colquhoun pondered. 'The men on the Clyde, Tyne, Wear, &c., have had a long practical training, and possibly could not be removed to a new sphere of labour without many difficulties and disadvantages'. Contestably, what can be implied from this assessment was that South Wales lacked sufficient men skilled in at least mechanical trades to support a shipbuilding industry. The pool of skilled labour in South Wales was on the whole employed by the coal, iron and steel industries. He might have conjectured that a likely penalty of there being a lack of skilled labour in South Wales was that the growth of a home-grown mechanical manufacturing industry would be curbed.

Moreover, the general manager of the Tredegar Iron & Coal Company further perceived another impediment to applying engineering technologies in South Wales. 'In technical education our Continental neighbours are ahead of us'. He hoped that training would be supplied in South Wales so that 'the staff of agents employed at the different works' would be able to 'adapt themselves quickly to any new condition of things that may arise'. Maybe to win over supporters for advancing technical education in South Wales he added: 'Formerly no great attention was given to determining the chemical properties of iron and steel, but the chemist is an indispensible person connected with every important establishment'.

Last in his survey, James Colquhoun saluted civil engineers for making it easier for train travel between South Wales and England. Under construction, between 1880 and 1886, was the four mile long Severn tunnel. The tunnel 'will give immense facilities for the carrying of coal to London and the south of England, and will be of great benefit to the South Wales trade generally'. The skill of the collier was an asset for tunnelling, and many of them accepted the dangers of such work.

downcast headgear, and became 'greatly battered'. The upcast shaft also 'bore evidences of the seriousness of the explosion'. Although the windows of the colliery's winding houses were broken, the winding engines were undamaged. Alarmingly wrecked was the Guibal ventilating fan, and also part of the building in which it was housed. Curiously, most of the fan house's window glass remained intact. The colliery's lamp room further escaped damage, but posted inside was a grim message. Seventeen lamp checks hung on hooks in the lamp room that belonged to men underground where most of them were doing a repair shift.

After being alerted by messages of alarm, company officials travelled to the colliery's pithead. Some news of the explosion got to Tredegar due to an employee of the L&NWR feeling its shock at Bedwellty Pits' signal box, a mile to the north of the colliery. The London & North Western Railway speedily 'placed an engine and van at the disposal' of the officials of the Tredegar Iron & Coal Company. James Colquhoun joined with the company's mineral agent and engineer, respectively Mr Stratton and Mr W. Hamilton, for the journey in the van to the colliery.

At about quarter to twelve on Saturday evening, just two and a half hours after the explosion, the colliery manager, Thomas Stratton, and his assistant, John Reynolds, bravely descended underground. The air they inhaled was of poor quality since there was no colliery ventilation. Their formation as colliery officials made them well informed about the dangers that they might have to contend with venturing underground in the aftermath of an explosion. Indeed, it seems highly likely that John Reynolds was the overman at Bedwellty Pits in 1865, and so had experienced the aftermath of that colliery's explosion.[64] Thomas Stratton and John Reynolds 'first went to the [underground] lodge-room of the pumpman (William Williams), whom they brought out alive'. The two officials then had to cope with the horror of finding mutilated, crushed, and burnt dead miners' bodies numbering fourteen. Some miners were found in sitting postures having died due to suffocation by 'after-damp'. As the rescue mission extended its reach, the manager and his assistant were joined by other officials and colliery worker volunteers. The travail continued for four, or maybe five, more days until the last two bodies were recovered, roadmen John Davies and Josiah Morris.

Lamp Check - Pochin Colliery, Tredegar Iron & Coal Company. Workers and colliery officials exchanged a check for a safety lamp before going underground. The checks were hung on a board that acted as a register of people present underground.
Courtesy of Amgueddfa Cymru National Museum Wales

Seventeen Pochin Colliery Lamp Checks

On Saturday, the 8th November 1884, at ten minutes past nine o'clock in the evening, a violent eruption of fumes, the manifestation of an underground explosion of gas, issued from Pochin Colliery's shafts.[63] 'Two of the large beams of wood forming the framing' of the downcast shaft headgear were wrenched from their iron sockets by the force of the eruption. Moreover, several cross-beams, 'very heavy pieces of wood', were hurled a distance on to the sidings of the L&NWR. A cage was 'blown up to the sheave' atop the

1884 Pochin Colliery Explosion – Victims being stretchered on the colliery's surface. The explosion killed sixteen men.
Western Mail, 12 November, 1884. Supplied by
Llyfrgell Gendlaethol Cymru/The National Library of Wales

Activity on the surface of the colliery, during the early period of the rescue mission, was watched by hundreds of bystanders. Recovered dead bodies were carried to the carpenters' shop, placed in coffins for sending on to the homes of the deceased miners. Early Monday morning, probably a smaller crowd of spectators watched the arrival by train from Newport of the chairman of the Tredegar Company, Benjamin Whitworth MP. Later that day, Donald Bain Assistant HM Inspector of Mines performed his duties underground. A distance from the pithead, a 'long and deep trench' was excavated by Pochin Colliery workers to bury the carcases of forty-three horses killed by the explosion.

By around Friday the 14th November, worker burial ceremonies had been conducted at cemeteries dispersed around west Monmouthshire. The Cefn Golau Cemetery saw seven men interred. Rev T. Theophilas, Vicar of Tredegar, Joseph Evans, a local Presbyterian minister and John Williams, the town's surveyor, united to lead the setting up of a relief fund for the benefit of the widows and orphans. Mourners at the Cefn Golau burials included James Colquhoun, Thomas Stratton and John Reynolds, and other officials of the Tredegar Iron & Coal Company.

On Tuesday the 25th November, at Tredegar's Temperance Hall, Monmouthshire's coroner, Martin Edwards, opened an inquest into the fatalities at Pochin Colliery. The coroner selected men who had no connection with the Tredegar Company to be members of the inquest's jury. The first case examined by the inquiry was that of Philip Pugh. 'Pugh was at the colliery soon after the accident, and was rather persistent in his offers to render assistance'. Indeed, he caused a spell of disorder that moved Police Inspector Williams to usher him away from the mouth of the shaft. The policeman scented that Pugh was 'under the influence of drink'. The persistent Pugh later charged forward, and fell down a shaft to his death. The jury returned a verdict of 'Accidental death' for Pugh.

Thomas Stratton was called as the first witness for the examination of the deaths of colliery workers. He was cross-examined by Hon A. Lytton of the Home Office. Afterwards Pochin Colliery officials, engine-drivers, pump men, and colliers were called as witnesses.

Such witnesses gave a picture of the colliery's operation. The colliery was spoken of as being 'a fiery one, but not exceptionally so'. A common view among the witnesses was that the pit had 'good ventilation'. Gas was not detected by underground officials' during checks made prior to the explosion. One witness said that 'there was a good deal of dust' in the colliery workings, but he had 'seen more in other places'. With the exception of one miner's lamp being found 'unlocked', all miner's lamps were intact. The lamps were of the Clanny type, which one witness cautioned were 'not the best to use where water' was 'falling, because if a drop touched the glass it might cause a split'. After the explosion, a search of one dead collier's pockets found two matches. Notices at the colliery prohibited the 'taking of matches' underground.

Three experienced colliery managers, all independent of the Tredegar Company, had inspected the colliery after the explosion.[65] The consensus view of this set of managers was that the condition of the colliery was 'excellent' and 'well laid out'.

Mr T. E. Wales, HM Inspector of Mines, made two notable comments. Although he was unhappy with the ventilation of one area of the colliery, generally he found no fault with the ventilation.[66] But, 'he believed that the coal dust added to the severity of the explosion, and the sooner the fact was appreciated in South Wales collieries where they fired shots the better'.

Following the Coroner's summing up the jury retired to consider a verdict. After returning to the inquiry's gathering, the jury's Foreman said:

We find that Thomas Lewis came to his death through an explosion which occurred at Pochin Pits on the 8th inst., but how the explosion was caused we have no evidence to show.

The jury's verdict applied to each of the deceased colliers, which for remembrance were:

John Bevan	married, of Blackwood (Fleur-de-Lys)
James Breeze	married, Tredegar
John Davies	married, Blackwood
William Evans	married, Hollybush
Evan Griffiths	single, Pittabach
John Harman (or Hamar)	single, Whitworth Terrace, Tredegar
William Havard	married, Troedrhiwgwair
John Jones [Shon yr haulier]	married, Blackwood (Bryn, Maesycwmmer)
Thomas Lewis	unknown, Bridge Street, Tredegar
Isaiah Morgan	married, Blackwood
Thomas Morgan	married, Hollybush [or Blackwood]
Josiah Morris	unknown, unknown
Gwilym Owen	unknown, Troedrhiwgwair
Henry Preece	married, five children, South Lane, Tredegar
William Scott [Scotty?]	single, Blackwood
John Williams	unknown, Whitworth Terrace, Tredegar

The Pochin Colliery explosion prompted some false speculation, and a bizarre recollection. The Home Secretary, Sir W. Harcourt, answering a question raised in the House of Commons, a couple of days after the Pochin Colliery explosion, stated that 'in his opinion the explosion was the result of shot firing'. Witnesses at the Tredegar inquest into the explosion, subjected to cross-examination, gave no information that verified the Home Secretary's opinion.

Reported days after the explosion was the premonition of a brewer, William Williams. In a dream, 'he saw Pugh fall down a pit, and warned him on Saturday'. The brewer traded at the Cambrian Arms, Tredegar. Williams' story about the demise of the befuddled Pugh was a gift to local campaigners seeking to ban the drinking of alcoholic drinks. The inquiry into the Pochin Colliery explosion was held at the town's Temperance Hall.

Coal Dust

The 1884 Pochin Colliery explosion occurred during the period when the accepted notion of the coal industry that underground explosions were solely due to the ignition of fire-damp was the subject of doubt. Nearly a decade earlier, an Assistant HM Inspector of Mines, William Galloway, had ventured to propose that coal dust floating in an underground atmosphere, being liable to ignition, was also a medium for spreading explosions. Galloway came up with this hypothesis after being party to inspecting the 1875 Llan Colliery explosion. His hypothesis was refuted by his superiors, and so he resigned from his post with the inspectorate.

Galloway then pursued a career as a consulting engineer, and persisted with research into the dangers of coal dust. In 1882, the underground workings of the Rhondda Fawr Valley's Llwynypia Colliery, owned by the Glamorgan Colliery Company, became his laboratory to test his ideas about coal dust. His controlled tests caused some violent underground explosions. Scientific papers he presented afterwards reported his tests' findings and conclusions in support of his initial hypothesis. Initially, his paper's conclusions were generally greeted with doubt. T. E. Wales's comments suggest that by 1884, within the HM Inspectorate, there was some appreciation that coal dust was dangerous as an explosion medium.

Moreover, James Colquhoun became personally acquainted with the ideas of William Galloway. In the wake of the 1884 Pochin Colliery explosion, Galloway examined the underground workings of Pochin Colliery with the general manager of the Tredegar Company. Galloway found:

That the flame of the explosion had penetrated into every working place in the colliery they had examined, with the exception of a small part of the big coal district, where there was a long heading in which the working places were quite free from any indication of the presence of flame, and on examining it carefully, and instituting inquiries, they found that the dust on that roadway was slightly damp in consequence of a water-cask having passed over it four times every twenty-fours, conveying water from a dip place to the lodge of the colliery.

Then, notably: 'The dropping of the water from the cask had been sufficient to wet the dust slightly, and that had prevented the flame of the explosion penetrating into the district'.[67] William Galloway, later knighted, would later acknowledge William Hood of Llwynypia Colliery as 'pioneer in this district [South Wales Coalfield] in watering the colliery roads, as a precaution against explosions'.[68]

Galloway's visit to Pochin Colliery caused James Colquhoun to action H. M. Stratton to explore ways and means for reducing the coal dust danger underground. During the years 1886 and 1887, H. M. Stratton did watering experiments at the colliery. One of his experiments saw hose-pipes spray water from stand-pipes set into a mains' pipe at every 30 yards. He also examined the notion that if 'the temperature of the downcast air were raised and saturated with moisture in the downcast shaft, the watering would be done automatically; because the reason why coal dust was formed along the roadways was that air coming down the pit was usually at low temperature which was gradually raised as it passed through the mine'.[69]

Stratton used a hose-pipe system to dampen coal dust. 'The spray had been tried at different times, but the objection was raised that it wetted the horses and the hauliers, and it was discontinued'. Yet, such an experiment had proved to be 'economical in every respect', and the horses 'seemed to be in a better condition since the watering had been regularly adopted'.

H. M. Stratton's experimentation with raising the temperature of the downcast air and saturating the downcast air with moisture appears to have been a novel undertaking at the time. He made reference to a review by Messrs Atkinson of 'five great explosions' and 'five of the most recent' explosions in the Durham Coalfield. The Messrs Atkinson review suggested 'a drastic remedy' not unlike H. M. Stratton's, who merits praise for trying to test the principle.[70]

A description of the 'apparatus' Stratton used for changing the nature of the underground atmosphere was not found. Nevertheless, 'it was very easy to do it in summer time, but as the weather got cooler, it was found that the difficulty proportionately increased'.[71] Upon finding during summer time 'no dust whatever in the working roads or working faces', he advocated enlarging the 'apparatus for giving heat to the intake air' during cold weather. He was also alert at the outset to 'much doubt as to the result in the way of damaging the roof, and causing many other inconveniences'. However, 'he was glad to say that with the exception of about the first 200 yards from the down cast pit, the system made absolutely no difference at all to the roof, or in any way acted prejudicially to the mine'.[72] However, Richard Bedlington, one of the three experienced colliery managers who had inspected Pochin Colliery after the 1884 explosion, was moved to offer a general appraisal of an aspect of Stratton's work. 'He thought it was very objectionable to raise the temperature of the intake air if it could be avoided, and equally good effects be produced by other effects'. Indeed, he advocated Mr Thomas's method at Ynishir Steam Coal Colliery. At Ynyshir, a 'series of pipes … carried along the main intake and up the headings, with spray jets at certain intervals, at those points which the experience of the manager found to be necessary'.[73]

Notably, several independent attempts were made over the period of years 1886 to 1887 aimed at reducing the coal dust danger in colliery workings of the South Wales Coalfield. The period might be considered as the first development stage for such mining engineering in the coalfield following William Hood's pioneering work at Llwynypia Colliery. During the period Henry W. Martin, another one of the three colliery managers that inspected Pochin Colliery after the 1884 explosion, tried two dust dampening methods at collieries of the Dowlais Company. The method trialled by the Dowlais Company that caught the interest of mining engineers involved a compressed air-water system producing a spray or mist at Vochriw (sic) and South Tunnel Pits.[74] Henry W. Martin reported that the 'system was working so satisfactory that he

was largely expanding its application'.[75] Thomas Forster Brown (1835-1907), a distinguished mining engineer, introduced another method for watering the dust at Harris's Navigation Colliery. He 'looked upon' the application of water 'as the great secret of safety in the future of the steam-coal collieries of South Wales'.[76] Time would tell if his optimism was justified, but the period's body of experimental work showed that some coal owners had heeded William Galloway's ideas.

Regarding the Tredegar Company's experiments they might have stalled by around 1887 since H. M. Stratton left the company to take a post in the North of England. Shortly after Stratton's departure from the South Wales Coalfield, James Colquhoun reflected upon his company's experiments. 'Of course the first main principle was, as a matter of safety, to get the mines watered; but at the same time it was desirable to know what expenditure any particular system involved'.[77] He might have been reproved by colliery workers for raising the cost aspect of engineering safety, but he deserves credit for having sanctioned experiments. The 1884 explosion at Pochin Colliery made the Tredegar Company realise that coal dust underground was as equally dangerous as gas.

Pochin Colliery – After 1884

Pochin Colliery stood remote from both Tredegar and a large village to its south, Blackwood. In the absence of factual data, as a guess, only a few hundred men worked at the colliery at the outset. During the middle of 1881, a 'resident' of Tredegar indicated his intention to build six cottages adjacent to the new colliery. Such an intention prompted an expectation that 'more' property 'speculators will come forward'. House building around Pochin Colliery was reckoned to be a 'necessity' and 'will be done by the company if not speedily taken in hand by private individuals'.[78] Indeed, such a pattern of house building was a common practice in the South Wales Coalfield. Yet, only a small number of houses were ever built on the threshold of Pochin Colliery.

One Pochin Colliery miner, Harry Flower of Blackwood, had absented himself from work on the day of the 1884 explosion to celebrate his nineteenth birthday. The young miner had endured thirteen weeks of work at the colliery without a day off prior to his birthday.[79] Harry Flower, like other miners for that matter, appears not to have left any further reminisces about working at Pochin Colliery. He and fellow miners might have been able to give rich details about the colliery's history after the 1884 explosion.

Information sourced concerns the colliery's officials, and some of its manning figures from the year 1903 to 1933.[80] Thomas Stratton was succeeded as the colliery's manager, probably in 1887, by John Reynolds, under-manager at the time of the colliery's 1884 explosion. From 1903, the Tredegar Iron & Coal Company colliery manager regime at the colliery shows that T. Reynolds served until 1923.[81] T. Reynolds, John Reynolds's son, was drafted from the Surveying Department to the colliery after the 1884 explosion.[82] He attended the Cefn Golau Cemetery burials of the Tredegar miners killed by the explosion as part of the Tredegar Company's party. T. Reynolds successor as Pochin Colliery manager was Mr H. Evans who held the post for at least ten years.

The Tredegar Company's operation of the colliery saw two peaks of employment. In 1911-15, around 1,600 workers worked at the colliery, whilst over the period of years from 1923 to 1926 around 2,100 men made journeys from afar to raise the pit's steam coal.

Youths, from at least Tredegar, who wandered south along Mynydd Bedwellty and teetered from the edge of Darren Ddu to sit on the Rocking Stone, cared little about the statistics of employment associated with Pochin Colliery. Generations of youths glanced down upon the colliery as they retreated home from the Rocking Stone after a brief exposure to danger. A spirit for adventure fitted youths for work in the coal mining industry.

ROCKING STONE AND POCHIN COLLIERY,
TREDEGAR.

W.4835.

Above: New Tredegar boys sit atop the Rocking Stone. Left to right: Leslie Shore, Martyn Gulliver, and Alan Shore.

Photographer William I. Shore - taken circa 1959
Pope/Parkhouse Archive

Opposite: The view of Pochin Colliery from alongside the rocking stone.

Presage of catastrophe?

Maybe young people of the Tredegar district would have been enchanted by an 'unusual incident' at the Tredegar Works in May 1888. One evening, men were engaged blowing out Number 3 furnace for repair purposes. The arrival of a flock of birds overhead caused work to halt. 'Hundreds' of the birds were 'overcome by the fumes and fell into the furnace and on to the ground, where they were picked up by the workmen'. The birds were described as brown in colour, white breasted, with a long beak, and a similar size to a wren. The *Western Mail* noted: 'People superstitiously inclined hold that the advent of the birds presage a catastrophe, but the probability is that they were foreign birds in passage'.[83]

Perhaps, though, it was an omen. On the western side of Mynydd Bedwellty, during the 1880s, a railway company, focused upon working the Rhymney Valley, believed it could make an extra fortune in the Sirhowy Valley.

Rhymney Railway Bill of 1888

During 1888, the Rhymney Railway Company championed a Bill in the Houses of Parliament to gain entry into the Sirhowy Valley. The railway company sought powers to construct a line from Cardiff to Nine Mile Point near the mouth the Sirhowy Valley. A Committee of the House of Lords met in at least July 1888 to test the company's case. The chief objectors to the Bill were the Alexandra Dock (Newport) Company, and other railway companies. Mr Pope QC, representing the dock company, observed: 'At present the Rhymney Railway was not in the Monmouthshire Valleys at all … which were practically in the hands of the Great Western'. Cornelius Lundie, general manager of the Rhymney Railway, submitted that he 'anticipated about a million tons' of coal traffic between the Sirhowy Valley and Cardiff. However, he

further appeared to have an ambition to move Ebbw Vale coal to Cardiff via the Rhymney Railway.

Questioning by the committee revealed some aspects of the Monmouthshire coal trade. James Colquhoun reported that the Tredegar Company 'shipped over 200,000 tons of coal last year at Newport, but they sent very little to Cardiff'. Regarding the Rhymney Railway's proposed route to ship coal at Cardiff, he observed: 'With increased railway facilities the shipments would increase at Cardiff'. The representative for the Newport and Abercarn Coal Company supported the Bill. He noted that his company was 'solely dependent upon the Great Western Railway. The present rate to Cardiff was 1s. ½d. They could do more business with that port if the carriage was less. His firm 'desired to send their coal to Cardiff for mixing purposes'.

Sir George Elliot, who declared his interests in Powell Duffryn and the Alexandra Docks, argued it was not necessary to take Monmouthshire coal to Cardiff for mixing. However, crucially from his point of view, the carrying of coal to Cardiff that otherwise would go to Newport would be 'detrimental to the town of Newport … and it would not benefit the Rhymney'.

The GWR had earlier invited Henry Tennant, general manager of North Eastern Railway Company, to tour the district 'with a view to advising them as to their position'. The House of Lords Committee heard Tennant state that 'if the new line was made, no prudent railway manager would make use of it for the conveyance of coal to Cardiff so long as the line from Cross Keys via Newport to Cardiff was available for the purpose'. He ended his submission saying: 'It seemed to him that the Rhymney Company were seeking to transfer the Great Western revenue to their own pocket'. The Midland Company and the South Western Railway Company also opposed the Bill.

The Committee of the House of Lords, Lord Basing in the chair, 'decided that the Rhymney Railway Company should have powers to make a line from Cardiff to Nile Mile Point, but here it will stop. It will have no running powers over the Great Western Railway, or London and North Western railway...'[84] Although the Rhymney Railway (Monmouthshire) Bill was passed in August 1888, that allowed a line of five miles to be built from Caerphilly to Nine Mile Point, the project never proceeded. Roger Kidner claimed that the 'Rhymney allowed itself to be bought off by the GWR offering a moiety of the traffic which it carried from western Monmouthshire to Cardiff'.[85]

James Colquhoun's submission at the July meeting of the Committee of the House of Lords shed no light upon the Tredegar Company's commercial stance regarding paying for railway services. His neutral stance might suggest that the company was content with the status quo, essentially using the L&NWR. However, he fostered change regarding the washing of coal.

Washing Coal

In 1892, the Tredegar Company invested in a coal washery process at Ty Trist Colliery that was an advance on what had been used by the company previously. Moreover, the company claimed that at Ty Trist was 'one of the finest washeries in South Wales'.[86] Before the years 1884-5, the Tredegar Company used the 'simplest process of all', known as the 'Trough System' that washed 300 tons of coal a day.[87]

For an iron making company, washing coal as part of the coke operation offered benefits like those revealed by James Colquhoun in circa 1885. 'Until recent years', he said, 'there had been difficulty getting rid of the impurities [like shale] in the coal. The coal was not worked for making coke alone, but the small was taken from the large coal, washed, and cleaned in the best possible way, and then made into coke. If it had not

been washed, it would have been useless for iron making'. By washing coal, and with improvements in the blast furnace at Tredegar, Colquhoun reckoned that a 'saving of about 12 cwts of coke on every ton of iron had been effected, besides the saving of limestone required for fluxing, and the expense of taking away in slag to the slag tip; so that putting it all together there was a very great and decided advantage in washing the coal, and in washing it as clean at could possible be done'.[88] The Ebbw Vale Company pioneered washing coal in Monmouthshire by installing a Bérard Machine in 1865.[89]

The general manager of the Tredegar Company declared that after around 1870 he made himself familiar with all the different coal washing machines marketed. Regarding the operation of the trough-machine, he recounted that 'until lately' the company 'used to wash the small coal (which comprised all the screenings from an inch and a quarter down to smudge) as it came direct from the collieries'. Perhaps the trough-machine process was used by the company first at Whitworth Colliery where in 1880 a coal-washing plant operated. Furthermore at Whitworth Colliery, a machine called a 'beeswing' moved small coal from the washery to coke ovens so making manual labour unnecessary.[90]

Nevertheless, James Colquhoun was frank about the Tredegar Company's initial experiences with coal-washing plant. There had been 'much difficulty in washing' the screenings 'successfully, because, as was well known, if the coal were not properly sized, the washing could not be done anything like so well'. Thus he sanctioned another trial: coal was ground first and then sent through the trough-washing machine. 'But that system did not do very well, because a large portion of the coal was carried away. What was left was very well washed, but there was too much waste of coal. The coal being so fine, it was carried

Coal washing plant at an unknown Tredegar Company Colliery that appears to use the Feldspar Washer operating principle. *Paul Jackson collection*

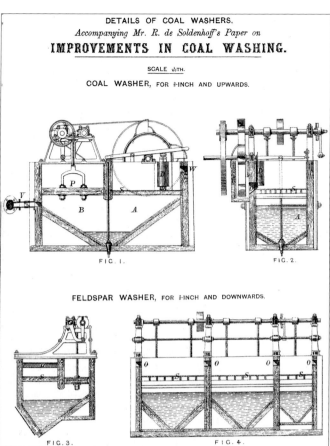

DETAILS OF COAL WASHERS.
Accompanying Mr. R. de Soldenhoff's Paper on

IMPROVEMENTS IN COAL WASHING.

SCALE ½TH.

COAL WASHER, FOR ⅜-INCH AND UPWARDS.

FIG. 1.   FIG. 2.

FELDSPAR WASHER, FOR ⅜-INCH AND DOWNWARDS.

FIG. 3.   FIG. 4.

The Feldspar Washer principle.   *Proceedings, SWIE: 1885, Vol. XIV*

away with the waste water. Some of it settled in the tanks, but a large proportion was lost altogether'.[91] Such a report suggests that he was unhappy with the trough-machine. However, being familiar with the pitfalls of such a machine, and with knowledge of other coal washing machines, he seemed adequately informed to make a decision.

During the South Wales Institute of Engineers' 1884-1885 session, as the Institute's President, James Colquhoun chaired a discussion of a paper about 'improvements in coal washing'.[92] The paper's author, R. de Soldenhoff, focused upon a development by Mr Lührig. Gluckhilf Colliery, Lower Silesia, Germany, was the place in 1867 where Lührig proved his development, which was called a Feldspar Washing Machine. During the machine's process of washing, shale fell through a bed of feldspar. Due to the specific gravity of coal being lower than that of shale, a flow of coal particles suspended in water exited from the machine at a level above the bed. A piston mechanism installed in the machine governed the washing process. The Feldspar Washing Machine was 'intended for washing coal of sizes from $^3/_8$ths of an inch down to impalpable powder'.

The operation of such a type of coal washing machine by the Dowlais Company around 1883 captured the interest of members of the Institute. Thus, the Feldspar Washing Machine became the subject of 'the criticising element of Institute' even though one member of the Institute inspected the Dowlais plant and thought it 'seemed' to be working 'exceedingly well'.[93] However, the main concern of members whose field of industry was solely coal was the 'large sum' of money needed for capital expenditure on such plant.[94]

The Ty Trist Colliery washery – erected in 1892 - together with the coke ovens. Photograph circa 1905.   *Paul Jackson collection*

Nevertheless, James Colquhoun concluded that the Feldspar Washing Machine had 'overcome the difficulties of coal washing, and was the best he had seen yet'.[95] He did not disclose the sum of money spent by the Tredegar Company investing in washing plant. However, he remarked: 'There was often much difficulty in getting the persons who attended to the coal washery to do their work with sufficient care and attention to always produce coal of equal quality'.[96] The noise and filth of a washery was not an attraction for workers who could be choosy about their place of employment.

Nevertheless, an advance like the Feldspar Washing Machine influenced Tredegar Company's future decisions concerning coal washing plant. In 1892 'one of the finest washeries in South Wales' was erected at Ty Trist, but the type of process used was not found.[97]

Associated coke oven developments also occurred at Ty Trist up until 1921. Fifty Coppée coke ovens operated at Ty Trist until their closure in March 1945.[98] The Tredegar Company's coke oven developments at Ty Trist spanned two decades with the Coppée ovens built in four banks of twenty thus culminating in a total of eighty ovens. The ovens were built and rebuilt as follows:[99]

Bank A	Built 1903	Rebuilt 1913 and 1927
do. B	do. 1903	do. 1915
do. C	do. 1906	do. 1920
do. D	do. 1906	do. 1921

Monmouthshire and South Wales Coal Owners' Association

Although change in terms of colliery plant and equipment became a feature of the company's activities, it remained a steadfast member of the Monmouthshire and South Wales Coal Owners' Association. In 1890, Benjamin Whitworth MP, as chairman of the Tredegar Company, was recognised by the Association as the company's 'Representative'. Yet, it was James Colquhoun, classed as an 'Associate', who served upon a committee key to keeping a grip upon the lively industrial relations matters of the South Wales Coalfield.

The administration of the 1875 Agreement was delegated to a Sliding Scale Joint Committee made up of an equal number of coal owners and workers' representatives. In 1890, James Colquhoun sat as one of the eleven employers' representative on the Committee. Moreover, he served as the chairman of the Association's Newport District Board that dealt with issues arising in the Monmouthshire part of coalfield.[100] Five years earlier, the vote of thanks he received as the retiring President of the South Wales Institute of Engineers praised him for the 'very able and zealous manner' in which he had served as President. Testimony was further given about his 'perseverance, the energy, and … great urbanity'.[101]

As a member of the Sliding Scale Joint Committee, Colquhoun witnessed some of the tussles between two notable personalities in the history of the South Wales Coalfield. The chairman of the committee was Sir William Thomas Lewis and its vice-chairman was William Abraham, who acquired the epithet of 'Mabon' – the Bard. In 1885, William Abraham (1842-1922), was elected a Liberal Member of Parliament for the Rhondda. He won fame in 1888 by bringing about a day's holiday every month for the colliery workers of South Wales, which was called 'Mabon's Day'.

Abraham had 'hammered out' with Lewis, as the employers' chief negotiator, the Sliding Scale Agreement of 1875. William Abraham's inclination was for co-operation between coal owner and workers. In the years 1882, 1887, 1890, and 1892, the Joint Committee met to ratify a continuation of the Sliding Scale. However, by around 1890, a number of developments outwith the South Wales Coalfield troubled Sliding Scale protagonists.

By 1890 at the latest, the Miners' Federation of Great Britain (MFGB) began 'to take shape' as a 'united federal movement' whilst a Miners' Eight Hours' Bill began a fumbling course through Parliament.[102] The MFGB opposed the Sliding Scale. The South Wales Association of Miners, a term used for the body of colliery workers' representatives that William Abraham led, was not affiliated to the MFGB.[103] Nevertheless, the South Wales Association of Miners 'were agreed broadly with the MFGB on hours and most other questions – except the sliding scale'.[104] Moreover, the South Wales Association of Miners was wary of the growing influence in 'Monmouth' of a MFGB 'enclave representation', whose leader in 1891 was William Brace (1865-1947).[105]

Although the rhetoric of the MFGB attacked the South Wales Association of Miners for its acceptance of the Sliding Scale Agreement, on the whole, colliery workers in South Wales generally earned higher wages than their MFGB counterparts. Maybe as a sign of comparatively sizable earnings by South Wales' colliery workers, the Agreement had to be modified in January 1892 to deal with a rise of absenteeism among workers, and 'heavy extras and allowances conceded' to them at a local level.[106]

Previously the Sliding Scale Joint Committee had attempted to mediate local disputes over extras and allowances. In the case of the Tredegar Company, the Joint Committee helped end disputes over colliers' working hours and cokers' wages, in the years 1889 and 1890 respectively. Also in 1890, the committee mediated on payment for digging clod[107] at Ty Trist Colliery, and the cost of men's travel to Pochin Colliery.[108] Regarding members of the Monmouthshire and South Wales Coal Owners' Association, the Sliding Scale helped make coal they raised a 'keen' competitor in the market.[109] Coal production in the valleys of South Wales and Monmouthshire had been become king in Great Britain.

Monmouthshire Coal around 1890

In 1889, the Tredegar Company, with an assured tonnage of 782,490 tons ranked in second place in the Monmouthshire league of coal producers.[110] The first place in the league was held by the Ebbw Vale Steel, Iron, and Coal Company at 890,948 tons. Just short of the Tredegar Company's output of coal, in third place, was John Lancaster & Company, centred upon Blaina in the Ebbw Fach Valley, which raised 741,245 tons. In fourth and fifth places in the output league respectively were: the Blaenavon Company at 478,500 tons, and Powell Duffryn at 389,727 tons attributable on the whole to two collieries, New Tredegar and the new Elliot. Placed in sixth place, mining the Pontypool district, was Partridge, Jones Company with 312,977 tons.[111] The total amount of coal raised by Monmouthshire and South Wales Coal Owners' Association member companies in Monmouthshire in 1889 was 5,114,492 tons.[112] The leading six member companies in Monmouthshire produced a seventy per cent share of the total raised. The thirty per cent share balance was due to coal production by ten other companies.[113]

Yet, how effective was the Tredegar Iron & Coal Company as a coal producer? The following analysis of colliery operations in Monmouthshire is offered to propose an answer to the question.

In 1889, the coal output per pit or level of the Tredegar Iron & Coal Company was:[114]

	Tons	
No. 7 Pit [Mountain Pit]	52,800	
Whitworth Drift	80,000	
Whitworth No. 1 Pit	39,475	} = 115,817 tons
Whitworth No. 2 Pit	76,342	
Ty Trist, No. 1 Pit	94,362	} = 183,098 tons
Ty Trist, No. 2 Pit	88,736	
Bedwellty Pits	155,382	
Bedwellty Levels	34,076	
Pochin Pits	170,317	

Regarding John Lancaster & Co. Ltd, coal outputs in 1889 were:[115]

	Tons
Lower Deep Pit	161,311
Hirwain Pit	141,024
Cinder Pit	129,737
Griffin Pit	132,150
South Griffin Pit	177,023

Bedwellty Pits. At the centre of the photograph is a Waddle fan that reveals that furnace ventilation was abandoned after the 1865 explosion.

Pope/Parkhouse Archive

From the above, both the Tredegar Company and John Lancaster each operated five collieries. Such a state continued until in 1891 when John Lancaster sank Griffin No. 3.[116] By 1891, the Tredegar Company had revealed no plans to sink a successor colliery to Pochin.

How productive were the Tredegar Iron & Coal Company's collieries compared with other Monmouthshire companies around the cusp of the 1890s? As a means to partly answering the question, a comparison with Powell Duffryn's New Tredegar Colliery as a Monmouthshire equivalent of Bedwellty Pits is presented first. Both collieries were opened within years of each other, so the colliery engineering was probably similar, and they worked adjacent mining ground. Bedwellty Pits, though, raised coal from seams at a shallower depth than at New Tredegar Colliery. In 1889, the output from New Tredegar Colliery was 194,648 tons of coal.[117] Thus, the output of Bedwellty Pits in 1889, at 155,382 tons, was twenty per cent less than New Tredegar Colliery.

Pochin Colliery's Monmouthshire peer collieries, in terms of the date of sinking, were Waun Lwyd owned by the Ebbw Vale Steel, Iron & Coal Company, and the Newport-Abercarn Black Vein Company's Celynen. In 1889, Pochin Colliery's coal output was 170,317 tons while Waun Lwyd Colliery produced 48 per cent more coal due to raising 252,249 tons.[118] In 1888, Celynen Colliery raised 445,000 tons of coal for the Newport-Abercarn Black Vein Company. In that year the consulting engineer to the Newport-Abercarn Company, Thomas Thomas, stated that the 'colliery was one of the largest and best arranged for the purpose of a large output'.[119]

The foregoing comparisons do not make a case for praising the Tredegar Iron & Coal Company for the management of its coal interests during its first two decades as a business. It would seem that Pochin Colliery had not been designed for a large output whereas Celynen Colliery had been. Maybe a village would have grown up around Pochin Colliery if the Tredegar Company had had greater ambitions for the colliery. Furthermore, the contrast between Bedwellty Pits and New Tredegar Colliery outputs suggests that Powell Duffryn was a more productive colliery operator than the Tredegar Company. Conceivably, Powell Duffryn's officials were much more demanding of colliers than their Tredegar Company counterparts. Perhaps also the colliers at New Tredegar were more productive than Bedwellty Pits' due to superior methods of working.

However, the business policy of the Tredegar Iron & Coal Company, unlike Powell Duffryn or the Newport-Abercarn Black Vein Company, involved juggling the wants of two industries, steel and coal. The Tredegar Company's investment in steel plant in circa 1880 probably delayed opening a successor colliery to Pochin Colliery.

Curiously the directors of the Tredegar Company in 1889, like those of the coal companies named above, had historical grounds for believing that further growth years lay ahead for coal. The upward trend in the South Wales coal trade from 1873 until 1889 had been inexorable.[120] In the year 1873 collieries of the coalfield supplied fourteen million tons to the market. In 1889, the South Wales Coalfield's output stood at twenty-eight million tons. The doubling of the coalfield's coal output over the sixteen years of the company's operation was clearly notable. Yet again, using this measurement as a reference, the Tredegar Company's coal mining performance over the corresponding period had not been as equally illustrious. Over the period 1873 to 1889, the company increased its total tonnage coal output from 535,000 tons to 782,490 tons that is by a factor of just under one and a third. However, the forgoing comparison uses as a premise that the Tredegar Iron & Coal Company was solely a coal company, which it was not.

Thus for equivalence, appraising the Tredegar Company's performance as a coal producer versus that of the Ebbw Vale Steel, Iron, and Coal Company might be relevant. The

Valentine's Series

Celynen Colliery, Abercarn.

Newport-Abercarn Black Vein Company's Celynen Colliery. A contemporary pit of Pochin Colliery.   *Pope/Parkhouse Archive*

Ebbw Vale Company's coal output in 1873 was 1,020,000 tons whereas in 1889 it was 890,948 tons.[121] The apparent decline in the Ebbw Vale Company's coal output may have been caused by a strike mentioned in its 1889 annual report.[122] The Tredegar Company' annual report for the same year makes no reference to a strike having an impact upon its coal operation, which suggests that the Ebbw Vale strike was a local one.[123] Although no fair comparison about coal outputs can be thus be made between the two Monmouthshire companies for the particular years of 1873 and 1889 it may be true to propose that the Ebbw Vale Company was still capable of producing around one million tons. If so, the Ebbw Vale Steel, Iron, and Coal Company coal operation stayed roughly constant between 1873 and 1889 whereas the Tredegar Iron & Coal Company's coal operation had grown.

Putting the immediately foregoing speculation aside, both Monmouthshire companies were intent in 1889 upon continuing to trade in steel and coal. The companies appeared to have contrasting fortunes pursuing the same business course. In June 1889, for the accounting year ending the 30th March 1889, the Tredegar Iron & Coal Company reported a profit of £23,692 8s. 6d.[124] Moreover, the Tredegar Company's profit in 1889 was better than the previous year's of £10,011 12s.[125] In 1889, the Ebbw Vale Company's gross profit of £10,915 17s.1d. had a rider: 'the [financial] loss on the working was attributed to the low prices [steel] and unprofitable trade during the first four months [March-June 1888], and to the subsequent strike'. Such a drab appraisal contrasted with that of the Tredegar Company's directors outlook: they were 'glad to report [in 1889] that prospects are brighter, the prices of coal having advanced considerably' and that they obtained maybe equal pleasure in reassuring shareholders that 'the steel and iron trades are … in a more hopeful condition'.[126] However, both companies' performances were ever vulnerable to the wayward nature of South Wales Coalfield industrial relations.

The 1893 Hauliers Strike[127]

On the 1st August 1893, workers at North's Navigation Company's Wyndham Colliery, Ogmore Vale, angered by a delay in an audit that preceded any adjustment in wages due to the Sliding Scale, ceased work. Ocean Company hauliers, at the Ogmore Collieries, also struck. The next day strikes took place at the Ocean Company collieries in the Rhondda Valley. On the 4th August, hauliers, underground enginemen, riders and shacklers at Lywnpia Colliery 'absented themselves from work'. The hauliers were prominent in their absence from work, and demanded a twenty per cent advance on their 'standard' per the Sliding Scale.

The strike spread across the coalfield. 10,000 colliery workmen met at Crumlin in the Ebbw Vale on the 9th August. A resolution supporting the hauliers' demand was carried at the Crumlin meeting, and afterwards several Monmouthshire collieries 'ceased operation'.

On the 15th August, the Monmouthshire and South Wales Coal Owners' Association met to set up an Emergency Committee. There was no Tredegar Iron & Coal Company representative on the Emergency Committee. On the 18th of August, due to 'the grave situation at various collieries', the Emergency Committee called for 'proper protection, both police and military'. By the end of the 18th August, the Emergency Committee had a plan for distributing military force to the districts of the coalfield. Regarding Ebbw Vale, Tredegar, Blaina, and Rhymney '200 infantry already furnished'. On the night of the 19th August 'a portion of the troops', detachments of the 14th Hussars, Inniskillen Dragoons, and the Devonshire and Bedfordshire Regiments, arrived in the South Wales Coalfield. According to the coal owners, the introduction of military forces had 'not been necessary in previous strikes'. Tredegar, unlike Rhymney and Ebbw Vale, did not become a camp for troops.

Almost simultaneously the workmen's representatives on the Sliding Scale Joint Committee appealed to the strikers to resume work. At Dowlais and Ebbw Vale collieries there was an immediate return to work. By early September, a large number of collieries in the South Wales Coalfield had re-started work. The six-and-a-half weeks' 1893 Hauliers Strike ended on the 11th September when Wyndham Colliery and Ogmore Collieries' workers commenced work. The workers at Wyndham Colliery and Ogmore Collieries, as its instigators, were not alone in having to ponder about how worthwhile the strike had been. In general, wages earned by colliery workers employed by Monmouthshire and South Wales Coal Owners' Association member companies continued to be regulated by the Sliding Scale as it had been before the 1st August 1893.

Regarding the Tredegar Iron & Coal Company, it lost twenty-one days of coal production at its collieries due to the 1893 Hauliers Strike. The company was affected by the strike from the 11th August to the 6th September. Individual collieries of the Ebbw Vale Steel, Iron, and Coal Company and the Rhymney Iron Company experienced a range of idle days due to the strike from three to eleven days. In accordance with the rules of the Monmouthshire and South Wales Coal Owners' Association, member coal companies were indemnified for costs arising from the strike. Nevertheless, the absence of general management leadership during the 1893 Hauliers Strike might have also had some bearing upon the loss of coal production at the Tredegar Company's collieries.

Death of James Colquhoun[128]

In October 1892, James Colquhoun resigned as general manager of the Tredegar Iron & Coal Company after nearly twenty years service. It seems that no successor to the post was recruited for some period afterwards. On the 18th May 1893, he opened the Town Hall in Tredegar. That he was invited to carry out such a duty was a sign of the esteem in which he was held in the town. The Monmouthshire and South Wales Coal Owners' Association's account about the 1893 Hauliers Strike by its secretary, W. Gasgoyne Dalziel, identifies James Colquhoun as a representative at a meeting held in August 1893, but puts a question mark after Colquhoun's name.

The general manager of the Tredegar Company suffered a medical stroke that may have caused him to retire to live at 'Abbotsford', Weston-super-Mare, by around October 1892. As an antidote to illness, during the summer of 1893, he spent a long holiday in the Highlands of Scotland. On the 21st November 1893, aged sixty years, he died following another stroke. His funeral at Weston-super-Mare saw a strong representation of Tredegar people like Mr W. Routledge, manager of the Tredegar Ironworks, and Dr and Mrs Brown. Present also at his funeral was Mr J. Bishop, a manager with the London & North Western Railway company.

James Colquhoun's move to Weston-super-Mare caused him to cease taking an 'active interest in local affairs'. He had served as a county magistrate for Monmouthshire, and as chairman of both the School Board at Bedwellty and the local board at Tredegar.[129] He had also been an active member of St. George's Church, Tredegar, for example chairing bible classes.[130] Maybe his Christian values had a bearing upon his conduct in business. Early in his office as general manager of the Tredegar Company, he showed a benevolent spirit by supporting the efforts of working men to found the Tredegar Workmen's Medical Aid Scheme.

Eulogies about James Colquhoun remark upon his services to the company, the South Wales Institute of Engineers, the Monmouthshire and South Wales Coal Owners' Association, and a variety of Tredegar societies. He was particularly recognised for having erected Bessemer and rail rolling plant at Tredegar at 'the lowest ebb' in coal, iron and steel trades. The newspaper obituaries read did not mention other technical achievements of his like pioneering the Number 2 Endless-Rope system in the South Wales Coalfield, and introducing compressed air systems into the company's collieries in 1893.[131] Nevertheless, the directors of the Tredegar Iron & Coal Company had some grounds to look back upon the period that Colquhoun had run the iron, steel, and coal operation with satisfaction. The shareholders of the company had regularly earned a dividend during his twenty years of service. Curiously no director of the company attended his funeral.

Also in 1893, the chairman of the Tredegar Company, Benjamin Whitworth, died. The company's deputy chairman, Henry Pochin, succeeded Whitworth. However, around a year later, the sixty-nine year old chairman offered an appeal to the company's directors: 'owing, however, to the pressure of his numerous business engagements, he wished to be relieved of a position that makes very large demands upon the time and energy of its holder'.[132] His request was accepted by the company's shareholders, and a successor company chairman was elected.

NOTES

1 TICC, op. cit., p.2. OS Ref No. SO 162047. Laura Elizabeth Pochin was born on the 14th May, 1854; 'The Late Aberconway', *North Wales Chronicle*, 13 Jan 1933.

2 'Rent Audit Dinner-At Bodnant Eglwys-Fach, near Conway', *North Wales Chronicle*, 6 Jan 1877.

3 'Rent Audit Dinner-At Bodnant Eglwys-Fach, near Conway', *North Wales Chronicle*, 6 Jan 1877.

4 Circa 1850, in a letter Mr Booker to Sir Henry de la Beche, a section of the Rudry [nr Caerphilly] Coal Measures were labelled 'Coal, Little Rock Vein or Pont-gwarth-yr-harn' (also spelt 'haiarn'). Later, at the respective Sirhowy Valley location, the label 'Brithdir' seam superseded its local name. Dr Henry Jordan, 'The South Wales Coalfield', SWIE, Vol. XXXVIII (1922), pp.125-126.

5 TCG, 'Monmouthshire & South Wales', Vol. XXV, 8 March 1878, p.386.

6 TCG, 'Monmouthshire & South Wales', Vol. XXV, 29 March 1878, p.507.

7 TCG, 'Monmouthshire & South Wales', Vol. XXV, 29 March 1878, p.545.

8 Charles Wilkins, *The South Wales Coalfield Coal Trade and its Allied Industries*. (Daniel Owen, 1888), pp.170-1.

9 TCG, 'Monmouthshire & South Wales', Vol. XVLI, 22 April 1881, p.612.

10 TCG, 'Monmouthshire & South Wales', Vol. XVLII, 1 July 1881, p.19.

11 TCG, 'Monmouthshire & South Wales', Vol. XVLII, 15 July 1881, p.102.

12 'Background Information to the Development of the Colliery [Oakdale]', hereafter BIDCO, p.4. The document was part of the late Albert John Edwards's papers, which is in the keeping of the Writer. The document carries no author's name, and clues suggest that it was written early in the 1960s. Document contents were found by the Writer to be on the whole authentic when compared with other research findings concerning the Tredegar Iron & Coal Company. All the thicknesses of the coal seams found at Pochin Colliery are taken from this source since it would seem highly likely that they were used by the company as a guide for estimating both the potential coal resources, and the depth of sinkings, for Oakdale Colliery.

13 TCG, 'Monmouthshire & South Wales', Vol. XVLII, 16 Sept 1881, p.362.

14 A classification of coal, in use in 1946, identified coal at Pochin Colliery as Bituminous II (coking coals) having volatile matter 22-30%; carbon content 88 to 91%; hydrogen 4.8 to 5.3%; and a calorific value range of 15,500 to 15,800 Btu/lb. The coal's caking properties ideal for making 'coherent coke'. SWC-RegRpt, pp. 20-21.

15 Charles Wilkins, op. cit. (South Wales Coal Trade), p.171.

16 An aspect of the headgears of Merthyr Vale Colliery (1869-73) were sections of 'wrought-iron bull-head rail bound together at intervals by wrought-iron bands riveted to the rail flanges'. See Stephen Hughes et al., *Collieries of Wales: Engineering and Architecture*. (Royal Commission on the Ancient and Historical Monuments of Wales), pp.52-4.

17 Charles Wilkins, op. cit., p.171.

18 Trevor Boyns, 'Communications and Commerce', op. cit., p.65, see D. S. M. Barrie, *A Regional History of the Railways of Britain, 12: South Wales*. (Inverness, 1994), p.73. The date for the acquisition by the L&NWR of the Sirhowy Railway from ME, 10 Oct 1903, p.10.

19 'Mr Davies' Retirement', ME, 10 Oct 1903, p.10.

20 'Sirhowy Railway', MM, 1 July 1865, p.1.

21 Charles Wilkins, op. cit., p.261.

22 William Smith, op. cit., p.13.

23 J. C. Carr and W. Taplin, op. cit., p.80.

24 K. C. Barraclough, *Steelmaking: 1850-1900*. (The Institute of Metals, 1990), p.83.

25 Robert Protheroe-Jones, *Welsh Steel*. (Amgueddfeydd Ac Orielau Cenedlaethol Cymru, National Museum & Galleries of Wales, 1995), p10.

26 Source Robert Hunt, *Mineral Statistics*, (1881) see Laurence Ince, op. cit, p.183 & p.1881.

27 Laurence Ince, op. cit, p.7.

28 Richard Laybourne, 'On the Bessemer Steel Plant Erected at Rhymney', SWIE, Vol.XI (1878-79), p.112.

29 TCG, 'Monmouthshire & South Wales', Vol. XXXV, 15 March 1878, p.427. Confirmation that Davy Brothers supplied the plant: 'Tredegar Steel Works', *The Journal of the Iron and Steel Institute* (hereafter JISI), (1883), p.297.

30 'Tredegar Ironworks', MM, 29 Oct 1880, p.5.

31 Source Robert Hunt, *Mineral Statistics*, (1881) see Laurence Ince, op. cit, p.183 & p.1881.

32 Description of the Tredegar steel plant compiled from: 'The New Tredegar Steel Works', *The Journal Iron & Steel Institute*, hereafter JISI, (1882), pp.679-80; and 'Tredegar Steel Works', JISI, (1883), p.297.

33 TCG, 'Monmouthshire & South Wales', Vol. XVII, 14 Oct 1881, p.622.

34 Richard Laybourne, 'On the Bessemer Steel Plant Erected at Rhymney', SWIE, Vol.XI (1878-79), p.110.

35 Richard Laybourne, op. cit., p.111.

36 *The South Wales Coal Annual* 1916, p.13.

37 'Tredegar', MM, 25 Aug 1882, p.8.

38 'Opening of New Steel Works Tredegar ', WM, 9 May 1884, p.4.

39 'Opening of New Steel Works Tredegar ', WM, 9 May 1884, p.4.

40 'Tredegar', *South Wales Daily News*, 13 June 1883, p.3.

41 'The Iron and Steel Trade', *South Wales Daily News*, 1 Dec 1883, p.4.

42 William Truran, op. cit., p.140.

43 Susan E. Demont, 'Tredegar & Aneurin Bevan: A Society and its Political Articulations', PhD Thesis, Cardiff University (1990), pp.36-37.

44 R. H. Walters, *The Economic and Business History of the South Wales Steam Coal Industry, 1840-1914*, (PhD thesis, Oxford University, 1975), p.17 and p.45 respectively.

45 'Death of Samuel Homfray Esq', MM, 17 Nov 1882, p.5.

46 'Newport Town Council', MM, 1 Dec 1882, p.8.

47 Discussion, 'Endless-Rope Haulage', SWIE, Vol.XIII (1882-1883), p.213.

48 Discussion, 'Endless-Rope Haulage', SWIE, Vol.XIII (1882-1883), p.213.

49 A full description of the use of No.1 endless-rope system at Lower Level, the Clay Level, Terrace Pit, and, Whitworth No. 2 Pit is given in James Colquhoun, 'Endless-Rope Haulage', SWIE, Vol.XIII (1882-1883), p.126-131.

50 James Colquhoun, 'Endless-Rope Haulage', SWIE, Vol.XIII (1882-1883), p.131.

51 James Colquhoun, 'Endless-Rope Haulage', SWIE, op. cit., pp.123-125.

52 The average distance used to make a calculation of ton per mile was 1,050 yards. The cost elements for a 300 tons per day operation comprised: ropes (0.204 d), trams (0.1d), grease and oil (0.1d), coals ((0.13d), repair to engines and boilers (0.1d), maintaining way (0.075d), and labour (0.624d), and the comparison was made with reference to a table of the paper. James Colquhoun, 'Endless-Rope Haulage', op. cit., p.126 and p.132 respectively.

53 In particular 'Adjourned discussion on Endless-Rope Haulage, op. cit., pp.214-221, and pp.254-256. An application of a Number 1 system at Cymmer Colliery was also a topic of the discussion.

54 James Colquhoun, 'Endless-Rope Haulage', op. cit., p.125.

55 James Colquhoun, 'Endless-Rope Haulage', op. cit., p.131.

56 'Discussion on Endless-Rope Haulage', op. cit., p.154.

57 'Adjourned discussion on Endless-Rope Haulage', op. cit., p.223.

58 'Adjourned discussion on Endless-Rope Haulage', op. cit., p.222.

59 'Adjourned discussion on Endless-Rope Haulage', op. cit., p.259.

60 'Discussion on "The System of Endless Rope – Haulage, at the Clifton Colliery, Nottingham', SWIE, Vol.XIV (1884-1885), p.75.

61 'Adjourned discussion on Endless-Rope Haulage', op. cit., p.213.

62 'President's Address', SWIE, Vol.XIV (1884-1885), pp.2-13.

63 Compiled from a number of reports, 'The Tredegar Colliery Explosion', WM, 10, 11, 12, 14, 20, 26, 27 November 1884.

64 'Tredegar Colliery Official Honoured', ME, 1 Oct 1904. The article reveals that John Reynolds was an official at Bedwellty Pits before 1880, and was party to the promotion of a collier, David Davies, to the position of fireman at the colliery.

65 The colliery managers were: Henry William Martin of the Dowlais Company; Richard Bedlington, and Archibald Hood – 'engaged in large collieries in South Wales and Scotland' who initially made a reputation as a mining agent in the Ayrshire Coalfield, and circa the 1860s became a partner in the Glamorgan Coal Company, which was centred upon Llwynpia Colliery.

66 The area of concern was the colliery's Standage Level. In his opinion, the ventilation would have been adequate if $16,000ft^3$ per minute passed through the area. However, the HM Inspector of Mines cast doubt upon the colliery manager's records that showed that such a performance had been attained.

67 Discussion, 'The Watering or Damping of Dusty Mines', SWIE, Vol. XV (1886-87), pp.100-101.

68 William Walker Hood was the son of Archibald Hood; see an earlier footnote.

69 Discussion, 'The Watering or Damping of Dusty Mines' op. cit., p.62.

70 Discussion, 'The Watering or Damping of Dusty Mines' op. cit., p.93.

71 Discussion, 'The Watering or Damping of Dusty Mines' op. cit., p.91.

72 Discussion, 'The Watering or Damping of Dusty Mines' op. cit., p.92.

73 Discussion, 'The Watering or Damping of Dusty Mines' op. cit., p.94.

74 Henry W. Martin, 'On Damping Dust in Mines ', SWIE, Vol.XV (1886-1887), pp.267-275.

75 Discussion, 'On Damping Dust in Mines ', SWIE, Vol.XV (1886-1887), p.315.

76 Discussion, 'On Damping Dust in Mines ', op. cit., p.317.

77 Discussion, 'On Damping Dust in Mines ', op. cit., p.319.

78 TCG, 'Monmouthshire & South Wales', Vol.XVLII, 19 August 1881, p.302.

79 W. W. Tasker, *Mid Valley Nostalgia: Hollybush, Markham Village, Argoed, Blackwood*. (D. Brown & Sons Limited, 1990), p.61.

80 *The South Wales Coal Annual*, for the respective years.

81 In 1917, T. Reynolds lived at Vale Cottage, Tredegar. *Monmouth Guardian*, 1 June 1917.

82 'Tredegar Colliery Official Honoured', ME, 1 Oct 1904, p.10.

83 'Singular Incident at Tredegar Works', WM, 11 May 1888, p.3.

84 'The Rhymney Railway Bill', MM, compiled from two editions: 13 July 1888, p.6, and 20 July, 1888, p.6.

85 R. W. Kidner, *The Rhymney Railway*. (Oakwood Press, 1995), p.30. The moiety saw the GWR pay the Rhymney Railway £10,000 a year for ten years.

86 TICC, op. cit., p.2.

87 Discussion, 'Improvements in Coal Washing', SWIE, Vol.XIV (1884-1885), p.314.

88 Discussion, 'Improvements in Coal Washing', op. cit., p.268.

89 Collieries of Wales: Engineering and Architecture, op. cit., p.126.

90 Charles Wilkins, op. cit., p.170.

91 Discussion, 'Improvements in Coal Washing', op. cit., p.314.

92 R. de Soldenhoff, 'Improvements in Coal Washing', SWIE, Vol.XIV (1884-1885), pp.88-102.

93 Discussion, 'Improvements in Coal Washing', op. cit., p.199.

94 Discussion, 'Improvements in Coal Washing', op. cit., p.199.

95 Discussion, 'Improvements in Coal Washing', op. cit., p.315.

96 Discussion, 'Improvements in Coal Washing', op. cit., p.198.

97 TICC, op. cit., p.2.

98 Evence Coppée invented the retort oven in 1867 with Ebbw Vale pioneering its use in South Wales in 1874. Most of the British Coppée ovens were erected in South Wales 'where they suited the local coal'; J. C. Carr and W. Taplin, p.54. Around 1870, Evence Coppée joined with Lührig to 'extend their business'; R. de Soldenhoff, 'Improvements in Coal Washing', op. cit., pp.89-90.

99 *South Wales Coalfield (including Pembrokeshire) – Regional Survey Report*. (HMSO, 1946), p.205.

100 W. G. Dalziel, *Records of the Several Coal Owner's Association of South Wales, 1864 to 1895* (hereafter RSCOASW). p.15.

101 'Vote of Thanks to the President', SWIE, Vol.XIV (1884-1885), pp.354-355.

102 R. Page Arnot, *The Miners: A History of the Miners' Federation of Great Britain 1889-1910*. (George Allen & Unwin, 1949), p.94 and pp.175-202 respectively.

103 Rt Hon William Brace MP, who served as secretary of the Monmouthshire branch of the MFGB, view of the South Wales Association of Miners was as 'an organisation or rather a semblance of an organisation. They have an organisation simply in numbers…'

R. Page Arnot, op. cit., p.204.

104 R. Page Arnot, op. cit., p.190.

105 R. Page Arnot, op. cit., pp.204-5.

106 RSCOASW, op. cit, p.197.

107 *Clod* – a mixture of sandstone and shale, was also called by other names like clift, bast, clunch etc. In faulted coal seams digging clod meant that a collier did not earn money producing coal.

108 RSCOASW, op. cit., p.114.

109 In 1898, Ben Pickard, elected MFGB president in 1889, petitioned a body acting as the British coalowners' association to end the Sliding Scale in South Wales and Monmouthshire and 'so prevent the keen competition of South Wales and Monmouthshire'. R. Page Arnot, op. cit., p.309.

110 'Assured tonnage' was used to calculate a company's subscription to the Monmouthshire and South Wales Coal Owners' Association contingency (strike) fund. The Association had the right to check the output books of every member. 'Subject to rounding for some companies in some years, the figures for assured output are a good approximation'. Letter, Prof. Trevor Boyns to Writer, 31 Aug 2015. RSCOASW, op. cit., p.22.

111 RSCOASW, op. cit, pp.22-23.

112 RSCOASW, op. cit, p.15.

113 The tonnage figure given for Monmouthshire excludes the Newport-Abercarn Black Vein Company that in 1890 was not listed as a member of the Association. In 1888, the company's only colliery, Celynen, was reported as having raised 445,000 tons of coal.

114 'Assured tonnage'. RSCOASW, op. cit, p.22.

115 'Assured tonnage'. RSCOASW, op. cit, p.22.

116 R. H. Walters, op. cit., p.45.

117 'Assured tonnage'. RSCOASW, op. cit, p.22.

118 'Assured tonnage'. RSCOASW, op. cit, p.22.

119 'The Rhymney Railway Bill', MM, 13 July, 1888, p.6.

120 Richard Watson, *Rhondda Coal, Cardiff Coal – The Insoles of Llandaff Coal Owners*. (City and County of Cardiff Libraries and Information Service, 1997), Appendix A, p.182.

121 'Assured tonnage'. RSCOASW, op. cit.

122 TCG, 'Monmouthshire & South Wales', Vol.LVII, 28 June 1889, p.920.

123 TCG, 'Monmouthshire & South Wales', Vol.LVII, 28 June 1889, p.921.

124 The Tredegar Company's financial year generally ended around the last day of March. In the company's 1923 annual report the financial year end date used was 31st March. In 1889, the Ebbw Vale Company used the same end date for the financial year as the Tredegar Company, which suggests that they both followed the same convention.

125 TCG, 'Monmouthshire & South Wales', Vol.LVII, 28 June 1889, p.920.

126 TCG, 'Monmouthshire & South Wales', Vol.LVII, 28 June 1889, p.921.

127 RSCOASW, op. cit., pp.179-207. The source for the following brief account of the strike.

128 Compiled from reports about James Colquhoun's death and funeral in *Evening Express*, 25 Nov 1893, p.1 and *Cardiff Times* [hereafter CT], 25 Nov 1893, p.8.

129 'Obituary', JISI, Vol. XLV, (1894), p.390.

130 MM, 30 Jan 1880, p.8.

131 TICC, op. cit., p.2. Although 'the first air compressor was installed in 1893' the company's history does state where it was sited .

132 'Tredegar Iron and Coal Company, Limited', *The Sheffield & Rotherham Independent*, 20 June 1895, p.7.

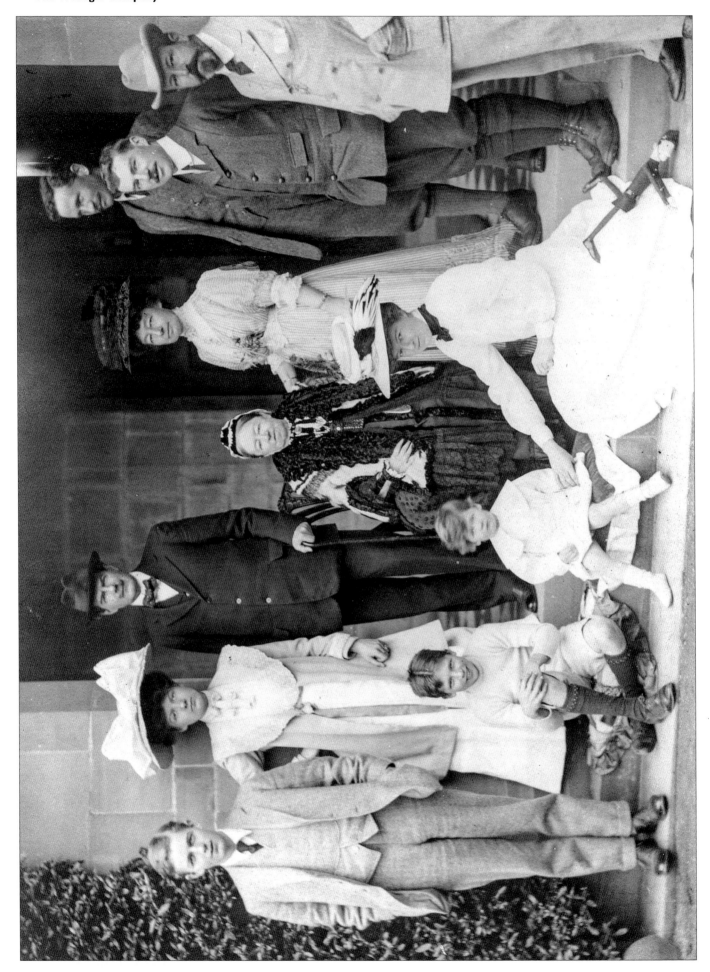

Chapter Four
McLAREN and a DARK SPOT

In 1894, Charles Benjamin Bright McLaren MP (1850-1934) became chairman of the Tredegar Iron & Coal Company by succeeding his father-in-law, Henry Davis Pochin.[1] Years previously, in 1877, he married Laura Pochin (1854-1933). After gaining a first class honours degree in philosophy at Edinburgh University in 1870, Charles McLaren left the city of his birth to finish his university education at Bonn and Heidelberg. Following a brief period of work as a journalist, he was called to the Bar by Lincoln's Inn. Charles McLaren successfully built 'a large Chancery practice' that dealt 'chiefly in company and mercantile cases'.[2]

In 1896, McLaren publically declared that to the 'best of his ability' he would uphold 'the standard of [Liberal] Radicalism'. He was for 'civil and religious liberty'.[3] He chaired meetings promoting women suffrage.[4] He first entered Parliament as the Liberal Member for Stafford in 1880 but lost his seat in 1885. After winning the Bosworth division of Leicestershire in 1892, he held it as Member of Parliament until 1910.

Almost in parallel with the development of his political career, his election as a director to the boards of a number of public companies enabled Charles McLaren to take an ever deepening interest in the affairs of industry. Marriage had granted his father-in-law an exclusive position to appraise his character, and values. Henry Pochin gradually handed over the monitoring of his industrial company interests to McLaren. In 1882, his son-in-law became a director of the then Sheffield based John Brown & Company, and so he probably learnt why that company had 'given up rail making in the early 1870s', and developed a heavy ship plate trade.[5] Pochin's interests also included Bolckow Vaughan and the Derbyshire based Staveley Iron & Coal Company, and McLaren became associated with both these companies.[6] No doubt for business meetings with his father-in-law, but also for pleasure, Charles McLaren 'spent much time at Bodnant'. His link with Wales was further strengthened in 1888 when he was elected to the Tredegar Iron & Coal Company's board of directors.

In 1890, the House of Commons heard McLaren speak in 'favour of an eight-hours' day in the coal mines', but with 'certain objections to dealing with this subject by legislation'.[7] During 1894, the second reading of the Miners' Eight Hours' Bill became a 'dead letter' due to a vote on an amendment. Also in that year, the Member of Parliament for Bosworth joined a Leicester Miners' Association meeting. He dealt with a remark made by a Leicestershire miners' agent, T. Chambers, who judged that the member for Bosworth's speech was 'from the owner's side the strongest argumentative speech delivered in the House that night'. Bosworth's MP said that 'his objections to the Bill, were after due consideration and discussion less serious than formerly, and as the representative of miners he felt bound to carry out the wishes of his constituents'. When opening the meeting's proceedings, he remarked: 'It was rather difficult to discuss labour questions apart from politics from his point of view, because they were so mixed up together'.

If McLaren, as a politician, needed reassurance for pursuing a radical Liberal agenda, then he may have been heartened by an aspect of the 1892 General Election: five Liberal Members of Parliament had previously been employed as coal miners. However, the voting at the election returned a Conservative government.

E. Wilson Taylor. Appointed Company Secretary around 1895.
Paul Jackson collection

Nevertheless, by the mid-1890s, the daily life of Charles McLaren's was hectic. He juggled duties as a lawyer, parliamentarian, and industrialist. As 'a man of abundant energy, of genial temperament and considerable charm' he appeared suited for such a life. Moreover, his personal qualities coupled with his mental ability gave grounds for believing that he could give effective leadership to a broad range of industrial concerns.

An early task for Charles McLaren was to identify the men he could trust to manage the Tredegar Company when pursuing his other duties. Around 1895, Edmund Petley, based at the company's London Office, retired as the company's secretary and E. Wilson Taylor became his successor. Petley, granted a pension of £300 per annum, had served the company from its founding in 1873. E. Wilson Taylor 'had long experience of the London Office'. However, at Tredegar two unknown appointments were made in key accountancy posts. The Tredegar Works' cashier and bookkeeper, respectively Mr Widdowson and Mr Bardley, had also retired with each receiving pensions of £100 per year.[8] However, one puzzling aspect concerns the holder of the post of general manager of the collieries and steel works, which seems to have been left vacant after James Colquhoun's retirement. Nonetheless, Charles McLaren's start as chairman of the Tredegar Iron & Coal Company coincided with an unrelenting slump in the steel market.

Opposite: McLaren Family, Bodnant House, circa 1900. L to R standing: Francis McLaren (1886-1917), younger son; believed to be either Florence or Elsie McLaren, daughters; Charles McLaren; (seated) Agnes Pochin (1825-1908), Henry Pochin's widow, and pioneering suffragette; Laura McLaren (née Pochin); gentleman unknown; Henry Duncan McLaren (1879-1953); unknown gentleman. Front row: unknown children with either Florence or Elsie McLaren.
Courtesy of McLaren Family

Steel and Coal

Although around 1894, the Tredegar Company and the Ebbw Vale Steel, Iron, and Coal Company, retained second and first places respectively in the Monmouthshire county league of coal producers, they shared a business quandary. Steel output in the United Kingdom stagnated at around 3¼ million tons per year over the years from 1887 to 1894.[9] Notwithstanding that in 1896 the United Kingdom steel industry 'still commanded well over a half the total world export trade in iron and steel' after '1890 Britain was fighting a losing battle against competitors securely entrenched behind protective barriers'.[10]

In 1893, the Tredegar Company reported that steelmaking contracts had 'fallen' as a 'heavy [financial] loss'. In July 1893, the company made known that 'in view of the serious loss attendant on the manufacture of steel', the directors 'decided to suspend steelmaking. The steelmaking plant and equipment, though, was to be kept in 'an efficient condition' until 'such time as improved trade permits of resuming it at remunerative prices'.[11] The impression that these decisions give is that the company had not 'abandoned' steelmaking in 1893. The company acted to cope with the 'lowest point of the "Great Depression" for the [British] iron and steel industry'.[12] The Ebbw Vale Company remained in coal, iron, and steel.

Coal production enabled the Tredegar Company directors to 'submit much more satisfactory accounts of working results', but the 1893 annual report also mentions 'large economies in the establishment charges', and changes in management. Moreover, during the financial year reported on in 1893, the company paid out £12,816 7s. 11d. for interest on debentures, loans, and charges such that the profit and loss account carried a debit of £7,752 15s. 7d., the amount written-off from the 'reserve and depreciation fund'. The fund's revised amount stood at £48,971 0s. 11d.[13]

Charles McLaren's father-in-law may have forewarned him that the chairmanship of the Tredegar Iron & Coal Company was likely to make large demands upon his time. As chairman, McLaren needed to retain the favourable support of shareholders willing, due to their wealth, to bear poor business times. In 1893, in keeping with the company's practice concerning elections to the board of directors, two directors 'retired', Hon Sydney Carr Glyn and James Wyllie. Both men were 'eligible for election' to the board, and it seems likely that at least James Wyllie was re-elected.

In the spring of 1895, a series of shareholder extraordinary meetings of the Tredegar Company were held. The advocate's skill of Charles McLaren played some part in winning shareholder approval for a reduction in the company's capital value to £1,088,335.[14] The 'large economies' mentioned above was set also to yield over two years a reduction in the company's 'indebtedness on loan accounts' by a total sum of £60,494 4s.[15] However, accountant arithmetic may have further bemused some shareholders. In the 1895 annual report, the Tredegar Company recorded a gross profit of £40,698 10s. 6d. Cash spent on the interest on loans and debentures whittled the gross profit down to £30,792 14s. 10d. In 1894, despite the company making a net profit of £20,550 12s. 11d., the shareholders agreed not to take a dividend. However, partly due to retaining the 1894 profit, the company realised in 1895 a net undivided profit of £51,343 7s. 9d. However, written-off the foregoing net undivided profit was £24,000 as an item described as 'royalty paid in advance'. The outcome, as far as the shareholders were concerned, was a dividend of just 3 per cent.

The financial adjustments reported in 1895 suggests a company still struggling to make ends meet financially, but the company's coal activity would have lifted the morale of some shareholders. The Tredegar Company's annual output of coal stated in its 1895 annual report was 893,318 tons, 'the largest quantity on record'.[16] The company's output performance defied general gloom in the South Wales Coalfield. 'During some months of the year' the coal industry had been 'adversely affected by uncertainty as to the continuation of the Sliding Scale agreement. At the last moment, however, an agreement was made between the representatives of the coal owners and the miners'. The company hoped that 'for some time to come steady work is assured under the amicable relations usual in South Wales between capital and labour'.[17]

Developments at Pochin Colliery were reassuring. The colliery's shafts having been deepened to a lower seam to find coal of 'excellent quality and thickness, with good floor and roof' on the 20th February 1894. The seam was viewed to be of 'considerable advantage to the company'. Underground coal handling was also improved at the colliery by installing a compressed air powered haulage system. The company's stock of railway wagons was also increased.[18]

In June 1895, in accordance with company practice, Henry Pochin and James Wyllie resigned as directors from the board. Following a shareholder election, the vacant seats on the board were taken by Walter S. B. McLaren MP, and Charles Paxton Markham. Walter S. B. McLaren (1853-1912), a brother of Charles McLaren, was the Liberal Member of Parliament for Crewe and a Bolckow, Vaughan & Company director. According to his daughter, Violet, Charles Markham was a 'stern and powerful man' who had prospered as an industrialist.[19] The centre of Markham's business interests was Derbyshire. He ran Sheepbridge, and Staveley Coal & Iron companies, and an engineering company, Markham & Co., Broad Oaks Iron Works, Chesterfield.

The new directors were instantly made members of the Works Committee that comprised three directors with its chairman being Charles McLaren. Particularly brought to the attention of the shareholders was Markham's 'long experience and practical knowledge of a similar class of business' being placed at the disposal of the company. As some idea of the role of the Works Committee, its members were said to be 'in constant touch with the colliery officials and sales departments of Tredegar and Cardiff'.[20] Such seemingly close involvement of directors in the operational side of a company may cast doubt upon the capability of management. However, the company's financial performance was largely governed by the state of the market.

In July 1897, Charles McLaren made a frank admission to the company's shareholders. 'The hope expressed in the last report [1896] that some improvement would take place in the coal trade later in 1896 was, unfortunately, not fulfilled'. The last half of 1896 saw a 'marked depression'. 'Scarcity of demand resulted in decreased [coal] outputs with the inevitable result of increased costs, so that the fairly satisfactory contracts which have been taken earlier in the year proved unremunerative'. Yet, despite the market, the company's collieries produced 889,556 tons of coal for the 1896-97 year, which was just a little less than the record year.

The outcome in 1897 for the Tredegar Company's shareholders was to receive another modest dividend payment. The profit 'for distribution' being £10,180 3s. 9d. Nevertheless, among the directors, the spirit of enterprise was not moribund. The directors won the approval of the shareholders for a business policy that envisaged two ways forward for the company.

In 1896, an intention of the directors was to 're-establish some of the former manufacturing industries at Tredegar'. After mid-1897, the relighting of two of the blast furnaces at the Tredegar Works signalled the implementation of the manufacturing aspect of the policy. Planned also was the 'erection of another rail mill, the extension and improvement of the existing foundry, and the re-starting, on a more modern basis, of the old brickworks'. The directors further declared that they were contemplating the 'erection of machinery for the manufacture of nuts and bolts'.[21] Although Tredegar town's people may have speculated about the restoration of steelmaking at the head of the Sirhowy Valley, they might have been more intrigued by the company's rapid preparations to sink a new pit, but this time in the Rhymney Valley. What would develop into a major aspect of the business policy's second way forward, an expansion of the coal activity, had begun.

Cwm Tysswg

The main aim of the company's coal policy was to expand the mining of the north-western swathe of property leased from the Tredegar Estate. The first action of the coal policy's plan, it seems, was to extend an underground roadway from Bedwellty

Pits to connect with the pit being sunk in the Rhymney Valley's Cwm Tysswg. Winning more coal from the Big Vein and Yard Coal appeared to have been the mining priority for the company. The Tredegar Estate would have savoured the prospect of a lift in income from its Cwm Tysswg property.

Preparations for the company's new pit, situated in the Rhymney Valley, were reported in July 1897 to be 'rapidly' proceeding'. The Tredegar Company's new pit stood on the 800 foot contour of the eastern side of the valley, and was about three-quarters of a mile north of Powell Duffryn's New Tredegar Colliery. Two decades earlier, trials by the Admiralty of bituminous coals from Monmouthshire ranked New Tredegar coal as the 'best'.[22] The colliery's coal was appraised by the Admiralty to be a 'hard' bituminous type and suitable for supply to coal stations around the world. Thus, the Tredegar Company had good reason to expect that a similar quality of steam coal could be obtained from its new pit particularly if the Rhas Las seam was worked.

However, the Rhas Las seam had a reputation for being 'fiery'. In 1875, twenty-three miners working the Rhas Las at PD's New Tredegar Colliery were killed by an explosion due to the ignition of gas.[23] Regardless, the Tredegar Company judged that it was acceptable to pursue ventilating Cwm Tysswg coal reserves from Bedwellty Pits, which stood a distance of about one-and-half miles eastward of the shaft sunk in the Rhymney Valley.[24]

Nevertheless, the Tredegar Iron & Coal Company's investment for the expansion of its coal activity was based upon some forecast of the future coal market. 'For some months in the autumn of 1897 slackness of demand [for coal] and great scarcity of tonnage at Bristol Channel ports seriously affected the regular work of the South Wales collieries'. However, late in March 1897, the company renewed a contract with the Great Northern of Ireland Railway to supply 60,000 tons of 'best steam coal' and received 'some Admiralty orders'.[25] Moreover, Cunard Steamship Company accepted tenders for the supply of steam coal from three South Wales coal companies of which two, the Tredegar Company and Lewis's Merthyr Navigation Colliery Company, 'secured' the largest portions of the 180,000 tons ordered.[26] Maybe such market interest during the 1897-98 year was a reason why Tredegar company collieries did not suffer 'a single day's stoppage', and so raised a total of 947,497 tons of coal to set a new annual output record. The McLarens may have been relieved by the form that the Tredegar Company's 1896 coal policy was taking.

In 1897, Charles McLaren MP earned the right to wear silk through being made a QC, but he 'gave up his law practice' and dedicated his life thereafter to running his wife's business affairs. Following her father's death, Laura McLaren inherited a wide portfolio of industrial investments that 'created logistical problems' to oversee first-hand. Henry Davis Pochin, aged 71, died in October 1895 at Bodnant House.[27]

In the Sirhowy Valley, also due to the 1896 coal policy, both Ty Trist No. 2 and Bedwellty No. 2 pits were 'deepened to the Ras Las seam'. As a result, 'at these points' coal had 'been proved of good thickness and quality'. Moreover, further coal reserves of 217 acres, situated south of Pochin Colliery, were leased from the executors of the late Captain Williams.[28]

1898 Lockout

Nonetheless, the generally poor state of the Tredegar Company's finances in the mid-1890s also tallied with colliery workers in the South Wales Coalfield earning relatively low wages under the Sliding Scale. Whereas in 1894 the coal price per ton of large steam coal was £10 8s., for the years 1895, 1896, and 1897 the prices were respectively £9 7s., £9 2s., and £9 3s.[29] Discontent among colliery workers over reduced wages led to the South Wales Association of Miners giving the Monmouthshire and South Wales Coal Owners' Association six months notice, as from the 30th September 1897, of its intention to end the agreement. The coal owners 'retaliated by giving notice of a lock-out as from the beginning of April 1898', and 'refused to negotiate'.

Consequently, a lock-out was imposed, and valley mining communities suffered considerable hardship. 'Without funds to sustain themselves' the South Wales Association of Miners sought and received help from the Miners' Federation of Great Britain. In public, William Abraham joined with at least William Brace of the MFGB 'Monmouth enclave' to campaign for an end to the Sliding Scale. However, Mabon urged within the South Wales Association of Miners Association that 'consideration be given to the owners' insistence on a renewal of the Sliding Scale'. Although the Government made an attempt to act as conciliator, the stance taken by the Monmouthshire and South Wales Coal Owners' Association held, and the 'Welsh miners were worn down'. 'After five months' lock-out they returned to work, defeated. They accepted the owners' terms [that included abandoning Mabon's Day]. They accepted the Sliding Scale'.[30] The agreement was for four years.

The day after the 1898 lockout ended the *Western Mail* judged that 'it has been the longest, most serious, the costliest, and cruellest, and has caused the most widespread misery, and destitution of any labour troubles which have affected the South Wales Coalfield'. Perhaps seeking objectivity regarding the *fait accompli* of an agreement added: 'It is one of the ironies of labour troubles that this result could have been attained four months ago'.[31]

'But', according to R. Page Arnot, 'the struggle had not been vain'.[32] In 1898, William Abraham responded to approaches from the MFGB, and led 'penitent Welshmen' into joining the Miners' Federation of Great Britain. In so doing he acceded to the aims of the union that included abolishing the Sliding Scale. The year 1898, Arnot proposed, was the date of the 'true foundation' of the South Wales Miners' Federation (SWMF).

Concerning the conduct of coal company chairmen during the lockout only one was known to have had the 'courage' to hold a public meeting with workmen. Charles McLaren met workers at a hall in Tredegar at which he 'ventured to say, that in the future, they [the workers] would have the same treatment as they had experienced in the past'.[33] Such an engagement suggests that Charles McLaren had no qualms about learning first-hand about workers' issues. Nonetheless, to meet workers, made needy by the lockout, whose temper might be roused by an insensitive comment, was a brave action. He had also to be as fearless in meetings with shareholders irritated by years of poor company performance.

The financial reckoning in the Tredegar Iron & Coal Company's 1898 annual report noted a £30,938 6s. net profit for distribution to shareholders. However, the directors of the company recommended to the shareholders writing-off £10,000 from this net profit. Moreover, although the directors had hoped to offer shareholders a dividend of 2½ per cent, the 'prolonged strike (sic)' of 1898 caused them to limit the dividend to 1¼ per cent, which was 'the same as last year'. The shareholders accepted the directors' recommendations. The company's 1898 annual report further mentioned a 'further issue of £30,000 four per cent first mortgage terminal debentures' for 'meeting' capital expenditure. No details were given about the company's plan for spending capital, but the new pit in Cwm Tysswg involved an unknown, but considerable sum of money.[34]

McLaren Merthyr Colliery[35]

In July 1898, the company reported that the Cwm Tysswg pit was 'sunk with great rapidity and economy, and the surface arrangements are now practically complete'. The pit's sinking had found 'the best seams of the Merthyr district, showing a total thickness of over 18 feet of coal, have been satisfactorily proved, and the coal has been found of excellent quality, with good roofs and floors'.[36] The shaft sunk by the company in the Rhymney Valley was 16 feet in diameter and reached, by 1898, 294 yards, which was coincident with the Rhas Las seam.[37] The shaft cut a section through: the Big Vein (5 feet 6 inches thick) at a depth of 250 yards; the Yard Coal (3 feet 8 inches thick) at 252 yards; the Polka Coal (3 feet 9 inches thick) at 292 yards; and the Rhas Las (which varied from 2 feet 9 inches thick to 5 feet thick) at 294 yards.[38]

McLaren No. I Pit. The first shaft sunk by the Tredegar Iron & Coal Company in the Rhymney Valley. In 1898, at 244 yards, the prized, but 'fiery', Rhas Las seam of steam coal was found. Note that the style for Tredegar railway wagons was now for the main name to be in an arc together with a diamond logo. Several are fitted with a coke crate – the extra planks above the top of the wagon – to increase the capacity as coke was less dense than coal and thus a greater volume could be carried. The coke ovens here can be seen on the right. Several wagons are also loaded with pit props, these were return loads from the docks.

Paul Jackson collection

Such findings of coal may have prompted more ambitious ideas about mining Cwm Tysswg. The company decided to create a discrete colliery in the Rhymney Valley. Sometime during the year before the end of March 1898, the company acquired the 'lease of a pit lately in the occupation of the Rhymney Iron Company, and from this a considerable area of coal in the north-western potion of the company's leasehold property can be economically worked'.[39] The pit, Pwll-Llaca, seemingly surplus to the Rhymney Company's needs, stood a mile and a half to the north of the Tredegar Company's new pit. The leased pit took its name from Cwrt-y-Llaca farm and was twelve feet by sixteen feet oval in plan and 154 yards in depth for access to the Yard coal. At this pit, in 1890, miners produced coal from the Red Upper Foot and Big Vein seams.

That the Rhymney Iron Company helped, for rental income, the Tredegar Company develop a discrete colliery adjacent to its area of activity did not square with a view of a concurrent observer of the coal industry about industry competition. 'There is no law more potent in its influence on industrial life than that of self preservation' contended the *South Wales Coal Annual* in an introduction to its 1912 coverage of the Rhymney Iron Company.[40] The Rhymney Iron Company could have chosen to frustrate the Tredegar Company's entry into mining in the Rhymney Valley by not leasing Pwll-Llaca Pit. However, perhaps the Rhymney Company had an urgent need for income even though it had quit steelmaking in 1891 'influenced by the then depressed state of the iron and steel industries, abandoned the manufactures of steel'.[41] Even as the 1890s ended the Tredegar Company gave an impression that re-entry into steelmaking remained an option whilst it pursued a coal expansion policy.

With the coupling of the Tredegar Company's Cwm Tysswg pit with Pwll-Llaca Pit, consistent with company's naming practice, McLaren Colliery came into being. The company made an early claim that the colliery's coal was associated with the 'Merthyr district'.[42] Smokeless steam coal, valued by navies around the world, was raised from under the Merthyr Tydfil district. McLaren Colliery coal, by the conventions of a qualitative coal classification followed at the start of the twentieth century was ranked as steam coal, but lay near the arbitrary steam - smokeless steam coal boundary.[43] The lower seams at McLaren Colliery especially possessed properties approaching that of smokeless steam coal. Consequently, McLaren Colliery's coal was placed on the Admiralty's List. As a clever commercial ploy, the company appended 'Merthyr' to 'McLaren' for listing the colliery in editions of *The South Wales Coal Annual*.[44]

The pit sunk by the company became more commonly known as McLaren No. 1. The pit initially featured a 65ft high timber headgear that was later substituted with a steel-framed headgear. Steam for the shaft's winding machinery was raised by three Lancashire boilers whose waste gases were vented via a 130ft high, circular in plan, chimney stack made from iron plate.[45] Pwll-Llaca Pit, as McLaren No. 2, was operated as the upcast by 1899.

McLaren No, 2's ventilation fan was powered by a Parson steam turbine. The 'expectation' was 'that the [fan] would produce 150,000 cubic feet of air per minute through the workings with a 3-inch gauge'.[46] The air movement capacity installed at the colliery was low compared with two other Rhymney Valley collieries. In 1895 a ventilation fan with a capability of moving 190,000 cubic feet of air per minute was in use at Powell Duffryn's Elliot Colliery.[47] Sunk simultaneously with the founding of McLaren Colliery, and four miles to its south, was PD's Bargoed Colliery where a fan of 500,000 ft^3 per minute was installed for ventilation.[48] Elliot Colliery and Bargoed Colliery were sunk to work coal seams at depths of 530 yards and 628 yards respectively.

After coal winding began in 1898, McLaren Colliery's output 'steadily increased to 1,200 or 1,300 tons a day'.[49] Such an output of coal was admirable when compared with the 1,200 tons per week expected in 1895 at Elliot Colliery after five years of operation.[50]

McLaren Merthyr coal won approval as boiler fuel to power naval ships.

McLaren Colliery stood next to the Brecon & Merthyr Railway line that ran from its northern terminus just over a mile north of the colliery, known as Rhymney (B&M), southward to Bassaleg (B&M) with connections to the GWR and Newport docks. A contract was agreed with the railway company to run a special colliers' train service so as to bring workers from afar to the colliery. Converted railway carriages were used for worker travel and featured 'bare wooden seats, boarded windows, with no light, and doors opened from the inside by passing the hand through a large hole cut in the door panel'. Instead of railway tickets, colliers used brass metal tokens to show that they were entitled to make the journey from their home station to Abertysswg station.[51]

Alfred Simeon Tallis

In September 1899, the Tredegar Iron & Coal Company made a crucial managerial appointment. Alfred Simeon Tallis became agent and manager of the company's collieries, and took up residence at Rhyd Hall, situated at the southern end of Tredegar.[52] Born on the 13th January 1863, he entered Stockport Grammar School on the 23rd September 1873. No record of when he completed his education at the school was found. The occupation of his father, Richard Tallis, was noted as 'mineral surveyor' in the school's records.[53] During Richard Tallis's career he worked in the North Wales Coalfield based in Hawarden, Flinshire and then from the early 1860s served as general manager of Timsbury Collieries, Somerset. At maybe fourteen years of age, A. S. Tallis joined David Davies & Company. In 1887, David Davies & Company and Davies, Scott & Company

Alfred S. Tallis
Appointed agent and manager of all the Tredegar Company's collieries in 1899. The photograph was taken circa 1905. *Paul Jackson collection*

were merged to form the Ocean Coal Company Limited. He left the post of agent for the Ocean Company's Parc and Dare collieries to remove to Tredegar.

Alfred S. Tallis already possessed links with both the towns of Tredegar and Ebbw Vale. On the 22nd November 1892, he married Miss Mary Frances Webb at Bedwellty Church. His bride was the daughter of Tredegar's vicar, Rev. Richard Webb. Their marriage would produce a daughter and three sons. His brother, John Fox Tallis, resided at Ebbw Vale where he was the general manager of collieries for the Ebbw Vale Steel, Iron & Coal Company.

Perhaps around the time that A. S. Tallis prepared for his wedding to Mary Webb he took stock of coal mining activities at the head of the Sirhowy Valley. If so he more than likely judged that the locality was a haven of calm compared with the mining maelstrom where he was employed. During the year 1889, there were 'rumours of large colliery undertakings' in the Rhondda Valleys: 'Four pits have already been "pegged out' by the surveyors, and others are expected to be taken in hand very soon'.[54]

Abertysswg

An early task for the general manager of collieries involved planning a village, which took its name from Abertysswg Farm, adjacent to McLaren Colliery.[55] The farm, whose earliest parts were dated to 1518, lay to the south-west of a Brecon & Merthyr Railway bridge that spanned the brook that drained Cwm Tysswg, but was destined to be covered by colliery waste.

Abertysswg village's housing was constructed on an elevated spot to the north of the colliery. The first phase of house building involved twelve houses near the colliery to accommodate

officials, and the colliery manager. The manager's home, McLaren House, was later known as the 'big house' by villagers. The first colliery manager appears to have been John Powell. He left a manager's post with the Rhymney Iron Company Limited to join the Tredegar Company in September 1898.[56]

E. E. Edwards later reflected that over the period from 1898 to 1907 the village grew. The village's 'terraced houses were to diverge from the central Park shaped to form an interesting and unique pattern in planning'.[57] The pattern, in plan, has been likened to that of an open-winged butterfly, and so the place acquired a nickname, 'Butterfly Town'.[58]

Tallis's instigation of town planning at Abertysswg may now be viewed as modest in scale. However, it was an early example of a move away from the unplanned towns and villages of the South Wales valleys sited adjacent to iron works, and collieries.[59] Two and a half miles northward from Abertysswg stood a local precedent that is called Butetown today. Founded as 'Newtown' in the early nineteenth century this 'small self-contained village' housed workers for Rhymney's Union Ironworks.[60] The building of Abertysswg also represented a sociological measure taken by the Tredegar Iron & Coal Company.

Within the South Wales Miner's Federation some siren calls were raised about coal companies using new houses as a means for enticing new workers to a colliery. The liberty of a worker to withdraw his labour in a dispute with his employer, whilst living in a house made available by his employer could be jeopardized. In 1890-91, a Scottish railway strike led to the eviction of railwaymen and their families from railway-owned housing on the grounds that the strikers had 'permanently left their employment'.[61] However, if a coal company pursued such a policy following a strike it risked being left with the cost of a village of vacant housing due to a boycott by unionised colliery workers, and an undermanned, and so unproductive colliery.

Nevertheless, the Tredegar Company's commitment to creating a village of new housing for its workers after 1898 deserved praise not censure. The provision of quality new housing for workers was an advance in conditions that only a killjoy could condemn. That Alfred Tallis was encouraged by Charles McLaren and his fellow company directors to think imaginatively about housing at Abertysswg speaks for a progressive attitude among the company's directors.

Maybe only the company's attempt to influence the conduct of the villagers' at leisure might prompt some sarcasm today. The company built its 'own McLaren Arms Hotel at Abertysswg which was opened in 1904'. Two decades later the company made a frank statement: 'The Directors have endeavoured to control the drinking facilities in the villages by setting up improved public-houses in place of the miserable taverns which existed in the neighbourhood, the licences of which the Company purchased and surrendered'.[62]

Probably, the company's policy was not approved of by objectors to the 'demon drink', beer. One of the mantras of some of the objectors to drink, 'Not on Sunday', was adopted. Not until the 1960s did Sunday drinking restrictions end in Monmouthshire, the county where McLaren Arms Hotel traded.

A Very Dark Spot

In 1899, the Tredegar Company experienced a sobering period. The company was pitched into a crisis. During that year, the 'financial position of the Company was so acute … that they appealed to the 2nd Lord Tredegar to assist them in recouping some of the outlay [regarding McLaren Colliery], and to allow them to deduct from the royalties, over a period of years, a sum equivalent to a sum of £50,000'.[63] A decade later the year would be reflected upon by Alfred Tallis 'as a very dark spot in the history of the Tredegar Company. The company then hardly knew whether they would be able to continue or be wiped out'.[64]

The owner of the Tredegar Estate proved to be as helpful to the Tredegar Iron & Coal Company as his ancestors had been with regard to the Tredegar Ironworks business. With a proviso, that the company 'kept the works going', Lord Tredegar granted the

Right: McLaren Arms Hotel, Abertysswg. Opened in 1904 under the auspices of the Tredegar Iron & Coal Company. The building has been razed.

Paul Jackson collection

Below: The company's General Offices, Tredegar. *Pope/Parkhouse Archive*

requested changes to the cost terms in the lease. J. H. Thomas later considered that Lord Tredegar's proviso 'had in mind, no doubt, the benefit that would accrue to the town of Tredegar, as a result'.[65] However, paying scrupulous attention to the landowner's proviso risked dire consequences for the company due to the continued poor state of the steel industry.

A possibility then on the eve of the twentieth century was the Tredegar Company being made bankrupt. Workers might have

mocked an idea that 'happily, if the capitalist has not been able to retain all the money which his enterprise has won for him, and bankruptcy has sometimes followed close in the wake of opulence, the wage earner has always been fed'.[66] Yet, workers could have relocated for employment, for example to the recently opened Powell Duffryn Bargoed Colliery. However, a chance boom in the market for coal also came to the aid of the Tredegar Company.

TREDEGAR IRON AND COAL CO. NEW GENERAL OFFICES.

'Surprising Prosperity'

In July 1900, Charles McLaren announced that the coal trade had returned 'extraordinary and surprising prosperity' when delivering the company's annual report.[67] In January 1899, the price of South Wales steam coal stood at 25s. a ton, which he remarked, 'many thought was a heavy price'. Yet on the day that he spoke about the company's business performance the price of coal stood at 27s. a ton. R. Page Arnot later observed that the first eighteen months of the Boer War (1899-1902) coincided with a leap in the price of coal.[68] Moreover, the war also affected the company's board of directors. Although Lt-Colonel Alexander Keith Wyllie was re-elected to the board, he had been posted to serve in South Africa. Nevertheless, the geographical market for Tredegar coal had also seen expansion: 'The Baltic were taking an increasing quantity, Italy was taking it, and the whole of the Mediterranean trade was increasing'.

The effect of such a buoyant coal trade was detailed in the company's annual report for the year 1900. The company's collieries raised 1,034,341 tons of coal. Charles McLaren reported a company profit of £104,147 on the working account for the year. The deduction from the gross profit of £11,176 for interest on loans, although similar to that incurred in the years 1893 and 1895 for example, could be viewed as being consistent with a company experiencing capital investment. As a signal that a considerable change was underway in the company's fortunes, in the annual report, McLaren offered a stirring proclamation: 'it was expected that the capital of the company would be replaced long before the leases ran out'.

The directors and chairman of the Tredegar Iron & Coal Company had further given thought to how they could 'induce the workmen to become shareholders'. A scheme that facilitated share ownership among workers offered a step towards some of the objects of socialism: worker ownership, and the control of

production. Charles McLaren canvassed that it was 'advisable to get labour and capital to combine' since it 'would save strife and engender a feeling of friendship between master and man, and an interest in the workman and his work'. Such a vision of industrial harmony was maybe as idealistic as the aims of socialists. Yet, whereas socialists could only plot political courses to achieve their aims the Tredegar Company conceived an idea for introducing worker share ownership.

The directors proposed splitting the company's 'A' grouping of shares so that £1 shares were made available. The £1 share was viewed as being a 'handy form of investment, as it attracted small investors'. The advocates of the company's worker shareholder scheme might have taken heart from the rise in coal prices. The Sliding Scale acted to lift workers incomes. Maybe if a subsequent sustained period of company worker well-being followed they might have been able to accrue surplus money to think about buying company shares. If so, workers would then have had to weigh up what kind of business they were investing in, and what the risks were for a return on their money in the future. In the year 1900, would shareholding workers of the company have objected to the ending of steelmaking at Tredegar?

Iron and Steel

According to a 1906 trade review, in January 1901 the directors of the Tredegar Company 'finally decided to relinquish the manufacture of steel to confine the operations of the Company to coal mining'.[69] Months earlier, in 1900, the company reported that it 'had turned what was a ruin into what was now a very compact little iron and steel works'.[70] The Tredegar Iron & Coal Company's fifty year history states that the company had abandoned steel making on a large scale in 1893, and that 'the production of pig iron ceased in 1901'.[71] However, other information raises doubt about the company's history concerning this matter.

A 12-ton seven-plank wagon with side and end doors built for the Tredegar Company by the Gloucester Railway Carriage & Wagon Co. and photographed in March 1912. The wagon was one of one-hundred ordered on the 8th January 1912 and paid for in cash at £69 10s each. Thi swas the last order that the company placed with Gloucester having dealt with them since the 1870s. Previous orders had been placed with the Midland Waggon Co. of Birmingham. Wagons built by Charles Roberts of Wakefield were also acquired via the Bute Works Supply Co. of Cardiff. In July 1900 the Tredegar Company reported that its annual output of coal exceeded 1,000,000 tons for the first time. Such a feat also involved just over 200,000 movements of 'Tredegar' railway wagons as then most would have been of 10-ton capacity delivering coal to the docks and returning empty to company collieries.

GRC&WCo.

Arthur Markham, a director of the company, speaking in 1904 at Tredegar, recounted 2nd Lord Tredegar's intervention into the affairs of the company. 'When the iron trade seemed to be in a better condition than it was now, Lord Tredegar gave a considerable sum of money to again start the furnaces, and the steel plant at Tredegar, his object being to see the hills of Tredegar Valley once more lit up'.[72] Thus the landowner's intervention appears to have led to the operation of a compact little iron and steel works from 1903. That year saw Lord Tredegar visit the works to light a blast furnace. Afterwards until 1908, a blast furnace and bar mill operation continued seemingly managed by the company. The blast furnace was blown out for the last time in 1908.[73]

At least one of the directors, Arthur Markham, was vexed by the company's continued operational tie with the iron and steel trade. In his 1904 speech he remarked upon the 'stress of competition' in the iron and steel trade and that the company had 'been unable to make iron' in the Tredegar district 'at a profit'.[74] He further pronounced that the town's people had seen 'the last flare'. His mention of a flare implied that no Bessemer converter had worked at Tredegar for a period before 1904 and so prompts the question: what other steel making process was being used by the company around 1900? Although a small scale steel making process might have been in use at the works, a search did not identify it. Nonetheless, maybe only in 1904 did it become conclusive that the company's involvement in bulk steelmaking had ended years earlier maybe in 1893 as noted in the company's fifty year history.[75] Regardless, it seems the Tredegar Company was enabled to creep away from operating in the iron and steel trade due to the ambitions of the manager of the Tredegar Works, L. D. Whitehead.

Whitehead Iron & Steel Company[76]

In 1903, L. D. Whitehead 'entered into a lease in partnership with his brother ..., A. V. Whitehead, to take over the Tredegar Puddling and Bar Mills'. L. D. Whitehead & Company initially focused upon rolling wrought iron, but in response to the market, 'reverted to the re-rolling of steel'. Furthermore, L. D. Whitehead visited the United States of America to inspect an advance in continuous and semi-continuous rolling process invented by a Mr Bedson. In 1907, the Whitehead partnership placed an order with Morgan Construction Company, Atlanta, Georgia, to design, make, and install the process at Tredegar. Regarding the supply of steel, this was more than likely purchased in billet form from a steel producer. A furnace re-heated the billets as a prelude to the rolling process. Maybe of greater significance to workers in the town of Tredegar, the placement of the order caused L. D. Whitehead not only to resign from his position with the Tredegar Company but to form the Whitehead Iron & Steel Company to manage the investment in the process supplied by the Morgan Construction Company. Also in 1907, the Whitehead Iron & Steel Company bought leasehold rights from the Tredegar Iron & Coal to use the site of the original Bessemer plant for installation of the Morgan Construction Company process.

As a pioneering adopter of the process in Great Britain, Whitehead's action was treated with scepticism by the British trade. Yet, British opinion was 'proved wrong', and in the following two decades Whitehead's Tredegar Works became a commercially successful producer of bars, special sections, wire rods, hoops and strips. In 1914, Whitehead Iron & Steel Company acquired a site in Newport for a continuous hoop and tube-stripping mill, which was the forerunner of other investments by the company in steel products manufacture.

Reflecting upon the Tredegar Iron & Coal Company's eleven years of converting iron into mass produced steel, from 1882 to 1893, this had proved to be a short period of activity compared with a century of smelting iron at the Tredegar Works. The company's decision to enter steelmaking in around 1880 was made in the hope of becoming a successful competitor in a market of promise. Today, over a century later, steel takes a 90 per cent share of the world's materials market. During the twentieth century the 'iron' in the Tredegar Company's title was retained maybe out of sentiment for past commercial success, a century of ironmaking for the supply to the world of rail for steam locomotive transport.

A cursory search found that Tredegar rail was once supplied to the French Northern Railway due to being part of a charge for an Open Hearth furnace at the French works of Terrenoire to make steel.[77] Maybe the constant recycling of steel rail gives grounds for a belief that the story of ironmaking at the head of the Sirhowy will last as long as steel is needed as a material. If so, some mine hewn from a Monmouthshire tract of the Tredegar Estate for smelting into iron might prove to be everlasting in its use.

Arthur Basil Markham

The observations of Arthur Basil Markham, made above, about the Tredegar Company and iron and steel making, act to mark his entry into the affairs of the company as a director. Born in 1866, he was the second of three sons and one daughter, Violet, of Charles and Rosa Markham. His mother was a daughter of Sir Joseph Paxton (1801-1865), the designer of the Crystal Palace that housed the Great Exhibition of 1851. His father, Charles Paxton Markham, became a director of the Tredegar Iron & Coal Company maybe in the mid-1870s. The family's 'substantial Georgian house', Tapton, overlooked the Derbyshire town of Chesterfield.[78]

Arthur Markham was educated at Rugby School, but was 'incorrigibly idle as a school-boy', and as 'young man he made various false starts before finding his place in the world'. However, again according again to his sister, he 'finally settled down at Chesterfield to study engineering, at Broadoaks Works, the property of his brother Charlie, who had already made a name for himself as an engineer'. Arthur opted to specialise 'on the mining side for which he showed aptitude and, having at last

Arthur B. Markham (1866-1916)
Coalowner with interests in coal companies in the Derbyshire, Nottingham, and Yorkshire coalfields in addition to the Tredegar Iron & Coal Company. Liberal MP for Mansfield from 1900 until his death. In 1911 he was made a baronet for services to politics.
Courtesy of Tony Hallam the author of 'The Family Markham' .

found his vocation'. He further 'set to educate himself, which he did with some thoroughness. He read widely and made a serious study of economics from Adam Smith to Karl Marx'. Perceptively, maybe, Violet Markham observed that her brother's 'mind was never pruned and disciplined as a mind is disciplined by hard work at school and University, but perhaps for that reason it always kept much of its natural impetuousness and vigour'. Nonetheless of meaningful significance, she reflected that 'both of us had grown up in a household always keen about politics and holding the Liberal faith'.[79] Indeed, at thirty-four years of age Arthur Markham stood as the Liberal candidate in a general election held in 1900 and was elected the Member of Parliament for the Mansfield constituency of Nottinghamshire.

Although Violet Markham's memoir about her brother Arthur conveys her high regard for him, she offers a frank appraisal about his character. He married in 1898 to become a 'devoted husband and father'. However, she noted that he was 'blessed (or cursed) in full measure with the Victorian urge to work, before which all domestic considerations had to give way. Hence the need for his family life to fit itself into an exacting schedule covering Parliament, the affairs of the South Yorkshire and South Wales coalfields, and a hundred other matters '. Moreover, 'his holidays were few or non-existent'. A driven man, he was also 'combative', and could be 'very brusque but his boyish smile that would light up his whole face took out the sting out of any rough word'.[80] His character contrasted with that of the Tredegar Company's chairman, Charles McLaren.

Would Arthur Markham upset the managerial ethos that McLaren had strived for so as to advance the directors' interests in a corner of industrial Monmouthshire? In 1906, Markham may have hurt the pride of some local people. Presiding at a Tredegar eisteddfod, the Derbyshire man was reported as observing:

'Men in the North, by some curious fate, were directors of many of the industrial concerns in South Wales. This was perhaps due to the fact they were more plain-spoken and not so much guided by sympathy and passion and feeling as the Welsh people. South Wales, unhappily, seemed to be a cockpit for disputes to a much a larger extent than in the North.'[81]

A Coal Company

Certainly around the year 1900, when confronting a business crisis, candidness among the directors of the Tredegar Iron & Coal Company would have been necessary. Indeed, Arthur Markham declared publicly in 1903 that 'the Tredegar Company could not be said to have had a very happy record for it during 20 or 30 years [. If] there was a concern run contrary to common sense and best management, it was this company'.[82]

Although the coal mining policy of the company in the 1890s may have been equally slated by its colliery workers, the conduct of commercial matters was beyond the workers' ken. The course to setting up an employee shareholder scheme, like attempts made to make real most radical ideas, needed to involve at least countering fallacies and suspicion among workers about how business is run. Nonetheless, in 1900, Charles McLaren declared: 'The directors proposed to set their house in order'. The first project tabled by the directors to meet this goal concerned an intention to 'work the collieries with electricity'.[83]

A Mysterious 'Force'[84]

Early in 1900, the Tredegar Iron & Coal Company secured the consulting engineering services of Maurice Deacon to design and cost a scheme for installing electricity at a number of the company's collieries. In July 1900, the company committed £60,000 towards the cost of contracting the associated engineering work from the 'profits of the current year [1901]'. It had been reckoned that a commissioned electricity scheme would save the company 10d. per ton of coal.

Around 1895, in Britain, when 'electricity was first introduced into mining work its use was confined to lighting, and at that time direct current was the recognized system'.[85] However, the Tredegar Company heeded Maurice Deacon's advice: to use the three-phase electricity system 'as the most suitable for their mines'. 'The whole scheme was then gone into by Mr Deacon and Mr Tallis on behalf of the Tredegar Company and Mr W. C. Mountain on behalf of the contractors'. W. C. Mountain was a director of Ernest Scott & Mountain Limited, an engineering consultancy firm, which the company contracted to finalise the electrical engineering and manage the installation work. The company's electricity system was 'put down in 1901 and 1902' at three of the Tredegar Company's collieries: Bedwellty Pits, Pochin Colliery, and Ty Trist.[86]

On the 3rd July 1903, a special train brought 160 members of the South Wales Institute of Engineers from Cardiff to the head of the Sirhowy Valley to inspect the Tredegar Company's 'electrical installation at the Pochin and Ty Tryst (sic) Pits'. Arthur Markham MP acted as host for 'representatives of all the colliery centres of South Wales'.

At a luncheon for the gathering, his jocular speech was well received if gauged by his listeners' bursts of laughter, and applause. 'Many people,' he claimed, 'seemed to have the idea that only good was to be found in their collieries, and feared that if they allowed anybody to visit their collieries they would take away and copy what might after all prove to be a bad design which they would be better without. Whilst this feeling prevailed it could not be expected that the rapid pace of industrial progress and improvement we see in the United States would take place in this country. Speaking for the Tredegar Company they had nothing to hide, and everything they had done they were willing to show visitors, provided the latter did not become a nuisance by coming on too many occasions.' He closed his speech saying: 'The directors were the first in South Wales, as before they were always the last, to move in the direction of electrical equipment, and they had not done this as an experiment, because in the Midlands and the North of England electricity had been used in pits for five or six years with beneficial results.'[87]

Later in 1903, W. Angus Scott of Ernest Scott & Mountain Limited gave a paper about the Tredegar Company's electricity system to the South Wales Institute of Engineers. He began his paper with a reflection: it had 'long been the fashion to speak of electricity as a mysterious 'force' and to attribute to everything connected with it occult characteristics, better suited to medieval wizardry than to modern science'. The following gives a summary of the description he gave of the 'first large installation' in the South Wales Coalfield of three phase alternating current [AC] electricity to power colliery underground haulage and pumping equipment.[88]

Sited on the surface of Pochin Colliery was one of the two electricity power generating plants erected for the company. The Pochin plant was housed within a 'plain stone building, with a floor measurement of 53 feet X 47 feet'. Steam, raised by two Lancashire boilers, was piped at 120 lb/in^2 to power two horizontal long-stroke coupled compound engines having automatic triple-expansion gear. Each compound engine developed 250 internal horsepower to drive a rope-driven set coupled to a three-phase generator unit rated at 200 kW. Thus, the Pochin plant generated 400 kW.

The 'power-house', as the stone building was called, also contained the main switchboard, with instruments and switches mounted on a panel made of marble. Electricity was transmitted at 500 Volts. The 'periodicity' of electricity supply, which was the term then used for frequency in cycles per second, was 40 Hz, which later became an exception to the norm of 50 Hz.

At the Tredegar Works, 30 Hz was preferred for electrical power, but Scott omitted this aspect in his description.[89] The works featured a Westinghouse electrical plant that comprised two horizontal compound engines with a generator mounted on the shaft between the cranks. Steam for the engines was raised in two Babcock and Wilcox boilers having the Meldrum system of forced draught, and 'by this means the company are able to consume waste product in the shape of coke, which previously found its way on to the tips'.[90]

Again with regard to the description of the collieries' electricity system, two electric cables ran from the Pochin power-house to

A Horizontal long-stroke coupled compound steam engine with automatic triple-expansion gear . developed 250 ihp. The kind of prime mover installed in both the Pochin and Ty Trist Power-Houses to drive, by a rope system, a three-phase generator of electricity.

Proceedings, SWIE: 1902-04, Vol. XXIII

A 200 kilowatt Three-Phase Generator.

Proceedings, SWIE: 1902-04, Vol. XXIII

Electric motor driven main and tail-haulage system installed underground at Pochin Colliery. Featured are 5 feet diameter drums that drew 14 trams each weighing about 26 cwt. The haulage rope ran at 5½ miles per hour. *Proceedings, SWIE: 1902-04, Vol. XXIII*

Electric motor driven endless-rope system installed undergound at Pochin Colliery. Rope wheel 6 feet diameter. Rope ran at 2½ miles per hour. *Proceedings, SWIE: 1902-04, Vol. XXIII*

enter the mouth of one of the colliery's pits. The electrical cables, three-core, insulated with vulcanised bitumen, were housed in wooden troughs 'the whole distance down the pit'. From pit-bottom distribution switchboards, located in 'special-rooms', cables ran out to supply power to motors.[91] The motors, with an operating range of 500 V to 550 V, rotated at 590 revolutions per minute. Installed in the Yard seam were three three-phase motors, each of 55 Brake (B.) h.p.. Two of these motors drove main-and-tail rope haulage gears whilst the remaining one powered an endless-haulage system. Installed in the Old Coal seam were four motors, two at 55 B.h.p. for haulage, one at 25 B.h.p. for pumping, and one 5 B.h.p. also for pumping.[92]

Under the floor of the underground main roads at Pochin Colliery electric cables were buried in steel conduits. One of the cables was placed at a depth of fifteen inches below the floor whilst the other cable was laid on puddle clay and protected by a single steel semi-tube. Hugh Bramwell of the Great Western Colliery Company, who saluted the pioneering achievement of the Tredegar Company's electricity scheme in the South Wales Coalfield, was to the fore in saying: 'as to where and how they should carry cables underground, one must be guided by the circumstances of each case'. The 'method adopted at Tredegar would be impractical' regarding 'most of the main roads he managed'. In the lower Rhondda Valley, Bramwell reckoned that an excavation of a gutter to bury a cable 'would start a movement of the ground'.[93] W. A. Scott accepted Bramwell's general principle, with qualifications. 'If the roads were bad and

the roof fairly good, the cables should be hung up. If the roof were bad and the floor good, then bury them. Both methods were carried out at Tredegar, but if the cable was going to be broken at all, he should prefer it broken under a foot of earth and clay rather than in the open heading'.[94]

Concerning the Ty Trist Colliery and Bedwellty Pits' part of the Tredegar Company electric scheme the consulting engineer wrote: 'Much interest lies in the magnitude of the plant, and in the fact that high-tension circuits are in use for transmission of power to Bedwellty Pits, some mile and a quarter distant'. A power-house was sited near Ty Trist Colliery to supply the Ty Trist and Bedwellty Pits with electricity. In general, most of the Ty Trist-Bedwellty Pits installations resembled those at Pochin Colliery. However, steam for the Ty Trist power-house was provided by four Lancashire boilers at 150 lb/in² to power three generating units rated at 250 kW, or in terms of maximum power of the engines – 400 internal h.p..

At Ty Trist Colliery, three three-core cables, steel-wire armoured over vulcanised bitumen carried electric current down the fan pit to the Yard and the Old Coal seams. Underground at the colliery, electric power operated: three main-and-tail haulage gears, driven by 55 B.h.p. motors; a 25 B.h.p. motor drove a converted haulage-gear; two 75 B.h.p. motors, each one

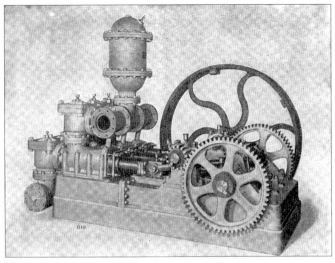

Electric motor driven three-throw shaft pump installed undergound at Pochin Colliery. 5-inch x 6-inch rams that delivered fifty gallons of water against a head of 800 feet. *Proceedings, SWIE: 1902-04, Vol. XXIII*

Electric motor driven two-throw shaft pumps. 4 inch X 6 inch rams that delivered 30 gallons per minute against a head of 120 feet.
Proceedings, SWIE: 1902-04, Vol. XXIII

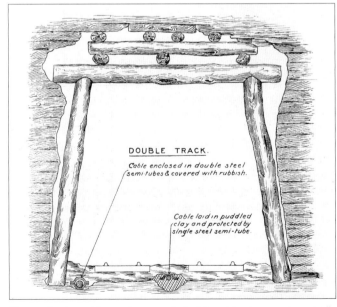

The method used for underground electric cable placement generally adopted by Tredegar Iron & Coal Company.
Proceedings, SWIE: 1902-04, Vol. XXIII

coupled to a pump, allowed water to be lifted from the Old Coal seam; and one 55 B.h.p. motor-pump unit raised water from the Yard Coal seam.[95] Individual rope drives were used to transmit electric power from the motors to pumps and haulage gear.

Electric current was fed from the Ty Trist power-house to Bedwellty Pits at 2,000 V by overhead bare copper lines. The copper wires were supported 'on discarded 90-lb double bull-head rails'. The power station's generation output of 500 V was transformed up to 2,000 V for transmission via the line to a step-down transformer at Bedwellty Pits. At the time Scott wrote about the Tredegar Company's electric scheme the Bedwellty Pits' installations were only partly finished. He noted that 'the power to Bedwellty Pits will be 150 h.p. when completed, and the loss on the line, including the transformers, will not exceed 8 per cent'. Moreover, that 'at present only one 55 horse-power motor is at work, driving a main-and-tail haulage. There will, however, be an endless-rope gear and a large pump presently set to work, each requiring about 55 horse-power'.

W. A. Scott disclosed that the capital cost of the Pochin Colliery aspect of the Tredegar Company electric scheme was £14,451.[96] He made a subjective remark: 'The whole of the buildings, both on the surface and underground, have been constructed by the Tredegar Company, who have spared no expense to make a thoroughly sound job of these, especially the foundations for the haulage-gears and the pumps underground'.

The consulting engineer appeared also to have approved of the Tredegar Company's conduct in commercial matters regarding plant and equipment purchases. Otherwise he would not have scorned the 'bugbear of the lowest bid' by suppliers if the company had adopted such a policy. Moreover, he would not have speculated: 'There is a tendency for contractors tendering on their own specifications to cut prices and put in an inferior job, which, unfortunately, is often accepted'.

Regarding operational costs of the Tredegar Company's collieries' electricity scheme, Scott reckoned that the cost of electric power at Pochin Colliery was 0.43d. per British Thermal Unit for an annual electrical consumption of 300,000 'Board of Trade' units (a unit was equal to 1,000 Watts for one hour i.e. 1 kW/hr).[97] The cost per unit for the pioneering colliery electric plant scheme in the South Wales Coalfield served as a useful reference for appreciating subsequent developments. A decade later, Powell Duffryn's Middle Duffryn power station generated electricity at 0.28d. per unit to serve its Aberdare Valley collieries.[98] The relatively cheaper cost of electricity production at Powell Duffryn's Aberdare collieries electric scheme compared with the Tredegar Company's can be attributed on the whole both to scale, and the use of steam turbines as the prime mover.

In circa 1903, steam turbines were said to be 'unquestionably coming into vogue'.[99] Scott acknowledged that the steam turbine 'was an excellent type of prime mover provided it were installed in large enough sizes, say over 800 kilowatts. Under that size he did not think it was so economical as the reciprocating engine, nor was it as economical on anything but full load'.[100] His argument suggests that the Tredegar Company incurred a reasonable operational cost taking its first step into the use of electricity for working three collieries.

Moreover, W. A. Scott also revealed that he was attuned to a principle for the application of colliery engineering for coal production: 'Efficiency was not everything in a colliery, as freedom from trouble and stoppage was worth a good few decimal points of efficiency'.[101] He knew that colliery plant had to run all day on a very heavy fluctuating load. Thus, he must have felt some joy when reporting that for the Pochin Colliery electric scheme, after two years of operation, there had not been 'a single motor to repair nor even to adjust a bearing'.

However, the hazards of electricity had to be respected. A pumpsman, 'shortly after the plant was installed', acted to change a fuse wire in a fuse box. The 'fuse wire was too long and got nipped between the lid and the case of the metal fuse box, the earthing was not perfect, and he received a shock which killed him'.

Objectively, there were also risks to life and limb maintaining mechanical systems. Early one morning, in late 1905, chargeman Samuel Brooking, duty mechanical engineer according to the company's rules, with a fitter, Peter Watkins, stood on staging in No.1 shaft Ty Trist Colliery to repair a steam pipe valve. The supply of steam in the pipe to the valve had been stopped on the colliery's surface beforehand. However, a misunderstanding about a signal to the surface led to a flow of steam in the pipe. The two men, maybe stunned by a rush of steam, or due to dodging flying mechanical parts, fell 110 yards to their deaths.[102]

Although the Bedwellty Pits-Pochin-Ty Trist electric system was not the cause of other fatalities, during the initial period of nine years, accidents occurred. A. S. Tallis revealed in 1911 that 'a number of workers received shocks on haulage roads, principally from haulage ropes and tackle, which had become charged owing to defective "local earths" situated near the various haulages and pumps. These earths were obtained whether by earth plates sunk into the strata or buried under water, neither of which were found reliable. This system was abandoned and now all the earths were brought to one or more earth plates on the surface, using the armouring of the cables as the earth return'.[103]

Tallis further highlighted in 1911, regarding the company's electricity scheme for the Tredegar district, that 'there were all together 9½ miles of underground cable and 5½ miles of overhead transmission'. Furthermore, he also mentioned that the company 'had recently installed exhaust steam turbine-driven sets'.[104] Indeed, the first mixed pressure turbine was installed by the company in 1908 at the Oakdale power-house, which is covered later.[105]

Regarding electric lighting, it seems to have been in use at Ty Trist, Whitworth, and Bedwellty Pits sometime earlier than 1903. A large electric lighting plant was provided at Ty Trist. The plant comprised a 100 kW single-phase AC generator, driven by ropes, from a compound condensing engine, producing 2,000 V, which was transformed down to 110 V for the lamps.

However, in 1903, W. A. Scott also announced: 'It is proposed to carry current over the Bedwellty Mountain to McLaren village, for lighting the miners' cottages'.

Mining coal at McLaren Colliery

The company built the village of Abertysswg so as to have a pool of labour available on the doorstep of McLaren Colliery. The village was also conceived around the time when the company aspired to 'engender a feeling of friendship between master and man'. An obstacle to realizing such an aspiration was the separation of company officials' housing from those of colliery workers', which was consistent with South Wales Coalfield practice.

Nevertheless, sited over a mile from the neighbouring village of Pontlottyn, the founding of Abertysswg offered some promise for the creation of good relations between colliery officials and local men. The village's population of hundreds was suited to fostering swift personal recognition among the migrants drawn to the place. Then, once a degree of familiarity flourished in the village, the McLaren Colliery officials were likely to become much more disposed towards village-based workers than travellers to the colliery for work. The marshalling of local men by officials for the descent down the pit probably involved less hassle than dealing with a late train of travelling workers. Moreover, the operation of the colliery became the foremost common interest of village residents. Gossip within the community also served in part to shape a local work ethic, some sense of ownership for the place of work, and maybe occasionally checked some misdeeds both at work and in the community. However, the foregoing speculations probably only became meaningful after 1907 when the 'unique pattern in planning' took concrete form at Abertysswg.

At the start to September 1902, a total of 777 men were employed at McLaren Colliery. Allotted to the day shift in the No. 1 Pit were 403 men with 214 men in the No. 2 Pit. Regarding night work, 110 men worked in the No. 1 Pit and 50 men in the No. 2 Pit.[106] Tredegar men made up a 'large percentage' of the colliery's manning. Rhymney Valley men from Pontlottyn, Rhymney, Tirphil, Troed-y-rhiw-fuwch, and New Tredegar also travelled to the colliery for work. Moreover, forty-two horses were deployed underground at the colliery.[107]

The colliery's miners worked a two-shift pattern with each shift being of ten hours duration. The day shift, called the 'coaling shift', produced 'hand-got' coal. The night shift miners did repair work so that the coaling shift was not held back from winning coal.[108] The way of working coal saw the use of the Longwall principle with a mix of 'the South Wales system, which had the stall roads 15 yards apart, but also to some extent on the "Barry" or "Nottingham system", in which the trams are taken up along the face, the stall roads being 60 and 80 yards apart'. All the coal seams at the colliery 'gave off fire-damp', and were 'of a dry dusty nature'.[109]

Miners and officials were issued with locked bonneted 'Clanny' lamps, made by Ackroyd & Best, at the colliery's lamp room before going underground. These lamps, whilst providing light, could also give an indication of the presence of fire-damp (methane gas). The flame in the lamp would feature a light blue-cap if the atmosphere contained less than a 5% part of gas. The size and nature of the flame and cap helped the lamp's user gauge the percentage of gas present. There was insufficient amount of oxygen to support combustion if there was more than a 15% share of methane in the atmosphere. However, the atmosphere became a latent explosive if the proportion of methane was within the range limits of 5% and 15% and in a mixture with a sufficient amount of oxygen. An enduring and sufficient source of heat was needed to cause the mixture to ignite. The most violent explosions occurred when a mixture comprised 9.5% of fire-damp and 90.5% oxygen. After an underground explosion, if a victim was alive, the after-damp made him drowsy, which was a prelude to death by choking.

On the 20th June 1902, a 'heavy' underground roof fall occurred at the northern corner of the west side of the colliery. The 'fall lay between No. 2 Heading tight through to Talybont Heading a distance of 120 yards'. The fall blocked the flow of air. Some miners were 'withdrawn to No. 2 Heading' to work while others dug an airway from No. 2 airway over the fall to No. 1 Heading. Two days later, the digging yielded some improved air flow, and no fire-damp was detected.

Several approaches were then tried to get the ventilation to function satisfactorily. Alfred Tallis and the colliery's officials discussed proposed approaches prior to carrying on work 'in a proper and workmanlike method'.[110] At the end of August an approach involved the opening of a stall in 'Thomas Amos's heading from No. 2 to No. 1 Heading'.[111]

An important external authority also inspected the colliery's ventilation. 'On several occasions in 1900, 1901, and 1902, Mr Martin, H. M. Inspector [of Mines] had drawn the attention of the colliery owners and their manager to the presence of gas in the mine at the time of the official inspection by his assistants, and to the general ventilations. Explanations had been offered in reply'.[112] Regarding the work to rectify the 'great fall' of June 1902, J. S. Martin seemed scathing: 'I myself was not satisfied that they were pushing on the ventilating passage through Amos Barry to Lewis William's heading as quickly as they might, and I entertain considerable doubt as to whether men should have been put to work in Gwilym Morgan's Heading in the return airway in face of a possible accumulation of gas, before the ventilation of the above was completely cleared and restored'.[113] Since the company's officials used a trial and error process to try to achieve satisfactory ventilation, this suggests that the view of an Inspector of Mines was one of many debated.

Of some import, 'some months before' September 1902 a 'new and more powerful fan had been ordered by the Company' but the delivery remained outstanding. McLaren Colliery's miners probably also complained 'about certain bad practices', but were 'ignored'.[114]

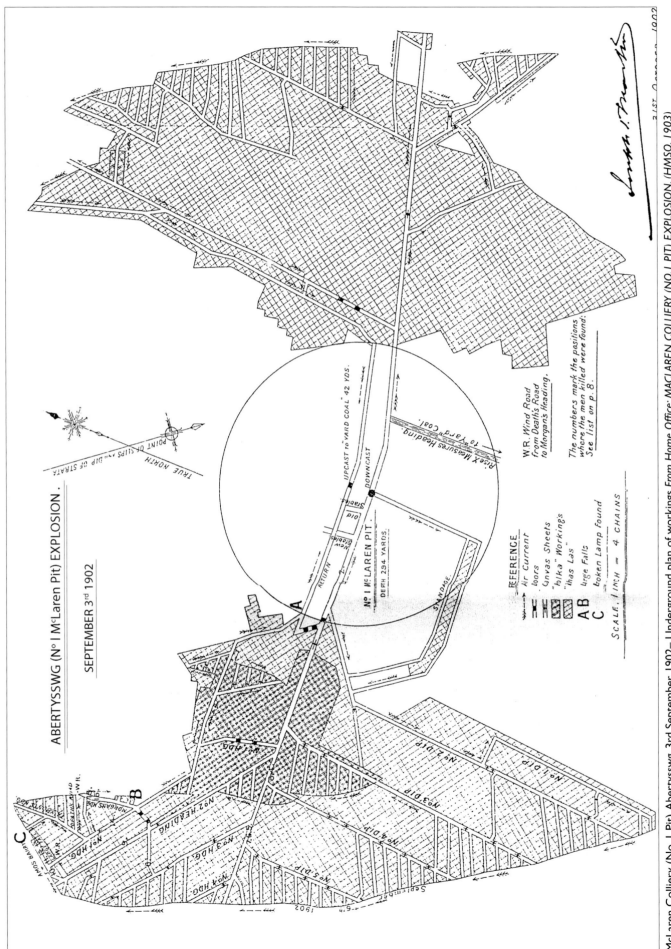

ABERTYSSWG (Nº I McLaren Pit) EXPLOSION.

SEPTEMBER 3rd 1902

McLaren Colliery (No. I Pit), Abertysswg, 3rd September, 1902– Underground plan of workings *From Home Office: MACLAREN COLLIERY (NO. I PIT) EXPLOSION, (HMSO, 1903)*

'A Cruel Time'[115]

On the night shift of Wednesday, the 3rd September 1902, at about 11.30 p.m., an explosion of fire-damp occurred at the northern corner of the western side of McLaren Colliery (No. 1) Pit. Before the explosion, 'several yards' of work remained so as to 'make good the ventilation' to a mining district in part defined by Amos Barry's Heading and Lewis William's Heading.[116] S. T. Evans KC, MP, later proposed that 'it appears clear that the origin of the explosion was an ignition of gas at one of two places in the extreme North and "Rise" corner of the Rhas Las workings off the No. 1 Heading'.[117] A strong blast of fumes raced from the explosion's origin. Near the source of the explosion, the blast dislodged stones and coal that crashed into roof support timbers, blew on-end trams, and one loaded tram was catapulted into a coal face.

Startled by the 'terrible retort' of the explosion were Pontlottyn haulier Tom Minton, and his 'young butty', Tom Rawlings, from New Tredegar. They were repairing timbers on the main roadway about 150 yards west of the No. 1 Pit, and so just under a half-a-mile from the explosion. Then a tornado of fumes arrived and 'knocked down' the pair of workers and 'light played fiercely about' Tom Minton's arm. Darkness. "Oh dear where are we?" whined Tom Rawlings.

A split second later, fifty yards from No. 1 Pit bottom, Thomas Lodwick of Abertysswg, a fireman on duty and 'in charge' of the west side of the colliery, was floored by the explosion's blast. He sustained 'burns about the leg'.

The fumes charged onwards. The Pit's winding-engine man, John Williams of Pontlottyn, 'heard a heavy sound like distant thunder'. Then he saw 'volumes of smoke' pour out of the shaft and 'knew that an explosion had taken place'. John Williams ordered banksman Ben Davies to go the 'Big House' to tell the colliery manager that 'something was amiss down below in the mine'.[118] The colliery manager, John Evans, had been in post at least four months having succeeded John Powell. In June, as manager, after an explosion at Guest, Keen & Nettlefold's Fochriw Colliery, he joined the rescue party.[119]

Underground, fireman Thomas Lodwick was helped by a miner, William Davies, to the pit bottom. However, Lodwick did not loiter at pit bottom, despite the discomfort of burns, he began a search. As he stepped westward he met Tom Minton and Tom Rawlings. Sensing Tom Rawlings's terror, he offered consoling words: 'Fechgyn, beth sydd y mater?' In English: 'Boys, what's the matter?' A tram loaded with timbers barred their way to the fireman. After clambering over the tram, Minton and Rawlings flinched and then froze. A 'poor horse' groaned and kicked. 'When the horse got a little quiet we passed the animal, and made our way out in the darkness, and we got to the pit bottom, and were the first to arrive there', recalled Tom Minton later. After medical treatment in the lamp room, the haulier commented upon his experience. 'Oh it was a cruel time', he moaned. Tom Minton died four days later at his home due to severe burns.[120]

Mr W. Taylor, surface foreman, was the first official to descend underground.[121] The foreman was 'speedily followed' by John Evans, David Roberts, the colliery's under-manager, and a 'strong rescuing party'.[122] The explosion's blast had shaken timber supports and so raised the risk of a roof collapse. Underground doors and sheets, used to control the flow of ventilation underground had been blown away.[123] The rescuers found it harder than normal to breathe. Halts had to be made to check for fire-damp and to sense for after-damp. Yet, five bodies were brought up the pit 'speedily', and others followed. Thomas Lodwick and a hitcher were raised alive to the colliery's surface.

By the early hours of Thursday the 4th September, bystanders encircled the pit head of McLaren No. 1. Some of the men that gathered at pit head volunteered to become rescuers. The crowd's numbers swelled to 'thousands'. People had been drawn to the colliery from 'all parts of the surrounding mining districts' with some fearing the loss of a family member. A 'large body of police' took up stations to keep order within the crowd, but 'had no arduous duties to perform'.

Doctors mustered on the colliery's surface to give medical help. The general practitioners were: Dr R. T. E. Davies of Abertysswg; Dr Nettleship of New Tredegar; and Dr H. Maunsell of Tredegar. Dr Davies 'promptly' descended the pit.

After the colliery's officials had taken stock of the effects of the explosion, messages were sent from the colliery to recruit the support of other qualified mining engineers. After gathering on the colliery's surface, at around one p.m. on 4th September, the engineers organised as two rescue teams, descended underground. In addition to Alfred Tallis, the mining engineers comprised: the twenty-three years old George G. Hann, manager of Bargoed Colliery; T. Gregory, manager of Llanbradach Colliery; Lewis Watkins, manager of Elliot Colliery; T. Reynolds, a Tredegar Company colliery manager; and William Morgan from the Rhymney Iron Company.

'The rescue party prosecuted their sad duties with splendid expedition'. The mining engineers led the search for injured and dead miners, and supervised small teams of colliers to clear roof falls. The clearing of major falls and timber repairing was expedited by David Roberts deploying teams of 'suitable' workmen in a relay of short shifts.[124] A mining engineer stood by also to safeguard such work. His tasks involved being alert to signs of roof collapse, watching for workman fatigue, and regularly performing gas checks like a fireman.

Possibly on the 4th September, but more likely on Friday, 5th September, the underground of McLaren Colliery saw fact finding tours made by three notable groups. The first group included Powell Duffryn's general manager of collieries, Edmund Mills Hann, the father of George Hann. Edmund Mills Hann was viewed by his peers as one of the leading mining engineers of the South Wales Coalfield.[125] He was known for being 'thorough' in 'all he did', and visited the colliery as the representative of the British Association of Colliery Managers. The second group comprised HM Inspector of Mines Joseph S. Martin, and assistant HM Inspector of Mines Mr Robinson. Last, delegates from the SWMF, its general secretary, Mr T. Richard, the miners' agent for the Rhymney Valley, Evan Thomas, and the SWMF's solicitor, Daniel Evans, visited the scene of the disaster.

On being raised to the surface, bodies of miners were stretchered to the colliery's Fitting and Blacksmiths Shop for identification.[126] 'The mournful operation of bringing the bodies to [the pit] bank was most reverently watched, and [after identification] as they were removed to their late homes they were carried between long rows of their sympathetic fellow-workmen'. Recalled decades later were the whispered remarks of McLaren Colliery workmen: 'The price of coal is high', and, 'There but for the Grace of God go I.'[127]

Around late Friday, 5th September, the death toll at McLaren Colliery stood at eleven men. Due to having 'sustained severe burns', the lives of the rescued William Baker and William Brown was uncertain. Four horses had been brought to the surface severely burnt. Lamp discs hanging on hooks in the colliery's lamp room told that three men of the night shift of the 3rd September 1902, had yet to be found.

'Posted at the colliery' were telegrams of sympathy that included one from His Majesty The King Edward VII and another from Sir Charles McLaren. In 1902, Charles McLaren was made Baronet of Bodnant. On the 10th September, accompanied by Alfred Tallis, he 'made a tour of inspection of the colliery and 'personally expressed his sympathy with several of the [victims'] families'.[128]

Employed underground at McLaren Colliery on the night of 3rd September 1902 were 110 men and 42 horses. Three men died in a roof fall, triggered by the explosion, whilst minding four horses that also perished. Several horses were 'very badly burnt'. Fifteen men were also injured by the explosion. An often reproduced illustration of a memorial to miners' lives lost in the South Wales Coalfield between the years 1837 and 1927, does not list the 1902 McLaren Colliery disaster.[129] Due to the explosion at McLaren Colliery in 1902 the death toll was sixteen men as listed in the table overleaf.[130]

Death Toll
McLaren Colliery (No. 1 Pit), Abertysswg
On the 3rd September 1902

Name	Age	Occupation	Injuries as Cause of Death	Address	Legacy[131]
William Rawlings	25	Timberman	Burned severely	6, Fothergill Rd, New Tredegar	
Thomas Minton	37	Haulier	Burned severely	3, Bridge St, Pontlottyn	
George Wilkins	41	Labourer	After-damp. Not burned	10, Charles St, Abertysswg	Widow. 8 children
George Grainger	32	do.	do.	86, Lower Row, New Tredegar	Single
Evan H. Evans	25	Collier	do.	6, McLaren Cottages, Abertysswg	Single
John T. Jones	23	Haulier	do.	12, Arthur St, Abertysswg	Single
Albert Williams	19	Labourer	do.	10, Upper Stanley Tce, New Tredegar	Single
Rees Jones	26	Labourer	Burned severely	3, Lawrence Tce, Troedrhiwfuch	Single
William J. Jones	17	do.	do.	30, Earl St, Tredegar	Single
John Jones	30	Collier	do.	The Garn, Tredegar	Widow. 4 children
William Baker	24	do.	Burned very Severely	23, Prospect Place, Tredegar	Widow. 2 children
William H. Brown	32	do.	do.	54, Queens St, Tredegar	Widow. 7 children
Gwilym Roberts	34	Haulier	do.	103, Vale Tce, Tredegar	Widow
Walter Griffiths	25	do.	Burnt, but not Severely	Arthur St, Abertysswg	Widow
Gwilym Morgan	41	Collier	do.	7, Barkley St, Abertysswg	
Azariah Probert	25	Haulier	do	High St, Rhymney	Single

The funerals of colliery workers killed by the explosion took place at locations remote from Abertysswg. With full military honours, Azariah Probert was buried at Graig, Rhymney. He had served with 'K' Company of the 2nd Volunteer Battalion of the South Wales Borderers. 'A large concourse of people' attended the funerals of Walter Griffiths and John Jones, of Mountain Ash, who were buried at Rhymney Bridge and Cefn Golau respectively'. The common land above Cwmsyfiog, south of New Tredegar, was where a number of separate funerals parties united for 2,000 people to form a 'solemn cortège' for the march to Bedwellty Church for the burial of William Rawlings, George Grainger, and Rees Jones. Mourning may have also occurred in England. Albert Williams' late father had lived at Cinderford. George Grainger was a native of Bristol.

The explosion also harmed fifteen McLaren men. The Abertysswg men injured were: William Bell, Tom Lodwick, and Tom Rees (boy). Four casualties lived at the hamlet of Tirphil: Tom Davies, Edward Harris, William Clewer, and Fred Woodward. Edward Morgan, Hugh Jones, and George Yeoman, respectively from New Tredegar, Rhymney, and Tredegar, were also harmed. Pontlottyn men injured were: J. H. Jones, Robert McDonald, and David Rees. Tom Rawlins, and James Morton from the hamlet to the south of Pontlottyn, Troed-y-rhiw-fuwch, were also on the casualties' list.[132] However, until at least the early 1960s there were at least eight men of the village who could vividly recall the effect that the colliery's explosion had upon people.[133]

The late Tom Minton's 'young butty', Tom Rawlings, seems to have escaped from the McLaren Colliery explosion uninjured. Yet, a newspaper's report about the terror he suffered might have gained him sympathy for the rest of his life. However, even a surfeit of pity, for the despairing widows, troubled orphans, and the injured with doubts about their prospects for re-employment, had little value. A source of financial support was needed by such people to stave off poverty.

The inquest into the McLaren Colliery disaster regarding Monmouthshire victims opened at the magistrate's court Tredegar before W. Berry Watford, the district Coroner, on the 6th September 1902. The inquest was adjourned for jurors to inspect the victims' bodies.[134] Later in September, the inquest reconvened. The ventilation of the colliery and the miner's lamp flame cap became issues between Joseph S. Martin, HM Inspector of Mines, and A. S. Tallis. The words between both men became 'heated'. Tallis at 'one point broke into sobs in the box, overcome with his feelings'.

The source of the explosion was not settled upon: 'Either near point C on the plan by "Amos's," "Barry," or by the fall at where Nos. 30 and 31 were working'. However, a 'large majority of the jury' concluded there 'is no one to blame in the matter in any way'. The jury offered two 'riders':

(1) 'it should be strongly kept before the colliers that their lamps should be put in a secure position';
(2) 'that gas showing in a lamp should be taken as a danger signal, and men not allowed to work in or near it until some responsible official has decided whether the position is safe or not'.

The Coroner then gave a 'formal verdict': 'That the deceased lost their lives by an explosion of inflammable gas in the No 1 McLaren Pit, Abertysswg, and by misadventure came to their deaths'.[135]

Late October, 1902, Sir Charles McLaren, on behalf of the Tredegar Iron & Coal Company, made presentations at Tredegar Town Hall to the '23 persons who were the most prominent at the earlier stages of the rescuing proceedings' at McLaren Colliery. The company's chairman 'felt that (and he was expressing the feelings of his co-directors) that the courage and the devotion shown by their friends upon that trying occasion were deserving of far higher praise than any poor words of his could accord them'. Twenty men, including colliery officials and colliers of the company, were given an inscribed silver English hunter watch, a £5 note, and a vellum scroll expressing the thanks of the company's directors. Alfred Tallis, John Evans, and E. H. Mitton, assistant colliery manager, were each presented with a silver cup as a token of the directors' 'recognition of their gallantry'. Sir Charles McLaren ended the presentation by moving 'a vote of sympathy with the bereaved, which was passed by the assembly standing'. The Tredegar Male Voice choir 'contributed to the programme'.[136]

Company motor car assigned for A. S. Tallis's use. Parked at The Circle, Tredegar. Chauffeur, with assistant, who may have driven Sir Charles McLaren and Alfred Tallis to Abertysswg to inspect McLaren Colliery and meet families of the victims of the 1902 explosion.

A. S. Tallis Photograph Album, Courtesy of the Tallis Family

Silver Cup presented by Sir Charles McClaren to Alfred Simeon Tallis following the 1902 McLaren Colliery explosion. John Evans, colliery manager, and E. H. Mitton, assistant colliery manager, were also presented with such a token of the company directors' appreciation for the actions they took after the explosion. *Frances Gard Photography*

Explosion's Aftermath

The Tredegar Iron & Coal Company's position regarding financial help to people affected by the explosion was made known seemingly almost immediately after the McLaren Colliery explosion. The Monmouthshire & South Wales Coal Owners' Association took charge of the administration for allocating financial help to people on behalf of the company. 'Every facility would be given for discharging the liabilities the Tredegar Company in this case. If any of the families were in need … they [the Association] … (would) be dealt with promptly'.[137]

Nevertheless, an Abertysswg relief fund committee was set up and held a public meeting at Pontlottyn Infants' School. Evan Thomas, miners' agent, detailed 'circumstances [that] would prevent some of the sufferers from benefitting from the Compensation Act, and where help was needed'. The issue had been raised with the company. A local appeal for donations to the relief fund followed the meeting. Moreover, a letter from the Tredegar Company advised the meeting of 'intended subscription lists [for the Abertysswg relief fund] at their Tredegar, Cardiff, and London offices'. Donations had also been made in a letter by Alfred Tallis (£5) and by other senior officials of the Tredegar Company.[138] This would suggest that the contributions made to the surviving victims of the McLaren Colliery explosion by the Monmouthshire and South Wales Coal Owners' Association were boosted to some extent by the Abertysswg relief fund.

As a sequel to the explosion at McLaren Colliery, in November 1902 a letter by A. S. Tallis appeared in the *Cardiff Times*. The letter tackled statements reputed to have been made by members of the Miners' Federation of Great Britain. William Abraham 'was reported to have stated to the Home Secretary that "the general theory set up at the [McLaren Colliery (No. 1) Pit] inquiry with the continuing work in an atmosphere laden with gas renders it imperative upon the miners' leaders to have the matter dealt with some authority that would not be confined within the narrow limits of the Coroner's Court"'. The Tredegar Company's general manager of collieries related that 'no such theory was put forward at the inquiry'.

McLaren Merthyr Colliery after 1906. No. 3 Pit headgear is seen on the left with the new, dominant in size, headgear for No. 1 Pit to its right. Coking plant is situated above the railway sidings in the centre of the photograph. Behind the chimney stack can be seen the terraced housing of McLaren Cottages, home to colliery officials, and the roof of McLaren House, the colliery manager's residence. *Pope/Parkhouse Archive*
Right: Lamp Check McLaren Colliery. *Philip Hatfield Photography/ A. J. Edwards Collection*

Robert Smillie, a Scottish miners' union leader, had 'found a large body of gas' during his visit to the colliery days after the explosion. He concluded that this, with other evidence, meant that the 'ventilation of the colliery was inadequate'. Tallis's reply cast doubt upon such a critic's practical appreciation of the 'fiery mines of South Wales'. Furthermore, Smillie had also canvassed for miners to be represented at explosion inquiries by expert witnesses such as those called by the management of McLaren Colliery and the Tredegar Company. Smillie's call caused Tallis to observe: 'This may be true in so far as workmen's evidence could hardly be considered expert evidence, but several of the workmen were called and gave evidence at the inquiry'.

Furthermore, Evan Thomas, the miners' agent for the Rhymney Valley, was reported to have said that the fireman at the McLaren Colliery inquiry gave evidence 'of finding small accumulations of gas and a cap showing in the lamps upon several occasions'. The evidence was used by Thomas as a case for legislation to put an end to the seepage of gas underground. Alfred Tallis registered that 'no legislation, which can be enacted, can possibly overcome these physical conditions'.

Mabon had apparently also asserted, "He had no hesitation in declaring that it was not safe, neither was it necessary, for mining operations in these days to be carried on in the presence of gas, which was indicated by a cap." He concluded: "It is impossible to expect the workman to rest satisfied until something more has been done to have this matter cleared up."

Tallis, in summary, observed that the colliers employed by the Tredegar Company took practical measures to accommodate the constant danger of underground gas in the pursuit of their livelihoods. He asserted that 'every facility was afforded to the Tredegar colliers to carry out this inspection and on each occasion they have availed themselves of their powers they have

invariably reported the mine to be safe'. The General Rule No. 38 of the Coal Mines Act 1877, he noted, had empowered 'the workmen employed in a mine to appoint two or more of their number to inspect the mine whenever they wish to do so, and forthwith make a true report of the results of their inspection'.[139] Ostensibly to some degree, from Alfred Tallis's perspective, his letter was a swipe against an ongoing ploy of leading miners' union representatives to discredit coal owners.

As a sequel, J. S. Martin, H.M Inspector of Mines, in early 1903, offered reflections about the McLaren explosion with reference to the report issued by S. T. Evans KC, MP.[140] However, he 'desired again to emphasise the importance of watering the road in fiery seams'.[141]

But in October 1902, at McLaren Colliery, the issue became a dispute about the cutting price of the "roof".[142] 500 men went on strike over the issue.[143] Early November, the Tredegar Iron & Coal Company issued summonses to twenty of the strikers for breach of contracts under the Sliding Scale agreement. At Tredegar Police-court the summonses were heard and 'the Bench considered there had been a breach of contract on the behalf of the defendants, and gave judgement for £1 10s. damages in each case and court fees, 8s. each'.[144]

1902 National Conciliation Board

In 1902 the Miners' Federation of Great Britain, though, had greater worries concerning workers' pay. 'By 1902 conditions had become less favourable for the Federation. The selling price of coal had dropped ....' Thus, early in 1902 coal owners outwith the South Wales Coalfield 'applied for a wages reduction of 10 per cent'.[145] Thus, a national Conciliation Board met in June 1902 to adjudicate upon the coal owners' application for a wages reduction.

Lord James of Herford (1828-1911) was a Board member. He 'at once set himself to get a clear understanding and acknowledgement of what factors should enter into the determination of wage rates'. He 'pressed' Benjamin Pickard, a Yorkshire miners' union leader, for guidance. Pickard dodged being snared by reasoning that led to a sliding scale. He would not 'admit that 'selling prices [of coal] was a factor, or indeed that any particular factor existed'. 'The variations in price of this commodity are settled not by any definite factor but by the *higgling* [sic] *of the market* [Arnot's emphasis] in which we use all our skill to outwit the mineowners. We want cheap labour. We want a living wage', asserted the Yorkshire man.[146] Factors such as coal owners' profit and coal output were also discussed at other meetings of the Conciliation Board to try to agree a formula for wage determination. However, in December 1902, after a miners' strike, the Federation 'demurred to accepting the figure presented by the employers'.[147] The Miners' Federation of Great Britain's haggling with the coal owners for better wages was deferred to the future.

Planning for future company collieries

Significantly in the Rhymney Valley the founding in 1897-98 of McLaren Merthyr Colliery coincided with the start of its owner becoming 'centred' as a coal business. The financial performance of the Tredegar Iron & Coal Company reported for the years 1900, 1901, and 1902 revealed that the company had begun to turn its fortunes around. The profits of the Tredegar Company were:

Year ended March	Profit
1900	£104,147
1901	£134,814
1902	£94,077 [148]

In 1902, the directors again attended to company colliery expansion by initiating steps to found a new colliery in the Sirhowy Valley. In making the decision to open Oakdale Colliery, seven and a half miles south of Tredegar, the directors 'hesitated to extend their financial obligations by taking other properties involving immediate additional outlay'. The caution was understandable since lingering in the memory of the company was the 'very dark spot' mentioned earlier. Moreover, an unsettling period of industrial relations was anticipated. Just after October 1902, saw the 'burial of the Sliding Scale' in the South Wales Coalfield. The miners' union leaders and coal owners were faced with a major issue: 'What would take its place?'[149]

Regarding the directors' hesitation, the Tredegar Iron & Coal Company risked forfeiting Llanover Estate trustees mining property that separated the steam coal takes of Pochin Colliery and the future Oakdale Colliery. Another coal company could make a bid to acquire the property. Moreover, the opportunity was foregone of contiguous working that offered the prospect of more efficient collieries' operation.

In 1902, Arthur Markham 'informed the [Tredegar Company's] board that he considered the Llanover minerals of such great value that he proposed to continue negotiations with a view to taking a lease of them on his own account, but that, if he were successful, he would give the company the option of acquiring the entire interest in them'.[150] His initiative gave birth to an idea about a Markham colliery being sunk in the Sirhowy Valley sometime in the future.

The Tredegar Company's decision to limit expansion to just one new colliery might soon afterwards have been judged by shareholders as wise. The following three years saw lower company's profits than those reported in the previous three years:

Year ended March	Profit
1903	£88,205
1904	£70,750
1905	£74,434 [151]

Managing the company's colliery workers during dips in the coal trade was not an easy one. Natural events could also disrupt the company's business.

On the 12th March 1905, the southern movement of coal from McLaren Colliery was stopped. A landslide at New Tredegar Colliery 'crumpled up for a distance of 300 yards' the Brecon and Merthyr railway line. The railway company 'got a temporary road through'. Coal wagon traffic though was restricted until double line working began on the 13th July. The disruption to transport coincided with a slump in the coal trade that closed the colliery for thirteen days.[152]

Developing McLaren Merthyr Colliery

Natural events, though, did not stop the company developing McLaren Colliery. In 1906, a No. 3 Pit was sunk to 373 yards, and made the upcast. The opening of No. 3 shaft 'enabled' the company to raise the colliery's output from 4,500 tons to 8,000 tons per week.[153] The company's annual report for 1906-07 noted that the new shaft had 'struck' the Old Coal seam, which was 'found to be of good section and quality'.[154] The No. 3 shaft cut through: the No. 2 Rhondda seam (also known in Monmouthshire as the Rock of Big Rock) at 27 yards, the Four-Feet at 244 yards, Nine-Feet (the Ras Las) 287 yards, and Old Coal (also called the Five-Feet Gellideg) at 361 yards.[155]

Also during 1906, transmission lines were erected to supply electricity from Ty Trist power-station to McLaren Colliery. The electrical current was generated at 550 volts then transformed up to 6,600 volts for transmission a distance of three miles to the colliery. At McLaren Colliery, a transformer 'stepped down' the current to 500 kW 3-phase current for powering the winding gear's 250 h.p. motor, pumping-plant, and the ventilating fan's 250 h.p. induction motor. The primary braking provision for the winding gear, driven by a using a British Westinghouse liquid resistance controller, was electrical, but provided with hand or foot control safeguards, and an overwinding facility.[156] Abertysswg homes and the McLaren Arms Hotel were also lit by electricity.[157]

Coking plant, of an unknown size and capacity, was erected at McLaren Colliery during its early years. However, in circa 1920, the company commissioned what was possibly a new washery at the colliery and the coking plant was upgraded. Implied from E. E. Edwards's later description of the colliery it ultimately featured a battery of forty coking ovens.

When the 1910s began, McLaren Colliery employed more men than any other company colliery. Under the management of John Evans, the colliery was manned by 1,510 and 1,813 workers in the years 1908 and 1913 respectively. He was succeeded in 1915 by David Kendrick who held the post for around two decades. Maybe earlier than 1930, James Roy Tallis (1901-1978), a son of Alfred Tallis, held the post, but in 1938 K. D. Woolley became possibly the colliery's last manager in the service of the company. Stalwart officials were also vital for colliery management.

Honouring a Colliery Official in 1904

In 1904, a former official at Pochin Colliery, David Davies, received a 'handsome testimonial' at a gathering held at the Castle Hotel, Tredegar.[158] The career of David Davies reveals that colliery workers of ability could gain promotion within the Tredegar Company. R. W. Tolfree,[159] in 1904 the manager of Bedwellty Pits, observed at the gathering that 'although a little man' David Davies 'was full of good sense and ability'. Moreover, his 'conduct' during the 'disastrous fire and explosion' in 1865 at Bedwellty Pits' was noticed.

In 1876, John Reynolds, then overman at Bedwellty Pits, 'spotted' Davies working 'under him as a collier', which led to him being promoted to fireman. Impressed by David Davies's performance as a fireman, the overman took 'the first opportunity' to recommend him to his superiors. Consequently, in 1880, Davies was made overman at Ty Trist Colliery, and in 1883 he was moved to Pochin Colliery in the same role. Davies then 'risked life and limb in exploring the dark and dangerous workings at Pochin Colliery after the appalling disaster' in 1884. Three years later, he was promoted to the colliery's post of under-manager. The under-manager vacancy was probably due to John Reynolds becoming the colliery's manager. John Reynolds further commented that as under-manager at Pochin Colliery, David Davies 'won' for himself 'golden opinions from masters and men' due to his 'intelligent and energetic management of that large undertaking'.

A written testimony about the colliery official was further read at the gathering. 'As an official' David Davies 'held the scales of justice evenly, ever fearlessly protecting the interests of your employers, and never knowingly or willingly doing an injustice to the workmen'. No doubt colliers with grievances against David Davies would have been galled by this aspect of the testimony. Moreover, many more colliers might have scorned the aspect's moral tone. Yet, its metaphor of striving for a balance between the needs of capital and those of workers reveals that some Tredegar Company colliery officials aspired to fairness in their conduct of man management. That such a principle of man management was publicly expressed was a sign that it would have been approved of by the company's directors, not least by Sir Charles McLaren.

Present also at the gathering was a collier, John Jones, who had worked under 'Mr Davies' for sixteen years. He tabled that the official had 'invariably held the balance between the company and workmen as justly as possible'. A scathing opinion of a collier's was unlikely to have been heard at such an event. Nevertheless, a collier who lauded an official in public did so knowing that he risked being abused by fellow workers if what he had said was false. John Jones's remark at least suggested that a degree of goodwill thrived between officials and some company workmen due in part to the conduct of man management by colliery officials.

The report of the career of David Davies also revealed that he had been a 'good teacher' to T. Reynolds, and that he was 'greatly indebted to many of the workmen, and he had learned a great deal from several of those present'. Seemingly *The Merthyr Express* had presented a portrait of a model colliery official. Maybe not done for such a purpose, the newspaper's article had further served to inform fledgling colliery officials that fairness in dealings with workmen was a valued aspiration of the Tredegar Company.

The gathering to honour a colliery official of the Tredegar Company in 1904 received lengthy coverage in a local newspaper, *The Merthyr Express*. Such press attention acts as a reminder about the high status that colliery officials held at the start of the twentieth century in the South Wales Coalfield. Moreover, the future employment prospects for company colliery officials and workers in the Sirhowy Valley appeared bright.

NOTES

1   Trevor Boyns, 'McLaren, Charles Benjamin Bright, first Baron Aberconway', *The Oxford Dictionary of National Biography*. The source of following unless otherwise referenced.
2   'Lord Aberconway', *The Times*, 26 Jan 1934, p.12.
3   'Hinckley Liberals and Mr McLaren MP', *Leicester Chronicle and the Leicestershire Mercury*, 27 June 1896, p.2.
4   'News', *The Daily News*, 27 June 1896.
5   J. C. Carr and W. Taplin, op. cit., p.131.
6   J. C. Carr and W. Taplin, op. cit., p.88.
7   'Mr C. B. McLaren and the Eight Hours' Question', *Leicester Chronicle and the Leicestershire Mercury*, 6 September 1890, p.3.
8   'Tredegar Iron and Coal Company, Limited', *The Sheffield & Rotherham Independent*, 20 June 1895, p.7.
9   J. C. Carr and W. Taplin, op. cit., p.164.
10 J. C. Carr and W. Taplin, op. cit., p.168.
11 'Tredegar Iron and Coal Company', WM, 5 July 1893.
12 J. C. Carr and W. Taplin, op. cit., p.165.
13 'Tredegar Iron and Coal Company', WM, 5 July 1893.
14 The paid-up capital was reduced by one-ninth, through the reduction by £6 of each £50 'A' share (on which £36 had been paid up) and by £4 3s. 4d. on each fully paid £25 'B' shares. Further the reserve fund of £43,333 was also 'absorbed' as part of the capital write down. Comment Prof. Trevor Boyns to Writer, 31 Aug 2015
15 'Tredegar Iron and Coal Company, Limited', *The Sheffield & Rotherham Independent*, 20 June 1895, p.7.
16 The annual coal output figure was for the twelve months prior to the 31st March, 1895, which aligned with the period covered in the Tredegar Company's annual report.
17 Tredegar Company, *The Sheffield & Rotherham Independent*, 20 June 1895, p.7.
18 Tredegar Company, *The Sheffield & Rotherham Independent*, 20 June 1895, p.7.
19 Violet Markham, *Friendship's Harvest*. (Max Reinhart, 1956), pp.4-5.
20 'Tredegar Iron and Coal Company', The Sheffield & Rotherham Independent, 20 June 1895, p.7.
21 TCG, 'Monmouthshire & South Wales', Vol.LXXIV, 16 July 1897, p.117.
22 The experiments at Portsmouth involved *Grinder*, a dockyard tug of 332 tons. New Tredegar Colliery coal generated 523.59 h.p., the highest recorded for Monmouthshire coals tested. Moreover, New Tredegar coal demanded less 'expenditure of labour in use', and was 'especially adapted for service abroad'. A tested Tredegar coal generated 469.89 h.p.. 'Welsh Coal and the Navy', MM, 3 March 1888, p.3.
23 Leslie M. Shore, op. cit., pp.38-42.
24 'I think wisely' was the comment drawn from Mine Inspector J. S. Martin in 1902 about the Tredegar Company's subsequent decision to change the initial 'communication' way from Bedwellty Pits, described later. T. Evans and J. S. Martin, Reports to His Majesty's Secretary of State for the Home Department on the Circumstances attending an Explosion which occurred at McLaren Colliery (No.1 Pit), Abertysswg, on the 3rd September, 1902. (HMSO, October 1902), [hereafter MER], p.11.
25 'Cardiff Coal Contracts', *South Wales Echo*, 29 March 1897, p.4.
26 Crawshay Bros., Ltd received the least share of the Cunard order. 'Large Coal Contracts', *South Wales Echo*, 20 May 1897, p.4.
27 Henry Davis Pochin left £13,263 16s. 9d. In addition to the Tredegar Iron & Coal Company, his shares in public companies also included at least: Metropolitan Railway, John Brown, Bolckow Vaughan, East Cannock Colliery, Globe Marine Insurance, Palmer's Shipbuilding, Sheepbridge, and Staveley Iron & Coal. 'Will of Mr Pochin', *The Sheffield & Rotherham Independent*, 25 March 1895.
28 TCG, 'Monmouthshire & South Wales', Vol. LXXVI, 15 July 1898, p.119.
29 Richard Watson, op. cit, p.185, which was sourced from John Williams, *Digest of Welsh Statistics*. (Welsh Office, 1985), I, p.337.
30 R. Page Arnot, op. cit., pp.280-288.
31 End of 1898 'Strike', WM, 2 Sept 1898.
32 R. Page Arnot, op. cit., pp.280-288.
33 'Abertysswg Library and Institute', ME: West Mon, Ebbw Vale, Sirhowy Edition, 30 Oct 1909.
34 TCG, 'Monmouthshire & South Wales', Vol. LXXVI, 15 July 1898, p.119.
35 OS Ref No. SO 134055.
36 TCG, 'Monmouthshire & South Wales', Vol. LXXVI, 15 July 1898, p.119.
37 S. T. Evans and J. S. Martin, MER, p.9.
38 MER, op. cit., p.11.
39 TCG, 'Monmouthshire & South Wales', Vol. LXXVI, 15 July 1898, p.119. 'Upwards of £36,000 had been expended' by the company 'during the year on the capital account'.
40 *The South Wales Coal Annual*. (1912), p.3.
41 *The South Wales Coal Annual*. (1912), p.7.
42 TCG, 'Monmouthshire & South Wales', Vol. LXXVI, 15 July 1898, p.119.
43 McLaren Colliery coal was classified in 1946 as follows: the upper seams were bituminous I : volatiles 17-23%; carbon ranged from 90-92%; hydrogen 4.3-5%, and calorific value 15,650 to 15,800 Btu/lb; and its lower seams were close to semi-bituminous, and granted the distinction of being 'caking steam' coal; volatiles 13-18% carbon

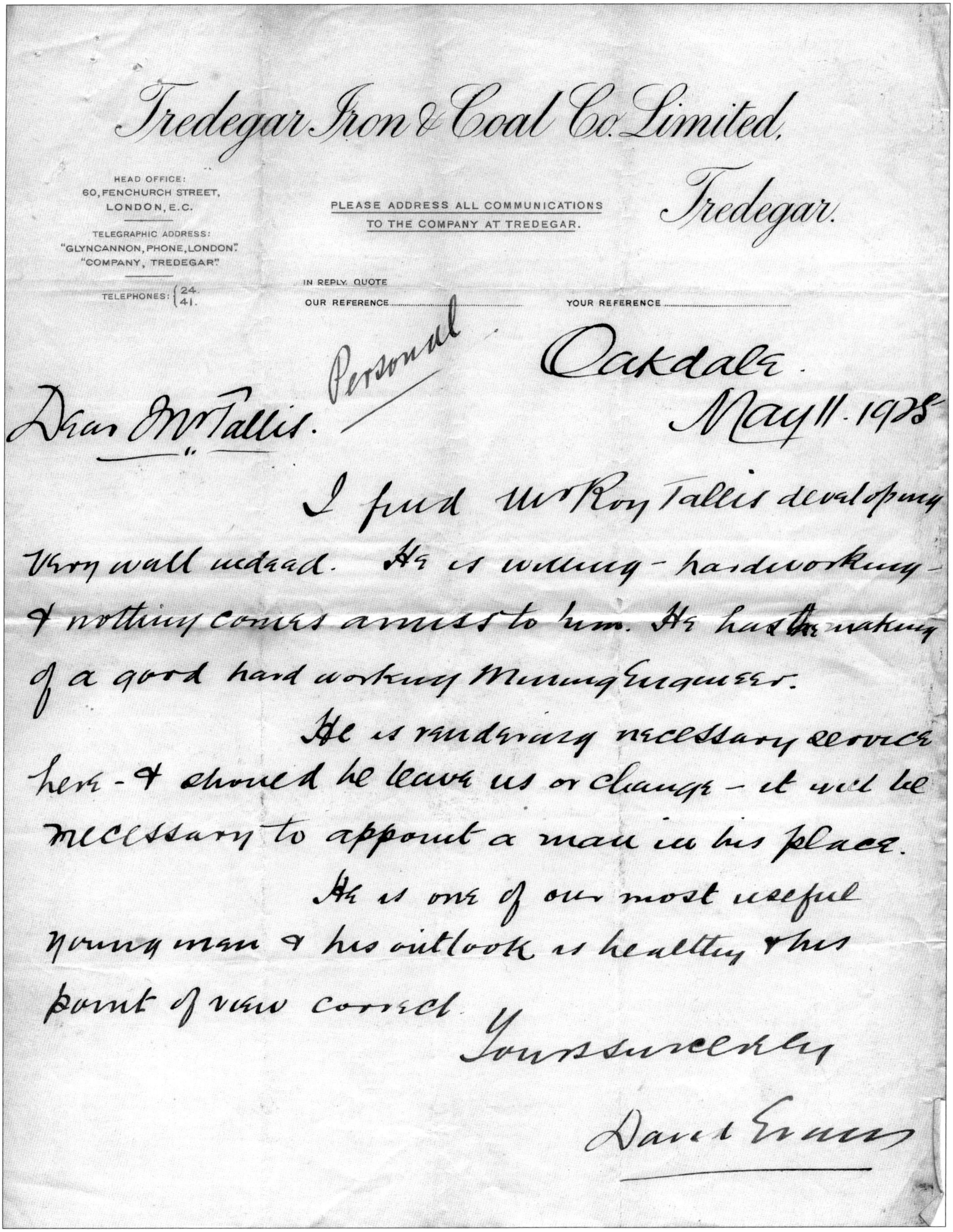

Tredegar Iron & Coal Co. Limited,

HEAD OFFICE:
60, FENCHURCH STREET,
LONDON, E.C.

PLEASE ADDRESS ALL COMMUNICATIONS
TO THE COMPANY AT TREDEGAR.

Tredegar.

TELEGRAPHIC ADDRESS:
"GLYNCANNON, PHONE, LONDON".
"COMPANY, TREDEGAR"

TELEPHONES: { 24.
{ 41.

IN REPLY, QUOTE
OUR REFERENCE...........

YOUR REFERENCE...........

Personal

Oakdale.
May 11. 1928

Dear Mr Tallis.

I find Mr Roy Tallis developing
very well indeed. He is willing - hardworking -
& nothing comes amiss to 'im. He has the making
of a good hard working Mining Engineer.

He is rendering necessary service
here - & should he leave us or change - it will be
necessary to appoint a man in his place.

He is one of our most useful
young men & his outlook is healthy & his
point of view correct.

Yours sincerely

David Evans

An appraisal of Roy Tallis prior to his appointment as the manager of McLaren Merthyr Colliery. David Evans, see more later, was the manager of Oakdale Navigation Colleries.
Courtesy of the Tallis Family

ranged from 90.5-92.5%; hydrogen 4.0–5%; and calorific value 15,600 to 15,800 Btu/lb., SWC-RegRpt, pp.20-21. As a generalisation, McLaren Colliery's coal was a superior free-burning coal compared with South Wales coal mined to its east and south-east.

44   As an example of use, in April 1912, 850 tons of 'McLaren Merthyr' coal bunkered the *Hai Chai*, a Chinese Navy cruiser, at Bute Docks, Cardiff. WM, 15 Apr 1912, p.8.

45   E. E. Edwards, *Echoes of Rhymney*. (Starling Press, 1974), p.52.

46   MER, op. cit., pp.11-12.

47   Leslie M. Shore, op. cit., p.60.

48   Leslie M. Shore, op. cit., p.92.

49   MER, op. cit., p.9.

50   Leslie M. Shore, op. cit., p.72

51   E. E. Edwards, op. cit., p.53.

52   'Mr A. S. Tallis JP: Prominent Colliery Owner Passes Away', *South Wales Argus* [hereafter SWA] 10 Sept 1927, p.6. In an article, 'The Abertysswg Explosion', ME, 27 Sept 1902, p.5, Tallis's early career was summarised as '22 years under the employ of' the Ocean Company, which would have meant that he entered the coal industry at four years of age. Maybe an inference from such an error is that he was employed by the Ocean Company for twelve years, which would suggest he entered the coal industry at fourteen years of age.

53   Email, Stuart Helm, Archivist, Stockport Grammar School, to Writer, 3 Dec 2014.

54   TCG, 'Monmouthshire & South Wales', Vol. LVIII, 13 December 1889, p.851.

55   Marion Edwards, *A Portrait of Rhymney, Vol. 1*. (Old Bakehouse Publications, 1994), p.100.

56   'Rhymney Colliery', WM, 26 Sept 1898.

57   E. E. Edwards, op. cit., p.53.

58   Marion Edwards, op. cit., p.102.

59   Roger Tanner, 'Why Wales is Different …when it comes to planning', *Cynllunio*, Winter 2013, p.7.

60   E. E. Edwards, op. cit., p.31. George III pennies; one dated 1804 and the other 1807 were found under a sill-board during repairs to one of the buildings 'some time ago' before 1974.

61   R. Page Arnot, op. cit., p.343.

62   TICC, op. cit., p.5.

63   William Smith, op. cit., p.14.

64   'Abertysswg Cottage Hospital', ME, 8 Oct 1910, p.10.

65   William Smith, op. cit., p.14.

66   TCG, Vol. XXXV, 17 May 1878, p.793.

67   'Tredegar Iron and Coal Company', WM, 4 July 1900.

68   R. Page Arnot, op. cit., p.310.

69   WCF: TI&C, op. cit., p.45.

70   'Tredegar Iron and Coal Company', WM, 4 July 1900.

71   TICC, op. cit., p.2.

72   'Grand Hospital Bazaar at Tredegar', ME, 22 Oct 1904, p.10.

73   The Iron & Coal Trades Review, 14 Aug 1908.

74   'Grand Hospital Bazaar at Tredegar', ME, 22 Oct 1904, p.10.

75   TICC, op. cit., p.2.

76   *The Iron & Coal Trades Review*, 18 Sept 1931, p.399.

77   K. C. Barraclough, op. cit., p.167. The charge was made on 20 July 1873.

78   Violet Markham, op. cit., pp.4-5.

79   Violet Markham, op. cit., pp.6-8.

80   Violet Markham, op. cit., p.14.

81   'Englishmen and Welsh Industries', CT, 11 Aug 1906, p.6.

82   'Electricity in Mines– Engineers at Tredegar', CT, 4 July 1903, p.7.

83   'Tredegar Iron and Coal Company', WM, 4 July 1900.

84   The main source for the section that follows: W. A. Scott, 'Electric Motive Power in Mines and Collieries', SWIE, Vol.XXIII (1902-1904), pp.235-303. W. A. Scott used the Ty Tryst spelling.

85   G. M. Harvey, *Colliery Electrical Engineering*. (Sir Isaac Pitman & Sons, 1924), p.20.

86   TCG, Vol. CI, 5 May 1911, p.885.

87   'Electricity in Mines – Engineers at Tredegar', CT, 4 July 1903, p.7. Arthur Markham also said: in 'America they were not quite as conservative as we were in our country. If a stranger went to America he was taken down every colliery, shown every working cost, and every detail connected within the mining industry, but in this country colliery working costs were considered a fetish, and a sacred institution which under no condition must be disclosed to a competing colliery owner.'

88   Discussion, 'Electric Motive Power in Mines and Collieries', SWIE, Vol. XXIII (1904), p.439.

89   TCG, Vol. CI, 5 May 1911, p.885.

90   'Electricity in Mines – Engineers at Tredegar', CT, 4 July 1903, p.7. The works was called the 'steel works' in the newspaper's report.

91   The starters of the motors were placed in a 'gas-tight case, filled with oil. The advantages of this action were as follows: The case, 'being full of oil, no gas can get into it; the oil absorbs the heat of any arcs at the contacts, and consequently these contacts do not burn; the heat in the resistance coils is also absorbed by the oil, and therefore, the switch can be in use much longer than if in air'. W. A. Scott, op. cit., p.249.

92   Described more fully by W. A. Scott as 'one set of three-throw dip-pumps – 4-inch X 6-inch rams, to deliver 30 gallons per minute against a head of 120 feet' and were placed on 'a trolley for easy transport'.

93   Discussion, 'Electric Motive Power in Mines and Collieries', SWIE, Vol. XXIII (1902-1904), p.452.

94   Discussion, 'Electric Motive Power in Mines and Collieries', SWIE, Vol. XXIII (1902-1904), p.535.

95   The Old Coal seam pumps were capable of dealing with 270 gallons per minute against a head of 680 ft. The Yard Coal pump offered the same capability, but against a lesser head, 450 ft.

96   Discussion, 'Electric Motive Power in Mines and Collieries', SWIE, Vol. XXIII (1902-1904), p.531. The total capital cost included: boilers, engines, generators, motors, haulage-gears, pumps, cables, switchboards, controllers, power-house and foundations, underground haulage and pump rooms, and all excavations. W. A. Scott identified that £7,930 was spent on generating plant; £5,705 on 'consuming plant' comprising haulage; and £1,809 on pumping. The sum of the foregoing cost allocations is around £1,000 more than that stated in the text.

97   Regarding the cost of electricity generated at the Tredegar Works this was 'under three-sixteenths of a penny per unit' and in 1903 it was believed that this cost could be reduced further. 'Electricity in Mines– Engineers at Tredegar', CT, 4 July 1903, p.7.

98   Leslie M. Shore, op. cit., p.155.

99   Discussion, 'Electric Motive Power in Mines and Collieries', SWIE, Vol. XXIII (1902-1904), p.443. 'The Metropolitan Railway Company were putting in ten 5,000 h.p. turbines; the Lancashire and Yorkshire Power Distributing Company twelve turbines'.

100 W. A. Scott judged that 'you must have plenty of condensing water and maintain a high vacuum; otherwise the steam turbine seemed to lose its efficiency as a steam engine in greater proportion than did the reciprocating engine'.

101 Discussion, 'Electric Motive Power in Mines and Collieries', SWIE, Vol. XXIII (1902-1904), p.535.

102 Samuel Henry Brooking (1854-1905) was the Writer's maternal great-grandfather. An inquiry decided that their deaths were 'accidental'. 'Colliery Horror', *Evening Express*, 15 Dec 1905, p.3, and 'Flange Blew Out', *Cardiff Times*, 23 Dec 1905, p. 4.

103 TCG, Vol. CI, 5 May 1911, p.886.

104 TCG, Vol. CI, 5 May 1911, p.885.

105 W. Angus Scott's remark, W. D. Woolley, 'Wyllie Colliery', SWIE, Vol. XLV (1929), p.401.

106 MER, op. cit., p.11.

107 'Terrible Colliery Explosion', ME, 6 Sept 1902, p.5.

108 George Greeve, 'McLaren Colliery Explosion', p.13. An unpublished paper, circa 1960, about the 1902 McLaren Colliery explosion. George Greeve interviewed around twenty Abertysswg people, aged between 70 and 90 years, who had recollections of the 1902 disaster. Archive Bargoed Library, Caerphilly County Borough.

109 MER, op. cit., p.11.

110 MER, op. cit., p.5.

111 'The Abertysswg Explosion', ME, 27 Sept 1902, p.5.

112 MER, op. cit., p.6.

113 MER, op. cit., p.5.

114 George Greeve, 'McLaren Colliery Explosion', p.3.

115 'Terrible Colliery Explosion', op. cit., 6 Sept 1902, p.5, various columns. The main source of the following description of the explosion.

116 Names for headings, or other features underground, were as useful for navigation as are street names marked on a town's plan. As a convention, it also served to recognise the work of a colliery worker for maybe opening a heading. MER, op. cit., p.3.

117 MER, op. cit., p.4.

118 George Greeve, 'McLaren Colliery Explosion', p.13.

119 Mine Explosion, CT 7 June 1906, p2.

120 'Death of T. Minton', ME, 13 Sept 1902, p.5, col.4. He was the

121 W. Taylor was killed on the colliery's surface sometime after the 1902 explosion.

122 MER, op. cit., p.3 and p.9 identify David Evans as the 'under-manager, but apparently he is more in the position of an overman at No. 2 Pit'. Press reports identify David Roberts as the under-manager for No. 1 Pit.

123 MER, op. cit., p.9.

124 George Greeve, 'McLaren Colliery Explosion', p.7.

125 Leslie M. Shore, op. cit., passim

126 The Writer's father, William (Bill) Shore, worked at McLaren Colliery around 1956 as assistant colliery engineer. Led by their father, the Writer aged circa eight years, and his younger brother, (Professor) Alan Shore, made a tour of the buildings on the surface of the colliery in around 1958. The workshop was inspected, but the Writer cannot recall any mention of the sad duty that it had once served.

127 George Greeve, 'McLaren Colliery Explosion', p.5.

128 'The Abertysswg Disaster', *Evening Express*, 10 Sept 1902, p.3.

129 See for example, Rayner Rosser, *Collieries of the Sirhowy Valley*. (Old Bakehouse Publications, 1996), p.102.

130 MER, op. cit., p.7, other than the 'Address' and 'Legacy' columns.

131 The 'Address' and 'Legacy' columns compiled from George Greeve, 'McLaren Colliery Explosion', pp.7-8.

132 A landslide, over decades, has destroyed nearly all of Troed-y-rhiw fuwch's houses.

133 In and around 1959, George Greeves of Abertywssg interviewed a number of village residents aged between seventy and ninety years for his article about the 1902 McLaren Colliery explosion. Among the men he interviewed were: James Addis, Thomas Arthur, Alfred Boughay, John Conboy, William Edwards, Lewis Jacobs, Joseph Mullings, and Thomas Owen. It seems that he only interviewed one woman, Miss Victoria Morgan.

134 'The Abertysswg Disaster', *Weekly Mail*, 13 Sept 1902, p.5.

135 'Abertysswg Disaster' and 'Painful Incident', CT, 4 Oct 1902, p.4.

136 The persons awarded watches were: D. Roberts, under-manager; Wm. Taylor, surface overman, who was to be killed in early November, 1902, trapped in a new tram tipping machine; Wm. Bebb, night fireman; Samuel Jones, pumpman; John Amos, fireman; Charles Jones, overman; P.C. Moore; D. Davies, fireman; George Skinner, fireman; William Jones, fireman, D. Jones, fireman; William Davies, collier; George Jones, fitter; George Yorath (Powell Duffryn Company); W. G. Morgan, collier; Wm. Davies, collier; John Jones, collier; Charles Jones, collier; Thomas Davies, labourer; and David Jones, master haulier. 'Abertysswg Disaster', CT, 1 Nov 1902, p.4.

137 'Assistance Offered by the Company', ME, 13 Sept 1902, p.5, col.4.

138 'Relief', ME, 27 Sept 1902, p.5, col.5.

139 'Abertysswg Explosion – Condition of the Pit', CT, 29 Nov 1902.

140 MER.

141 'Dry & Dusty Mines', *Evening Express*, 23 Jan 1903, p.3.

142 'South Wales Coal Trade', *Evening Express*, 8 Oct 1902, p.2.

143 'Colliery Dispute at New Tredegar', *Evening Express*, 6 Oct 1902, p.3.

144 'Breach of Contract by Tredegar Colliers', *Evening Express*, 19 Nov 1902, p.4

145 R. Page Arnot, op. cit., p.311.

146 R. Page Arnot, op. cit., p.313.

147 R. Page Arnot, op. cit., p.315.

148 'Tredegar Company', ME, 17 June 1911, p.8.

149 R. Page Arnot, op. cit., p.317.

150 'Tredegar Company', ME, 17 June 1911, p.8.

151 'Tredegar Company', ME, 17 June 1911, p.8.

152 'Brecon and Merthyr Line', CT, 19 Aug 1905, p.10.

153 E. E. Edwards, op. cit., p.53.

154 'Tredegar Iron & Coal Co.', CT, 8 June 1907, p.5.

155 Source gives depths in feet and inches. Ray Lawrence, The Coal Workings of the Caerphilly County Area, p.131.

156 'Electricity in Mines', *South Wales Weekly Argus* [hereafter SWWA], 2 June 1906.

157 WCF: TI&C, op. cit., p.47.

158 'Tredegar Colliery Official Honoured', ME, 1 Oct 1904, p.10.

159 R. W. Tolfree died in late May 1917, and was buried at Cefn Goleau Cemetery. He was described as being 'manager of Bedwellty Collieries'. 'Late Mr R. W. Tolfree', *Monmouth Guardian* (Rhymney) and *Bargoed and Caerphilly Observer* [hereafter *Monmouth Guardian*], 1 June 1917.

On the cusp of the twentieth century the future of the Tredegar Iron & Coal was put in jeopardy partly due to the capital expenditure commitment to open McLaren Colliery shown above. With a proviso that the Tredegar ironworks continued to be operated, Lord Tredegar generously agreed to help the company through a financial crisis. The nation gained during the Great War since the colliery's coal was listed by the Admiralty as suitable for powering battleships of the Royal Navy.

Pope/Parkhouse Archive

Special train used to deliver guests of the Oakdale Navigation Collieries Limited to the ceremony that opened Oakdale Navigation Colliery on the 20th April, 1907. The train is composed of four- and six-wheeled saloons hauled by a Great Western 0-6-0ST which is stopped alongside a temporary water tower, possibly built for the occasion. To the left above the train invited guests are assembled at the colliery site whilst others wander at will along the railway which is part of Hall's Road.

A. S. Tallis Photograph Album, Courtesy of the Tallis Family

Chapter Five
OAKDALE COLLIERY

By 1906, the Tredegar Iron & Coal Company had fostered an image of having entered a 'period not of decline but rejuvenation' in one part of the coal trade's press. Forecasted was that with the company's 'products established in every important market; with its old and new collieries equipped with the latest machinery which engineering skill had evolved for economically working the coal, and efficiently preparing it to give the best results to consumers; with an extensive tract of unworked seams, containing Welsh steam coal of the first class … everything points to a long and successful future for the Company'. The company was also assessed as being run by 'an energetic and experienced body of directors and officials'. In 1906, the directors of the Tredegar Iron & Coal Company were: Sir Charles McLaren Bart, MP; Messrs Arthur Markham MP, Charles John Stoddart, George Andrew Barkley, Walter S. B. McLaren, and Lt-Colonel A. K. Wyllie CB.[1]

Regarding the company's chairman, in 1906 his standing in British industry was extolled as being 'one of the principal and best known figures in the commercial life of the Kingdom'.[2] However, the coal trade press article gave no insight into the nature and degree of the chairman's involvement in the company's activities. In a much later consideration of McLaren's career as an industrialist, it was proposed that he attended to the 'financial aspects of the companies of which he was chairman, leaving the day-to-day management in the hands of others'.[3]

The Tredegar Company was managed via two distinct functions: the operation of the collieries, and a commercial function. The commercial function had to be proficient at contract tender bidding, and negotiating sales agreements with coal customers to win coal orders. The function's ability to foster goodwill with customers might also have proved of benefit to company sales during poor trading conditions. The function's ability to perform the task of arranging the movement of coal from pit heads was also essential for keeping customer goodwill.

The company's two chief commercial offices were located in London and Cardiff. The London Office manager, appointed in 1901, was H. O. Monkley with H. Kendrick serving as the manager of the Cardiff Office in the Exchange Buildings from January 1904. Before July 1907, the London office was deemed as 'inadequate for the extended business of the Company', and so more 'commodious offices' were acquired at 60, Fenchurch Street and occupied that month.[4]

Regarding the company's coal distribution from the Sirhowy Valley, in 1906 the work of the London & North Western Railway was fundamental. However, coordination with the Great Western, the South Eastern & Chatham, and the Metropolitan railway companies were also needed for Tredegar Company wagon movements in Great Britain. Among the customers for Tredegar coal to fire locomotive boilers were the foregoing railway companies with the Chatham and Irish companies.

Moreover, the 'greater portion of the output' from the Tredegar Company was shipped abroad for coaling steamers at foreign ports, and for railways or works in 'every part of the world'. A 'proportion' of coal was thus 'shipped into the bunkers of trading steamers and liners at Cardiff, Newport, Southampton, Birkenhead, and London'. Nevertheless, 'large quantities' of coal were distributed to other places to supply the home market.[5]

Coal order requests from commercial clerks affected the output of the company's colliery washeries. 'Washed peas and washed nuts' were processed by the washeries for 'steam-raising purposes at works of every description', and in 1906 a 'strong demand' prevailed. South Wales and Staffordshire were the chief geographical markets for the company's coke output.[6]

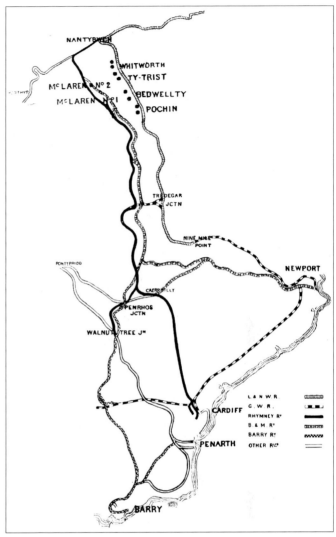

Tredegar Iron & Coal Company collieries in circa 1906 and their railway links with South Wales ports. *Paul Jackson collection*

The above gives just a hint about activities that engaged office-bound clerks in Cardiff and London. Clerks charged with the logistics of moving coal had to be deft coping with transport hitches. Congestion on the South Wales Coalfield railway network was particularly acute during a boom for coal, but a train's derailment, or a locomotive's failure, could occur at any time and disrupt coal distribution. Life in the company's commercial offices could be hectic co-ordinating the supply of colliery coal production to customers, but there was a gulf in the conditions of work between commercial clerks and a coal-face worker.

The toll of miners' deaths and worker ill health stained any claims made about the value of the coal industry to the economy of the world, but it had been a spur for the workers of Tredegar to set up a local worker's medical scheme. Yet, there was a glaring gap in local health care.

Tredegar Cottage Hospital

The idea about a hospital for the Tredegar district arose before 1902. However, in August 1902, a Tredegar Cottage Hospital Committee met at which the Tredegar Company promised a donation of £250 towards the hospital fund and £25 per annum towards maintenance.[7] A hospital scheme was then designed by a group of representatives drawn from a Library Committee, a Workman's Committee, and a Sick Fund Committee.[8]

On the 14th September 1903, a ceremony held in Tredegar's Bedwellty Park marked the start to building a hospital. 'Stones were laid by Mrs A. S. Tallis on behalf of the Tredegar Company, Mrs (Dr) G. A. Brown for the townspeople, and Mrs A. Onions as representing the working man'. The hospital's architect was E. A. Johnson of Abergavenny, and the building work was undertaken by Tredegar's D. John Vaughan. Regardless of the 'laudable object' of the scheme, at the stone laying ceremony, the chairman of the Hospital Scheme, A. S. Tallis, revealed that 'the townspeople had not yet extended the support to the movement which could be expected of them'.

A speech by the miners' agent, Alfred Onions, contains clues to why some support was being withheld. He said: 'some people professed to believe that there was no identity of interest between colliery companies and workmen, but in this case at any rate there was a general identity of interest. Employers were financially responsible to some extent for repairing injuries to their workmen and he hoped the Tredegar Company would be amply repaid for their interest in this movement by their injured workmen receiving better and speedier cures. (Applause.) He hoped the hospital would not suffer from prejudice'.[9] Maybe the prejudice was due to some people asserting that it was the duty of the company to pay for all the hospital's building and running costs.

The Tredegar Cottage Hospital cost £4,126 to build and furnish. 'Eighty per cent of the workmen balloted in favour of it, and decided to contribute one half-penny per week per man to the cost of maintenance, amounting to £360 a year'. The company met its promise of £25 per year, and 'it was hoped that from other sources close upon £100 per annum would be forthcoming' for maintaining the hospital.

On Monday the 3rd October 1904, for the opening of Tredegar Cottage Hospital, 'all the local collieries were idle for the occasion'. The weather 'was excellent'. A 'large throng welcomed' 2nd Lord Tredegar at Sirhowy Railway Station. A procession marched from the Temperance Hall to the Town Hall where a luncheon for guests took place. The occasion was enriched by the singing of the Tredegar Male Voice Party, conducted by E. R. Edwards.

After the luncheon, Mrs A. S. Tallis handed over a 'suitably' inscribed gold key to Lord Tredegar for the formal opening of the building. He remarked that he 'had never felt so much gratification … to present the [Bedwellty] park to the people of Tredegar as he did that day. (Cheers.) … Sometimes they heard remarks not flattering to great landlords; sometimes they heard that great men had too much land. He could almost say on this occasion he felt gratified that he owned some land, and that it did not belong to speculative builders who would use it to get money out of it for themselves alone'. He then 'declared the hospital open and inspected it throughout'.[10]

Tredegar Cottage Hospital comprised a ground floor and upper floor. The ground floor catered for nine patients in a large ward, and further featured an anaesthetic ward, two private wards, a sitting room for nurses and doctors, a dispensary, and offices. Provided on the upper floor were six bedrooms, a bathroom, and staff accommodation.[11] The main entry into the hospital building lay on the town's Park Row side with a frontage overlooking parkland.

The hospital project, though, was burdened with debt. According to Alfred Tallis, '£1,675 had been received [for the cost of the hospital], and it was hoped that the forthcoming bazaar would clear most of the building debt off'.[12]

Over three days in October 1904, a 'grand hospital bazaar' was held at the Market Buildings. Teams of women, mainly wives of the company's officials and the town's businessmen, attended ten 'charmingly decorated' stalls at the bazaar that displayed 'exquisite goods'. The builder, D. John Vaughan, dared to suggest in public that 'the social effect of the bazaar' had been considerable having brought 'the ladies together in spite of election differences, fiscal reform, or fiscal regression'. His remark was reported as having prompted laughter.

'Distinguished visitors', Lord and Lady Llangattock, attended the bazaar's first day. Lord Llangattock was amazed at Tredegar's 'pluck to build a hospital without having the money to pay for it, and he hoped their energy would be rewarded by a speedy liquidation of the debt'.

Arthur Markham was the bazaar's chief visitor on the second day. He 'first apologised' for the absence of Sir Charles McLaren and Lady McLaren. He then recollected that his family had been 'connected with the Tredegar Company since its formation'. 'Therefore everything that made for the welfare of the people employed by the company must be of gratification not only to himself, but to his family'. He then observed 'with regard to the hospital it was necessary there should be a place for men meeting with accidents should be taken' and urged 'all sections the necessity of contributing to its funds. There should be no shadow of doubt and of difficulty of removing the debt of £2,000'.[13] The tally of the bazaar's takings was £1,310.

As a local initiative, the cottage hospital was noteworthy. As a model of public health care, the hospital complemented a local workers' medical scheme. The cottage hospital was in the van of an associated movement that saw similar facilities provided in the valleys of the South Wales Coalfield after 1896 following the opening of a cottage hospital at Mountain Ash, Glamorgan.

The construction of the Tredegar Cottage Hospital fulfilled local ambition without any public authority aid. A landowner gifted the site for the building. The capital cost of the initiative was ultimately met from workers' contributions. The publically declared donations by the Tredegar Company aided fund raising, and it gave Alfred Tallis and other company officials licence to engage in the scheme.

As an act of trust in the 'strength of the workmen's contributions', the Tredegar Company observed discretion about lending money to service payments associated with the hospital's capital expenditure.[14] Publicly, the hospital scheme's apparent financial debt prevailed until at least 1908. In January 1908, Mrs A. S. Tallis opened a new ward at the hospital to cater for women and children. A. S. Tallis praised the 'donation of £1,000 made by the workmen towards the hospital'. He further related that 'since the opening of the Hospital, four years ago, 126 in-patients had been treated and 918 out-patients, with 1,912 cases visited by district nurses'.[15] No record was found of the nursing staff's names during the hospital's first decade. However, in May 1916, Miss Gertrude Thomas, sister at the Research Hospital, Cambridge, was appointed matron of the Tredegar hospital.[16] Alfred Tallis became the hospital's figurehead, but the durability of his place in local life relied upon him successfully progressing the opening of a new colliery.

Oakdale Navigation Collieries Limited

On Saturday the 20th April 1907, at one o'clock in the afternoon, Mrs Lucy Markham cut the first sod to mark the founding of Oakdale Colliery.[17] William Clay Hepburn was the manager made responsible by the Tredegar Company for the Oakdale sinkings. The colliery's name was a departure from the company's custom of saluting the surname of a director, but its origin remains to be found. No geographical feature in the vicinity of the new sinkings carried the Welsh language's equivalent of Oakdale, 'Dyffryn Derwen'. The extent of the Oakdale's mining property was 2,900 acres.[18] The colliery's coal reserves were estimated to be 80 million tons.[19]

Oakdale Colliery's coal property was leased from landowners other than the Tredegar Estate. The surface ground for the sinking lay roughly on the 650 foot contour on the edge of a dell that elbowed into the eastern side of the Sirhowy Valley. The new colliery stood a mile north-north-east of the village of Blackwood, which was served by a L&NWR station. Regarding coal wagon traffic, the colliery was served by the GWR's Penar Branch line opened in 1886, which was used by a special train to bring the company's guests to witness the sod cutting ceremony.

Mrs Lucy Markham stands just to the left of the doorway into the marquee pitched for use at the cutting of the first sod for Oakdale Navigation Colliery.
A. S. Tallis Photograph Album, Courtesy of the Tallis Family

Scene of the cutting of the first sod ceremony on the 20th April 1907.
Mrs Lucy Markham is seen holding the ceremonial spade.
A. S. Tallis Photograph Album, Courtesy of the Tallis Family

An early stage in the construction of Oakdale Navigation Collieries. More or less at the centre of the photograph are shown the North Pits wooden headgear, used for sinking, and to its left the winding house. The substantial retaining wall is in the process of being built.

Pope/Parkhouse Archive

The ceremony attracted 'a large company of guests from London, the coal shipping ports of Cardiff, Barry, and Newport, and towns in the vicinity'. Some guests attended out of courtesy to the Tredegar Iron & Coal Company. The event was a stage for furthering commercial business. Nevertheless, it can be proposed, the attendance emphasised the high level of interest that a South Wales Coalfield colliery investment commanded in the first decade of the twentieth century. Moreover, many of the guests were a class of people who had prospered due to industry and commerce and not because of a landowner's income. Such people appreciated that private investment in the colliery was being staked upon the future of the steam coal market. A newspaper registered that the event was 'a red day in the upper part of the Sirhowy Valley, marking as it does the initiation of a great colliery enterprise'.[20]

Nonetheless, the Tredegar Company had acted with caution. The company had earlier formed a subsidiary company, Oakdale Navigation Collieries Limited. The subsidiary company's initial share capital was £200,000 with £50,000 allotted to the Tredegar Iron & Coal Company, and 'as and when additional money is required, it is proposed that further allotment of share capital, or issue of loan capital, be made available as the directors think advisable'.[21] Thus the directors also reserved the right to liquidate Oakdale Navigation Collieries Limited if it proved to be non-paying, so as to shield the Tredegar Company from financial liabilities. The circumspection of the company's directors was no doubt due to the sour lesson of the dark spot of 1899.

Lucy Markham's brief speech, after being handed a spade for her to dig into Sirhowy Valley ground, gave a hint of a likely hazard of sinking. Although received with loud cheers the wife of Arthur Markham said, 'I hope the directors will be successful in striking good, thick seams of coal without encountering water.' In around 1900, a trial sinking three miles south of the colliery site, at Gelligroes, was 'abandoned because of excess water'. Moreover, three decades earlier, the sinking of Pochin Colliery had been dogged by feeders of water.

Nevertheless, at the outset, the company's plan for Oakdale Colliery was much bolder than for McLaren Colliery. The lease taken by the Oakdale Navigation Collieries Limited enabled coal to be taken from at least, in descending order into the earth, the Mynyddislwyn seam, the Brithdir seam for household use, and the steam coal measures.

Regarding early references to Oakdale Colliery, in a list of South Wales and Monmouthshire collieries, it is linked with 'Gwrhay'.[22] The Nant Gwrhay, an eastern subsidiary to the Sirhowy River, drained a small valley a half a mile to the north of Oakdale Colliery. The 'Gwrhay' reference is thought to concern the Oakdale Company working a level in the small valley. The Mynyddislwyn seam, over the course of most of the previous century, had been accessed via Gwrhay levels. Three levels, and also a pit's shaft, appear to have been operated in the small valley before 1916 according to an Ordnance Survey map. In 1909, the Oakdale Company employed twenty miners at Gwrhay. The employment of workers at the Gwrhay operation peaked at 101 for several years before, and including, 1918, when mining ceased.[23] The Oakdale Company further purchased the Waterloo Level, opened in 1815 and named to mark Wellington's defeat of Napoleon in battle. The level, or levels, since two are marked on the aforementioned Ordnance Survey map, lay adjacent to, and to the east of, the Oakdale Colliery sinkings.

Oakdale Colliery's 'principal' sinkings of two shafts, later differentiated as the North and South Pits, each twenty-one feet in diameter, were sunk to a steam coal seam reckoned to be at a depth of around 680 yards. The diameter of the shafts was equal to those sunk at Powell Duffryn's Penallta Colliery in the Rhymney Valley between 1906 and 1910. Such a shaft diameter was greater than others sunk before in the South Wales Coalfield. The North Pit was made the colliery's upcast that also involved ventilating the Waterloo Pit, dealt with shortly.

The North Pit was to be 'made available for working' Old Coal 'when desired'. At the outset, the company made a decision to

The construction at a similar stage but looking in the opposite direction. Note the wagon on the right lettered for Tredegar Brick Works.

Pope/Parkhouse Archive

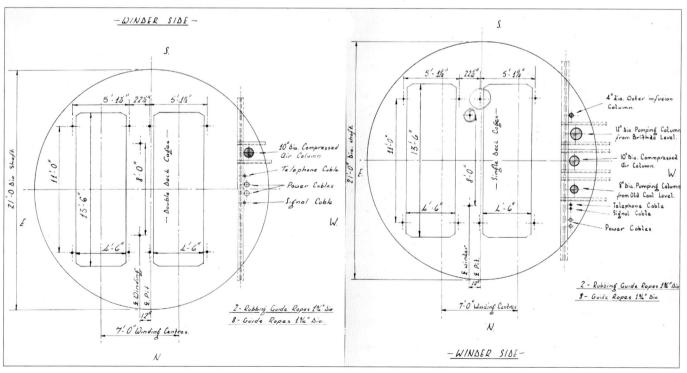

Two shaft layout diagrams for Oakdale Colliery. On the left is the one for South Pit, to the right that for North Pit. The diagrams show how the cages were arranged to give space in the shaft for pipework etc. The cages in the South Pit were double deck, those in the North Pit were single deck. Both shafts had rope guides.

National Coal Board South Western Division No. 6 Area Drawings No. ADO SK.627 and SK.727 dated 15-10-62; A. J. Edwards collection

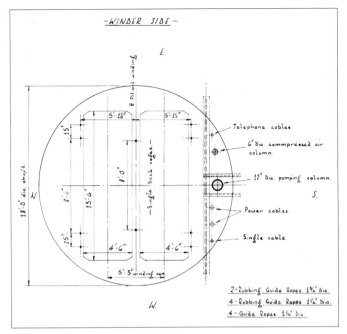

─ WINDER SIDE ─

Telephone cables

6" dia. commpressed air column.

12" dia. pumping column.

Power cables

Single cable

2 - Rubbing Guide Ropes 1¾" dia.
4 - Rubbing Guide Ropes 1¼" dia.
4 - Guide Ropes 1¼" Dia

Waterloo Pit Diagram Oakdale Colliery
National Coal Board South Western Division No. 6 Area Drawing No. ADO SK.726 dated 15-10-62; A. J. Edwards Collection

postpone working of the colliery's lowest seam in the steam coal measures, the Old Coal. The finding of 'excess water' during the Gelligroes trial sinking warned that there was a higher chance of flooding in the lowest coal seam compared with upper seams.[24]

With regard to working the Brithdir seam, the Oakdale Company sank a shaft of sixteen feet in diameter, and called it the Waterloo Pit. In 1909-10, 100 workers were employed at Waterloo Pit.

The Tredegar Company put its people in charge of managing the Oakdale Colliery venture. In 1907, the duties of the Tredegar Company's E. Wilson Taylor, and Alfred Tallis, were widened to include accountability for the colliery. Wilson Taylor and Tallis were appointed respectively managing director and general manager of the Tredegar Company in July 1906.[25] Messrs Scott and Leggatt of Cardiff were appointed consulting electrical engineers to the company. Offices at Tredegar appear to have been the base for the complement of engineers, surveyors, and maybe draughtsmen assigned to design, order the plant and machinery, layout, and construct the colliery.

By April 1907, 'a large number of men' were already employed excavating ground to build engine houses. The engineering of the colliery was to span a number of years, and maybe those involved became so focused that they gave little attention to other matters.

Profits, Coal Prices, and Politics

The 1907 annual report for the Tredegar Iron & Coal Company detailed a profit on working accounts of £128,603 16s. 1d., and that 1,604,599 tons of coal had been raised by its collieries. The company's capital spend during the year reported was £27,393 16s. 1d. The net profit was stated at £123,051 8s, and the directors proposed a shareholders' dividend of 7½ per cent. During the spring 1906 there was 'little movement in the prices of coal … but an upward tendency developed in the autumn [of 1906] and the high level which was subsequently reached' was maintained. In 1906, the average price per ton of large steam coal was 12.s. 4d., but in 1907 it rose to 14s. 9d.[26]

In July 1907, the company's directors correctly predicted a 'satisfactory' business outlook due to being in a 'position to take advantage of the enhanced prices'.[27] Thus, for the year preceding the end of March 1908, the company returned a net profit for distribution to shareholders of £183,276, which represented a peak

amount during the first decade of the twentieth century. In 1908, the shareholders were paid a lucrative ten per cent dividend.[28]

Early in July 1908, the House of Commons debated the Coal Mines (Eight Hours) (No.2) Bill. The debaters included Keir Hardie and two directors of the company, Arthur Markham and Sir Charles McLaren.[29] James Keir Hardie (1850-1934) was the Labour Party Member of Parliament for Merthyr Tydfil. Hardie, a Scot and a socialist, first made his mark as a young militant miners' leader in the Ayrshire Coalfield.

In the Coal Mines (Eight Hours) (No. 2) debate, the Merthyr Tydfil MP contested that the 'great question was whether the Bill would increase the cost of production'. One of Hardie's arguments was that 'the profits now being made in the coal trade were amply sufficient to meet the increase of the costs'. He then detailed the 'enormous profits' made by a number of coal companies across the British Coalfield before advocating that the profits could be used 'to meet the extra cost without calling upon the customer'.[30] A taunt of his appeared to be directed at North of England coal owners, but it might have had a more general intention. The coal owners 'were the men, who out of their bloated dividends were providing money to mislead the country in regard' to this Bill.

The MP for Mansfield spoke in support of the Bill after Hardie. Arthur Markham began by observing that 'all prices were mere speculation and must of course, be determined by the state of the market for the time being. It was impossible and indeed ridiculous that any Member of the House should say that the price of coal would increase …' Afterwards, in a subsequent contribution to the debate, he declared that he and Sir Charles McLaren were directors in a 'large company in South Wales which produced 1,500,000 tons of coal per annum', viz. the Tredegar Company. Markham then took issue with William Brace, MP for South Glamorgan. He held that Brace ought to have based his speech's review of profits made by South Wales coal companies upon 'a fair average'. Indeed for 1908-1909, the Tredegar Iron & Coal Company returned a lower profit than the year previous, £93,419 and a lower dividend, five per cent.[31] He further contested that the House of Commons had heard a flawed appreciation of the factors that shaped profit making. The 'Socialist party', he carped, told people regarding the distribution of profit that miners 'received 5 per cent and the owners 95 per cent. He then stated:

> For every £1 paid in wages the companies got 2s. 6d., or in other words for every £100 paid in wages profit was £12 10s. If a Socialistic Government took over the mines, as the Hon. Member for Merthyr Tydfil desired, there would only be an addition of £12 10s. on every £100 paid in wages at present. That was of course after allowing for all the costs of equipping and sinking collieries and interest on the capital involved … There was no use referring to special collieries. Coal mining depended on whether the conditions were favourable. Good collieries could make money whilst other collieries adjoining lost money.

Markham ended his speech observing that 'from his own experience, he believed that the profit made on coal-mining as an average was not 6 per cent on the capital value'.

Concerning the 'cost that would be entailed by the Bill', Arthur Markham asserted that it 'depended entirely on the men themselves'. In the South Wales Coalfield men 'worked longer hours than any other part of the country, except some districts of Lancashire'. Yet, the adoption of eight hour per shift, double shift working in the South Wales Coalfield was unlikely since 'the men had always raised possible objections to the modern methods of working'.

Although Sir Charles McLaren predicted an extra shilling rise in the cost of South Wales coal if the Bill was passed, he supported the Eight Hours' movement. After declaring he 'was largely interested in South Wales' he pronounced that 'he was prepared to meet that increased cost without the slightest apprehension. Welsh coal was an article of first necessity not only in this country, but all over the world, and if they must have Welsh coal they must be prepared to pay the price'. He further foresaw that the 'men would get better conditions of labour, and it would necessarily reduce profits of the producer of coal. If he got the shilling out of his foreign customers, he did not see why he should not cheerfully support the Bill'.

If Tredegar Company workers were worried about the prospects of reduced incomes due to working reduced hours due to an Eight Hours Act of Parliament, some Westminster news gave them cause for cheer. In 1909, the Liberal Chancellor of the Exchequer, David Lloyd George, tabled his 'People's Budget'. Moreover, concerning the residents of Abertysswg, in October 1909 they looked forward to using a new facility that promised to be of benefit to their social lives.

Abertysswg Library and Institute[32]

Members of Parliament Henry D. McLaren and Thomas Richards united to lay foundation stones for a library and institute building at Abertysswg. The October day was one of continuous torrential rain. Torrents of water rushed down the surrounding hillsides. The services of Captain W. H. Price and his 'gallant' fire brigade enabled the ceremony to take place. The ceremony's guests dutifully left shelter 'under the hospitable roof' of the McLaren Arms Hotel to witness brief acts of masonry.

The architect of the Abertysswg Library and Institute was A. F. Webb, Alfred Tallis's brother-in-law, whose earlier work included buildings in Tredegar and Blackwood. His Abertysswg building enabled both self-motivated ordinary people to further their education in an extramural way, and local cultural and leisure activities to be organised. The building's plan comprised: a lending library of 3,000 volumes; a librarian's office; a general reading room; and a ladies' room. A concert hall to seat 700 people occupied the building's upper floor. Other rooms were provided such as two 'large committee rooms', and 'retiring rooms' for artistes. The electric lighting, and heating 'by low pressure hot water pipes' made the building a convivial gathering place.

The building's budget was £3,280. The 'best red facing bricks' and Forest of Dean stone dressings were some of the materials that the workers of Fleur-de-lis builder, Theo. Matthews, used to construct the library and institute.

Ainon Chapel was the stage for speeches after the foundation stones were laid. David Aggex, deputy manager of McLaren Colliery, spoke first. He recounted that initially the 'workmen at Abertysswg had formulated a scheme for the library and institute and they purposed paying half-penny a week towards the maintenance and to get the management of it'. An ambition of a workmen's committee was to grow the library's stock of books and literature. In 1909, James Davies was the chief spokesman of the committee with D. O. Williams its secretary. The committee was also keen to have a place for 'concerts, entertainments, and eisteddfodau, and meeting together'. Building plans were shared with Alfred Tallis who 'helped them a good deal in the matter'. With workmen's support, 'a penny a week towards defraying the expenses of such a building, and getting the books to cultivate their minds', the committee took action.

The thirty years old Liberal MP for West Staffordshire, son of the company's chairman, paid tribute to the workmen's committee for their 'enterprise' after Aggex's speech. The Eton, and Balliol College, Oxford, educated Henry Duncan McLaren thought 'that the work of building an institute like theirs was a remedy for many of the social evils they suffered'. Men and women could 'gather together for talking and reading and various pastimes'. Moreover, an institute was 'also a very good counter attraction to the public house'. He believed that the committee had 'set an admirable example for other towns, and districts less fortunately situated than theirs'.

That evening Ainon Chapel was the venue for a Liberal Party meeting at which Rev. E. Roberts spoke in favour of the Chancellor of the Exchequer's 1909 budget. 'He was sure that all Liberals and working men could approve a policy of

placing the heaviest burden on the broadest shoulders'. Henry McLaren supported the motion by highlighting the budget's three objects: the extension of an Old Age Pension; 'to provide for a larger navy'; and to raise money to make effective social reforms. It has been said that the budget gave birth to the Welfare State, but the Chancellor of the Exchequer, David Lloyd George, asserted that it was 'a war budget'. Thus, the Liberal Government was enabled to fund the building of eight Dreadnought class battleships, which would need Welsh steam coal to power their propulsion systems.

Lib-Lab

Thomas Richards did not attend the Liberal Party meeting at Ainon Chapel. He had entered the House of Commons as the Liberal Member for the West Monmouthshire constituency after a by-election in 1904. His absence from the meeting was due to a radical change in the way that the Miners' Federation of Great Britain engaged with national politics. Roy Gregory, writing in 1968, considered that within Welsh mining communities 'at the turn of the [twentieth] century the stuff of politics was still the grievances of nonconformity and of Welsh nationalism, and the Liberal party was still the vehicle of protest, uniting all classes in opposition to the established church and the English gentry'.[33] Although in West Monmouthshire Welsh nationalism was a weak force due to the area being home to a growing Anglo-Welsh population, other facts support Roy Gregory's view. For example, from 1885 up to and including the 1900 general election, the constituency vote favoured the Liberal candidate. No 'fiery militant brand of Socialism' challenged the Liberals in the constituency. Indeed, it would seem true to conclude that: 'Loyalty to the Liberals', during the period defined above, 'went very deep among Welsh miners, and, for all the undoubted unrest in the coalfield, a new political party, breaking fresh ground, could not help but find the going hard'.[34]

Between 1900 and 1902, regarding its parliamentary representation policy, the Miners' Federation of Great Britain aligned with the Liberal Party through co-operation with Liberal Associations.[35] In 1904, Thomas Richards, the general secretary of the SWMF, was adopted 'with the greatest of reluctance' as the Liberal candidate for the West Monmouthshire constituency.[36] Some middle-class based Liberal Associations were opposed to working class trade unionists using an alliance with Liberals to stand for Parliament. Arthur Markham was a pragmatist about the Lib-Lab alliance as his conduct up until circa 1910 in Derbyshire reveals.[37] Regardless, Richards, as a 'Lib-Lab', pronounced that 'he knew the Liberal programme and enthusiastically supported every item of it' when he first canvassed for votes in West Monmouthshire.[38]

The election of Thomas Richards and his kind to Parliament, though, gifted a local Socialist agitator a lever for promoting dissent. An agitator could propound a thought among miners: coal owner Liberal MPs would safeguard their interests ahead of their miners when labour issues were raised in Parliament.

Then, in 1909, the MFGB 'belatedly followed the example of all the other major unions and joined the Labour Party'.[39] Thus, Richards's sponsor, the Miners' Federation of Great Britain, asked him to resign the Liberal whip and take the Labour one. Significantly, with hindsight, the die was cast. The political bond made between miners' leaders in the South Wales Coalfield and the Labour Party became a factor in South Wales Coalfield miners spurning Liberalism for Socialism. In 1911, a branch of the Independent Labour Party was formed at Tredegar.

However, Thomas Richards's switch in political party allegiances did not appear to alter his conciliatory attitude towards coal owners like the Tredegar Company. During his speech at the laying Abertysswg institute's foundation stone he declared a hope: 'That the joint operation of today will always be continued, and that the institute may be a common ground for both masters and men where all differences may be amicably settled.'

Government Actions

The year 1909, when the 1908 Coal Mines (Eight Hours) Act came into operation, was judged by Arthur Markham in June 1910 to be an 'anxious' one for the Tredegar Company. Nevertheless, he claimed that the company won the 'most hearty cooperation of the men' for applying the Act. The 'tact of Mr Tallis', he believed, during associated negotiations had fostered such cooperation.[40] Nonetheless, in 1911, the company's collieries lost four days to stoppages due to matters associated with the Eight Hours Act.[41]

Following the abandonment of the Sliding Scale the coal owners and miners' union representatives agreed to operate a Conciliation Board to settle worker wages in the South Wales Coalfield. However, the introduction of the Eight Hours Act caused the coal owners of the coalfield to seek 'a rearrangement' of the end date of the Conciliation Board agreement. A rearrangement was agreed but on the 1st January 1910, the workers' representatives gave notice 'that they wished to terminate the agreement'. After a further 'number of meetings' between both parties it 'was found impossible' to reach 'a mutual agreement'. An initiative by the Government's Board of Trade led to an agreement between the parties, and this was signed on the 8th April 1910.[42]

Crumlin Rescue Station

Another department of Government had earlier used the threat of more legislation, advocated by the Liberal Home Secretary, Herbert Gladstone, to cause the South Wales Coalfield coal owners to provide colliery rescue services.[43] Thus, in the year 1910, a milestone event in the history of coal mining in Monmouthshire occurred. In July, the Crumlin Rescue Station was opened. The station became the second after Aberaman's in the Monmouthshire and South Wales Coalowners' Association scheme for 'better protection of the lives of the men employed in the South Wales Coalfield'.[44] The Tredegar Company was not represented at the opening. However, by April 1912, the company subscribed money to the Monmouthshire Collieries Rescue Association, formed on the 31st December 1911. Thereafter subscriptions from around two dozen Monmouthshire coal companies were pooled by the Association so that the costs of the Crumlin Rescue Station's building and plant, equipment, and running expenses were met.[45]

Opening of Abertysswg Workmen's Institute[46]

In July 1910, the Abertysswg Library and Institute, known familiarly as the Workmen's Institute, was opened. Henry D. McLaren MP attended the event with another director of the company, Lt-Colonel A. K. Wyllie. Lady McLaren had been invited to perform the opening ceremony, but her son informed that at a 'late hour' she 'had an urgent message from the Young Women's Liberal Federation, of which she was president and treasurer. The question they had to consider was the policy of the Association in regards to votes for women'. Mrs A. S. Tallis carried out the ceremony using a golden key to unlock the door of the building.

Another aspect of Henry McLaren's speech drew much applause. He recounted that his mother, a company shareholder, 'desired to promote the welfare of those who lived in the villages [associated with the company]'. He then said: 'We are not here as directors solely for profit. We are responsible for the well-being and happiness of those we employ. We are bound up together. You can say I am only seeking for the success of the Tredegar Company. Gentlemen you are as much a part of the Tredegar Iron and Coal Company as I am. Our responsibilities are the same. We depend upon you and you depend upon us. Your welfare and happiness depends upon the success of the Tredegar Company. It would, indeed, be very wrong to consider this responsibility does not extend to the wives and children of our employees. We consider as much their welfare as we do the commercial success of the Company.'

As a public statement, his declaration espoused a coal company's aspirations, but the relationship between a coalowner and colliery workers was a complicated one. Around the same year, Arthur Markham's sister, Violet, a progressive Liberal, led a social venture in a new mining community, Woodlands, situated in Yorkshire.[47] Decades later she reflected: 'a mining community … looked no less askance at the sister of a capitalist and owner who talked brightly about drawing neighbours together and suggested clubs and classes to that end'. The suspicion she met was 'wholly intelligible'. 'You cannot in the history of an industry disregard every human factor and in practice, if not in theory, treat workers like automatic machines for making money, and then expect a fine flowering of the human spirit among such men'.[48]

Nonetheless, Henry McLaren ended his speech expressing the hope that the institute 'would become the centre of life and a place of healthy recreation and instruction'. Since the Abertysswg Library and Institute was the idea of local workers, Violet Markham's observations might be discounted. Yet, he also advocated that the building be a 'venue for political instruction'. Was his mind open to the prospect of the institute becoming a school for Socialist learning?

Lt-Colonel Wyllie revealed in his address that the Tredegar Company had donated a total of £600 to the cost of the institute. He then extended praise to the colliery workers 'subscribing their penny per week' to the cost fund. 'You and we will jointly see this thing through,' he added. Although the company underwrote the cost of the institute as work on it progressed, it did so in trust that the workmen would reimburse the company the money.

The institute was set to realise the expectations of the village's community. An eisteddfod was held at the building that year's month of August, and became a regular event for years afterwards. Abertysswg men honed competitive skills in billiards at the institute. In 1916, a team representing the village won the first division of a Rhymney Valley billiards league.[49] The institute became a training ground for many billiard and snooker players, and some of them reached a world class standard.

Miners' Reasonableness

For a period around 1910 Henry McLaren was one of the owners' representatives on 'The Board of Conciliation for the Coal Trade of Monmouthshire and South Wales'. During his 1910 speech at Abertysswg he stated that he 'was proud' to be associated with the workers' representatives for West Monmouthshire, William Brace, Walter Lewis, and Alfred Onions, and saluted Thomas Richards MP. He judged that 'the present Conciliation Board was one of the best things they ever had. They knew that by careful deliberations peace had been maintained in the coalfields for many years'. McLaren further praised 'the [company's] miners on their reasonableness and the integrity of their representatives'. It would seem that his father's wish, to 'engender a feeling of friendship between master and man', had been cultivated between the Tredegar Company, as a master, and the representatives of their workmen. However, were William Brace, Walter Lewis, and Alfred Onions more accommodating as union leaders than others in the South Wales Coalfield?

After August 1910 a workers' strike endemic spread from the Rhondda Valley's Cambrian Combine's Ely Pit across the South Wales Coalfield.[50] By September, production at collieries in the Rhymney and Monmouthshire Valleys came to a halt. Although colliery workers in the Rhondda and Aberdare Valleys were to stay on strike for many months, the Tredegar Company's annual report for 1910-11 does not mention any colliery stoppages due to the strike.

However, sustaining any amicable relations between coal owners and miners' leaders into the future was doubtful. David Evans, in his 1911 appraisal of the 1910 strikes, thought that tension existed within the SWMF between its established leaders and some of its younger miners' agents. He identified that some of the 'younger leaders' were 'Socialist imbued with Communistic theories concerning the relations of Capital and Labour'. The objective of such young leaders' agitation was to bring forward the day when the workers took over the means of production.

In June 1910, Arthur Markham chaired the annual Tredegar Company meeting of shareholders. He was roused to respond to what he judged to be 'pure and unadulterated nonsense' circulating about 'labour's share of the profits'. His 'notice' had been 'called a few months ago to a statement that for every £3 earned [by the capitalist] the worker got one'. Regarding the Tredegar Company, he tabled that 'the dividend represented 10 per cent of the wages they paid—for every pound they paid the men got 18s. and the company 2s'. The two shillings, he went on to say, 'represented the return to the shareholders for their capital embarked, and although they put money to reserve it was not more than necessary for depreciation which occurred in all mines'.[51] Although Markham did not identify who was advancing an analysis of labour's share of the profits that differed from his own, it seems likely that he was attempting to defend capitalism against its critics. However, he opted not to augment his analysis with a disclosure about the Tredegar Company's expenditure upon worker welfare, mine's rescue, and health initiatives.

Abertysswg Cottage Hospital[52]

In late 1911, Miss Mary Edith Humphrey became the first Matron of Abertysswg Workmen's Hospital. She had been trained as a nurse at the Royal Free Hospital, London, and afterwards held the position of Night Sister, and Sister of a male surgical ward.[53]

The unfurnished Abertysswg Cottage Hospital was opened earlier on Monday the 3rd October 1910, by 1st Viscount Tredegar using a golden key. Godfrey Charles Morgan, 2nd Lord Tredegar, was created Viscount Tredegar in 1905. The building, designed by A. F. Webb, and built by Theo. Watkins of Pengam, cost £2,500. The hospital featured: a men's ward for four beds; a private patients' ward; an up-to-date operating theatre; an equipped X-ray room; a consulting room; an out-patients' room; nurses' and matron's sitting rooms; kitchens; bathrooms; and a bedroom for staff.

The opening of the hospital was like a regal occasion. A special train brought Viscount Tredegar to Abertysswg. The music of the Abertysswg Silver Band added zest to the occasion. There was a 'large concourse of people'. Many people were well-dressed, which was a show of self-esteem among the villagers. The McLaren Arms Hotel was the venue for a luncheon and toasts.

The luncheon gave the area's landlord a stage for his wry wit in a speech. His presence caused Alfred Tallis, who spoke for the company's directors, to reflect upon the Tredegar Company's 'very dark spot'. Lord Tredegar was thanked for his 'generosity' at a time when the company was in a perilous financial state.

W. Stephen Davies, the company's agent, spoke before the general manager and addressed the topic of capital and labour. He was reported as saying:

'At the present time there was a tendency to accentuate differences between capital and labour, and one could not help feeling that although capital had its rights and labour had its rights, there was a difficulty in defining where one ended and the other began. In this undertaking [the founding of the hospital] both had joined together on one common platform to mitigate the sufferings which accrue to labour. He hoped the feelings of toleration and frankness that must arise from the consideration of mutual interests would be maintained. From experience he knew very well that when workmen and management were brought together to discuss matters a good feeling sprang up.'

Alfred Tallis also addressed the topic after declaring that 'the Tredegar Company was a prosperous company now'. 'He trusted that workmen and owners would combine to work in harmony together each doing the best they could for each other. He was afraid there were serious times ahead, and it behoved all of them to exercise patience and forbearance with each other, without trying to force their individual views down another's throat'.

The workers' spokesman was Mr J. Edwards, the deputy Rhymney Valley miners' agent. He acknowledged that 'everything in Abertysswg depended upon the company. The company was one of the strongest in Wales, he believed, and it had required a great deal of enterprise to push that place. He hoped that the workmen would continue to work hand in hand together. A great deal of the success had been due to Mr Tallis'.

Edwards's appraisal of the strength of the company, measured in terms of annual output of coal, in the South Wales Coalfield was true. By 1911, the Tredegar Company competed for the second spot in the coalfield's output league. The company's rivals for such a rank were Ocean Coal, Ebbw Vale, and GKN Limited (Dowlais).[54] Powell Duffryn Steam Coal Company stood top of the coalfield's league. Also in 1911, the company's chairman, Sir Charles McLaren, was raised to the peerage as Lord Aberconway of Bodnant.

Rhymney Valley Rescue Station

On Monday the 30th January 1911, the Rhymney Valley Rescue Station was opened at New Tredegar. The building's cost, £2,000, was shared between Powell Duffryn, the Rhymney Iron Company, and the Tredegar Iron & Coal Company. The station stood adjacent to Elliot Colliery, and was the third opened under the Monmouthshire and South Wales Coalowners' Association mines rescue scheme.

W. Stephen Davies, and John Evans, McLaren Colliery's manager, represented the Tredegar Company at the opening. Standing among many guests, they witnessed a rescue exercise performed by a squad representing the Aberaman Rescue Station. The exercise took place in 'galleries of the building … charged with smoke and sulphur'. Afterwards, W. Stephen Davies observed in a speech that 'as far as the partnership in this trinity of this present undertaking was concerned the Tredegar was the smallest'. Powell Duffryn was the dominant partner. Nonetheless, as a man who began work as an underground door boy, seemingly in the Mountain Ash district, Davies said 'that every one who held a responsible position in connection with colliery work looked upon any means of mitigating suffering with a favourable eye'.[55]

Nevertheless, commercially, the Tredegar Company would have been troubled after the 6th January 1911. 'Fearing interference with the regularity of their supplies [of coal] from South Wales on account of the stoppage of work at collieries there, a number of Liverpool shipowners turned their eyes northward to seek for supplies'.[56]

A year of the Great Unrest

The five year period from 1910 up to the outbreak of the Great War has sometimes been called the time of 'Great Unrest'. An epidemic of industrial disputes hit the economy of the United Kingdom during the period. Socialists, syndicalists,[57] and the trade union movement campaigned for worker control over the economic system.

In February 1911, Walter Lewis, the Rhymney Valley miners' agent, in contrast, held a sanguine outlook concerning industrial relations.[58] Regarding his union's relations with coal owners in the Rhymney Valley, he thought that 'they go on in a more desirable way than many other places'. Concerning his dealings with the valley's colliery officials, 'they managed to get around a table and discuss their differences and part as good friends as they could'.

At odds with such behaviour, in August 1911 two hundred men ran amok in Tredegar. Shops, mainly owned by Jewish people, were damaged and rifled. A. S. Tallis, as a Justice of Peace, coordinated action to bring law and order to the district. The Riot Act was read twice. Police force and a contingent of Worcester Regiment soldiers were used to deal with the trouble. However, 'hundreds' Tredegar people publically 'made clear their support for those convicted' of crimes that occurred during the riot.[59] Across the South Wales Coalfield, more or less coinciding with the Tredegar riot, other Jewish shops were subjected to attacks.

The 'ant-Jewish' riots in the coalfield have since 'attracted a surprisingly large literature, especially among historians concerned with British anti-Semitism'.[60] In 1997, W. D. Rubenstein

OAKDALE COLLIERY, SHOWING SIDINGS.

PUB. BY CHIVERS,
OAKDALE POST OFFICE.

Sinking began in 1907 and was completed in 1911 for Oakdale Navigation Collieries Limited, a Tredegar Iron & Coal Company subsidiary. On the left is headgear of the Waterloo Pit, for working the Red Ash otherwise known as the Brithdir seam. The two headgears on the right are the North Pit (left) and South Pit (right) for working the steam coal seams. The power-house's cooling towers stand behind, but just to the right of Waterloo Pit. The two van style railway vehicles that can be seen also appear in the view of the special train on the occasion of the cutting of the first sod (page 94) where it can be discerned that one was lettered 'Oakdale Colliery'. That in the view here both vehicles are isolated leads to questions as to their exact use.

Pope/Parkhouse Archive

Philip Hatfield Photography.A.J. Edwards Collection

Right: Oakdale Lamp Check

discounted that the riots were premeditated, considered that the 'anti Jewish component' had 'constantly been exaggerated', and observed that the 'great majority of Welsh people demonstrably reacted to these riots with horror'.[61] He also noted that 'a number of specific economic causes of hostility to Jewish shopkeepers were offered in the local press at the time especially the alleged 'rack-renting' of one Jewish property-owner in Tredegar, and claims that some Jewish shopkeepers had unjustifiably raised the prices of necessary commodities after the two days' railway strike'.[62]

However, if any Tredegar Company worker took part in the riot then it was not due to a shortage of money in their pockets. 'An abnormal percentage of miners' absented 'themselves from work in the [Tredegar Company] pits' in the summer of 1911 due to it being 'exceptionally hot'.[63]

In June 1912, the Tredegar Company attributed a part of the fall in its coal output to 'serious labour troubles which had affected the South Wales Coalfield throughout a greater part of the year [1911-1912]'. The company's annual coal production fell from 1,822,933 tons the previous year [1910-1911] to 1,558,821 tons. The company did not elaborate upon the nature of the labour troubles, but it seems likely the company's operation was disrupted by at least a railway strike and a seamen's dispute. Nevertheless, the Tredegar district saw none of the worker militancy that upset life in the Aberdare and Rhondda Valleys particularly in 1910. Indeed, as a contrast, the Tredegar Company's directors broadcasted in 1912 that the 'relations between the company and the men continue to be of a friendly character'.[64]

Nevertheless, people in Tredegar may have been troubled by Alfred Markham's declaration in mid-1910 that 'it would not be necessary to sink any more pits on the Tredegar royalty'. Candidly he added that the 'future of the company so much depended' upon Oakdale.[65]

Engineering Oakdale Colliery

At Oakdale Colliery 'sinking was … completed to the steam coal measures in 1911'.[66] The South Pit, the downcast and commissioned as the colliery's winding shaft, was sunk 680 yards to the Upper Rhas Las for steam coal. Much later in the life of the colliery, the term 'Nine Feet' was preferred to Rhas Las. The North Pit was sunk to 685 yards, but was later deepened

to 720 yards to work the Old Coal (later labelled as either 'Five-Feet' or 'Gellideg'). The Waterloo Pit sinking was 'much delayed by water', but at 286 yards, the Red Ash seam, locally called the Brithdir, was opened.

The Tredegar Company's 1923 history claimed that Oakdale Colliery was 'equipped with the most modern and up-to-date appliances'.[67] A comparison between Oakdale Colliery and Powell Duffryn's Rhymney Valley Penallta Colliery, sunk in 1906, offers a test of that claim.[68]

At Oakdale Colliery, two winding houses were erected to serve the colliery's steam coal pits. By 1907, such an arrangement for winding was outmoded. The winding house built at Penallta Colliery accommodated two steam winding engines.[69] Moreover, the Penallta Colliery boiler plant lay adjacent to the winding engines so piped steam heat losses were minimised.

Ten Babcock & Wilcox double drum water tube boilers were erected to raise steam at Oakdale Colliery. A mechanical chain grate stoker fed coal into the combustion chamber of each boiler. The steam was piped a distance to the winding engines. In the case of supplying steam to the North and Waterloo Pits the length of piping was considerable. The length of steam pipe runs at Oakdale Colliery meant that more heat was wasted before powering winding engines than at Penallta Colliery. The boiler steam losses also meant that the Tredegar Company forfeited an amount of saleable steam coal.

Water for the colliery's steam raising plant was piped from Penyfan Pond,[70] sited on the 1,000 foot contour of Mynydd Pen-y-Fan, a southern continuation of Cefn Manmoel. The pond had been engineered as a water reservoir for the Ebbw Vale spur of the Monmouthshire canal system.

Regarding the choice of steam winding engines for Oakdale Colliery, British coal industry convention was followed. Oakdale Colliery's South Pit engine was of the simple type having cylinders of 42-inch diameter by 7 feet stroke, and operated with steam gauged at 120 lb/in². A simple type of steam winding engine was also installed at the North Pit and featured 36-inch diameter cylinders by 7 feet stroke. Coal from the Waterloo Pit was raised by a simple type of steam winder with cylinders of 22-inch diameter by 5 feet stroke. Powell Duffryn contemplated using electric winding at Penallta Colliery, but after economic

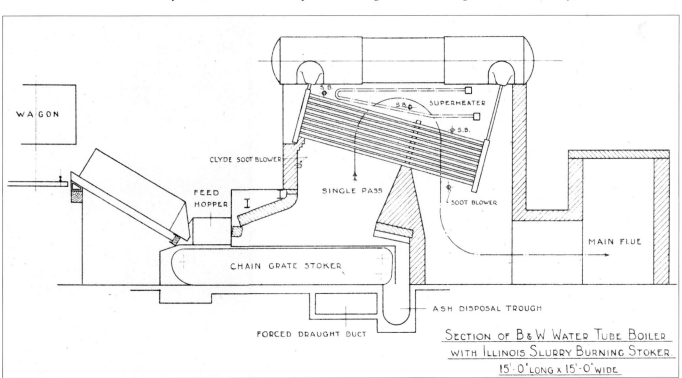

Section through a Babcock & Wilcox boiler used at Oakdale Colliery.
Folio of Technical Information – Oakdale and Wyllie Collieries, compiled by Jack Edwards circa 1946. A. J. Edwards Collection

comparisons opted for powerful compound winding engines. Powell Duffryn had already learnt from experience at its Bargoed Colliery that compound winding engines wasted less coal for steam powering than simple engines.[71]

Selecting a winding engine supplier seemed at the time to be an easy matter. Twenty-three United Kingdom winding engine builders traded according to a survey of the period circa 1880 to 1910.[72] Maybe vested interests guided the choice made for Oakdale Colliery since its winding engines were made by Markham & Company, Broad Oaks Iron Works, Chesterfield. The winding engine company made its first engine around 1869, and survived nearly eighty years designing and building steam winding engines, which suggests they enjoyed a favourable reputation.[73] Indeed, a neighbouring coal owner in the Ebbw Vale was persuaded by the merits of Markham & Co winding engines since two of them were installed circa 1908 at Navigation Colliery, Crumlin.[74] No ties were found between the owner of Navigation Colliery and the Chesterfield winding engine maker.

All the winding engines at Oakdale Colliery drove semi-conical drums, which were an advance in winding drum design.[75] The pioneer of the design was Powell Duffryn, whose term for it was 'semi-spiral drum'. The semi-spiral drum became a British coal industry standard, and known by the term 'bi-cylindro-conical' drum.[76] By 1965, the North Pit winding drum wound a rope of 1¼ inch in diameter rope whereas the South Pit's rope was 1⅞ inch diameter. Latch and Batchelor then supplied the ropes at lengths of 834 yards for both pits.[77]

One building on the surface of Oakdale Colliery, due to its duty, size and capacity of its installed machinery, merited attention for being modern. The power-house would become an electrical power station of some significance. By 1905, Powell Duffryn operated from Middle Duffryn an electrical power scheme to serve its Aberdare Valley collieries, which was a major technical advance in the history of the South Wales Coalfield.[78] Although the Oakdale Colliery power-house arrived shortly after Powell Duffryn's Aberdare Valley development, the Tredegar Company was well practised in the use of electric power and ably directed technically by consultant electrical engineers W. A. Scott and his associate, Leggatt.[79]

The initial investment in electric power at Oakdale Colliery did not fully use the power-house's floor space. The building's size was set in anticipation of future colliery developments in the locality, which are described later. In 1911, installed in the power-house were two 1,000 kW mixed pressure turbo-alternators, generating 3,000 V, and 50 Hz, and believed to have been supplied by Willans-Dick Kerr. The electric power was initially used for sinking pumps, ventilating fans, haulage, and other surface requirements. The power supplied at 3,000 volts was reduced to 500 volts for sinking pump operation.[80]

Regarding colliery ventilation, Oakdale Colliery's plant and equipment was equal to the best then being deployed in the British coal industry like that at Penallta Colliery. Installed at Oakdale Colliery were two Sirocco fans, each 154 inches in diameter. Powell Duffryn installed identical sized Sirocco fans at Penallta Colliery.[81] Such a Sirocco fan moved 500,000ft³ of air per minute at 6-inch water gauge. At Oakdale Colliery one of the fans, commissioned in 1913, was steam driven by a Belliss compound vertical engine whilst the other, commissioned in 1909, was a variable speed electric motor of the Cascade type supplied by Oerlikon.[82] Thus in the case of the failure of electricity there was a backup mechanical contingency available.

The respective heights of the Oakdale's South and North Pits' steel lattice headgears, height being defined as the vertical distance from the pit bank to the centre line of the sheave, were 78 ft 6 in and 83 ft. Both structures were supplied by Rees & Kirby, Morriston. Sheaves – sometimes called pulleys – of twenty feet in diameter spinning on the South and North Pits' headgears indicated winding in progress. The Waterloo Pit's headgear was 55ft high and it supported sixteen feet diameter sheaves.[83] By 1965, wound at the Waterloo Pit were flattened strand ropes sized at 1⅝ inch. Latch and Batchelor then supplied the ropes at a length of 410 yards.[84]

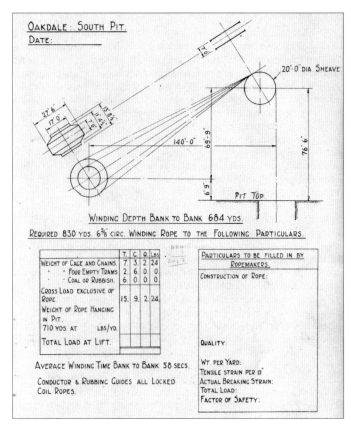

Oakdale Navigation Collieries - Particulars of Ropes - South Pit.
Folio of Technical Information – Oakdale and Wyllie Collieries, compiled by Jack Edwards circa 1946. A. J. Edwards collection

Each pit was assigned a duty. The North Pit moved men and materials, and at the outset its cages were single decked. In 1930, the plan was to introduce double decked cages to raise Old Coal at a 'later date'. However, a survey in 1969 of the colliery's shaft capacities suggests that no such action was ever taken.[85] Regarding winding at the Waterloo Pit single deck cages were used. The cages that shuttled up and down the South Pit had two decks so that four trams were carried. One lift of a South Pit cage brought five tons of mined coal to the colliery's surface.[86] The accumulation in weight of saleable coal raised to the pit bank was the ultimate measure of whether, or not, the investment in colliery buildings, plant and machinery was worthwhile.

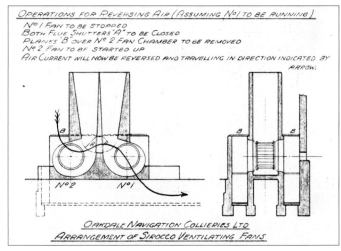

Oakdale Navigation Collieries Ltd – Arrangement of Sirocco Fans. Drawing dated 8th April, 1927.
Folio of Technical Information – Oakdale and Wyllie Collieries, compiled by Jack Edwards circa 1946. A. J. Edwards Collection

Underground Development Phase

In 1911, as the South Pit's shaft neared the desired Upper Rhas Las seam, the sinkers met geological disturbances, faults. William Hepburn's reading of the geology in the vicinity of the bottom of South Pit gave rise to ideas that the disturbances ran east and west, which later proved to be the case. Of equal interest to him was the thickness of the Lower Coal Measures defined as the distance between the Brithdir seam and the Rhas Las seam. In 1922, the thickness at Oakdale Colliery was reckoned to be 481 yards. At Llanhilleth Colliery, 2½ miles north-east of Oakdale, the thickness was 296 yards whilst at Cwmcarn Colliery, 4½ miles south-east of Oakdale, it was approximately 250 yards.[87] Nonetheless, Hepburn's mining plan was to drive a main road, in the form of a level, into the Upper Rhas Las seam.

However, the supposed Upper Rhas Las was soon found to present another problem of nature. 'The roof of the seam which is 4 ft to 5 ft thick is a close-grained "clift" of argillaceous shale, whilst the floor is fireclay'. Clift was a general term used in the South Wales Coalfield to describe many types of shales, and in terms of relative strengths of rocks, clift was among the weakest. Clays were the weakest of all rocks met in coal mining.

It is proposed that the Tredegar Iron Coal Company assigned from its other collieries a number of its most experienced miners for Oakdale Colliery's development phase.[88] William Hepburn knew that even such a gang of able miners would make slow progress. The use of dynamite in disturbed ground would have been viewed as foolish. Work, done with hand tools, involved awful conditions. The environment at the bottom of the shaft was warm and dusty. Poor ventilation prevailed until the Sirocco fans were commissioned. Worryingly for the company during the initial phase of opening out from the South Pit bottom,

variability in the coal yield was met. 'One week huge amounts of coal were wound whilst the next, supplies would run short. Elsewhere a seam five feet thick would dwindle, and almost disappear, a few yards along'.

Then, Tom Edmunds's gang of miners, having driven 100 yards 'to the east side' from the North Pit, experienced a roof fall. 'In the rubble' of the roof fall was noticed a 'much larger-lump of coal'. Then, on 'probing the hole created by the fall it was found that the real [Upper] Ras Las seam was there, the original had only been a secondary seam'. 'Discovered' was 'that the [Upper] Ras Las and Polka seam running separately at Pochin merged at Oakdale into one seam nine feet thick'.[89]

The discovery was potentially lucrative for the company, but made absurd the colliery's mining engineering plan. 'The South Shaft had been organised and laid out to take the most of the coal wound. To raise the pit bottom to the level of this newly discovered seam 'would create many difficulties and much financial strain' on Oakdale Navigation Collieries Limited. However, one consequence 'was a decision to raise the level of the North Shaft by thirty feet bringing the North "Pit Bottom" to the level of the new seam'. This was accomplished quickly partly since most of the 'sinking' team were still at Oakdale, 'many having decided to make, the new, modern colliery their permanent place of employment'. The emphasis *during* colliery development *then* switched to the North Pit from the South Pit, 'until this shaft could be brought into use'.[90]

Advancing a main underground roadway that was wide enough for two trams to run side involved experienced miners excavating and timbering the way forward supported by gangs of other miners. Horse pulled trams were led by hauliers to and from a pit bottom. As the roadway advanced other miners

General view of Pit Bottom Sidings at Oakdale Colliery.

Advanced Copy, Proceedings, SWIE, 1930

ensured that timbers installed were safe, and if not, made repairs. Skilled miners were ever alert to noises issuing from their surroundings so as to anticipate a roof fall.

The toilsome nature and scale of the foregoing work left a lasting impression. Nearly two decades later the company gave a seemingly vivid account of the work: 'As the road was driven through the pit pillar[91] (which has a diameter of approximately 680 yards) considerable difficulty was experienced in keeping them open. The crush was enormous and the fireclay also pucked,[92] or lifted very badly, and timber would last only a few days. On getting out of the pit pillar there was an improvement, but …These sections of roads often guttered up very badly and occasionally fell wide above the rock beds and were very difficult to timber and properly close.'[93]

Steel arch roof supports

Keeping open underground roads at Oakdale Colliery, during the development phase, proved to be 'prohibitively' expensive. For example, stone arches, side walls and girders placed near the pit bottom lasted 'very little time indeed', and had to be replaced. The acute need for a solution initiated the use of steel arch roof supports, first introduced at Oakdale Colliery in 1913, which were 'put in as fast as was possible.[94]

Manufacture of steel arch supports by the company was a benefit of hesitance over ending steelmaking. The company established around the cusp of the twentieth century a central engineering works at Tredegar. A small mill had been retained at the works to make rails of light section for the company's collieries.[95] The company's fifty year history registers colliery engineering innovations that it had introduced by the end of 1922, but omitted an appreciation of the company's achievement regarding steel arch roof supports.

During the period of years 1903-12, the annual average for fatalities in the mining industry of Britain was 1,313. The cause of 10 per cent of the fatalities was underground explosions. Press coverage of colliery disasters may have given the impression to people living outside mining communities that explosions were the main cause of miners' fatalities. However, it was the 'daily and regular toll of accidents due to isolated, and comparatively small falls of rock from the roof that, in the aggregate account, for the greater number of fatalities'. During the period of years 1903-12, forty-five per cent of colliery workers' deaths were due to falls of ground, either at the coal-face or associated roadways. At the start of the twentieth century there was clearly a humane reason 'for an improved method of supporting the roof and sides so that the coal-face and adjacent roadways should be kept free of falls and their attendant dangers'.[96]

'In the early days of the coal industry timber was relatively cheap, and was exclusively used in the maintenance of underground roadways'.[97] Timber props 'would creek and groan' and so alert colliery workers about a likely roof fall. As a rough guide to relative strengths, the tensile strength of mild steel is greater than dry Douglas Fir by a factor of 3.7.[98] Steel roof supports appear to have been first introduced around 1890 by W. W. Hood in the Rhondda Valley. With the removal of a coal seam the sheer weight of the strata could cause supports to buckle. Wooden pit props would snap in half. Steel supports, having an insufficient section, would fail abruptly. Into the 1920s the adoption of steel roof supports was generally discouraged in the South Wales Coalfield due to tradition, safety fears, and the practice of not moving timber from underground waste dumps.[99]

After 1913, the Tredegar Iron & Coal Company faced down tradition and advanced the use of steel roof supports. In 1920, the company revealed that at Oakdale Colliery the 'steel ring system', as it was called, 'had six times the life of timber supports, and was equally effective from the point of view of safety and of efficiency in allowing the officials to deal with the coal dust problem'.[100]

However, not until 1930, when Robert James presented a paper to the South Wales Institute of Engineers paper, 'Steel Arches and Steel Props for Underground Support', did the

company's innovation win wider notice. In the paper he noted that 'largely due to the pioneer work and perseverance of one or two collieries, and in particular the Tredegar Iron and Coal Company' the use of steel arching is 'rapidly extending' at least in the South Wales Coalfield. The evidence for the 'efficiency' of steel arching became apparent after the 1926 strike: 'From all quarters came evidence that in collieries where steel arches or other form of steel support had been in general use it was possible to re-open roadways to transport after little if any repair work'.[101]

In 1931-32, the acting president of the Institution of Mining Engineers declared with regard to steel arch girders that in 'South Wales there are more in use than in any other district'. He added: 'The Tredegar Steel & Coal Company (sic) makes its own arch girders, and brought them into their own pits, and so had several more years' experience with them than anybody else'.[102] Thus the Tredegar Company won another tribute for leading the advance in the use of steel arches in the British coalfield. The advance was of benefit not only to colliery safety, but to the company since by 1923 its works manufactured steel arch roof supports not only for 'domestic consumption', but were 'largely sold for colliery purposes throughout' Great Britain.[103]

Above & next page : Steel Roof Supports for underground usuage made and supplied by the Tredegar Iron & Coal Company.
From Tredegar Iron & Coal Company Ltd, Catalogue of Steel Arches, Rails and Colliery Requisites. A. J. Edwards collection

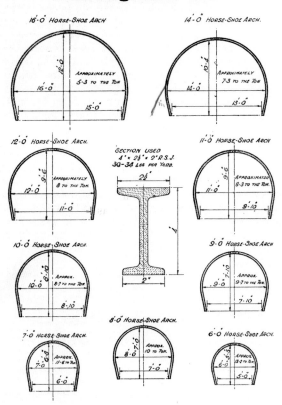

Steel Roof Supports for Underground Use

The correct size Bolt and Nut for these Arches is
2½" x ¾" Square, Square, Square.

Section and Fishplates
used for all Arches shown

NOTE.—FOR 16 FT. ARCHES THE WEIGHT OF THE SECTION IS INCREASED
TO 34 LBS. PER YARD.

Fishplate for Arch

Scale : 1 inch = 1 foot.

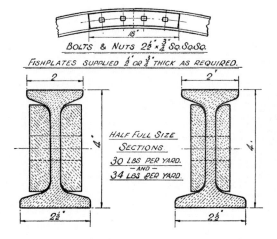

ALL THE ARCHES APPEARING IN THE CATALOGUE CAN BE MADE WITH
EITHER HORSE-SHOE OR STRAIGHT SIDES AS REQUIRED.

THE HEIGHT OF ALL ARCHES CAN BE VARIED TO MEET INDIVIDUAL REQUIREMENTS.

'Oversubscribed'

Regarding the development of Oakdale Colliery, although the Upper Rhas Las was reached by sinking in 1911, coal for sale purposes was not raised until the next year.[104] During the course of the 1911-12 business year, the directors of the Tredegar Company judged it 'advisable' to raise £150,000 by debentures 'secured upon the Oakdale property'. The Tredegar Company's 1912 annual report, issued June 1912, advised that 'the [earlier] hope of a considerably increased output' from Oakdale Colliery had not been realised. Nevertheless, the 'over-subscribed' response to the issue of Oakdale debentures suggested no disenchantment among shareholders concerning the venture.

Indeed, as a result of seemingly prudent financial management during the 1911-1912 year, the Oakdale Navigation Collieries Limited's share capital was increased by £160,000, the 'whole of which was taken up' by the Tredegar Company.[105] Thus, in 1912, the share capital value of the Oakdale Navigation Collieries Limited grew to £360,000. Perhaps the agent for the Tredegar Estate regretted that a Morgan of the past had not acquired the ownership of the mineral rights leased to Oakdale Navigation Collieries Limited.

Godfrey Charles Morgan, 2nd Baron, 1st Viscount Tredegar (1831-1913) Shown with his favourite Skye Terrier, 'Peeps'. Painted by John Charlton (1849-1917). Godfrey Charles Morgan inherited the Tredegar Estate in 1875. He supported the actvities of the Tredegar Iron & Coal Company and was a generous benefactor in the old county of Monmouthshire.
© *National Trust Images*

Death of the 1st Viscount Tredegar

It would seem that Viscount Tredegar's opening of Abertysswg Cottage Hospital was the last duty he performed in a community associated with the Tredegar Iron & Coal Company. Godfrey Charles Morgan died in 1913. During his period of stewardship of the Tredegar Estate, which began in 1875, the income of the Tredegar Mineral Estate, less tax, rose from around £15,000 per annum to an average of £88,000 calculated over six years, 1906 to 1912. In the year of 1913 the income of the estate, less tax, attained its peak, at £112,819.[106] Such an amount of wealth in the pocket of one individual stirs resentment among sections of the public.

A budget of the Liberal Government, 1905 to 1908, delivered by Hebert Asquith as Chancellor of the Exchequer, introduced a rising scale of death duties on estates valued at over £150,000. The wealth that Godfrey Charles Morgan left in his will to his nephew, Courtney, was thus reduced by death duties. During his lifetime, though, he had been a 'generous public benefactor' as evidenced not least by him giving land for the building of the Tredegar Cottage Hospital.[107]

Godfrey Charles Morgan had acted like his predecessors. He encouraged industrial development of the Tredegar Estate. He died in the year when the South Wales Coalfield reached its zenith in annual output of coal, nearly 57 million tons. He seems to have garnered goodwill and respect within at least the elite of the key towns in the eastern part of the South Wales Coalfield that on balance had prospered. He was made a Freeman of both Cardiff and Newport. Maybe fittingly, a statue of the 1st Viscount Tredegar, to the southern front of Cardiff's civic centre buildings, stands with other statues of men that once had an impact upon the economy of Wales.[108]

Workers at Bedwellty Pits, McLaren, Pochin, and Ty Trist collieries may have felt a link with the late Tredegar landowner on seeing his statue. A walk around the civic centre of Cardiff may have been used by visitors to kill time before watching rugby at the Arms Park, or soccer at Ninian Park. After 1919, the statue's feature of 1st Viscount Tredegar, in army uniform upon a horse, might have caused some workers to recall their dislike of the officer class. Yet, there would have been workers who would have respected Godfrey Morgan for his courage in battle. In 1854 during the Crimea War, astride his horse, Sir Brigg, as a captain in the 17th Lancers, he saw action in the 'Charge of the Light Brigade'. Regarding watching sporting heroes in Cardiff, the Viscount Tredegar's statue had no meaning for an Oakdale Colliery worker strolling around the civic centre.

Early years – Operational Oakdale Colliery

By the spring of 1914 the development phase of Oakdale Colliery was a tale for the remaining members of the pioneering gangs of miners to tell new recruits. In 1909-10, the number of persons employed at Oakdale and Waterloo-Gwrhay collieries stood at 235 and 120 respectively. By the end of 1912, the numbers employed at Oakdale had leapt to 700 whilst at Waterloo-Gwrhay numbers fell to ninety. In the year 1914, 1,800 workers earned wages from Oakdale Navigation Collieries Limited.[109]

Oakdale's colliers became familiar with the network of underground roadways for the movement of men and coal. From each 'pit bottom' two trunk roads were driven, one in a western direction and the other in an eastern direction. An underground trunk road was known as a 'main level' at the colliery. In what may be described for convenience as the South Pit eastern sector, a third main level was opened, which became known as 'John Williams's'.[110] Northwards and southwards from the main levels colliers hollowed out a series of passageways, known either as 'headings' or 'dips'. Use of the term 'heading' at Oakdale implied that the passageway was driven with a rise in the strata whereas a 'dip' passageway's course fell with the dip of the strata. At Oakdale Colliery, the headings, or dips, were driven off a main level at intervals of sixty yards.

Stalls, passageways dug out at right-angles from the headings or dips, were the work stations for winning coal. A stall was worked by a collier and an assistant, known in the local vernacular as a 'butty'. The collier and his butty worked a two-shift system, 'day' and 'afternoon'. The collier was paid on a piece-work basis with only the weight of large coal counting towards his wages. Small coal was 'a gift to the coal owner'. The butty was paid out of the collier's wages. Thus, youths under sixteen years of age were preferred as butties since they earned the lowest wages underground due to custom and practice. A sixteen year old butty was assigned to a heading's collier, and at eighteen years of age, if he was 'considered proficient, was given his own stall'.

Used at Oakdale Colliery was the Longwall method of mining. The method was enacted by colliers removing coal from a continuous face, or 'wall' of a seam. Concerning the Rhas Las seam, by 1920, its thickness was found to vary between 3ft and 5ft 6 inches.[111] With the coal removed, the overlying strata settled into the cave-like space—known as a 'gob' in the South Wales Coalfield but as a 'goaf' in other mining areas of Great Britain.

With a firm swing of a mandrel a collier cut coal from the face of a seam. The tempo of the swing, as well as being a sign of a man's physical fitness and stamina, gave a rough measure of a collier's output during a shift. As a generalization, coal is a relatively brittle rock. With the collier's need being to win large coal, his control of the blow of the sharp point of a mandril needed finesse.

Cut large coal was then loaded by hand into trams for dispatch to the colliery surface. A collier's wage was based upon a cost rate per ton of large coal. The butty used a two handed scoop known as a 'box' to transfer smaller sizes of coal into a tram. Dismissal from work was the penalty for using a shovel to load a tram. The collier knew that a shift of tram movements, each tram carrying stacked coal, secured for himself and his butty reasonable wages. The carrying capacity of a tram used at Oakdale was twenty-five hundredweights. By careful stacking of coal, much more than one ton of coal was moved in a tram. Another incentive for care in stacking was to limit the amount of small coal arisings due to large coal pieces being damaged in transit to the colliery's surface.

Horses moved trams underground. The size of a tram used at Oakdale Colliery was larger than those used at other company collieries, and so was the gauge of the tram road. At Ty Trist Colliery the gauge was two feet wide whereas at Oakdale it was two feet ten inches. Initially, a stable for twenty horses was provided below ground, and sited on the east side of the pit. By 1929 'almost a hundred horses were stabled'. Typically geldings, 'the horses were magnificent Shire bred horses some as much as fifteen hands high' and in 1929 'one of them was entered for the Horse Show at Olympia'. At Oakdale 'each horse worked 9 shifts per week maximum as allowed by law'. The feed and care of the horses 'was always first class'.[112] The colliery's surface featured a 'huge granary and stables', of which, the stables were used for the treatment of sick and injured horses. Feed for the horses underground was mechanically mixed and bagged for distribution.

On the colliery's surface, a pair of screens, one for sorting steam coal and the other 'Red Ash' coal, selected coal for washery treatment. Messrs Plowright, of Chesterfield, supplied the screening plant. For screening steam coal, in 1930, three tipplers were operated with one rubbish tumbler. The Red Ash facility featured one tippler with large 'cobble' coal picking belts.

Oakdale Colliery's washery was supplied by Messrs Simon-Carves, of Stockport. The design of the washery utilized the Baum principle, and offered an operational capacity of 125 tons per hour. The coal was either delivered to the washery by wagon or from the screens.

Washed coal was loaded directly into railway wagons for distribution to locations beyond the bounds of the colliery. The wagons were hauled from the colliery's sidings into the loading position by a GWR locomotive. The colliery's sidings seem to have been connected to the Collier's Arms junction of the Penar Branch of the Great Western Railway by April 1913.[113] The Tredegar Company surveyor responsible for setting out the colliery's railway sidings was William Woolley.[114] The subsequent groundwork placed the sidings' rail level lower, at 40 feet, than the colliery's surface.[115] Such engineering made needless the employment by the company of shunting engine crews, which was the Tredegar Company's practice at previous collieries.[116] Maybe such an aim was apparent to old hands of the Tredegar Company. Yet, many decades later the aim might be inferred from reading the associated comment in the Tredegar Company's 1930 description of Oakdale Colliery: 'no locomotive is required, all sidings being worked by gravity'.

The marshalling by the GWR of railway trains marked a start to the dispatch of Oakdale Colliery's steam coal to customers around the world. A range of percussion sounds issued. Railway wagons' buffers crashed together. The motion of chain links gave rise to a range of triangle-like tones. Bystanders heard a seemingly constant bass drum sound, and maybe felt the earth tremor as an outbound train of fully loaded wagons moved.

The locomotive's whistle operated by one of the crew on the GWR outbound train, might have served to crow that the GWR had denied the L&NWR a lucrative contract. At the outset of the Oakdale Colliery operation over 1,000 wagons for coal a week were marshalled in the sidings. Convoys of departing wagons of coal were the culmination of the toil of colliers and 'butties' who had been assigned to win coal in stalls by officials overseen by the colliery's manager.

Although Oakdale Colliery may have represented modern colliery engineering, the colliery management-officials' structure was the same as the one depicted in the Tredegar Iron Company's 1865 Rules and Regulations. Moreover, like for all collieries, a colliery manager's lineage developed. William Hepburn served as the colliery's first manager. In 1915, the holder of a First Class Manager's certificate David Evans succeeded Hepburn as the colliery's manager with David Aggex as under-manager. Evans's employment with the company began as a collier's 'butty'. Prior to his move to Oakdale Colliery, he was colliery manager at Ty Trist Colliery. It has been claimed that Evans's 'first move was to bring the experienced officials from Ty Trist and Pochin collieries to Oakdale'.[117] He was described as being 'a typical Welshman, with boundless energy and resource' and served in 1920 as the chairman of the South Wales branch of the British Association of Colliery Managers.[118]

David Evans held the Oakdale Colliery manager's post until 1924 when he was promoted to agent for the colliery company, thus replacing William Hepburn, who retired from the company. Evans was succeeded as colliery manager by Dan Morgan, whose career with the company began as an apprentice surveyor. Morgan later served not only as Oakdale Colliery's manager but also as the Oakdale Company's agent from 1930. Morgan's predecessor as agent was D. Kendrick who succeeded David Evans in some year after 1926, but before 1931. Kendrick had been promoted to agent having been the manager of McLaren Colliery for two decades. Dan Morgan seems to have remained in overall command of the colliery until the late 1930s when George Jones, more familiarly known as George 'Wrexham', who died in August 1946, became the manager.

William Hepburn and then David Evans, up until 1924, were the manager's held accountable for Waterloo Pit and Level. In 1925, T. Pritchard was made manager of Waterloo Pit and Level and held the position until 1933 when D. Morgan took on the dual manager's role which Hepburn and David Evans had performed before 1924.[119]

By July 1914, the colliery's weekly output attained 15,000 tons.[120] In operation was a colliery with the prospect of producing at least three-quarters of a million tons of coal a year. The colliery's potential annual output more or less equalled the total amount of coal produced by the Tredegar Iron & Coal Company in one year a quarter of a century earlier. Key to Oakdale Navigation Collieries Limited achieving such a prospect was the recruitment of a pool of labour, numbering thousands, many of which ideally lived near the colliery. The Tredegar Company copied the Abertysswg project by building a village to house Oakdale Colliery's officials and workers.

Oakdale Navigation Collieries' Management Office – in 1943 known as the Colliery Top Office. South Pit Headgear in background.
A. S. Tallis Photograph Album, Courtesy of the Tallis Family

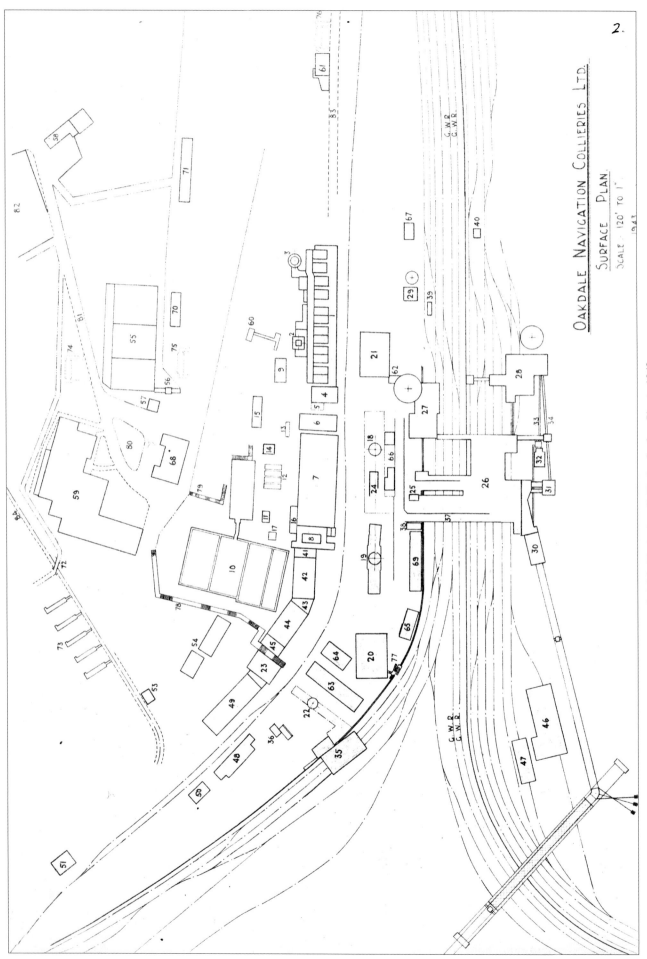

2.

OAKDALE NAVIGATION COLLIERIES LTD.

SURFACE PLAN.

SCALE - 120' TO 1"

1943

Oakdale Navigation Collieries Surface Plan in 1943.

Index to Surface Plan:

1. Boilers;
2. No. 1. Chimney
3. No. 2 Chimney
4. Feed Pump House
5. Ash Hoist
6. Turbo-Compressor House
7. Power-House
8. Fans
9. Boiler Shop
10. Cooling Towers
11. Chlorination Plant
12. Steam Accumulators
13. Compressed Air Receiver
14. Fire Pump House
15. Transformer House
16. Pump House
17. Surface Haulage
18. South Pit
19. North Pit
20. North Winder
21. South Winder

22. Waterloo Pit (House Coal Pit
23. Waterloo Pit Winder
24. Full Tram Creepers
25. Weighing Machine
26. Steam Coal Screens
27. No. 1 Washery
28. No. 2 Washery
29. Flocculation Plant
30. Ropeway Bunker & Driving Station
31. Small Coal Bunker
32. Tip Haulage
33. Rubbish Conveyor
34. Small Coal Conveyor
35. House Coal Screens
36. Creeper & House
37. Empty Tram Creepers
38. Battery House
39 & 40. Weighing machines
41. Sharpening Shop
42. Smiths' Shop
43. Mechanics Office
44. Fitting Shop
45. Carpenters' Shop

46. Tram Shop
47. Wagon Shelter
48. Electrical Shop
49. Stores
50. Sawmill
51. Dust Plant
52. Granary
53. Village Haulage
54. Ponds
55. Office Ponds
56. Alfloc Water Treatment
57 & 58. Garage
59. Pithead Baths
60. Stone Crusher
61. Sub-station
62. Switch House
63. Oil Lamproom
64. Cap Lamproom
65. Welding Shop
66. Pitmen's Cabins
67. Laboratory
68. Top Offices
69. Bottom Offices

70. H. C. Huts
71. Hut
72. Footbridge
73. Incline Shelters
74, 74 & 76. Shelter
77. Retaining Wall Steps
78. Colliery Approach Steps
79. Steps to Power Plant
80. Garden
81. Approach to Offices & Baths
82. Glan Rhiw House
83. Black Horse Path
84. Village Incline.

Folio of Technical Information – Oakdale and Wyllie Collieries, compiled by Jack Edwards circa 1946. A. J. Edwards Collection

Oakdale Navigation Collieries viewed from the western side of the Sirhowy Valley. The headgears (l-r) are: Waterloo Pit; North Pit; and South Pit. The building in the foreground to the left is the coal screens. the Power House roof can be seen to the right of the cooling towers.
Pope/Parkhouse Archive

NOTES

1   WCF: TI&C, op. cit., p.46 & p.49.

2   WCF: TI&C, op. cit., p.46. Sir Charles McLaren also sat on the boards of: Metropolitan Railway; Barry Railway; Palmers Shipbuilding and Iron Company as its chairman; John Brown and Company, Limited, one of the main Yorkshire coal owners; Sheepbridge Coal and Iron Company, with collieries in Derbyshire; and the Newstead Colliery Company with collieries in Nottinghamshire. Mention could also have been made that in 1899 John Brown acquired the shipbuilding yards of James Roger Thompson on the River Clyde, which was claimed that year to be the 'best equipped and successful shipyards and engine works in the United Kingdom'; see Ian Johnston, *John Brown & Company*. (Dunbartonshire Libraries, 2000), pp.99-100.

3   Trevor Boyns, 'McLaren, Charles Benjamin Bright, first Baron Aberconway', *The Oxford Dictionary of National Biography*.

4   'Tredegar Iron & Coal Co.', CT, 8 June 1907, p.5.

5   WCF: TI&C, op. cit., p.49.

6   WCF: TI&C, op. cit., p.49.

7   'Tredegar Cottage Hospital', *Weekly Mail*, 16 Aug 1902.

8   'Tredegar Cottage Hospital', CT, 8 Oct 1904, p.4.

9   'Tredegar Cottage Hospital', CT, 19 Sept 1903, p.4.

10 'Tredegar Cottage Hospital', CT, 8 Oct 1904, p.4.

11 'Tredegar Cottage Hospital', CT, 19 Sept 1903, p.4.

12 'Tredegar Cottage Hospital', CT, 8 Oct 1904, p.4.

13 'Grand Hospital Bazaar at Tredegar', ME, 22 Oct 1904, p.10.

14 It seems that not until 1923 did the company reveal that it gave 'every encouragement and financial support' to workmen's welfare schemes from which it may be inferred also health schemes; TICC, op. cit., p.3. Moreover, BIDCO, p.13, also presented an instance of the company's lending practices that supported Oakdale village's community 'social' schemes.

15 'Tredegar Hospital', CT, 4 Jan 1908, p.4.

16 She was the daughter of Mr J. D. Thomas JP who lived at 'Bronrhiw', Maesycwmmer, Rhymney Valley. Her sister, Blodwen Thomas, was matron of Gelligaer Isolation Hospital, Pengam (Glamorgan). 'Tredegar', *Monmouth Guardian*, 19 May 1916.

17 *The South Wales Coal Annual*. (1908), p.34. OS Ref No. ST 185989.

18 TCG, 'Tredegar Iron and Coal Company Limited', Vol.CII, 1 Dec 1911.

19 'Hotel for Oakdale Model Village', *Monmouth Guardian*, 13 March 1914.

20 'Sirhowy Coalfield', *Weekly Mail*, 27 April 1907, p.4.

21 'Tredegar Iron & Coal Co.', CT, 8 June 1907, p.5.

22 *The South Wales Coal Annual*. (1908), p.102.

23 *The South Wales Coal Annual*. (the years 1914 to 1918).

24 Mining at Oakdale Colliery's eastern neighbour Crumlin Navigation Colliery, in the Ebbw Vale, sunk between 1908-1911, was also troubled by underground flooding.

25 'Tredegar Iron & Coal Co.', CT, 8 June 1907, p.5.

26 Richard Watson, op. cit, p.184, which was sourced from John Williams, *Digest of Welsh Statistics*. (Welsh Office, 1985), I, p.337.

27 'Tredegar Iron Co.', *Weekly Mail*, 7 July 1906, p.4.

28 'Tredegar Company', ME, 17 June 1911, p.8.

29 'Coal Mines (Eight Hours) No.2 Bill', *House of Commons Debates*, Vol. 6, 6 July 1908.

30 Keir Hardie put his case not on profits per se but 'on the premium at which these companies were being sold in the market'. He claimed that the 'purchase of shares' was a 'very fair indication of the earning power of a colliery' company. The companies he chose were: the Ashley and Tidlsley Colliery Company whose shares were selling at a premium of 205 per cent, North's Navigation Colliery Limited (105 per cent), Bear Pit Colliery Company (1183/4), Bowhill Coal Company Ltd (335), Fife Coal Company 'where an eight hour day had long been in operation' – 500 per cent, and the Wilson Clyde Coal Company (321).

31 ME, 17 June 1911, p.8.

32 ME, 30 Oct 1909, p.8.

33 Roy Gregory, *The Miners and British Politics 1906-1914*. (Oxford University Press, 1968), p.120. His summary was based upon Sir Reginald Couplan, *Welsh and Scottish Nationalism*. (1954), p.216 et seq.

34 Roy Gregory, op. cit., p.187.

35 Roy Gregory, op. cit., p.19.

36 Roy Gregory, op. cit., p.122.

37 In 1910, Sir Arthur Markham Bart made it 'clear that the Chesterfield seat would always be at the disposal of the Derbyshire miners'. Roy Gregory, op. cit., pp.149-151, and also pp.159-165.

38 *South Wales Gazette*, 11 Sept 1904.

39 Roy Gregory, op. cit., pp.24-5.

40 'Eight Hours Bogey', CT, 25 June 1910, p.7.

41 ME, 17 June 1911, p.8.

42 *The South Wales Coal Annual 1911*, pp.43-52.

43 Leslie M. Shore, op. cit, p.133.

44 'Safety of the Miner', CT, 16 July 1910, p.7.

45 'Monmouthshire Collieries Rescue Association'. TCG, 19 April 1912, p.798.

46 ME, 30 July 1910.

47 At the 1919 General Election Violet Markham CH stood as a candidate, 'polled heavily', but was not returned as a MP. 'Election Results', *The Brecon County Times*, 2 Jan 1919, p.5.

48 Violet Markham, later CH, op. cit., p.9.

49 *Monmouth Guardian*, 14 Jan 1916. The article stated that the team 'looked certain of winning' the division after beating Bargoed by a margin of 231 points.

50 See: David Evans, *Labour Strive in the South Wales Coalfield 1910-11*. (Educational Publishing, Cardiff, 1911).

51 'Eight Hours Bogey', CT, 25 June 1910, p.7.

52 ME, 8 Oct 1910, p.10.

53 *The British Nursing Journal*, 4 Nov 1911, p.375.

54 Trevor Boyns, 'Growth in the Coal Industry: the Cases of Powell Duffryn and the Ocean Coal Company', ed. Colin Baber and L. J. Williams, Modern South Wales: *Essays in Economic History*. (University of Wales Press, 1986), table 2, p.155.

55 ME, 4 Feb 1911, p.10.

56 TCG, Vol. CI, 6 Jan 1911, p.13.

57 Syndicalism's aim was workers' control of industry by revolutionary means such as by 'direct action'. Tom Mann was one syndicalist who tried to influence the course of the strikes that hit the Rhondda and Cynon valleys in 1910. During the pre-war period, militant, young, South Wales Coalfield miners were thought to be much more likely to be persuaded to follow syndicalism than their counterparts elsewhere in the British Coalfield. See Henry Pelling, *A History of British Trade Unionism*. (Pelican, 1963), p.135 and p.142.

58 ME, 4 Feb 1911, p.10.

59 Susan E. Demont, op. cit., p.48.

60 See footnote No.2, W. D. Rubenstein, 'The Anti-Jewish Riots of 1911 in South Wales: a Re-examination', *Welsh History Review*, Vol. 18, 2 (1997), p.667.

61 W. D. Rubenstein, op. cit., p.669.

62 W. D. Rubenstein, op. cit., pp.689-690.

63 TCG, 'Tredegar Iron and Coal Company Limited', Vol.CIII, 14 June 1912, p.1207.

64 TCG, 'Tredegar Iron and Coal Company Limited', Vol.CIII, 14 June 1912, p.1207.

65 'Eight Hours Bogey', CT, 25 June 1910, p.7.

66 *Oakdale Colliery*. (The Tredegar Iron and Coal Company, Limited, 1930). The colliery's coal had properties more or less identical to Pochin Colliery's according to a classification used in 1946, see earlier.

67 TICC, op. cit., p.2.

68 *Oakdale Colliery*. (The Tredegar Iron and Coal Company, Limited, 1930).

69 Leslie M. Shore, op. cit, pp.121-126.

70 Named 'Pound-y-Coedcae' on the 1916, with 1938 additions, 25 inch OS map.

71 Leslie M. Shore, op. cit, p.91.

72 George Watkins, 'The Development of the Steam Winding Engine', *Transactions, Newcomen Society*, Vol. 50 (1978-79), p.23.

73 George Watkins, 'The Development of the Steam Winding Engine', op. cit., p.19.

74 George Watkins, *Stationary Steam Engines of Great Britain, The National Photographic Collection, Volume 4: Wales, Cheshire & Shropshire*. (Landmark, 1993), p.120.

75 The South Pit's semi-conical drum's dimensions were 18ft to 30ft diameter. North Pit's and Waterloo Pit's semi-conical drum's dimensions were both the same, 10 ft to 15 ft diameter.

76 Leslie M. Shore, op. cit, p.100.

77 *Winding Engine Data* – A. J. Edwards. (NCB). From the papers of A. J. Edwards in the keeping of the Writer.

78 Leslie M. Shore, op. cit, pp.94-7.

79 Comment, A. J. Edwards to Writer, 18 Feb 2007. In around 1950, W. A. Scott acted as the Seconder for Albert (Jack) John Edwards's application for Associate Membership of the Institution of Mechanical Engineers. Jack Edwards recalled visiting Scott at his

80 From the evidence of Alfred S. Tallis to a Parliamentary Departmental Committee, 'Electricity in Mines'. TCG, Vol.CI, 5 May 1911, p.886.

81 Leslie M. Shore, op. cit, p.127.

82 *Folio of Technical Information – Oakdale and Wyllie Collieries*, compiled by Jack Edwards circa 1946, pp.42-43. From the papers of A. J. Edwards in the keeping of the Writer.

83 Leslie M. Shore, op. cit, p.100.

84 *Winding Engine Data* – A. J. Edwards. (NCB). From the papers of A. J. Edwards in the keeping of the Writer.

85 *South Wales Area (Eastern), Chart Showing Shaft Capacities*. (NCB). Hereafter 'SWA (E) Shaft Capacities'. A. J. Edwards papers in the keeping of the Writer.

86 On the 2 May 1969, the payload per wind was rated at 5 ton 8 cwt. For comparison, Bargoed Colliery South Pit's payload per wind was noted as 6 ton 12 cwt, and Penallta Colliery's at 6 ton on 21 Oct 1969. Taff Merthyr Colliery, opened as a Powell Duffryn-Ocean Company joint venture, was ranked as the highest payload per wind in the South Wales Area (Eastern) Area on the 20 Feb 1971 at 7 tons. SWA (E) Shaft Capacities.

87 Jordan also reasoned that Oakdale Colliery's 'Fault points to Crumlin, and it is, probably, one of the Faults proved near the bottom of the Crumlin Navigation Pits'. Dr Henry Jordan, 'The South Wales Coalfield', SWIE, Vol.XXXVIII (1922), pp.122-123.

88 Proposed after discussions with Phillip Price, Health & Safety Manager, Lee Tunnel Project. Phillip Price began his career in mining at Bargoed Colliery. Emails 24 Sept 2013.

89 BIDCO, op. cit., p.5.

90 BIDCO, op. cit., p.5.

91 The pit pillar was a zone where only minimal mining took place. The zone's purpose was to limit subsidence on the pit's surface where the colliery's main surface plant and machinery was erected. Subsidence affected machinery parts alignment that was not good for operational reliability.

92 'Puckings' was the term used in the South Wales Coalfield for 'floor blow', which was when soft strata, exposed due to the working of a seam, rose if the local ground pressure had not been relieved through mining another seam.

93 *Oakdale Colliery*. (Tredegar Iron and Coal Company, Limited, 1930) [TI&C1930 hereafter], p.5.

94 TI&C1930, op. cit., p.5.

95 TICC, op. cit., p.2.

96 Robert James, 'Steel Arches and Steel Props for Underground Support', SWIE, an advance copy of the paper, (1930), pp.2-3. Statistics: Figure 1, reproduced from the report of the Chief Inspector of Mines, TCG, 2 Aug. 1929.

97 Robert James, op. cit., p.5.

98 Steel was also superior to wood in terms of relative crushing loads, which in general was a more crucial factor than tensile strength. The strength properties of timber are not as consistent as that of steel due to the presence of knots, decay due to fungus, and being exposed to wet weather on the colliery surface. See Robert James, op. cit., pp.22-23.

99 Leslie M. Shore, op. cit, pp.115-6.

100 Information given by the colliery manager, David Evans, to Prince Albert. 'Surprise Royal Visit, Prince Albert among the Welsh Colliers', WM, 17 Jan 1920, p.19.

101 Robert James, op. cit., p.6. Larch or fir was usually used for props, and 1,246,000 loads (a load represented 53 ft3 of timber) of pitwood was imported into South Wales in 1928.

102 Discussion, *Transactions-Institution of Mining Engineers*, Vol. LXXXII (1931-1932), p.426.

103 TICC, op. cit., p.1.

104 'Coal [at Oakdale Colliery] was first raised in 1912'. TICC, op. cit., p.2.

105 TCG, 'Tredegar Iron and Coal Company Limited', Vol.CIII, 14 June 1912, p.1207.

106 William Smith, op. cit., p.113.

107 He also donated land in Newport from which the later city has benefited from with the founding of Royal Gwent Hospital, the Athletic Ground, and Belle Vue Park. David Freeman, op. cit., pp.9-10.

108 Statues include David Lloyd George, the coal owner and trader John Cory, and Lord Ninian Crichton-Stuart, a member of the Bute family.

109 Employment figures sourced from *The South Wales Coal Annual* (per respective year).

110 Further examples of names for headings at Oakdale Colliery have been recorded as 'Mawrs', 'Jonah Prices', 'Bricki's Level', and 'Tom Powell'. BIDCO, op. cit., p.6.

111 'Surprise Royal Visit. Prince Albert Among the Welsh Colliers', WM, 17 Jan 1920, p.9.

112 BIDCO, op. cit., p.16 & p.17 regarding use of geldings.

113 R. A. Cooke, *Western Valleys*. (Black Dwarf Lightmoor), p. 40/67.

114 Woolley, William Downing, Application for membership of the Institution of Civil Engineers, 14 March 1936.

115 'Oakdale Colliery', dated 12 Aug 1957. Papers of A. J. Edwards in the keeping of Writer.

116 When bargaining for better wages, drivers and other members of the crew employed by the Tredegar Company to operate their shunting locomotives used at least go-slows to frustrate the dispatch of coal from collieries. The company's cash flow was adversely affected, and customer goodwill tested. Such an impediment was not repeated at Oakdale due to colliery engineering. Comment A. J. Edwards to Writer, circa 2007.

117 BIDCO, op. cit., p.9 & p.15.

118 'Surprise Royal Visit', WM, 17 Jan 1920, p.9.

119 Manager names sourced from *The South Wales Coal Annual* (per respective year). George Thomas's nickname from the notes of A. J. Edwards, which are in the keeping of the Writer. Seemingly David Evans made his first step on the company's managerial ladder as under-manager for both Ty Trist and Whitworth Drift.

120 'Oakdale Miners' Achievement: New Hospital to be Erected', *Llais Llafur*, 18 July 1914.

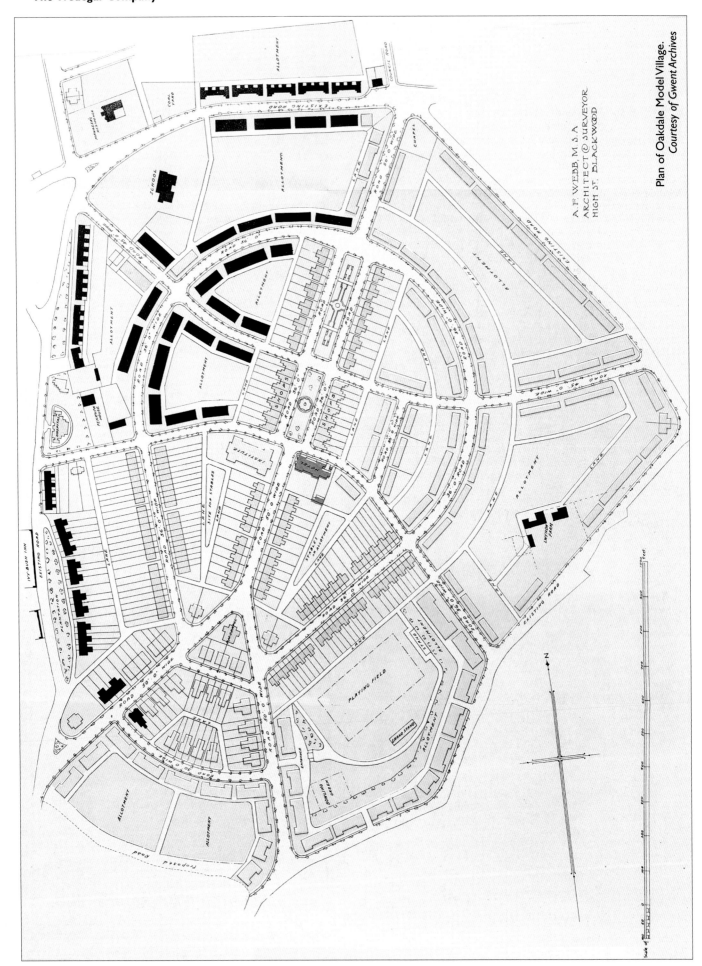

Plan of Oakdale Model Village.
Courtesy of Gwent Archives

A.F. WEBB, M.S.A
ARCHITECT & SURVEYOR
HIGH ST. BLACKWOOD

Chapter Six
MARKHAM & WAR

Early in the eighteenth century a Sirhowy Valley landowner, John Moggridge, embarked upon 'an experiment for the improving of conditions for the labouring classes of society, in the hills of Monmouthshire'.[1] He chose the western side of the valley for his experiment. Thus, on five acres of land known as Y Coed Duon (Black Wood) the village of Blackwood was born. Oakdale Navigation Collieries stood about a mile north-north-east of the centre of the village.

The housing at Blackwood, as featured on the 1914 Ordnance Survey, was less than a quarter of that shown for the town of Tredegar. The L&NWR's Blackwood Station was a useful starting point for exploring the village. Situated south of the station, for just under a mile, stood a string of houses on both sides of a road which a walker could use to make a journey up or down the valley. The string of houses would be developed as the future town's High Street. However, in 1914, seen on a walk down the valley on the road from the station were western road offshoots that accessed housing situated on higher ground. Maybe some Blackwood men and boys had taken employment at Oakdale Colliery. However, many more workers were needed for Oakdale Colliery than the village of Blackwood could have supplied.

The scarcity of colliery labour in the Sirhowy Valley was made worse by other deep-mine colliery openings. Within an area subscribed by a four mile radius around Oakdale Colliery, in the Rhymney Valley, Powell Duffryn added to Penallta Colliery by sinking Britannia Colliery in 1911. Furthermore, in the Ebbw Vale, within the same area, Partridge, Jones & Co. Ltd, over the period of years 1908-11, sunk Navigation Colliery at Crumlin, and, in 1912, Ebbw Vale Steel Iron & Coal Co. Ltd opened Cwmcarn Colliery. A boom in new house building within the area was an inevitable result of such a concentration of colliery investment.

The creation of Oakdale village captured the interest of Sir Arthur Markham Bart. He was awarded a Baronetcy in 1911. He had previously instigated a village scheme to serve the new Brodsworth Main Colliery near Doncaster, Yorkshire. The 'model' village of Woodlands was built in a 'beautiful park' that belonged to 'an old country house made uninhabitable by the sinking of the pit'. He 'carried out the scheme in the teeth of great opposition of less enlightened views of his fellow directors [of the Brodsworth venture]'. Markham sent his opponents a fierce written rebuke:

Why should you think it inevitable that colliers should live in a state of filth and piggery? If you try and make good clean homes and help social work, this tends to make better men …. After all, the theory that each man represents so much money or profit to the company by the amount of coal that he gets and that the obligation of the employer ceases when he has paid him his wages is utterly wrong. This is a question you have never really thought about. I want you to turn your mind for my sake to a higher ideal.[2]

Official Opening of Oakdale Model Village circa 1913. The central stage used for the event became the village's bandstand, but it no longer survives. The houses belong to Aberconway Place.
A. S. Tallis Photograph Album, Courtesy of the Tallis Family

Oakdale Village Workmen's Institute that was opened in 1917.

A. S. Tallis Photograph Album, Courtesy of the Tallis Family

It did not appear necessary for Sir Arthur Markham to send such a missive to fellow directors of the Tredegar Iron & Coal Company regarding a village for Oakdale Colliery. Abertysswg had set a new benchmark in South Wales Coalfield housing development. Moreover, regarding the health and social welfare of miners and their families, a pattern in care for the company's employees had emerged. The company played an encouraging role in the founding of Tredegar Cottage Hospital, Abertysswg Cottage Hospital, and the Abertysswg Workmen's Institute. The thinking of the directors of the company appeared to embody benevolence towards their employees. Maybe such thinking defines an enlightened coal owner. If so, it might also be contended that radical Liberalism had taken concrete form for the good of some working people. Paternalism, though, was apparent in the way the company wished to control at least the drinking habits of miners.

Sir Arthur Markham was 'largely responsible for the inception and carrying out of the model village' at Oakdale. The Tredegar Company held a competition, with a prize of £100, to find a village layout plan. The prize was won by A. S. Tallis's brother-in-law, A. F. Webb. Seventy-five acres was assigned for the village with an allocation of ten houses per acre.[3] The layout plan placed a central road as the village's main axis around which transverse streets were arranged in a concentric pattern. The site of the village stood just above the 700 foot contour.

Oakdale village housing had features that would have amazed Tredegar people. An Oakdale house was fitted with a 'large coal burning range, with an open fire heating a large oven at the side, with a boiler set in the back to heat the water and a bathroom'. According to Ralph Thomas writing in 1986, such fittings 'must have been a revelation' to most of the first occupants of these houses.[4]

An estimated million bricks were made at Tredegar Works to construct the village's houses and other buildings. By 1912, the village's Syr Dafydd Avenue houses were ready for occupation, and not long afterwards, colliery officials and families viewed Penrhiw Terrace houses. Penrhiw farm, at one end of Penrhiw Terrace, was acquired to house the colliery's chief engineer and his family. The building of 'Glan Rhiw', a detached home for the colliery agent, caught the interest of all the first villagers. After 1912, houses on Beech Grove, Markham Avenue, Llwynon Road, and Ashville became available for workers to rent to accommodate their families. The village's Central Avenue also took form. Once resident, the workers' families had grounds for at least one gripe. Following a dispute over charges between the company and the electric installation contractor, only Syr Dafydd Avenue enjoyed the benefits of household electricity. The rest of the villagers had to wait until 1930 to use electricity. Regardless, most of the new residents would have been pleased with the results of the £100,000 the company spent by around 1914 on creating the village.[5]

News about the prospects both for employment at Oakdale Colliery, and a better standard of home life at Oakdale village, travelled. 'People from Pontypool, Abertillery, Tredegar, together with some from afar as Gloucester and Somerset' were attracted to the new village.[6]

The company further encouraged the building of a hotel, the establishment of churches and chapels, and a workmen's institute. A provisional full licence for the hotel was approved at a Licensing Session at Tredegar in March 1914 despite opposition from the Temperance Party and the Free Church Council. The application for the licence was made by Lyndon Moore, Newport, in the name of A. S. Tallis. Moore's deposition stated that the application was 'made in the name of a gentleman whose position was a sufficient guarantee of its bona-fide nature', and that 'all profits above four or five per cent made from the hotel business would be devoted to local philanthropic purposes'. The licence obtained for the hotel caused the licence for an existing public house, The Black Horse, to be revoked. The Oakdale Hotel was erected at an estimated cost of £4,000, and managed by a subsidiary of the Tredegar Company, Abertysswg Hotels Limited.

The Tredegar Licensing Session heard A. S. Tallis speak for the Oakdale Hotel. He stated that it was the objective of the Tredegar Company to 'promote temperance by taking control of the hotel themselves, and he considered it unkind of the chapel people to oppose the application, seeing that the company gave them free sites for their chapels in the village'.[7] Maybe the snub Tallis suffered suggested that chapel people were more righteous than a coal owner. Nevertheless, the missionary work of Christianity within the new community of Oakdale was furthered due to the generosity of the Tredegar Company. Within the bounds of the new village were erected chapels for the Primitive Methodists (founded in 1914), Baptists (1916), Presbyterian Methodist (1916), and churches for the Anglican Church in Wales (1921), and for Roman Catholicism (1926).[8]

If Alfred Tallis's personal reputation was slighted by local chapel people, he may have gained credit among other villagers for promoting Oakdale Workmen's Library and Institute. The minute book for the Oakdale Workmen's Institute notes that its first annual meeting took place in April 1913. 'A memorable date' was the 20th August 1913 since A. F. Webb presented a design proposal for the institute. Ralph Thomas's later speculation seems true: 'Do we see here the hidden hand of Mr Tallis, remembering who Mr Webb was?'[9] The institute building was built opposite the Oakdale Hotel, on the other side of Central Avenue, and opened on the 10th September 1917.

In late 1914 house building by the Tredegar Company gained national attention in *Garden Cities and Town Planning*. The journal featured an article about Welsh housing schemes by Edgar L. Chappell of the South Wales Garden Cities and Town Planning Association. Oakdale village had arrived a decade after a future for 'Garden Cities' had been first advocated.[10] Chappell identified Oakdale as being 'one of the best *model* villages … now being built'. Before stating such a plaudit, he observed that 'most of these new centres of population hardly deserve to be called "garden villages", but they do conform to some garden city principles'.[11] Perhaps it was due to Edgar L. Chappell that the affix 'model village' became linked with Oakdale. Moreover, Sir Arthur Markham 'always held' that Oakdale was a 'much better' village than his pioneering Woodlands, which also acquired the 'model' affix.[12]

By the summer of 1915, Oakdale village featured 310 homes, two chapels, a 'well-managed' hotel, and progress was being made to open a church school. From the company's perspective: 'there was everything to make the place desirable'.[13] The web of connections made due to chapel and church life, social contact at the hotel, and the camaraderie that arose from colliery work, encouraged neighbourliness among the first Oakdale villagers. The social life of the village, according to one account about its origins, became organised after 1914.

The village's brass band later brought the name of Oakdale to the attention of audiences of critical listeners. During the 1920s the band was judged the Class 'A' Champions of Wales and was presented with the Prince of Wales Trophy, and at Belle Vue, Manchester, took fourth place in the British Championship. Such success was due reward for men who spent their leisure hours playing music after working underground to win coal for Oakdale Navigation Collieries Limited.

Markham Steam Coal Company

By the 1920s, Oakdale Colliery had established links with a neighbour, Markham Colliery. Arthur Markham's farsightedness and persistence ended in August 1910 with the Markham Steam Coal Company signing an agreement with the Llanover Estate trustees to take steam coal from 1,000 acres of land around Abernant-y-Felin in the Sirhowy Valley.[14] The Markham Steam Coal Company's first colliery, and as it would prove to be its only one, was sited just over two miles north-north-west of Oakdale Colliery, on the 775 feet contour of Cefn Manmoel, otherwise roughly one hundred feet elevation above the eastern bank of the River Sirhowy.[15] Also in 1910, with the assignment of William Woolley by the Tredegar Company to the

Markham Steam Coal Company as colliery manager, a start was made to engineering Markham Colliery.

During the spring of 1911, the directors of the Tredegar Company acted to acquire the Markham Steam Coal Company. With shareholders' approval, the company accepted an offer made by Arthur Markham to buy the entire share capital of Markham Steam Coal Company.[16] The share capital comprised 200,000 shares.[17] In June 1911, the Tredegar Company directors acknowledged it was 'under a great obligation to Mr Markham for his generous and disinterested services in this very important matter'. The recompense that the Member of Parliament for Mansfield received from the Tredegar Company was 4 per cent interest on money he had spent on legal expenses and preliminary sinking work with respect to the Markham Steam Coal Company.

The Derbyshire man appears to have been overly generous striking such a deal with the Tredegar Company in 1911 considering the state of his personal finances for the preceding years. From April 1908 up until the end of 1911, Markham had 'staked' his personal fortune upon opening Bullcroft Main Colliery, Yorkshire. The sinking of Bullcroft was beset by feeders. His sister, Violet, later reflected: 'Arthur faced little short of financial disaster'. A technical solution was eventually found and a 'valuable mine [was] brought into production'. She reflected decades later that the 'immense anxieties' of the 'risky [Bullcroft] venture' damaged the health of her brother, Arthur'.[18]

Markham and Mines Safety

The period of years around 1911 saw Sir Arthur Markham campaigning for improvements in mines safety. On the 11th May 1910, an explosion at Wellington Pit, Whitehaven, Cumberland, killed 136 workers. His Majesty's Inspectors of Mines report about the Wellington Pit disaster, written by [later Sir] Richard Redmayne, included a proposal that electric lamps 'should be provided in place of oil safety lamps' for some underground circumstances.[19]

According to Scandrett, seemingly with reference to practice at Ty Trist Colliery, in 1894 the Tredegar Company replaced 'old safety lamps with electric battery lamps'.[20] The action by the company was farsighted, and the motive for their use humane.

But the Wellington Pit inquiry's report proposal about electric safety lamps also made reference to three disadvantages. The 'main disadvantage' was the lack of an instrument within an electric lamp for detecting explosive gas. Another doubt concerned the security of an electric light's on-off switch. That an electric safety lamp gave a 'sort of search light effect, but a rather worse general lighting effect than an ordinary old safety lamp' was also deemed to be a disadvantage.[21]

The Wellington Pit report was the cue for Markham to offer 'anonymously' a prize of £1,000 to find the best electric lamp design.[22] His anonymity was secured by the Government acting as the prize sponsor. Knowledge of the prize immediately encouraged hope in at least the South Wales Coalfield that 'there will no doubt bring to the market various forms of [new] electric lamps'. In around 1911, A. Leighton Stevens informed that electric miner's lamps had been 'extensively' used in the one of the 'North-country collieries', and adopted by 'all rescue stations'. He further commented that the practice of using secondary batteries to operate an electric light had drawbacks. Nevertheless, he believed that 'from the point of safety the electric lamp should certainly hold its own … though it has the disadvantage of being unable to detect fire-damp'.[23]

In 1912, the prize for the best electric lamp design was awarded to a German inventor, whose name was not found. His design was afterwards supplied by CEAG (Concordia Elektrizitäts Aktien Gesellschaft), Cologne. In 1911 just 4,298 electric safety lamps were used in the British Coalfields. As a measure of the effect that the prize had, by 1914 the numbers had leapt to 75,707.[24] The Sir Arthur Markham prize was the catalyst that later led to the wide adoption of electric safety lamps in the British Coalfields.

Violet Markham held that as a Member of Parliament, health and safety in mines was 'always' her brother's 'first concern'.

During the passage of the Mines Bill in 1911, the Member of Parliament for Mansfield and the Chief Inspector of Mines, Richard Redmayne, met frequently at the Home Office, and sometimes there were 'stormy encounters'. In debates about the Bill in the House of Commons, and at Grand Committee meetings, Arthur Markham spoke as an 'advocate' for 'more stringent measures' for the protection of colliery workers.

A read of Hansard bolsters Violet Markham's claim that her brother acted as the 'self-appointed watchdog' of the Bill's progress.[25] He sought changes to many clauses of the Bill ranging from details, like the use of detaching hooks for the winding of cages, to policy matters such as qualifications and selection of mines inspectors. John Evans, manager of McLaren Colliery, visited the House of Commons to observe the Committee overseeing the Bill. He judged that 'with the exception of Sir Arthur Markham none of the other members knew anything about the subject with which they were called upon to deal'.[26] Some of the MP for Mansfield's proposed amendments to the Mines Bill passed into law, but some coal owners may have been pleased that one of his quests for change failed. Markham challenged the regulation that colliery managers were held accountable for colliery safety. He 'did not see why an owner should be divorced from the management of his mine', and was 'perfectly willing to be summoned and to pay a penalty, or go to prison if necessary' for cases where neglect of duty was proved against himself as a coal owner. In the Sirhowy Valley, William Woolley was shouldering for the first time the onerous duties of a colliery manager.

William Woolley

William Woolley's 1910 assignment to manage Markham Colliery served as a promotion for the twenty-six year old. Born in 1884, he was educated at King Edward VI School, Chelmsford, and Wycliffe College, Stonehouse, Gloucestershire. He entered the coal industry 'by pupillage' at eighteen years of age with Messrs Graham Brothers Collieries, North Staffordshire. In 1905, at twenty-one years of age, he joined the Tredegar Iron & Coal Company as Assistant Surveyor under T. Greenland Davies, who in 1934 was HM Mines Chief Inspector for the Northern Division. Also in 1905, Woolley began technical classes in mining, won two examination prizes, and in 1907 obtained a First Class Manager's certificate. He was then appointed under-manager at Bedwellty Pit, where he worked until the end of 1909 when he was given the opportunity to observe the opening of a colliery. In 1910, as surveyor, he laid-out the railway sidings for Oakdale Colliery. The Markham Steam Coal Company made him responsible for sinking two shafts, laying out extensive railway sidings, the erection of colliery buildings, and the installation of plant and machinery.[27]

An Explosion in a Pit[28]

The sinking of two shafts at Markham Colliery was contracted to Fred Piggot of Caerphilly. A previous job for a gang of Piggot's workers was sinking the then deepest shafts in the South Wales Coalfield at Bedwas Navigation Colliery, Rhymney Valley.[29] In May 1912, the North Pit sinking at Markham Colliery was suspended at a depth of 385 yards. A large store of water had accumulated at the foot of the pit. Large pumps were ordered for the extraction of the water. However, work continued in the North Pit building a brick liner for the shaft, and forming a lodge room in the vicinity of a landing stage located at 250 yards below the surface.

On Saturday the 18th May 1912, David Griffiths, winding engineman North Pit, sat out an undemanding day of work. There was no regular lift of spoil from excavating the pit bottom. At some moment he took time to watch George Jones, a mechanical chargeman, supervise the fitting of suction valves to a barrel used to bail water from pit bottom. Griffiths was in the company of a mechanic, and a banksman. Close to the three men hung a bowk – a basic design of cage for moving men and materials. The bowk hung over the North Pit ready to be loaded with the barrel. Then at some time before two o'clock in the afternoon, David Griffiths was startled when the windows of the winding house 'splintered

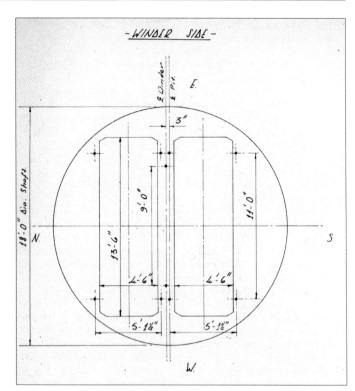

North Pit Diagram Markham Colliery. National Coal Board South Western Division No. 6 Area Drawing No. ADO SK.739 dated 15-10-62.
A. J. Edwards collection

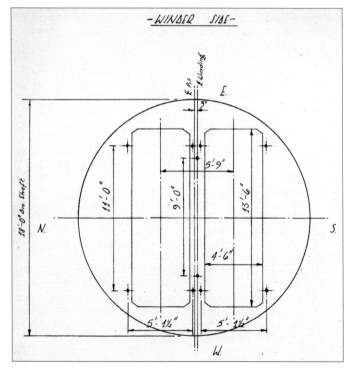

South Pit Diagram Markham Colliery National Coal Board South Western Division No. 6 Area Drawing No. ADO SK.739 dated 15-10-62
A. J. Edwards Collection

to pieces and a cloud of dust and smoke came up the pit, which completely obscured it' from his view. He 'did not hear the noise of the explosion in consequence of the roar of [electric] dynamos in the engine-room'. Markham Colliery was 'equipped entirely by electricity including the winding of the coal'.[30]

The explosion released a surge of air up the North Pit with hurricane force. 'Two of three [men] are supposed to have fallen down the shaft after the explosion and the other man's body', reported to be Caerphilly's Thomas Patrick, seemingly employed as a banksman by Piggot, 'was found about 100 yards from the pit' on the surface. 'In a banksman's cabin yards away [from North Pit] were Henry Simmonds and Walter Bainbridge. The cabin was wrecked but the men escaped with a few minor scratches'. The bowk and water barrel were 'blown away', and the pit's headgear 'was very much damaged'.

Two sinkers were known to be in the North Pit digging out the lodge room. A quarter of an hour after the explosion one of these men was heard to yell, "What's the matter."

At around 2 p.m., managers Alfred Tallis, William Woolley, and W. Stephen Davies met on the colliery's surface. The managers took stock of reports like those about after damp.

The managers were joined later by a squad of Crumlin Rescue Station staff. At 5. 30 p.m., a team comprising: William Woolley, Sgt Wimborne (Crumlin Rescue), James Joseph Leach and Llewelyn Howells (both of the Tredegar Company) 'equipped with Draeger apparatus and accompanied by a canary to give warning of the state of the atmosphere, made a slow descent in an improvised bowk'. William Woolley ventured into the pit having not worn breathing apparatus before. After 'considerable difficulty', due to meeting hazards like tangles of ventilation pipes and other wreckage, the team reached the landing stage for the lodge room. A sinker, James Snashnell of Argoed, was found alive but 'badly burnt about the arms and head'. The sinker revealed that his 'butty' had fallen down the shaft. Snashnell was raised to the surface where a large crowd of people had gathered.

North Pit rescue missions recovered, in total, five bodies. The victims were: George Jones (single); Michael Carrol (single), fitter; Bert Legget, (single) fitter, all from Argoed; Thomas Patrick, (married), Caerphilly; and George Gubtripp (single) sinker. Six weeks earlier George Jones's father, also George Jones, had been killed at nearby Llanover Colliery.

On the 20th May, J. B. Walford, district corner, opened an inquiry into three of the victims at Tredegar Police Court. The inquiry was adjourned with an observation that it concerned the 'biggest disaster … in that district' since the one at McLaren Colliery a decade earlier. Subsequently the cause of the Markham North Pit explosion became unsettled business. Put forward was the idea that a 'blower' of gas had entered the shaft above the landing stage at 250 yards. Although sinking had cut through old disused workings it was considered a 'remote possibility' that gas escaping from them leaked into the shaft since in 'the course of sinking the shaft was bricked and cemented'. Furthermore, there was no obvious explanation for gas ignition. Locked lamps were used underground, and no explosives were used to expedite sinking.

Sir Arthur Markham attended the 20th May inquiry, and spoke on behalf of the Markham Steam Coal Company and the Tredegar Company. He 'desired to express' the directors 'deepest and most profound sympathy with the relatives of these poor men who had suffered in the deplorable calamity'. Before the inquiry he inspected the effects of the explosion. According to Violet Markham, her brother was 'no surface owner but was constantly down the pit where he met workers on the actual coal-face as man to man – on their side a man they learnt to trust. He was always accessible; every worker knew he could see the "boss" for the asking if he had a request or a complaint to make'.[31]

Markham appears to have been profoundly moved by the North Pit explosion. The sinking of the *Titanic* had occurred the previous month. He reflected that 'the great disaster in the Atlantic loomed largely in the public's mind at the present time, but he believed that these men had met their death [in North Pit] under equally, or even in more tragic circumstances which the public did not understand or appreciate'. He claimed that the rescue had created history in being the first to make use of breathing apparatus. He extolled the first rescue team for doing 'noble work' and in a 'brave way'. 'It was indeed a source of great gratification that there were always men found ready when fellow men's lives were at stake to risk their own to save those who were in danger', he was reported as saying. From a position

of authority, both as a coal owner and as a campaigner for better mines safety, he also asserted that the rescue team that first entered North Pit had 'effected one of the most gallant rescues ever made in the history of coal mining'.

On the 27th September, *The London Gazette* announced: 'His Majesty the King has been graciously pleased to award the Edward Medal Second Class to William Downing Woolley, Arthur Thomas Wimborne,[32] James Joseph Leach, and Llewellyn Howells'. The bravery and humanity shown by the first team to enter Markham Colliery's North Pit after the explosion on the 18th May received national recognition.

The directors of the Markham Steam Coal Company were also impressed by the heroism shown by James Davies, a grandson of whom later lived at Markham village. The company gave James Davies a watch inscribed with a tribute for his action during the 1912 North Pit tragedy.[33]

Llewellyn Howells, on the left, and James Leach. Tredegar Company rescuers after the 1912 Markham North Pit explosion. Both men, with the colliery manager, William Woolley, and Arthur Wimborne, leader of Crumlin Rescue Station, were awarded the Edward Medal for their demonstration of 'bravery and humanity'.
From The Merthyr Express. *Supplied by Llyfrgell Gendlaethol Cymru/ The National Library of Wales*

Markham Colliery

Sinkers completed their work during 1913. The colliery's shafts were both 18ft in diameter. The North Pit, the upcast, is believed to have been sunk to a depth of 617 yards and the Ras Las lay at 523 yards with the Old Coal (Five-Feet/Gellideg) seam at 598 yards.[34] The seams were steam coal.[35] The South Pit seems to have been 500 yards deep. The thickness of the Lower Coal Measures at Markham Colliery was measured at 468 yards, which was thirteen yards less than at Oakdale Colliery.[36]

Concerning colliery engineering, Markham Colliery was in the van of a technical revolution in the South Wales Coalfield.

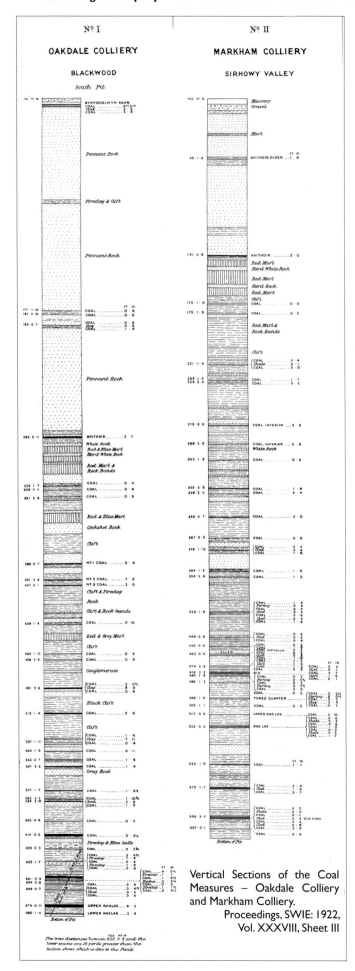

Nº I

OAKDALE COLLIERY

BLACKWOOD

South Pit

Nº II

MARKHAM COLLIERY

SIRHOWY VALLEY

Vertical Sections of the Coal Measures – Oakdale Colliery and Markham Colliery.
Proceedings, SWIE: 1922, Vol. XXXVIII, Sheet III

The South Wales Coalfield's first operational application of electric winding took place at Maritime Pit, Pontypridd, in 1908. Ferndale Colliery, Rhondda Fach Valley, adopted electric winding shortly afterwards. Powell Duffryn's Britannia Colliery in the Rhymney Valley was not only the third site in the coalfield to wind coal by electric winder, but the first colliery to be powered solely by electricity in the British Coalfields.[37] Markham Colliery appears to have been the fourth South Wales Coalfield colliery to use electric winding, and was probably the second all-electric one in the British Coalfields. The source of the colliery's electricity supply was Oakdale Colliery's power-house.[38]

Markham Colliery's winding engines were powered by 600 V DC electric motors made by Siemens Schuckert, and used the Ward Leonard system of control.[39] The 'peak load', which concerned lifting from pit bottom a stationary, fully loaded cage, called for the supply of electric power having the equivalent of 1,400 horsepower.

The winding engines drove 12ft to 18ft in diameter bi-cylindro-conical drums made by Markham & Company, Chesterfield. For a brief period, drums wound flattened strand ropes of 1¾-inch in diameter. However, by 1965 at the latest, these ropes had been replaced with Latch and Batchelor 1½-inch diameter locked-coil ropes supplied in lengths at 715 yards, for the North Pit, and 600 yards for the South Pit.[40] Both the North Pit and the South Pit were available for either service, or coal raising purposes. The winding time for the 600 yard North Pit was ninety seconds whereas the wind up 483 yards of the South Pit took fifty-one seconds.[41]

The colliery's winding plant and equipment was installed in one winding house thus following Powell Duffryn's lead in the British Coalfields at Penallta Colliery.[42]

The height of the colliery's headgears, from the pit bank to the centre line of the sheave, was sixty-five feet. The Rees and Kirby made headgears were of lattice steel construction. The sheaves were sixteen feet diameter.

In June 1971, National Coal Board (NCB) engineers assessed the colliery's winding system, and their data suggests that the original cage system remained in service. The cages were described as single deck. The payload per tram was 1 ton 10 cwt. Raised per wind were two trams. The corresponding details for Oakdale Colliery, and the original cage system, were: 4 trams per wind, payload per tram 1 ton 7 cwt.[43]

Markham Colliery, on opening, was among the best ventilated in the South Wales Coalfield at the time it became fully operational. Two Waddle fans of 18ft diameter each producing 400,000ft³ of air per minute were installed at the colliery.[44]

Until the colliery was equipped with screens and a washery coal was removed to Oakdale for preparation before dispatch to customers. Inwards and outwards sidings for railway wagons were laid and opened to serve the colliery over a period of years between 1911 and 1914.[45]

After overseeing the opening of Markham Colliery William Woolley remained as manager until 1914 when he was appointed Tredegar Company's assistant general manager. Woolley was succeeded by J. H. Austin who managed the colliery for seven years. In 1924 J. H. Austin was made a colliery agent with D. Davies succeeding him as colliery manager, who then served in the post until at least 1933.

With Markham Colliery, Sir Arthur Markham enabled the Tredegar Company to establish a 'continuous mineral area of ten miles in length' in the Sirhowy Valley from the southern limit of Oakdale Colliery's coal take to the northern boundary of the South Wales Coalfield. Such dominance of the northern reaches of the Sirhowy Valley by the Tredegar Iron & Coal Company's may have troubled the Bargoed Coal Company.

The Llanover Estate had two decades earlier leased to the Bargoed Coal Company the working of the Brithdir seam in an area that separated the Oakdale-Markham steam coal territories. The Bargoed Coal Company sunk Abernant Colliery in 1883 about half-a-mile southward of the future site of Markham

MARKHAM'S COLY HOLLY BUSH.

Markham Colliery in circa 1913. The winding house housed two Siemens Shuckett electric winders.

Pope/Parkhouse Archive

MARKHAM'S COLLIERIES, Nr. TREDEGAR 267.

Markham Colliery's headgears.
Inset: Markham Steam Coal Company Lamp Check.

Pope/Parkhouse Archive
Philip Hadfield Photography. A. J. Edwards collection

Colliery. At Abernant Colliery the Brithdir seam lay at a depth of 160 yard and was three feet thick, and was claimed to be the source of the finest blacksmith coal in South Wales. In 1916, the company employed 418 miners and fifty-nine surface workers at Abernant Colliery.[46] Three years earlier the company employed sixty-five more miners at the colliery, which might suggest a drift of former workers to jobs at Oakdale and Markham collieries.[47]

In 1906, the Bargoed Coal Company acquired the Llanover Colliery from Christopher Pond, a Blackwood coal owner. The colliery was perched on a platform elevated just above the eastern bank of the Sirhowy River, and sited between Markham and Oakdale collieries. The Brithdir seam, at 183 yards, was worked at the colliery.[48]

In 1909-10, in the vicinity of Llanover Colliery, but on the western side of the valley, C. Pond supplied coal from his Primrose Colliery for making gas, household, and manufacturing use. The colliery operation appears to have become known as Primrose & Rock Colliery after 1911. As a guide to the range in numbers of miners' employed at Primrose Colliery in 1909 it was fifty-five and in 1913 it was seventy-five.[49] Christopher Pond's coal business, he operated a number of other small coal operations in the area, survived despite being ringed by much mightier coal companies like the Tredegar Iron & Coal Company. The Bargoed Coal Company's market reach was also greater than Pond's since it had shipping and commercial offices in the vicinity of Cardiff Docks at 50 George Street. The trade in Sirhowy Valley coal gave employment for male clerks in Cardiff.

Right: Brithdir Seam Workings, North End of Sirhowy Valley.
Proceedings, SWIE: 1934, Vol. L

Below: Llanover Colliery. Sinking may have begun before 1906 by C. Pond so as to work the Brithdir seam. In 1906 the colliery was acquired by Bargoed Coal Company who began, or completed, sinking work. The one shaft colliery was linked underground with Abernant Colliery for ventilation. *Pope/Parkhouse Archive*

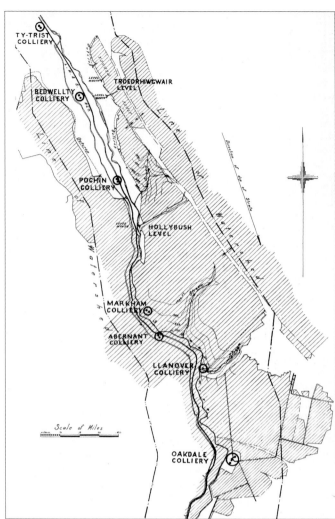

Llanover Colliery Argoed. Nr Blackwood. 409

Cardiff Offices

In 1914, like the Cardiff offices for the Tredegar Iron & Coal, and Oakdale Navigation Collieries, the Markham Steam Coal's shipping and commercial offices were to be found in the Exchange Building. However, after 1916, it seems that the shipping and commercial functions for the three companies were moved to the Imperial Buildings, Mount Stuart Square, under one commercial manager, Norman J. McNeil. By 1922, the shipping activity for the three companies, and most likely the commercial function as well, came under the ownership of Tredegar Associated Collieries & Shipping Company Limited.

Coal – Rewards & Risks

For the year that closed the end of March 1914, the Tredegar Company, including its subsidiary coal companies, produced 2,279,000 tons, which was an increase of a quarter of million tons on the previous year.[50] 'Something like 10,000 men' had been employed to produce the coal, and the corresponding total worker wage bill incurred by the company for the year was £900,500. The average wage a company worker earned was 35s. to 36s. a week.

The period saw 'the migration into the high-wage South Wales Coalfield of large numbers of agricultural workers from South and mid-Wales, Somerset, and Devon' and large numbers of men 'mostly from Bristol, Gloucester and the Midlands'.[51] Indeed, the village of Oakdale became home to some people drawn from the Marches and the West Country.

Moreover, in July 1914, the Tredegar Iron & Coal Company budgeted to build five hundred houses to create Markham Village.[52] In February 1914 and July 1915, the Bedwellty Urban District Council passed plans for the Markham Steam Coal Company to build houses to create the village.[53] The village was situated to the north of Bedwellty Church. In 1915, the village was referred to as Markham Garden Village.[54]

Newcomers to the South Wales Coalfield around 1914 would have been alive to the dangers of underground work. An explosion at the Universal Colliery, Senghenydd, in October 1913, killed 439 men. Regarding lowering the risk of underground explosions, in July 1914 the Tredegar Company ordered a 'special plant for all their collieries for the production of stone-dust' for spreading underground. Lord Aberconway declared it was 'the right thing to do', and claimed that the company was 'sparing no expenses to make their collieries safe in every particular [way] in which science could help'.[55]

Whitworth Colliery Fatalities

Nevertheless, coal mining remained a dangerous occupation. In February 1914, during a Saturday afternoon's shift at Whitworth No. 1 Pit, the whereabouts of three men gave rise to concern. A futile 'hurried search' was made, and assistance was called from the Crumlin and Rhymney Valley Rescue Stations. A rescue station team found the missing men 'suffocated by foul air, dead in an unused heading'.

The victims were: John Parsons, colliery under-manager, forty-four years of age, who lived at Arthur Street, Tredegar, whose dependents comprised a wife, seven children, and four other children; William Harris, overman, forty-four years, Vale Terrace, Tredegar, left a wife, and two children dependent; and William Watkins, fireman, twenty-five, James Street, Tredegar, also a married man left a wife and two children. Although Parsons had only served as under-manager at the colliery for just under a year, he had been an official at the colliery for twelve years having served first as a fireman and then as an overman. John Parsons's body was recovered by Sgt A. T. Wimborne of the Crumlin Station. Wimborne had earlier given Parsons full training in the use of rescue breathing apparatus.

An inquiry into the accident, before J. B. Welford, District Coroner, was held at the Police Station, Tredegar. The jury concluded that the men had been suffocated by foul air in the heading, and that a 'grave error of judgment' had been made by the officials. The verdict: 'death by misadventure'.[56]

A Colliery Manager's Promotion

With the expansion of the Tredegar Iron Coal Company's collieries, that also included two collieries as subsidiary companies, Oakdale and Markham, another tier of management, agents responsible for overseeing a set of colliery managers, strengthened. It seems that A. S. Tallis was the first collieries' agent of the company. However, at the time of the opening of Abertysswg Cottage Hospital, W. Stephen Davies reported as collieries agent to Tallis as the company's general manager. The set of collieries that W. Stephen Davies was held accountable for in 1910 was not found, but in 1917 he was answerable for Bedwellty Pits, McLaren, Pochin, Troedrhiwgwair (a level),[57] Ty Trist, and Whitworth collieries.[58]

Late summer 1914 saw the promotion of John Evans to agent for the Markham Steam Coal Company, and sub-agent over McLaren Colliery. He had served as manager of the Rhymney Valley colliery for nearly thirteen years, and gained 'wider influence'. He held offices as: president of the Colliery Official's Association of South Wales and Monmouthshire, president of the Rhymney Valley Baptist Association, and as councillor and chairman of the Rhymney Urban District Council.

John Evans heard tributes paid to himself at a gathering at the Workmen's Hall, Abertysswg, just before Christmas 1915. A newspaper report detected 'eulogistic terms' used at the gathering. However, many of those praising the senior colliery official held respect for a rule: 'You shall not bear false witness against your neighbour'.

Evan's successor as manager of McLaren Colliery, David Kendrick, recalled that on hearing about the colliery's officials moves to organise the gathering, 'the workmen expressed a wish to join in the congratulations'. Kendrick had 'worked under' Evans for nearly thirteen years, and claimed that the workmen's interest 'displayed' the 'general popularity in which Mr and Mrs Evans were held'. Punctuality, according to Kendrick was one of Evans' 'great characteristics'. 'All officials' had to 'observe this' at the colliery 'and they in turn tried to institute this into the men'.

Alfred Tallis told the gathering that John Evans was a 'sound man'. He 'confessed that upon many an occasion that advice [from Evans] had been put into practice, and had worked well'. With regard to what seems to have become the company's management ethos, he reflected:

> It was very difficult these days to hold the scales fairly and justly between employer and employee, but he had every confidence that Mr Evans had always tried to do the proper thing, and if there were times when he may have appeared to have not been as lenient as he might, he had, undoubtedly, tried to be just.

In certain circumstances, John Evans had to act with robustness when managing men. Alas the company's general manager did not elaborate upon the circumstances that had caused Evans not to show mercy. However, overman Charles Jones was closer to the realities of managing a pit than Tallis. Jones viewed his former manager as a 'gentleman'. Evans 'always treated' him and other officials 'kindly and always gave them good advice'. He remarked upon a 'good trait' of his former boss: 'if he had occasion to censure an official he would not do so before the men'.

The gathering also listened to the views of David Evans, recently appointed manager of Oakdale Colliery. He observed that John Evans 'was a firm disciplinarian, a rigid and austere manager, but, nevertheless was a good friend to all'. The incompatibility between the new agent's past conduct and his ability for nurturing fellowship went unexplained. Maybe it was Nehemiah Phillips who provided a clue to why such an incompatibility existed. As the agent for Powell Duffryn's collieries in the Rhymney Valley, Phillips noted at the gathering that 'a colliery manager's life was a lonely one because he was generally the only one in the place' where a colliery operated.

The report about the Abertysswg gathering may be considered invaluable for four reasons.[59] First, the report gives a rare sketch

John Evans
McLaren Colliery Manager 1902-1914
and Agent, Markham Steam Coal Company'
Monmouth Guardian and Bargoed and Caerphilly Observer. 24th April, 1914.
Supplied by Llyfrgell Gendlaethol Cymru/The National Library of Wales

of the character and conduct of a colliery manager employed by the Tredegar Iron & Coal Company. A search found no other similar report.

Second, although on the whole workers held jaundiced, sometimes scathing, opinions about coal industry managers, a degree of regard prevailed at least with respect to the education process that produced a colliery manager. Regarding John Evans, it appears that he had earned the respect of one of the oldest workmen at McLaren Colliery, Tom Price, of Brynteg Crescent, Rhymney. The worker valued Evans for being a 'self-made' man, and 'endowed with great abilities, and achieved the distinction of passing as a first-class manager'. However, at least one fellow colliery manager, J. P. Gibb, not present at the gathering, held the view that 'as long as a colliery manager kept his colliery safe and made it pay he was a first-class man, but no sooner did an accident occur at the colliery then there was nothing too bad to say about him, and that everything which he should have done had been left undone'.[60]

Third, Nehemiah Phillips' frankness revealed that a colliery manager posting was a lonely one.

Last, John Evans assumed a leadership role in the community to which he was assigned by the company. He was acknowledged at the gathering for having 'given a fair share of his time for the welfare of the inhabitants' of Abertysswg and 'the advancement of social reforms'. He could have chosen not to have become active in chapel life and civic affairs, accepted the solitariness of his posting, concentrated upon the operational matters met running McLaren Colliery, and pursued his own leisure interests.

As the honoured mining engineer of Abertysswg, Evans appears to have continued to reside in the village whilst serving as an agent for the Markham Steam Coal Company. A search failed to find information about the closing years of his life. Although he is not named as the agent for the Markham Company in the *South Wales Coal Annual* for 1916, he was alive in 1919, when he may have retired from the company.

The Abertysswg gathering was held whilst armed conflict on the continent of Europe and at sea was in progress. Earlier, sometime after 11 p.m. on the 4th August 1914, the First Lord of the Admiralty, Winston Churchill, issued an order for the Royal Navy to 'commence hostilities with Germany'. South Wales steam coal had long held the monopolist position for fuelling the boilers of His Majesty the King's ships. Colliery workers became likely recruits for the armed forces.

The Early Years of War

At the outset of the war, only the Tredegar Company's McLaren Merthyr coal was listed by the Admiralty for supply to the Royal Navy. Thus, coal won from under Cwm Tywssg was deemed to 'possess unique evaporative power' for battleship propulsion. Moreover, since the stoked coal gave off little or no smoke, the commander of a British battleship was gifted the advantage of surprise for attacking a German naval ship. Then, during the course of the war, 'Tredegar' coal, as a general term, was ranked among the 'Second Admiralty Coals'.[61]

The persons employed at Tredegar Company collieries in 1913 offers a rough indication of the company's potential for supplying coal for the defence of the realm:

	No. of Persons Employed
Bedwellty Pits Nos. 1 & 2	1,351
McLaren Merthyr	1,833
Oakdale (with Gwrhay)	804
Markham	190
Pochin	1,691
Troedrhiwgwair	68
Ty Trist Nos. 1 & 2	1,196
Whitworth	880

As mentioned earlier, for the year that closed the end of March 1914, the company's colliery workers produced 2,279,000 tons. Reported for 1913, the Tredegar Iron & Coal Company and its subsidiary coal companies employed 8,013 persons.

The company's Markham Colliery offered the promise of a lift in the company's annual total output once manning grew. The colliery's annual output potential appeared to be around 420,000 tons using the Oakdale-Markham collieries' cage payload per wind ratio for prediction purposes.[62] Moreover, the colliery's coal, regardless of it not being initially on the Admiralty's supply list, was a vital fuel for merchant ships.

A month or so after war had been declared at least two hundred men employed at Markham Colliery went on strike for two days. No notice of the strike was given to the colliery's management. The strike concerned a dispute about the price-list for 'ripping top'.[63] Such a dispute might be viewed as a parochial issue in which the new employees of the Markham Steam Coal Company sought to assert the value of their labour. However, as the hostilities in Europe got underway, a Miners' Federation of Great Britain (MFGB) quest for better wages and conditions was in process, which encouraged many strikes at collieries across the British Coalfields. In Tredegar, brief distractions from industrial relations conflict occurred.

Some households in the townships within the ambit of the operation of the Tredegar Company received notices of the deaths of a family member. John Powis of Dukestown, aged twenty-one, serving with the 1st Battalion, South Wales Borderers, was among the first men from the Tredegar district to be killed on the Western Front. His death occurred on the 29th September 1914.[64]

In October 1914, a recruiting campaign by the 3rd Monmouthshire (Reserve) Regiment was held in the town. A battalion of 450 men of the regiment paraded through Tredegar. Major Ford had a clear aim for the parade: 'They had not come there to play, but to do business, and he hoped to take back two hundred to three hundred men' to the regiment's headquarters at Abergavenny.[65]

Warfare presented Tredegar Company colliery workers, like others employed in the South Wales Coalfield, with other dilemmas. In March 1915, William Brace MP presided over a meeting of the SWMF's Executive Council that debated a letter from the secretary of the MFGB, Thomas Ashton, that workers' Easter holidays be curtailed. The executive had also received a similar communication from the Admiralty's Cardiff representative due to the Royal Navy's urgent need for Welsh steam coal. The executive agreed to the requests, and granted a further concession, that 'no holiday be asked for a May Day demonstration of the Federation'.

However, some members of the SWMF's executive at the March meeting were mandated to be party to resolving disputes about coal price lists at both Markham and Celynen North collieries.[66] Both collieries were reported to be in a state of 'sinking' in 1915.[67] The row over the price list at Markham Colliery endured for at least seven months.

Such a stalemate contrasted with the drive by the Monmouthshire Regiment to raise a third battalion. A recruitment rally in April 1915 at the Drill Hall, Rhymney, was lauded as successful.[68] A number of colliers employed at McLaren Colliery may have volunteered at the rally to follow the steps of other company employees to the trenches dug to define the Western Front.

At Ypres on the 21st July 1915, Captain William Clay Hepburn, who had left his position as Oakdale's colliery manager, was deployed with the 172nd Company, Corps of Royal Engineers, and assigned to the 1st Battalion Monmouthshire Regiment (Territorial). He oversaw the driving of an underground gallery in the direction of the enemy's line to counter similar German tactics. The British miners unearthed a German 1,350 pound explosive device partly prepared for detonation. The miners were 'successfully withdrawn by the united efforts of Captain Hepburn and two officers working under him'. He was awarded the DSO for 'conspicuous energy and good work'.[69]

Later in 1915, another soldier familiar with the dangers of working underground at Oakdale Colliery was awarded the Military Medal. The South Wales Borderer Sgt David George Morgan, a collier at Oakdale until enlistment, had shown the intuitive reaction of a miner to a fellow human being's plight. He 'carried a wounded officer out of danger under fire'.[70] The amity that flourished among colliery workers was a virtue of value, but sometimes it caused group stubbornness.

At Markham Colliery, in October 1915, there was a four day strike. The strike was prompted by a workers' demand for all the colliery's miners, then numbering 800, to attend the funeral of a 'comrade killed in the pit'. The colliery's manager, J. H. Austin, 'was unable to consent' to the miners' demand, but 'agreed to allow anyone who desired to attend the funeral to leave at 1.30 p.m., and eventually arrangements were made for a train to take the men who wished to attend the funeral to Tredegar'.[71] The dispute suggests that life in the Sirhowy Valley went on as normal in spite of warfare.

Although army recruitment was not helped by news about the toll of death in war, reports about the actions of men like Captain Hepburn and Sgt David George Morgan were a boon for associated rallies. However, a perhaps less than discreet aside by a recruiter at April's Rhymney Drill Hall rally was that a 'regrettable' aspect of enlistments was the 'number of single men from the collieries of the Company that had given their services to the King and Country, was very disproportionate to the married men'.[72]

The War's effect upon Coalmining

In the summer of 1915, Lord Aberconway informed shareholders at the company's annual meeting that the 'younger men had gone [to war] and the older men being left, the production per man was not so good as it used to be'. The company was 'faced with a daily shortage of between 10 and 20 per cent by absenteeism. Being older men, some were probably absent due to ill health, but yet the percentage of absent men was larger than it would have been in ordinary time'. Moreover, Aberconway was 'sorry to say' that 'the payment of higher wages, instead of encouraging men to work, induced them to work fewer days'. Concerning the company's employment numbers overall, the chairman reckoned that 3,080 company workers, 'about 20 per cent', had enlisted.[73] His figure of 3,080 begs the question about what baseline figure he used. A comparison between company's employment numbers, including subsidiary colliery companies, published in *The South Wales Coal Annual* for 1914 and 1915, reveals a fall of 18 per cent, but a decline in numbers of only 1,845.[74] However, during the course of the war, 800 Oakdale Colliery workers enlisted.[75]

Earlier, in October 1914, W. Stephen Davies, the company agent, met a deputation of Whitworth Colliery workers led by Alfred Onions the miners' agent. He told the deputation that the company had served notice about closing the colliery since its manpower was 'depleted by men having joined the colours'. He further mentioned that due to the war the company could not fulfil coal supply contracts in France, Germany, and Belgium, and this was a secondary reason for closing the colliery. W. Stephen Davies also warned that both the operations of Ty Trist, from which it was likely that Whitworth Colliery's coal take would be worked in the future, and Bedwellty Pits 'would be stopped' unless there was 'considerable improvement'.

Tredegar colliery workers 'crowded' a room at the Town Hall to hear Alfred Onions's report about the W. Stephen Davies meeting. There was a fear that the 'whole town' as well as Whitworth Colliery's workers would be affected by the closure. Yet, although in October 1914, 650 persons worked at the colliery, around 280 men had left the colliery since 1913. Alfred Onions raised laughter in the room by mentioning hearsay that the colliery had become known as 'old men pits'. However, he gloomily added that about twenty-five men at Oakdale Colliery and 100 men at Waterloo Level were also under notice about being laid off from work. The meeting's chairman, Walter Conway, counselled that 'they all knew that the position of the men [at Whitworth Colliery] was helpless, and he knew no power or influence to compel the company to keep open the collieries'. Although the SWMF had been told about the plight of the workers at Whitworth Colliery, those present at the Town Hall meeting heard that union funds, being depleted, made support for any protest strike action unlikely. The meeting carried a motion that the Tredegar Company be asked to withdraw the pending notices so that 'men can gradually be drafted to other collieries'. As a consequence, a deputation of workers met A. S. Tallis.

On meeting the delegation, the general manager repeated that the scarcity of men due to the war had made it 'impossible to keep' the colliery 'going at a profit'. However, Tallis advised that 'work would be available for the whole of the [Whitworth] men at Markham and Oakdale collieries'. He also advised that the company 'would do their best to find places for the old men, a considerable number of whom were employed at Whitworth Colliery'.[76] In June 1915, Lord Aberconway reported that Whitworth Colliery had become 'unremunerative, and would probably not be opened again', which proved to be the case.[77]

The Tredegar Company was further troubled by an adverse trend in working costs. Between 1909 and 1914, such costs had increased by 3s. 2d. a ton. The introduction of a workman's war bonus of 17½ per cent had added another 1s. 1d. per ton to the company's large coal costs.

The coal operation was also hindered by a shortage of materials. Scarcity had caused pitwood prices to double. 'Stores such as iron, steel, and machinery had all gone up in price, which made a material difference in the cost of getting the coal'.

Moreover, the coal export market had collapsed in Europe. Nevertheless, the company sought not to upset 'valuable and friendly connections with customers' by enforcing contract clauses upon those unable to take contracted quantities of coal.

Whitworth Colliery. Closed in late 1914. Peak manning, 870, occurred in 1911 when 793 men worked underground.   *Pope/Parkhouse Archive*

Furthermore, the company strove to 'supply heavy arrears of contracts they entered into under the old prices' even though it could have sold coal at higher prices. A seemingly prudent action by the company was appreciated by one customer who voluntarily paid an extra 1s. per ton on the contracted price.

Although the business year that closed at the end of March 1915 had been a 'very stormy one' for the Tredegar Iron & Coal Company, Lord Aberconway conceded that it 'had got on fairly well. There had been a 'shortage' of coal output, but the company made a profit of £157,253.

Profits made in Wartime

Sir Arthur Markham had earlier confronted the issue of profit making by coal owners at a time of war. According to Violet Markham:

As a coal owner he took a very strong line from the first on the limitation of profits. It was intolerable to this capitalist that some men should make money while others were dying in their country's defence. On the outbreak of war he wrote immediately to Mr Asquith urging the importance of stabilising wages and profits in the coal industry. Nothing immediate was done ... [78]

In June 1915, at the Tredegar Company's annual ordinary general meeting of shareholders, Markham contended that 'no one should want to make money out of the war'. Moreover, with a hint of a rebuke, he said: 'And so if the shareholders received the same dividends as before the war they could not complain'. As a prelude to giving details about where the coal market's coal price setting mechanism was at odds with normal times, he blamed Government for any excessive profits being made. 'It was impossible for one company to make a stand for reasonable price. It was for Parliament to take it up, and he strongly held the view that limitation of profit was desirable'.[79]

A Price of Coal (Limitation) Bill was read in the House of Commons in July 1915. A month earlier in the House, the MP for Mansfield reported the 'enormous prices' being paid for Welsh steam coal by the country's Allies, particularly France and Italy. Before the war, the Italian Navy paid 17s. per ton for steam coal but charges had doubled to 35s. Inferred from his speech, the Tredegar Company had a contract to supply coal to Italy. For controlling purposes, he advocated that a limit be put on the price of coal at the pit head.[80]

Regarding the Price of Coal (Limitation) Bill, he told MPs that it was 'absolutely worthless'. About a 'horrible position in South Wales', he censured the Government for having 'failed to take steps whatever to let people who are making the profits know they ought not to make them, and if they make them to take them back'. The 'people' in his statement were coal owners, coal merchants, and ship owners, but who was profiting most from the gain in coal prices was unclear. Sir Arthur Markham accused 'all of them' for wanting to 'get their finger on the pudding'. He candidly disclosed, again by inference, that the Tredegar Company had been making 'substantial profits' even when delivering coal sold at 1914 prices. Nevertheless, he had opened his House of Common's speech aware of the affect that the wellspring of wartime profit for the coal trade was having upon the mood of the country's miners. He contested that if the Government had sorted out the coal price matter earlier 'you would have no strike in South Wales today'.[81]

On the 15th July 1915, the 200,000 miners employed in the South Wales Coalfield went on strike. One factor that caused the strike was lingering bitterness among the miners about the way in which the Monmouthshire & South Wales Coal Owners' Association had forced the SWMF to enter the 1910 Conciliation Board Agreement. Another causal factor was 'frustration' among miners that the minimum-wage provisions of the 1910 Agreement denied them a wage rise. The strike was also a display of anger by miners about not receiving greater earnings whilst the coal owners reaped a profits 'bonanza'.[82] A settlement of the strike was reached in August, but it did nothing to 'resolve the fundamental dispute between the [South Wales] owners and miners'. 'Combat' between the Monmouthshire & South Wales Coal Owners' Association and the SWMF would 'continue throughout 1916'.[83]

Oakdale Cottage Hospital[84]

In October 1915 an event in the Sirhowy Valley provided a moment of distraction from at least the industrial relations battle in the South Wales Coalfield. Watched by a large crowd of people, Lt-Colonel A. K. Wyllie, a director of the Tredegar Company, opened Oakdale Cottage Hospital using a gold key handed to him by Mrs A. S. Tallis. The hospital cost £3,988 to build with expenditure on furnishings and equipment being between £700 and £800. The funds for building and equipping the hospital were raised by the workmen donating 1d. for each pound sterling earned as wages. Although the company declared a donation of £250 to the hospital build fund, at the time of the opening, the accrued colliery workers' subscription stood at £2,296.[85]

The hospital's foundation stones had been laid earlier on the eve of war in July 1914. The laying of the foundation stones was a sign of Oakdale Village's 'phenomenal progress' according to a newspaper.[86] Lord Aberconway, representing Oakdale Navigation Collieries Limited as its chairman, asserted in a speech before he laid the first stone: 'Nothing showed the progress their country was making more than in medical attendance in hospital establishments, and in everything which tended to promote the well being and the health of their growing population'. Regarding progress in the South Wales Coalfield, he continued:

There was a time when a new colliery village was built—and it seldom was built on decent lines—the first thing they did was to put in a public house. They had got a little beyond that stage now, and they thought of hospitals, institutes, schools and places for public worship. With those ideas before them no one could say that this country was on the down grade.

Aberconway had no need to boast about how the Tredegar Company had helped to shape social progress in its coal mining territory. Oakdale village was a concrete statement of the company's efforts to improve the life and wellbeing of some of its employees. Nonetheless, he registered his respect for the actions of working men. The cottage hospital was 'not provided by the company; it was the work of the miners themselves'. The hospital, he vouched, was a 'monument to the independence, energy, and foresight of the men who were employed at Oakdale Colliery'. The hospital scheme was 'not a work of charity; the example so successfully set by Tredegar would be followed and a levy made towards [the hospital's] maintenance out of their wages at their own request'. 'The scheme indicated the modern spirit which was actuating the working class of this country. They no longer desired to be the object of charity, but they wanted good wages, better living, and plenty of work, and [a] given that they were prepared to undertake their responsibilities like other citizens'.

The opened Oakdale Cottage Hospital offered eleven beds for patients to 'make a speedy recovery' from accidents or illness. Grim news from the Western Front also meant that hospital beds in Great Britain were being used to nurse the casualties of warfare. As July 1916 began, at Mametz Wood on the Somme, Welsh miners who had enlisted in the 38th (Welsh) Division saw action. The winning of Welsh steam coal to power the fleets of the Royal Navy had no interest for former miners engaged in trench warfare.

Oakdale Cottage Hospital – Opened in 1915.

A. S. Tallis Photograph Album, Courtesy of the Tallis Family

Wm. Daniel.   Dd. Jones.   Chas. Young.   Saml. Fileo.   J. L. Herbert (Sec.)   Alf. Cruickshank.   John Lloyd.   Gwilym Morgan.

Thos. Morgan.   Wm. Morgan.   Francis Webb.   Wm. Thomas.   D. J. Vaughan.   Miss A. Bramwell (Matron.)   Miss F. Ford (Sister.)   David Hughes.   Danl. Davies.   James Darnell.   D. J. Phillips.

Elijah Patfield   Thos. Smith   Hy. Bowen   L. D. Whitehead   Dr. G. A. Brown   A. S. Tallis   H. E. Mitton   T. L. Davies   Francis Rowland   John Jones
(Vice Chairman.)   (Vice-Chairman.)   (Vice-Chairman.)   (Vice President.)   (Vice President.)   (Chairman.)   (Trustee.)   (Trustee.)   (Treasurer.)   (Trustee.)

Oakdale Cottage Hospital – Management Committee.   *A. S. Tallis Photograph Album, Courtesy of the Tallis Family*

Disorder

In July 1916, Lord Aberconway reported that Government controls were affecting the Tredegar Company. A year earlier, he also had been frank with shareholders: 'he strongly held the view that the limitation of profits was desirable'.[87] However, the task fell to him to tell shareholders about the 'heavy obligations' of an excess profits tax. Concerning actual profits earned at the Oakdale and Markham collieries, the Treasury had taken a 53 per cent and 34 per cent share respectively. He held that both collieries had not made excess profits. He bemoaned an effect of the tax: 'there was less of an incentive to keep [colliery] costs on a low scale when the greater part of their earnings were taken by the Chancellor of the Exchequer'. Nevertheless, the company's financial performance for the 1915-1916 year was more than sufficient since shareholders were awarded a 10 per cent dividend.

Aberconway also revealed the company's coal output for the business year that closed at the end of March 1916 was 132,000 tons less than an unknown previous year's total collieries output. He related that 'partly due owing to high wages there had been bad working, there being a large percentage of absentees among the men who, if they did their duty to their country, would be working more time than less'. Two years earlier, in October 1914, Alfred Onions had raised the issue of absenteeism with workers at a Tredegar meeting, and appealed to them to pay attention to the company's complaint.[88]

Furthermore, in July 1916, Lord Aberconway was strident criticising the Government. He claimed 'that the employers had loyally carried out its provisions but for some reason Government' had, without consulting the employers, 'in absolute defiance of their own agreement' given the 'men an extra 15 per cent'. He accused the Government of having conceded the wage rise due to the 'agitation of the men'.[89] Maybe as an implication from the foregoing: members of the Monmouthshire & South Wales Coal Owners' Association would not have made a concession. Thus,

the company was party to what *The Times* called the 'The Curse of South Wales and the virtual private feud which was impelling the nation's safety'.[90] Later in November 1916, members of the Monmouthshire & South Wales Coal Owners' Association were charged in a leader of *The Times* for having a 'grasping policy' with regard to earning 'immense wealth' from a coalfield that they were 'trustees ... to the nation'. The newspaper's leader further advocated that the ownership of the South Wales Coalfield be 'transferred to someone' better.[91] Days later, Asquith's Government used the Defence of the Realm Act (1916) to 'assume control of the country's collieries, and immediately applied its authority to South Wales'.[92]

Sir Arthur Markham

The fifty years old Sir Arthur Markham's stance regarding the Government taking command of the British coal industry will never be known. On the 3rd August 1916, the Member of Parliament for Mansfield died suddenly 'from an attack of angina' at Newstead Abbey.[93] David Lloyd George, the Minister of Munitions, reflected: 'Many members differed from his views, and still more from his methods, but no one, I am sure, doubted for a moment either his sincerity or his patriotism. He had an utter fearlessness and a courage which I have never seen equalled in the most trying circumstances'.[94]

The death of a coal owner rarely won the respect of the whole of a mining community. Nevertheless, newspaper reports read about Markham's death just mention that he had been a director of the Tredegar Iron & Coal Company, and omit mention of the effect that he had had upon a corner of Monmouthshire. After around 1904, Sir Arthur Markham appeared to act as the company director with the most presence in north-west Monmouthshire. The degree to which he involved himself in the operation of collieries is unknown, but he was a critic of excessive autocratic managerial power.[95] His bluntness was probably resented at times by many company officials and workers.

For example, his opinion about no further engagement by the company in the iron and steel trade in 1904 ran counter to hopes in Tredegar. Regardless, his direct dealings in company affairs generally appear to have had constructive intentions. When the company was financially constrained, his independence of mind, courage for taking business risk, and persistence, led to the company expanding its coal mining territory. The formation of the Markham Steam Coal Company not only enabled the Tredegar Company to grow but created jobs for workers.

Some of Markham's counsel fell on deaf ears. He made the valid observation that the ratio of distribution of the whole of the earnings of company shareholders to workers as wages was much less than that vaunted by critics of capitalism. If his early calls to the Government to control the profits made by coal companies at the outbreak of war had been acted upon then the subsequent strife between coal owner and the coal industry's union may have been less bitter.

More than likely most colliery workers employed by the Tredegar Company maligned his local presence as being for the pursuit of a wealthy man's interests.[96] Such a partial view was a bar to valuing a down to earth man who was an adept businessman. Worker prejudice made them unlikely to concede that Sir Arthur Markham did not conform to their idea of the archetypal South Wales Coalfield coal owner. Regarding issues like mines safety and worker housing his outlook was far more progressive than most British coal owners. The miners in the constituency he served for years, Mansfield, though, appeared to regard him highly. During his Parliamentary career, he won an ever increasing vote at General Elections. At least in the Sirhowy Valley the Derbyshire man's contribution to the expansion of the Tredegar Iron & Coal Company could be seen as Markham Colliery and Markham village.

Under the Control of Government

In July 1917, Lord Aberconway addressed the subject of Government control at a company meeting. He told shareholders that the company's assets 'were not yet public property'.[97] Such circumstances enabled him to contend that 'if the [Government] Controller allowed them to keep their collieries in thoroughly efficient condition they ought not to complain of what was going to be done. He would be satisfied if nothing was done by the Controller which would injure the future prospects of the company, and he did not think that anything of that kind was likely to be done'.

Prior to July 1917, coal distribution was a priority for the Controller of Coal Mines. In May 1917, the Controller introduced a scheme that regulated the shipping of coal 'as far as possible at the port nearest to the collieries'. Thus, the 'output of Monmouthshire collieries would go to Newport'. But, by early summer of 1917, the export of coal from South Wales was hampered 'by lack of tonnage facilities, one of the fruits of a German submarine campaign. Coal could with difficulty be dispatched to France and Italy, where there was extreme need'.[98] Nevertheless, steam coal was also hauled in trains, nicknamed 'Jellicoe Specials' after Admiral John Jellicoe, from not least McLaren Colliery to other British ports to bunker the battleships of the navy.[99]

The chief protest of the Tredegar Company's chairman, in July 1917, was prompted by Government concessions concerning colliery worker wages. He thought 'that the shareholders were treated on a very much worse basis than the coalminer. Their men was getting fifty-five per cent increase in wages over the new standard, which was equivalent to 130 per cent increase on the old standard. … but the shareholders were not getting any increase or bonus of any kind'.

The chairman's protest, though, was less than candid. Some of the company's shareholders had invested not to benefit solely from yearly dividend earnings, but from long-term financial gain arising from capital growth. The company's post-war development plans were of more interest to such investors. Nevertheless, Lord Aberconway was acutely aware that some

shareholders had grounds to grouse. Government control had caused shareholders to forego a peak, during the years of the war, in dividend earnings. Indeed for the business year that closed the end of March 1917, the company returned a profit of £208,717, which not only represented a 10 per cent rise on the previous year's profit, but was the peak profit made during the war.[100] The forthright Sir Arthur Markham, had he lived, would more than likely have publicly deplored shareholder grousing at a time of war. At the company's July 1917 meeting, shareholders learnt about capital growth prospects.

Lord Aberconway told the shareholders that the company 'had taken a new coalfield, a very large area to the south of Oakdale' with the aim of developing it after the war. 'They might have diminution of profits after the war, but there was not a colliery company whose position was so well secured as theirs', he claimed. Lt-Colonel A. K. Wyllie seconded motions at the shareholder meeting concerned with the company's 1917 report, and the shareholders' dividends.[101] The Wyllie surname may also have become a contender for the name of a future colliery.

According to a history of the Tredegar Estate, its agent, Charles Forestier-Walker, was the instigator of the idea that led to the Tredegar Company declaring its intention to extend its coal property south of Oakdale's. He 'persuaded' A. S. Tallis to secure for the company mineral rights for, in total, 2,000 acres. The idea may have originated due to earlier frustrated dealings between the Tredegar Estate and Burnyeat, Brown and Company that owned Nine Mile Point Colliery.[102] The Sirhowy Valley's Nine Mile Point Colliery stood just over a mile-and-a-half south-south-east of the site intended for the Tredegar Company's colliery development.[103] Nine Mile Point Colliery's coal property was contiguous with that granted to the Tredegar Company by the Tredegar Estate due to negotiations with Charles Forestier-Walker. Nonetheless, it was apt that the Estate's Agent put such an idea to Alfred Tallis.

In 1916, Tallis was promoted to managing director of the company with William Woolley appointed as general colliery manager.[104] In July 1917, Woolley became embroiled in a dispute that seemed to have affected Ebbw Vale and Tredegar colliery workers simultaneously. A subsequent strike involved a total of 12,000 men of which 4,000 were associated with Tredegar collieries.[105] The dispute with the Tredegar Company was about wage payments.

Food Rationing and Disputes

By the end of 1917, discord was a facet of 'the food question' in Tredegar. A Local Food Committee had operated for at least six months previously. The local Trades and Labour Council called a meeting in January 1918 to discuss the question. The meeting's main speaker was Thomas Richards MP, who still served as secretary of the SWMF. The Member of Parliament's mention of 'danger' lurking in the town's queues for food handouts was a sign of the discord. He further 'uttered a note of warning that violence [in queues] was not going to remedy the situation'. 'Patience', he recommended, was needed in Tredegar when food rations were being distributed.[106]

One case of deprivation notified to the Ministry of Food concerned 'colliers having to work with bread and jam, and even dry bread, in their boxes'. As a moan, it may have been dismissed as absurd and trivial by people who had never worked at the coalface. The case was accompanied by a warning: 'that should a stoppage of work ensue the responsibility would not be on the workmen'. The threat of a strike aside, miners needed an intake of food containing thousands of kilocalories in total to sustain a productive shift of work at the coalface. The Ministry of Food dispatched a ton of margarine to Tredegar around the 30th January.

On the 3rd February, a Tredegar meeting heard calls for the resignation of the Local Food Committee. The mood of the meeting appeared to be: 'In view of the apparent failure of all steps by the organised workers to equitable distribution and the refusal of the Food Committee to resign, the meeting recommended the workers of the town to call a general stoppage of all industries'. The motion, viewed as 'a drastic' course by the miners' agent, Alfred Onions, was carried at the meeting. The motion's seconder, Walter Conway,[107] secretary of Tredegar's Medical Aid Society, a member of the Independent Labour party, tabled that 'the weapon [a stoppage] would not be used rashly or foolishly'.[108] It seems that a subsequent reconstitution of the membership of the Food Committee tempered the 'agitation' among the 'organised workers'.

Sometime before the 8th February 1918, Thomas Richards MP joined a deputation to meet the Government minister responsible for food rationing, Lord Rhondda.[109] By the end of February, the Tredegar Urban District Council, with the 'sanction of Lord Rhondda', had added three Labour representatives and one Co-operative Society member to the Food Committee.[110] The mood of the February meeting suggested that colliery workers would have blamed the Urban District Council for any stoppage of work used to protest against the food problem. The Tredegar Company would have found no solace in not being accused of causing such a strike.

At Oakdale Colliery, in April 1918, work stopped due to a miners' dispute about unloading rubbish. The company chided the men for not raising the issue 'in the usual way'.[111] The dispute was resolved.

In mid-May 1918, a dispute at Markham Colliery was discussed at the Blackwood offices of the Tredegar Valley District of the SWMF. One of the 'points in dispute' was an action by the company to stop a share of a day's wage from the earnings of a number of men who had 'conveyed home the body of a colleague' killed at the colliery.[112] A short time before, a Combine Executive Committee had been formed with the aim of uniting union representation at the separate collieries of the Tredegar Iron & Coal Company and its affiliated collieries to jointly negotiate with the company. The company chose not to meet with the Committee regarding the Markham dispute. Alfred Onions, the miners' agent for the District, reacted by saying: 'It is not unlikely that unpleasant developments may take place as a result of the attitude of Mr Tallis'.[113] A strike followed at Markham Colliery and was a cue for strikes of sympathy at company collieries.

Later in May, a Joint Disputes Committee of the South Wales Conciliation Board met to try to resolve the Markham Colliery dispute. The stance taken by the Monmouthshire and South Wales Coalowners' Association at the Board meeting was 'that immediately the men resume [work] they can bring before the Board any question which they consider in dispute at the colliery'.[114] A settlement to the strike was reached late-May, and the company admitted to the 'injustice' of its action, and paid the men for the amount docked from their wages.

The Markham Colliery dispute seems to have raised the hackles of a man who, in a newspaper article, claimed he had taken part in the strike. Probably for anonymity, he used 'A. G.' for his signature as the author of an item of reflection about the strike in the *Monmouth Guardian*.[115] Patriotism may have triggered his apparent fury:

Employers and employees are equally guilty of a grave offence against our boys in the trenches, who are fighting hard, and sacrificing all in the defence of the Welsh coal mines and the homes of the miners. To come out on strike when the greatest of all battles is in progress, is not only suicidal, but the equivalent in moral effect to five divisions of Germans being hurled against the British.

The views of A. G.'s were either insightful if true, or defamatory if false. He judged that only a fraction of the miners knew why they were involved in a sympathy strike. He contended that more or less all the speeches delivered at the mass meetings were 'fiery oratory of the Anarchical type'. As a witness of meetings: 'the impression [he] formed during the last few days is that some of the leaders of the agitation locally have revealed in true perspective the spirit of "firebrands"'.

According to A. G., some miners invoked the tag of 'Hindenburg's day' for a crucial meeting held during the course of the strike. The tag may have been used for irony, but by chance it was an omen. In late-September 1918, British and Allied armies breached the Hindenburg Line. On the 11th November, the armistice was signed that ended the Great War as it was then called.

Death Toll

The cenotaphs later erected in Tredegar, Abertysswg, Blackwood, and Oakdale remember local men who fell in battle, or who perished at sea during the war. Most of these men had once been employed by the company. In summary: at Abertysswg the names of forty-four men are recorded on the village's cenotaph; at Blackwood forty-two men; at Oakdale thirty-four of which three of them had associations with Argoed; and at Tredegar 407 men. Over 4,000 men from Tredegar fought in the war.

The loss of kith and kin in the war was felt widely. In May 1915, the miners' agent Alfred Onions was notified of the death of his son, Lieutenant Wilfred Onions.[116] In 1917, Hon Walter Francis McLaren MP, an officer in the Royal Flying Corps, was killed whilst flying.[117] The Tredegar community would have particularly mourned news about fatalities of local men. On the 29th December 1915, the quarters of the 3rd Monmouthshire Regiment, at Elverdinghe Chateau, Ypres, was the target of German shelling. Town's people later read of the deaths of four men from the Tredegar district due to the shelling: Sergeant Snell, Private R. Pugh, Private Probert, and Private D. Thomas, with among the missing, Lance Corporal Harris. Four Tredegar men were also wounded. There were also 32 casualties, later revised up to 38.[118] The shelling at Elverdinghe Chateau appears to have cost the most lives of Tredegar district men in one day of the war. The survivors returned to their homes in the north-west of Monmouthshire with memories of warfare, which troubled some of them for the rest of their lives. One survivor of the war, William Clay Hepburn, demobbed from the Corps of Royal Engineers in the rank of major, was appointed agent to Oakdale Navigation Collieries Limited.

Political Agitation

By 1918, most of the company's workers were familiar with the ideals of socialists. In 1914, Archibald Fenner Brockway, later Baron Brockway of Eton and Slough in the County of Buckingham, contended that the Labour Party stood for 'freedom under a system of public ownership where every worker will have equal voice in the conditions of life and labour'. The 'Labour Party has stood true because it is a working class party'. The Liberal Party was accused of being a 'Capitalist Party. It is a tool of Capitalism'. 'The Liberal Party is not only financed by capitalists, the Liberal Party in the House of Commons is largely composed of capitalists. No less than 30 Liberal M. P.'s are reputed to be millionaires'. Sir A. B. Markham, and Hon. F. E. McLaren were listed among the thirty Liberal MPs named by Fenner Brockway. Fenner Brockway was unequivocal: the 'object of the Labour Party is the overthrow of Capitalism'.[119]

In 1917, some Oakdale Colliery workers attended a local meeting of the Independent Labour Party where they heard 'Comrade' G. Phillips speak. He called upon them to 'organise themselves … to combat the Capitalists in the class struggle'.[120] He warned that the 'Capitalists were organising their forces to crush the workers'. If he had spoken in the locality in 1918, Phillips might have decreed that the introduction that year by the Tredegar Company of a pension scheme for their officials and clerical staff was an act of Capitalist 'class antagonism'.[121] The start by the company in 1918 of an officials' salary bonus scheme, regulated by the yearly dividend paid to shareholders, was also a gift for the left-wing. Socialists could claim that the bonus scheme was an incentive scheme that would sustain a coercive management force so as to extract more gain for the Capitalist through the 'expropriation of the worker'.

Maybe the election in March 1919 of officers for the Monmouthshire and South Wales Coalowners' Association gave socialist agitators a bonus for stoking animosity within the Tredegar Company's territory. A. S. Tallis was elected chairman of the Association.[122]

Sankey Commission

The start of Tallis's period of office occurred in the eye of a Government-coal industry storm that hit the coal owners like a hurricane. In January 1919, the Miners' Federation of Great Britain pressed for higher pay and less hours worked per day. The MFGB also threatened a national coal strike.[123] As a result, at the end of February, Lloyd George set up a Coal Industry Royal Commission. Sir John Sankey was the Commission's chairman.

In mid-March, the Government accepted the Sankey Commission report that recommended higher worker wages and a reduction of one hour in the working day. Notably, Sir John Sankey recommended, coupled to a limitation on strike action, the nationalisation of the coal industry. Three independent members of the Commission judged that no case had been put that gave 'any reasonable ground for belief that the coal industry could or would be as efficiently conducted by the State in the future as private enterprise in the past'. The MFGB officials of the Commission, although endorsing the recommendation for nationalisation, rejected the proposal for the limitation of the right to strike.[124] The MFGB, the coalowners, and Government reached an agreement that excluded nationalisation. At the end of the year, a speech in favour of the nationalisation of the mines was delivered in Tredegar by Frank Hodges, the general secretary of the union.[125]

Tredegar colliery workers who heard Hodges speak may well have been persuaded by the case he put for nationalisation, but some were more eager to hear that action was afoot to win for them improved wages. A nationalised coal industry was for the future. The Tredegar Iron & Coal Company had earned a £171,976 profit for the business year that closed at the end of March 1918.[126] All Tredegar Company's workers were acquainted with the nature of an autonomous local private coal company whose financial performance gave them immediate grounds for a wage rise.

Markham Colliery, sunk between circa 1911 and 1914, was probably the second all-electric colliery in the South Wales Coalfield. The colliery's screens and washery are shown to the left. During later years of the Great War 930 men were employed at the colliery. The peak in employment of workers, at 2,591, occurred in 1928. In 1947, 930 workers were employed to win coal. *Pope/Parkhouse Archive*

NOTES

1   Ewart Smith, *Blackwood Yesterday Book 1.* (Old Bakehouse Publications, 1991), pp.5-6.
2   Violet Markham, op. cit., p.10.
3   'The Prince's Visit', WM, 17 Jan 1920, p.10. Moreover, as clues to the nature of Alfred Markham's contribution, during the planning of Woodlands, he took 'immense trouble … calling many working people and their wives into consultation, but of course in a first venture we made plenty of mistakes'. Violet Markham, op. cit., p.19.
4   Ralph Thomas, *Oakdale: The Model Village.* (1986, Village Publishing), p.26. Text suggests that BIDCO was used as a source for this book. Thomas's bibliography refers to Fred Hopkins, *Sixty Years at Oakdale Colliery*, which agrees with earlier speculation that BIDCO was written in the 1960s.
5   'Hotel for Oakdale Model Village', *Monmouth Guardian*, 13 March 1914, p.6.
6   Ralph Thomas, op. cit., pp.25-26.
7   'Hotel for Oakdale Model Village', *Monmouth Guardian*, 13 March 1914, p.6.
8   Ralph Thomas, op. cit., pp.36-40.
9   Ralph Thomas, op. cit., p.28.
10   Ebenezer Howard was the originator of the term Garden City in a book he published in 1902, *Garden Cities of Tomorrow*. Howard played a leading role in creating both the 'First Garden City', Letchworth, Hertfordshire, and the second, Welwyn Garden City. Martin S. Briggs, *Everyman's Concise Encyclopaedia of Architecture.* (Dent, 1959), p.143.
11   'Housing in South Wales', *The Amman Valley Chronicle and East Carmarthen Times*, 10 Dec 1914, p.3.
12   Violet Markham, op. cit., p.9.
13   'Tredegar Iron & Coal Co.', *Monmouth Guardian*, 2 July 1915, p.1.
14   'Development of Sirhowy Valley', *Weekly Mail*, 16 July 1910, p.10.
15   OS Ref SO 168020.
16   'Tredegar Company', ME, 17 June 1911, p.8.
17   TCG, Vol.CII, 4 August 1911. The value per share was not stated. New articles of association were also adopted to enable the directors of the Tredegar Iron & Coal Company to control earnings made from returns on the Markham Colliery investment.
18   Violet Markham, op. cit., pp.11-12. During the sinking of Bullcroft there were periods when water spilled over the brims of the shafts. Arthur Markham was 'urged' by his brother, Charles, 'to cut his losses and abandon the pit'. Arthur Markham 'refused absolutely' to heed his brother's advice, and in 1909 used a German process, which in principle, froze the ground around the shafts.
19   R. A. S. Redmayne, 'Report on the Circumstances attending the Explosion and Underground Fire which occurred at the Wellington Pit, Whitehaven Colliery, on the 11th May, 1910'. Home Office, 31 Jan 1911 [Hereafter: 'Wellington Pit Inquiry]. Sourced: Cumbria Archives (Whitehaven). pp.26-27.
20   W. Scandrett, *Old Tredegar Vol. 1.* (Starling Press, 1990), p.93.
21   Wellington Pit Inquiry, op. cit. footnote, p.27.
22   Violet Markham, op. cit., pp.11-12.
23   A. Leighton Stevens, 'A New Safety Lamp', SWIE, Vol. XXVIII (1910-11), p.505.
24   A. V. Jones & R. P. Tarkenter, *Electric Technology in Mining: the Dawn of a New Age.* (Peter Pergeines, 1993), p.38.
25   See particularly: 'Coal Mines Bill', *House of Commons Debates*, 17 March 1911.
26   'South Wales Colliery Managers'. *Monmouth Guardian*, 3 April 1914, p.1.
27   Woolley was awarded the Board of Education (South Kensington) Bronze Medal and the Richardson Medal presented by the Ebbw Vale Steel Iron & Coal Company. William Downing, Application for membership of the Institution of Civil Engineers.
28   'Sirhowy Disaster ', WM, 20 May 1912, p.3, and 'Explosion in a Shaft', ME, 25 May, 1912.
29   Leslie M. Shore, op. cit, p.145.
30   'Tredegar Company', ME, 17 June 1911, p.8.
31   Violet Markham, op. cit., p.10.
32   *The London Gazette*, 27 Sept 1912, p.7108. In the citation Wimborne's surname was given as 'Winborn'. In a newspaper report, 'Tragic Colliery Accident at Tredegar', *Monmouth Guardian*, 27 Feb 1914, concerning another rescue involving the Crumlin Rescue Station sergeant, his surname was spelt 'Wimburne'. His surname was spelt 'Winborne' in 'Sirhowy Disaster ', WM, 20 May, 1912, p.3, and 'Explosion in a Shaft', ME, 25 May, 1912, and was thus adopted for

use in the text. An apology is offered to any descendant of this brave man if the surname adopted in the text is wrong.
33   W. W. Tasker, op. cit., p.53.
34   Dr Henry Jordan, 'The South Wales Coalfield', SWIE, Vol. XXXVIII (1922), Sheet III. The Brithdir seam was met at a depth of 131 yards, and the Elled at 463 yards yards.
35   The properties of Markham Colliery's coal was similar to Pochin Colliery's, see earlier footnote.
36   Dr Henry Jordan, 'The South Wales Coalfield', SWIE, Vol. XXXVIII (1922), p.124.
37   Leslie M. Shore, op. cit, pp.121-125, pp.147-150, p.154, and p.160.
38   A search did not find information to confirm whether, or not, Oakdale Power-House's electricity generation capacity was the same as detailed earlier in the text, or had been increased to power Markham Colliery.
39   G. M. Harvey, *Colliery Electrical Engineering.* (Pitman, 1924), pp.144-148. The Ward Leonard system provided a 'very high degree of control over the winder, smooth and steady acceleration and regenerative braking'. At PD's Britannia Colliery the Ilgner system was used, which involved a higher capital cost than a Ward Leonard system.
40   *Winding Engine Data* – A. J. Edwards. (NCB). From the papers of A. J. Edwards in the keeping of the Writer.
41   Data regarding winding at Markham Colliery. *File 82: Electric Winders No. 6 Area.* (NCB). From the papers of A. J. Edwards in the keeping of the Writer.
42   Leslie M. Shore, op. cit, p.121.
43   SWA (E) Shaft Capacities. Oakdale Colliery's capacities were assessed on 2nd May 1969.
44   John Cornwell, *Collieries of South Wales, Vol. 1.* (Landmark, 2001), p.167
45   R. A. Cooke, *Western Valleys.* (Black Dwarf Lightmoor), p. 40/47.
46   W. W. Tasker, op. cit., pp.46-5.
47   Ray Lawrence, op. cit., p.121.
48   Ray Lawrence, op. cit., p.122.
49   The *South Wales Coal Annual*, p.113, and p.113, both 1909-10, and 1913.
50   'Greater Safety in Mines: Tredegar Company's Experiment'. *Monmouth Guardian*, 3 July 1914, p.1.
51   Attributed to H. S. Jevons in Roy Church, *The History of the British Coal Industry, Vol. 3, 1830-1913; Victorian Pre-eminence.* (Clarendon Press, 1986), p.223.
52   'Greater Safety in Mines: Tredegar Company's Experiment'. *Monmouth Guardian*, 3 July 1914, p.1.
53   'Bedwellty Urban Council'. *Monmouth Guardian*, 27 Feb 1914 (for 42 houses) and 16 July 1915, both p.1.
54   'Bedwellty Urban Council'. *Monmouth Guardian*, 29 Jan 1915, p.4.
55   'Greater Safety in Mines: Tredegar Company's Experiment', *Monmouth Guardian*, 3 July 1914, p.1.
56   'Tragic Colliery Accident at Tredegar'. Monmouth Guardian, 27 Feb 1914, p.1.
57   Troedrhiwgwair Level, sited to the south of Tredegar [OS Ref SO 155071], accessed the Brithdir seam within Cefn Manmoel whose coal was used to make household gas. The Level became a company operation after the closure in 1901-2 of both the Bedwellty Level and Whitworth Drift.
58   *The South Wales Coal Annual 1917*, pp.284-5.
59   'Abertysswg Citizens Honoured', *Monmouth Guardian*, 24 Dec 1915, p.1. The article does not give the age of John Evans, but Alfred Tallis records that on meeting him for the first time he 'was then an old and respected official'.
60   'South Wales Colliery Managers'. *Monmouth Guardian*, 3 April 1914, p.1.
61   Llewellyn J. Davies & D. Owen Davies, *South Wales Coals.* (Cardiff, 1919), p.6.
62   The pay load ratio being 60/108 i.e. 3 tons (Markham) over 5 tons 8 cwt (Oakdale).
63   'Argoed – Dispute at Markham's', *Monmouth Guardian*, 16 Sept 1914, p.2. The colliery's manning figure was taken from *The South Wales Coal Annual 1914*, p.113.
64   Paul Jones, email, 31 Jan 2015.
65   'Monmouthshire Recruiting', *Monmouth Guardian*, 16 Oct 1914, p.1.
66   'The Welsh Miners – Shortening the Holidays', *Monmouth Guardian*, 26 March 1915, p.1.
67   *The South Wales Coal Annual 1915*, p.211 & p.212 respectively.

Celynen North Colliery was owned by Newport, Abercarn Black Vein Steam Coal Company Ltd.

68 'Recruiting Meeting Rhymney', *Monmouth Guardian*, 9 April 1915, p.1.

69 'Tredegar-S.W.B's Hero', *Monmouth Guardian*, 10 Sept1915, p.3.

70 'Tredegar-Military Medal', *Monmouth Guardian*, 15 Dec 1915, p.3. Sgt Morgan's home address was 36, York Terrace, Tredegar.

71 'Collier's Funeral and a Strike', *Cambrian Daily Leader*, 9 Oct 1915, p.1.

72 'Recruiting Meeting Rhymney', *Monmouth Guardian*, 9 April 1915, p.1.

73 'Tredegar Iron and Coal Co.', *Monmouth Guardian*, 2 July 1915, p.3.

74 *The South Wales Coal Annual 1914*, and *1915*. In 1914, the total numbers employed by the company including Oakdale and Markham was 10,257, p.113 & p.115. The corresponding employment numbers for 1915 were 8,421, p.211 & p.213.

75 'Surprise Royal Visit. Prince Albert Among the Welsh Colliers', WM, 17 Jan 1920, p.9.

76 Seemingly the SWMF's funds were depleted due to aid given to unemployed miners in the anthracite district of the South Wales Coalfield. 'Tredegar Industrial Clouds', ME, 31 Oct 1914, p.2.

77 'Tredegar Iron & Coal Co.', *Monmouth Guardian*, 2 July 1915, p.3.

78 Violet Markham, op. cit., p.24.

79 'Tredegar Iron & Coal Co.', *Monmouth Guardian*, 2 July 1915, p.3.

80 *House of Commons Debates*, Vol. 72, 17 June 1915.

81 *House of Commons Debates*, Vol. 73, 19 July 1915.

82 Factors proposed as the cause of the 1915 South Wales Coalfield strike see Barry Supple, *The History of the British Coal Industry Vol.4: 1913-1946 The Political Economy of Decline.* (Clarendon Press, 1987), pp.64-65.

83 Barry Supple, op. cit., p.74.

84 'New Cottage Hospital', *Monmouth Guardian*, 29 Oct 1915, p.1.

85 'New Cottage Hospital', *Monmouth Guardian*, 29 Oct 1915, p.1.

86 'Oakdale Miners' Achievement: New Hospital to be Erected', *Llais Llafur*, 18 July 1914, p.4.

87 'Tredegar Iron & Coal Co.', *Monmouth Guardian*, 2 July 1915, p.3.

88 'Tredegar Industrial Clouds', ME, 31 Oct 1914, p.2.

89 'Tredegar Iron and Coal Co.', *Monmouth Guardian*, 7 July 1916, p.4.

90 *The Times*, 22 Nov 1916.

91 *The Times*, 27 Nov 1916.

92 Barry Supple, op. cit., p.76.

93 Violet Markham, op. cit., p.33. During the last months of his life, Sir Arthur Markham became the tenant of Newstead Abbey, the former home of the poet Lord Byron.

94 'Sir Arthur Markham', *Cambrian Daily Leader*, 8 Aug 1916, p.1.

95 During the First World War, Sir Arthur Markham was a leading critic of Lord Kitchener's role at the War Office. With regard to the supply of munitions, Markham 'urged what was needed above everything in administration was decentralisation, delegation and division– principles the exact opposite of those which ruled at the War Office'; Violet Markham, op. cit., pp.26-27. As an example of Sir Arthur Markham's criticism of Lord Kitchener see 'Prime Minister's Statement', *House of Commons Debates*, 15 June 1915.

96 Sir Arthur Markham left £733,290 gross. His will gifted money to the poor of Mansfield. 'Sir A. Markham's Will', *Cambrian Daily Leader*, 14 Nov 1916, p.1.

97 'Tredegar Company's Prospect's', *Monmouth Guardian*, 6 July 1917, p.1.

98 Sir R. A. Redmayne, *The British Coal-Mining Industry During the War.* (Clarendon Press, 1923), pp.127-128.

99 See for information: Keith Turton, 'Admiralty Coal Traffic in World War One: the Jellicoe Specials', *Railway Archive*, issues 19 & 20.

100 Trevor Boyns, 'The Coal Industry', in *The Gwent County History, The Twentieth Century*, Vol. 5, ed. Chris Williams, Andy Croll, and Ralph A. Griffiths. (University of Wales Press, 2013), [hereafter 'Trevor Boyns-Gwent Coal Industry'], table 3.3, p.39.

101 'Tredegar Company's Prospects', *Monmouth Guardian*, 6 July 1917, p.1.

102 William Smith, op. cit., p.15.

103 Although Risca Colliery stood at the mouth of the Sirhowy Valley, geographically, Nine Mile Point Colliery was the valley's most southern colliery.

104 'Mr A. S. Tallis JP: Prominent Colliery Owner Passes Away', SWA, 10 Sept 1927, p.6.

105 '12,000 Miners on Strike', *Cambrian Daily Leader*, 28 July 1917, p.1.

106 'Tredegar: Food Question and War Aims', *Monmouth Guardian*, 11 Jan 1918, p.3.

107 Walter Conway (1873-1933) was orphaned early in his life, and so spent a number of his early years in the Bedwellty Workhouse. He worked as a miner before taking the post as secretary of the Medical Aid Society.

108 'The Food Problem: Tredegar: Workmen's Threat', *Monmouth Guardian*, 8 Feb 1918, p.1.

109 David Alfred Thomas (1856-1918), Lord Rhondda, later 1st Viscount Rhondda. In 1906, as chairman of Cambrian Collieries, he initiated in the Rhondda Valley a colliery company acquisition policy that by 1913 was known as Consolidated Cambrian Limited. As head of what was tagged the Cambrian Combine, he acquired notoriety among Rhondda miners for the bitter strike of 1910-1911.

110 'Tredegar Food Control Committee: A Reconstitution', *Monmouth Guardian*, 1 March 1918, p.1.

111 'Tredegar Valley Miners', *Monmouth Guardian*, 12 April 1918, p.4.

112 'A Terrible Indictment', *Monmouth Guardian*, 31 May 1918, p.3.

113 'Tredegar', *Monmouth Guardian*, 10 May 1918, p.2.

114 'The Tredegar Strike', *Monmouth Guardian*, 17 May 1918, p.3.

115 'A Terrible Indictment', *Monmouth Guardian*, 31 May 1918, p.3.

116 'Late Lieu. Onions', *Monmouth Guardian*, 21 May 1915, p.1.

117 'Lady Aberconway', *The Times*, 5 Jan 1933, p.12.

118 'Tredegar Men in the Casualty List', *Monmouth Guardian*, 7 Jan 1916, p.3.

119 'The Failure of Liberalism VII—What is the Alternative?', *The Pioneer*, 14 Feb 1914, p.6.

120 'Oakdale Branch I. L. P.', *The Pioneer*, 30 June 1917, p.4.

121 The pension scheme was funded through an equal share of contributions from the Company and the employees. The pension was paid on retirement at sixty-five years of age with the maximum being half the salary 'payable' at fifty-years with the maximum being £350 per annum. TICC, op. cit., p.3.

122 'The Coalowners', *The Cambria Daily Leader*, 24 March 1919, p.1.

123 Neville Penry Thomas, *A History of British Politics from the Year 1900*. (Herbert Jenkins, 1956), p.79.

124 A. K. McCosh, *The Case Against Nationalisation of the Coal Mines.* (Scottish Colliery Owners, 1944), p.11.

125 'The Nationalisation of the Mines', *Monmouth Guardian*, 26 December 1919, p.3.

126 Trevor Boyns-Gwent Coal Industry, table 3.3, p.39.

HRH Prince Albert meets Oakdale Colliery miners, January 1920. It is believed that Oliver Harris, SWMF's Executive member for the Tredegar District, is the man wearing a white scarf who stands to the right of the Prince. First to the left of the Prince is David Evans, colliery manager, with , next left, Major W. Hepburn DSO, company agent. *A. S. Tallis Photograph Album, Courtesy of the Tallis Family*

Chapter Seven
TRAUMATIC TWENTIES & WYLLIE

At the start of the Twenties, from the standpoint of its workforce, the Tredegar Iron & Coal Company was the power that held sway over their livelihoods. The colliery worker probably classified the company's chairman, directors, and managing director as the 'coalowner'. The worker reviled the 'coalowner' for the perceived scheming that denied them wage rises. However, for a decade at least, the Government had been involved in coal industry wage settlements. During the war, the MFGB further twisted the Lion's tail to win generous worker wage rises at the expense of the coalowner. Yet, widespread anger remained among colliery workers about the profits made by British coal companies during the Great War.

Regarding the leaders of the Tredegar Company, most of the colliery workers knew them albeit not personally. In 1920, the seventy year old Lord Aberconway had been associated with the company's affairs for three decades. A. S. Tallis had emerged by the start of the twentieth century as the public figurehead of Tredegar. After he removed from the town in 1913, leading townsmen feared that his interest in the well-being of Tredegar would fade,

and as a result the location's importance to the company would diminish.[1] However, his house move appears to have anticipated his promotion to managing director. He moved to live in 'Lwyn Celyn', a large house set in countryside to the north of Caerleon, which positioned him for ready access by road to Newport and the collieries of the company, and by rail to Cardiff and London for business. Nevertheless, the fostering of a new relationship between township and the company's hierarchy began in 1916 when William Woolley occupied Rhyd Hall, Tredegar.

Royal Visit to Oakdale Colliery[2]

A highlight in the company's history occurred on Friday the 17th January 1920. HRH Prince Albert, aged 24 years, second in Order of Succession to the Crown, later the Duke of York, made a 'surprise' visit to Oakdale Colliery and its associated village and hospital. The Royal party was chauffeured in a convoy of cars from Newport High Street Station. The party included: Alfred Tallis, Norman McNeil, Cardiff Office commercial manager, W. Strong, commercial manager at Tredegar, and

HRH Prince Albert, later HM The King George VI, meets Tredegar Company managers at Oakdale Colliery, January 1920. On the doorstep of one of the colliery's winding houses. Left to Right: Major W. Hepburn DSO, company agent; HRH Prince Albert; A. S. Tallis, managing director; David Evans, colliery manager. The men are each holding a fireman's stick. *A. S. Tallis Photograph Album, Courtesy of the Tallis Family*

Captain C. S. Mason of the Industrial Welfare Society of which Tredegar Company directors were members. The prince was the society's president. Major William Clay Hepburn, William Woolley, David Evans, colliery manager, and H. J. Rake, chief mechanical engineer, were the first men introduced to the prince at the colliery. At the time, the colliery employed 2,700 men who produced 14,500 tons of coal a week, which if sustained yielded an annual output of around three-quarters of a million tons.

Prince Albert donned overalls for an underground tour. At pit bottom, he met David Morgan, under-manager, who guided the Royal party to view: the New East district, 'the main haulage dip, ... the South Pit bottom, and 'into the West Slum'. En route, under the instruction of collier John Badham, the prince used a mandrel to cut coal, a piece of which was kept by him as a souvenir. The prince had a 'chat' with the 'driver' of 'Paddy', a pit pony.

On shaking the hand of Charles William, Prince Albert heard the collier say, "I hope the Majesty's Viceroy will win the Lincolnshire. I shall have a couple of pounds on it!" 'Roars of laughter' erupted as another collier 'chimed', "And I placed a shilling or two up and down." Charles William, wearing 'a mischievous grin', then appealed for more Welsh butter. "I have had only one ounce of butter to come to work since last Saturday, and how can you expect us to increase the output of coal on one ounce of butter?" Rationing of food remained an issue.

There were further presentations to the prince. He talked to George Wilson, a fireman, and chargehand Thomas Powell. He accepted an invitation from George Robins, chairman of Oakdale Horticultural Society, to plant a tree in the village square to commemorate the visit.

On the colliery's surface, the prince stepped from a cage to hear national and Welsh melodies played by the Oakdale Brass Band, conducted by T. Proctor. He mixed with a group of miners getting ready to descend the pit, and was introduced to Edward Gibben. The 'well-built, grey haired miner' of sixty-five years of age had worked as a 'collier for 35 years'. The prince was impressed by Edward Gibben's 'long run' in a 'hard' job. He later met Oliver Harris, checkweighman, SWMF's Executive member for the Tredegar district. The prince's guides for inspections of the winding house and the power-house were H. J. Rake and W. A. Hutchings, chief electrical engineer. On returning to the colliery offices, David Evans offered to the prince a gift, the fireman's stick used during the tour underground, and it was accepted.

Prince Albert next looked around the village and inspected 32 Syr Dafydd Avenue. After crossing the house's threshold, he shook a hand of Fred Noakes, a 'cheery ex-serviceman'. Mr and Mrs Fred Noakes had four sons. The prince learnt that Noakes had lost one finger fighting with a Welsh regiment at the Battle of Ypres in May, 1915, and two other fingers were 'smashed on the Somme'. After being discharged from the army, he got work at the colliery, but 'had the misfortune to lose' his left hand. However, the hospital had been 'very kind' and supplied him with an artificial arm. The prince attentively listened to Noake's tale.

Mrs Noakes was struck by how 'carefully the prince examined' the house. Observing that Fred Noakes wore working clothes, the prince asked his wife if they were usually 'dropped on the mat' upon her husband arriving home. Mrs Noakes replied, "No. We don't treat our men as bad as that. We let them take off their clothes in front of a nice fire." She judged the prince to be a 'young gentleman ... a handsome one–with a sunny smile on his face'.

The royal visit ended with an inspection of Oakdale Cottage Hospital where the prince's escorts were Dr Rankin, Matron Wolverage, and its chairman, David Aggex. The prince considered the hospital's X-Ray facilities to be 'among the finest in the country'. He took afternoon tea at Major and Mrs Hepburn's residence before motoring to Newport to catch the train for London.

Shortly afterwards, the prince wrote a letter to his mother, Queen Mary, in which he gave his impressions of the visit. It 'was very interesting and I got a very good reception from the miners. I talked to a number of them and they seemed quite contented .... They have a whole village to themselves which was built by the company, and the miners run the clubs, etc, entirely themselves ...'[3] Oakdale Colliery and its village had, beyond anybody's belief at the time, hosted a visit of the future HM The King George VI, and the naming of York Avenue at Oakdale recalls his visit.

The 1920 Coal Strike[4]

For the 'two years after the Armistice, the market for British coal remained buoyant and its values greatly inflated'.[5] On the 15th July 1920, the Executive of the Miners' Federation of Great Britain presented the Controller of Coal Mines with demands for: a reduction in the price of domestic coal, and flat rate wage increases for workers.[6] On the 26th July, Sir Robert Horne, President of the Board of Trade, rejected the union's demands and proposed a tribunal, or as an alternative to a flat rate for pay, a wage based upon a tonnage rate. The Miners' Federation rebuffed the minister's proposals, but negotiations continued. On the 16th October, following a ballot, a national strike began that ended on the 3rd November 1920, after an agreement was reached between the Board of Trade and the Miners' Federation.

However, the British coal industry was struggling due to poor general trading conditions and foreign competition. The Tredegar Company, between 1st April 1920 and the end of March 1921 produced 1,835,671 tons. Speculatively, if the Tredegar Company's collieries had been working fully then an extra one million tons of coal might have been realised.[7]

The 1920 British coalfield strike had at least two consequences. An Emergency Powers Act was passed that empowered the King to proclaim a state of emergency if a strike risked harm to the economy of the nation. On the 31st March 1921, the 'trustees ... to the nation' for the running of the coal industry during Great War, the Government, ended its control powers.

Some Sirhowy Valley events

In the spring of 1921, a landslide to the south of Bedwellty Pits gave rise to some alarm.[8] Around 800 men were employed at the colliery up until 1922. By early 1923, the Tredegar Urban District Council judged that the Bedwellty Pits' landslide had settled down.[9]

Around 1927, the 'Pochin' landslide, as it then was called, extended a distance of nearly one mile from just north of Pochin Colliery to south of Bedwellty Pits. A study of the landslide at the time observed that 'the slipping of the soil and subsoil' had carried 'a large quantity of colliery refuse'. The study also noted that a trench had been 'cut through at the toe of the tip', from which it was concluded that the 'colliery tip is *not* [Professor Knox's emphasis] pushing this mass downhill'. In 1966, Knox's conclusion caught the interest of an inquiry into the 1966 Aberfan disaster. A coal tip above the village of Aberfan slipped and

Landslide between Bedwellty Pits and Pochin Colliery.

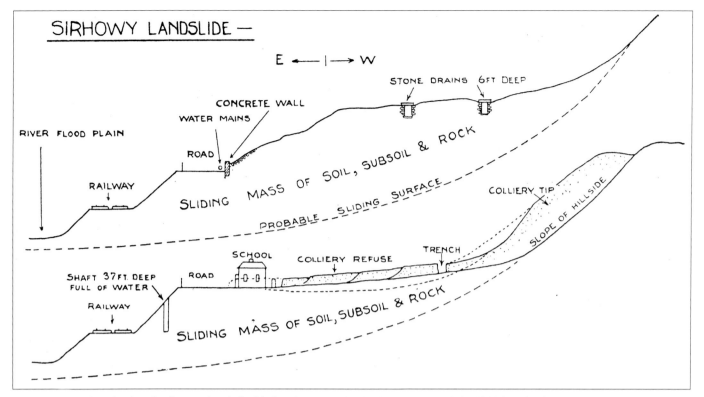

SIRHOWY LANDSLIDE —

Figure showing that the slip of colliery refuse halted before hitting a school, which anticipated the 1966 Aberfan disaster.

Proceedings, SWIE: 1927/28, Vol. XLIII

killed 116 children and 28 adults. However, the Pochin landslide became a burden first for the Tredegar UDC and then for its successor councils. Indeed, 'the uneven movement of the sliding mass necessitates almost continual repair work on the roadway', noted in 1927/28 for the A4048, has remained a bugbear.[10]

In 1921, the Tredegar Company tendered for the supply of 'British' coal to the Tredegar UDC for making town gas. Later that year, the council awarded a contract for the supply of coal for making gas to the company with Troedrhiwgaer Level named as the coal's source.[11]

Sometime around 1921, a doctor, A. J. Cronin, joined the Tredegar Medical Aid Society for general practice. Dr Cronin had previously practiced at a village in one of the Rhondda valleys where he found social life to be 'grim'.[12] In comparison, 'Tredegar was a colliery town, too, but it was trim and clean set on the verge of still unspoilt hill country. There were several decent stores, a public library, and one – could scarcely believe it – a town hall where moving pictures were shown twice a week'.[13] Familiar with parts of his native Scottish Highlands, he 'found a wild beauty on the high, bare heath' where in the summer he took 'prodigious walks' gathering 'whinberries' for 'deep-dish pies'. Thus, Dr Cronin became partial to a home-made dessert delicacy of the South Wales valleys. Moreover, he cherished the 'cold nights' sitting 'reading, talking, arguing' in front of a 'blazing fire' at the house provided for him by the Tredegar Medical Aid Society. As an employment perk, 'coal was plentiful and free'.[14]

Unemployment in 1921

In the year 1921, the coal output of the South Wales Coalfield fell by a third compared with 1920. In April, in the wake of the Government ending its control of the coal industry, the coal owners demanded a reduction in colliery workers wages. The colliery workers refused to go to work, and a lock-out was imposed that lasted three months. A sequel to the lock-out was an upsurge in local unemployment. Around the start of September, between 1,600 and 2,000 men were idle in Tredegar. Concerning other districts of Monmouthshire, in Abertillery 3,200 men were unemployed, in Ebbw Vale between 4,000 to 5,000 men, and in Nantyglo and Blaina 3,000 men.[15]

The unemployed were organised to make a protest. On the 7th September 1921, an estimated 5,000 men representing Monmouthshire's mining towns and villages marched on Tredegar's Workhouse. The protest was timed for a meeting of the Board of the Bedwellty Guardians. A role of the Bedwellty Guardians was to provide relief as cash under the Poor Law Act. Tredegar's unemployed colliery workers were not alone in finding that any relief granted by the Bedwellty Guardians was below a subsistence level.

Aneurin Bevan[16]

One of the leaders of the march was Aneurin Bevan. Born in Tredegar in 1897, he entered the coal industry as an underground worker at Ty Trist in 1912. He moved on to work at Pochin Colliery where in 1916, at nineteen years of age, he was elected chairman of the colliery's lodge, a SWMF position not unlike that of a trade union convenor of shop stewards at a manufacturing company. He was one of the protagonists in the creation of the Tredegar Combine Executive Committee. During the 1918 Markham Colliery strike he served as the Committee's deputy chairman, and toured the South Wales Coalfield to 'seek support for the strikers'. He had by then become a 'prodigious' reader of literature, poetry, and political texts loaned to him by the Tredegar Workmen's Library. In 1918, funded by a South Wales Miners' Federation scholarship, he began two years of study in Marxist economics and labour history at the Central Labour College, London.

Maybe it was before Aneurin Bevan studied in London that he won a local following for 'the towering arrogance with which he treated the employers'. As a member of one union delegation he had a 'violent argument' with W. Stephen Davies, agent of the Tredegar Company. Davies concluded: 'Look here Bevan, there isn't room in this Company for you and me.' 'I agree,' replied Bevan, 'and I think you ought to go.'

An evolving relationship between the Tredegar Valley Miners' District and the South Wales Miners' Federation at the time may also have spurred Bevan to assert local union power. Harold Finch took up a post as clerk at the Blackwood offices of the Tredegar Valley Miners' District offices in 1918.[17] He found on

A photograph of Aneurin Bevan (1897-1960) as young man. At nineteen years of age he was elected chairman of the South Wales Miners' Federation lodge at Pochin Colliery. A protagonist for the creation of the Tredegar [miners'] Combine. Entered the House of Commons as Member of Parliament for Ebbw Vale in 1929. Served in the 1945 Labour Government as Minister of Health. The founder of the National Health Service.   *Courtesy of Tredegar History and Archive Society*

joining the Tredegar Valley Miners' District that: 'In those days the Federation was a loosely-knit organisation, each valley or area having its own autonomy with miners' agents and other agents responsible to the membership of the area'. However, at the time he 'entered the Miners' Offices at Blackwood there was an increasing tendency to consult the central office and seek the guidance of the secretary, the Rt Hon Thomas Richards'.[18]

In 1919 the Tredegar Labour Party was formed, and Aneurin Bevan became a member. 'Bevan insisted to those' who thought of becoming Communists: 'You will cut off yourself from the main stream of the Labour Movement'. Michael Foot deemed that Bevan 'was a firm Marxist but his Marxist training taught him never to freeze his own mind in rigid attitudes'.

Protests against the Bedwellty Guardians

Regarding the protest on the 7th September 1921, Aneurin Bevan was among the delegates that met the Bedwellty Guardians. The delegation's main contention being that 'new circumstances had arisen which made the amount of relief from now on absolutely inadequate', and 'impressed' upon the Guardians the 'urgent necessity' of assistance for the unemployed.

After the meeting, Aneurin Bevan spoke to the assembly of men. His employment status at the time was found to be unclear. However, it is believed that his name was blacklisted by the Tredegar Company regarding re-employment, which if it was the case enhanced his authority when asserting: 'What was urgently needed was immediate action to make the Government come to the relief of the Guardians, and this could only be done by continual agitation. Failing that direction, they should get to

contact with other boards and trade unions to bring pressure to bear upon' the Government. Other voices were heard bemoaning the insufficiency of financial help.[19]

Six days later an estimated at 8,000 men, from mining communities across Monmouthshire, gathered again in Tredegar. Apparently 'excellent good humour' issued from the men during their hikes in 'drenching rain'. The crowd of men 'greatly appreciated' being served bread and cheese and tea upon their arrival at the Workhouse, but these were the only gifts they received.

A deputation 'from the demonstrators' appeared before Bedwellty Guardians' board to present an unemployment pay scheme proposal and to voice complaints. However, not only did the Poor Law Act not allow the Guardians to 'pay relief in money entirely', but the call for funds had put its financial solvency in jeopardy.

At the meeting Aneurin Bevan asked the Bedwellty Guardians to 'violate the Poor Law in many respects – '. The Guardians' Clerk intruded: 'You are going to put us in gaol'. Bevan continued: 'Unless something was done they were going to see a serious outbreak in the country, and they wanted to prevent that if possible'.[20] The deputation withdrew from the meeting to tell thousands of men again about impasse.

A series of other meetings occurred afterwards to discuss the issue. At one, Evan Davies, the Member of Parliament for the Ebbw Vale constituency, created in 1918, told members of the Bedwellty Guardians that 'he was in sympathy with the problem they were up against'. He advocated that 'the one sensible policy to adopt was to inform the Government that it was impossible to carry out the administration of poor law with the responsibilities lying on their shoulders'. He urged the Guardians to ask for 'the re-assembly of Parliament to deal with the unemployment problem, because they believed it was a greater menace to the nation as war and famine, and unless something was done immediately it was the surest road to revolution they ever had in this country'.[21]

In April 1922, Aneurin Bevan was elected a Tredegar Urban District councillor for the West Ward. *The South Wales Weekly Argus* described him as an 'ex-student' and 'a great debater'.[22] Michael Foot later claimed that Bevan 'used the Council Chamber as a platform for attacking the [Tredegar] Company', which was not confirmed in a read of the Tredegar UDC's minute book up to late 1926.[23] However, rivalry as debaters might also have been a feature of the Bevan-W. Stephen Davies spat mentioned above. According to Harold Finch, W. Stephen Davies was a 'fluent speaker'. Finch, who would later rise to prominence in civic life, further noted that the Tredegar Company agent served as a councillor on the Tredegar Urban District Council serving in 1920 as chairman.[24] The council's minute book suggests that Aneurin Bevan took a greater interest in the plight of the unemployed.[25]

On the 27th January 1923, he was one of the leaders of a further march of the unemployed to Tredegar Workhouse.[26] He later recalled that 'we locked the Guardians in for two days'. In his opinion they were not 'annoyed with us, for they were in the main our own people. They were one with us in our attitude to the parsimony of Whitehall'.[27] The sympathy of the Bedwellty Guardians did not win the unemployed an extra penny whereas coal orders taken by the Tredegar Company gave a glimmer of hope of work for at least idle Tredegar men.

Coal Market and Employment

Around 1922, the company was vulnerable as ever to hazards outwith its control. During the months of May and June in 1922, demand for Welsh steam coal for export fell away, resulting in 'a serious drop in prices'. The 'adverse tide' turned. Exceptionally, some Tredegar coal was shipped across the Atlantic 'in consequence of American requirements, due to the prolonged strike in the United States of America'. Moreover, 'the demand from Europe was quite good and the prices remained steady at a reasonable level throughout the autumn' of 1922. 'Notwithstanding a certain amount of competition from

America', for the first half of 1923, a 'good market' for Tredegar coal prevailed.[28] Indeed, Lord Aberconway claimed that the 'Welsh coal trade' had 'practically recovered the position it occupied before the War'.[29]

In 1922, the Tredegar Company employed 9,218 persons at its collieries, which compared with 1913 was a rise of 1,205. However, over that time period, the distribution of employment at the company's collieries had seen notable change:[30]

	No. of Persons Employed in 1922 (+ or – vs 1913)
Bedwellty Pits Nos. 1 & 2	780 (-571)
McLaren Merthyr	1,419 (-414)
Oakdale[31]	2,703 (+1899)
Markham	1,392 (+1202)
Pochin	1,615 (-76)
Troedrhiwgwair	82 (+14)
Ty Trist Nos. 1 & 2	1,227 (+31)
Whitworth	nil (- 880)

Moreover, around the time of the second march on the Tredegar Workhouse, employment prospects seem to have improved in the Sirhowy Valley. For the twelve months that ended the 31st March 1923, the Tredegar Company recorded growth in the number of its employees to 11,731 men and its collieries produced a total of 2,917,328 tons of coal.[32]

The colliery workers of the Tredegar Company had during that period of twelve months also adopted double shift working. Such a pattern of working, common in the Midlands Coalfield, was a 'somewhat new departure' in the South Wales Coalfield.[33] Indeed, in the South Wales Coalfield 'the system

was opposed, often vehemently' by colliers. The introduction of double shift working confounded 'traditions and customs', and had 'implications for earnings and safety because of the need for colliers on the alternative working shifts to share a stall'. Moreover, in the 1902 SWMF rule book rule V stated a 'commitment "to oppose the system of Double Shift except where absolutely necessary for the purpose of ventilation"'.[34] However, during the period reported, the company 'lost practically no time through strikes' that suggests that the company's workers, maybe fearful of the prospect of unemployment, accepted the change to double shift working without much dissent. Local pride, though, may have been hurt in 1923, when the company made it clear that coal raised at Tredegar, Oakdale, and Markham collieries was sold as 'Tredegar' coal.

Regardless, the seemingly healthy state of company employment was apparent elsewhere in the Sirhowy Valley. In Tredegar, a comparatively small pool of unemployed colliery workers sought work.[35] The company's engineering works and steel mill were 'fully employed'. The steel mill manufactured arched roof supports and light rails for the collieries. The company's 'busy' wagon shops saw both the assembly of new wagons and repair work.

Tredegar Iron & Coal Company's Jubilee Year

The foregoing picture of employment in 1923 gave the Tredegar Iron & Coal Company grounds to celebrate in some style a jubilee: the company had 'existed' for fifty years. Yet, only a 'little statement' was issued giving a history of the company.[36]

During five decades of operation, the statement noted, the company's shareholders had authorised a total of £2,395,954 financial investment on the capital account and special work for the development of Monmouthshire mining property. The statement omitted to mention that such enterprise had seen a

The Company's Tredegar Works – Wagon Shop.

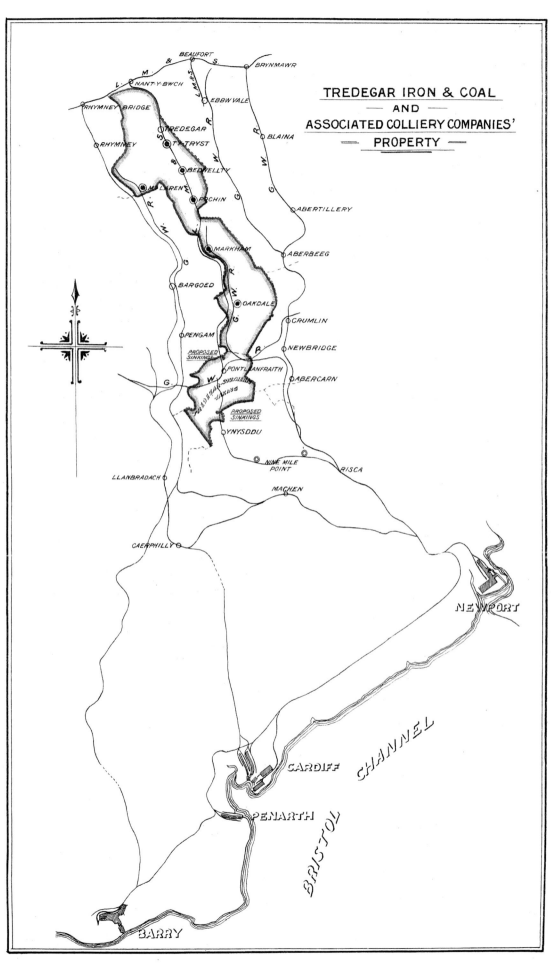

TREDEGAR IRON & COAL
— AND —
ASSOCIATED COLLIERY COMPANIES'
— PROPERTY —

Tredegar Iron & Coal and Associated Colliery Companies' Property at the time of the company's 50 years Jubilee in 1923.

doubling of worker employment over the five decades. In 1869, the then Tredegar Company employed 5,200 people.

The company's directors claimed in the statement that they had 'ever regarded the welfare of the workers'. The two model villages, Oakdale and Markham, were cited as evidence in support of their claim. 'There are 5,000 people living in the 1,000 houses which the company owned'. Credit was given to the 'workmen' for setting up workmen's institutes. In 1923, company officials and workmen's representatives joined Welfare Committees with one aim being to lay-out recreation grounds in Abertysswg, Oakdale, and Tredegar.[37] Although the company revealed that it had given 'every encouragement and financial support' for the setting up institutes, it did not admit to playing a role in the advance of the health care of workers. However, in June 1923, the company made a donation of £1,500 to the Tredegar Cottage Hospital for a new operating theatre to 'commemorate the Jubilee of the Company'.[38]

The jubilee statement asserted that the company had had 'remarkable freedom from serious mining accidents'. Such an assertion might speak for the prevailing definition for 'serious mining accidents'. Omitted was mention of the thirty-two company employees in total killed due to explosions at Pochin Colliery and McLaren Colliery in 1874 and 1902 respectively. Nevertheless, the late Sir Arthur Markham's example made true the directors' belief that they 'always kept the safety of their workmen in the forefront' and so had 'adopted every method of minimising the risks' of mining. Legislation, though, had 'also moved rapidly in the direction of the workmen' during the previous decades. Indeed, the company paid out in the financial year that ended on the 31st March 1923, the total sum £122,638 for workmen's compensation, health insurance, and 'betterment', which was a 'development never contemplated in the early years' of the company.

The company used the jubilee statement to gripe about its tax bill. The total tax paid by the company for the year 1873-1874 was £4,815. The company's tax assessment for the year 1921-1922 was put at £193,784, of which £67,187 was 'in discharge of local rates'.

The company noted that shareholder numbers had grown from forty-six in 1873 to some 3,000 in 1923. The prospect of attracting new shareholders occurred in 1923 since the company paid a high dividend, 12½ per cent, due to the company recording a profit of £234,022.[39] A company investment opportunity arose in 1923 since a resolution was passed to increase the capital of the company to £2,000,000 'by the creation of 480,000 new 'B' shares of £1 each'.[40]

The 'very dark spot' linked to the founding of McLaren Colliery was not mentioned in the company's jubilee statement, but it may have still haunted the memory of the company's chairman. Although at the 1923 meeting of shareholders he boasted about the 'great financial success' of the company, he counselled financial prudence. Lord Aberconway advocated that instead of 'paying a much larger dividend or bonus in cash, [or] to capitalise certain reserves and to issue a bonus in fully-paid shares to all the shareholders in proportion to their paid-up holdings', that an even larger cash balance be retained by the company. The company's accounts made known a 'large' cash balance 'amounting to half a million of money'. He candidly admitted that the 'money had been put aside many years past, to meet during the War and subsequent to War possible claims (most of which I am glad to say had not arisen), has been earned in the Sirhowy Valley, and we think it ought to be spent as far as possible in the development of that valley'.[41] Consistent with such an aim, he announced that the company proposed to 'proceed forthwith with the sinking of … two shafts at Penycwarel, near Ynysddu, in the Sirhowy Valley, and this colliery will be known as Wyllie Colliery'.

Wyllie Colliery[42]

The site chosen for Wyllie Colliery stood about two miles south of Blackwood on the western side of the Sirhowy Valley. The site was described by William Woolley in 1929 as 'limited and difficult', and was selected to 'keep well away from known large faults in this area'.[43] The site lay in a rural scene that offered an eastern outlook towards a hillside locally known as Mynyddisllwyn Mountain where in fields sheep and cattle grazed. St. Tudor's Church, which stood near the top of the mountain, owed its origin, circa 1102, to the monks of Glastonbury Abbey. After 1906 in fields to the north of the church, annual sheep dog trials were held.[44] However, although interest in the sheep dog trials flourished, the memory of the decades of fame that household coal mined from levels driven into Mynyddisllwyn Mountain faded.

At some date before the 29th June 1923, the Tredegar Iron & Coal Company registered 'The Tredegar (Southern) Collieries, Ltd' with Wyllie Colliery as its asset. As a subsidiary company, Tredegar (Southern) Collieries was set up 'on the same lines as Oakdale and Markham Companies. That is to say, the whole of the share capital will be subscribed for and found by our company [Tredegar Iron & Coal]'.[45]

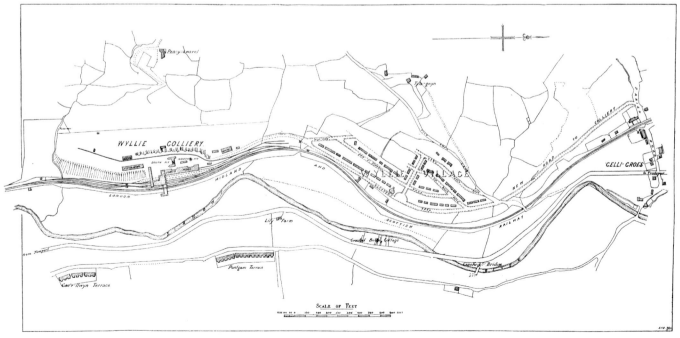

Wyllie Colliery and Village.

Proceedings, SWIE: 1929, Vol. XLV

Lt-Colonel A. K. Wyllie CB chaired the company's 1924 annual meeting. During the meeting he informed shareholders that the directors had 'been good enough to honour me by naming the Wyllie Colliery'. 'Despite the bad weather', he announced that 'good progress' had been made founding the colliery. 'An approach road about two miles in length' had been constructed for colliery access. 'Shortly' to be made available for use were the 'junctions connecting the colliery sidings with the London Midland & Scottish (LMS)'. The 1921 Railway Act had caused in Britain the amalgamation of railway companies, and as a result the L&NWR line of the Sirhowy Valley became an asset of the LMS. The availability of the sidings would 'enable' the company to 'proceed with the erection of the necessary sinking equipment'. 'Well in advance' were 'the 'somewhat heavy excavations for the colliery surface works and sidings'.[46]

The colliery was designed to be 'worked entirely by electricity'.[47] A. S. Tallis directed the work that conceived the colliery's layout and general design. Messrs William Angus Scott & Partners, consulting engineers, oversaw at least detail design. Even in the 1920s, it seemed remarkable that William Woolley felt it necessary to observe that 'few people recognised what an extensive amount of genuine civil engineering there was in the lay-out of a colliery surface. When they had to push tubs everywhere they would realise what their old friend 'Gravity' did for them in the more modern collieries' like Wyllie.[48]

Regarding the colliery engineering schedule, William Woolley noted that 'not until the end of 1924' did work begin regarding 'the [Wyllie] pits and permanent engine houses' and other colliery plant and equipment. The sinking contract was awarded to Frederick Piggot of Caerphilly. Two shafts, centres fifty yards apart, each 20ft in diameter, were sunk to the steam coal seams. On the 7th November 1924, seventy-one weeks of actual sinking of the South Shaft began. Shaft sinking halted for the erection

Workers employed sometime between 1924 and 1926 by Frederick Piggot of Caerphilly to sink Wyllie Colliery. Frederick Piggot had earlier been contracted to sink at least Bedwas Navigation Colliery and Markham Colliery. In 1919, Piggot sold his Caerphilly home, 'The Beeches', which adapted, became the Caerphilly District Miners' Hospital. *Courtesy of Amgueddfa Cymru National Museum Wales*

of the head-frame. On the 30th August 1926, at a depth 629 yards, after ninety-four weeks of activity the South Shaft was completed. The excavation of the North Shaft began on the 13th January 1925, and ended on the 21st September 1926, at a depth of 598 yards to the 'bottom of the sump' having entailed ninety weeks of work of which sixty-eight weeks concerned sinking.

According to the company's general manager of collieries, two factors guided the decision to make electricity the prime power source of the colliery. The 'successful experience' of operating the electrically-equipped Markham Colliery, was the first factor. The last factor was a 'lack of an adequate supply of water' for steam raising plant in the vicinity of Wyllie Colliery.

The colliery's electrical power was provided by Oakdale power-house that had greater generating capacity than in 1911 when only two 1,000 kW mixed pressure turbo-alternators were used to generate 3,000 V at 50 Hz. Added to the mixed pressure turbo-alternators after 1911 were the following items of 3 phase 50 Hz generating plant: one 5,000 kW 6,600 V, mixed pressure turbo-alternator, condenser and accessories by Messrs C. A. Parsons & Co., Newcastle upon Tyne; one 3,000 kW, 3,300 V, mixed pressure turbine by Messrs Willans and Robinson, with Westinghouse alternator and surface condenser; and one 7,500 kW, 6,600 V, mixed pressure turbo-alternator by Messrs Brown-Boveri, with surface condenser accessories by Messrs Allen, Sons & Co. As a result, in 1929, the power-house generated nearly 30,000,000 Board of Trade units[49] of electricity per annum, of which a 35 per cent share was distributed to Oakdale Colliery, 32 per cent to Markham Colliery, 26 per cent to Wyllie Colliery, and the balance to Tredegar's collieries and works.

Two electric transmission cables were laid from the Oakdale power-station to Wyllie Colliery. The district to the north of the new colliery was appraised as 'fairly thickly populated and likely to become more so'. The length of each cable was around 3½ miles, and mainly run in an earthenware trough filled with bitumen. Each cable comprised six copper wire cores of $0.125in^2$ section, and carried 6,600 volts. For most of a cable's run it was paper insulated, lead covered and single wire armoured. However, submarine type cable was used where 'permanently waterlogged' ground lay. At Wyllie Colliery, two Messrs Metro-Vickers, 'step-down' transformers 6,600/3,300 V were placed in 'fire proof cubicles external and detached from the main engine-house'. The transformers enabled the underground plant to be supplied at 3,300 V and subsidiary surface machinery at 550 V. The main underground substation was located at a depth of 520 yards.

Wyllie Colliery – Excavating North Pit, 30th January 1925.
Proceedings, SWIE: 1929, Vol. XLV

Wyllie Colliery – Engine House.   *Proceedings, SWIE: 1929, Vol. XLV*

Installed in the colliery's winding house, 283 ft long, having a roof span of 41ft, was all the important plant and machinery. An inspection of the building would see the colliery's winding engines, fan motors, air compressors, main electrical switchboard, and other equipment.

Messrs Markham & Co., Chesterfield, supplied the drums and mechanical components of the winding engines whilst the electrical parts and its brake were supplied by Siemens-Schuckert. Ward Leonard control was utilised. The engine brakes were of the post type applied at each side of the drum, which was bi-cylindro-conical with the small diameter being 12ft and the larger diameter 18ft. The winding specification comprised at least fifteen criteria. The major criteria being: ultimate output of coal per hour of 171 tons; net weight of coal per wind 2.7 tons; number of winds per hour 63; weight of cage and bridles 4¾ ton; number of trams per cage: two; and the winding rope weighed six pound per foot.

After the colliery had been sunk it was noted that the 'bulk of water' issued from the sides of the shafts. The seepage in the shafts, and from elsewhere in the pit, was collected in a 'storage bay'. The normal seepage rate was about 12,000 gallons/hr. Two Mather & Platt pumps and motors were installed in the North Shaft, level with the storage bay, to raise water to the surface. Each pump was capable of lifting 36,000 gallons/hr of water up a total head of 1,670 ft, which is roughly 557 yards. The pumps ran at 1,480 rpm driven by slipring motors with short-circuiting gear of 450 h.p..

In the case of the South Shaft, little or no water seepage occurred during sinking, suggesting that it could stay dry into the future. However, 'every precaution' was 'taken' in order to gauge any risk to the colliery's pumping facilities if a build up of a head of water did occur in the shaft. One precaution involved the foot of the shaft being bricked up to a depth of 622 yards. At the bottom of the shaft, 'a reinforced concrete plug or raft of 4 feet thick' was formed to act as a foundation for a 'ring of brickwork 9 inches thick with 3 inch cavity' as the footing for a concrete lining up to at least the 570 yards landing. The foot of the shaft was then filled with pit rubbish up to the 610 yards depth mark where another reinforced concrete raft was built, and for convenience referred to as the 'upper raft'. The pit rubbish provided a kind of soakaway for water. The key control facility was a piping arrangement plumbed in order that the pressure of any water collecting underneath the upper raft could be gauged at the 570 yard level. Subsequently it was found that the pressure of collected water varied 'slightly' with that accumulating in the sump of the North Shaft.

The colliery's ventilating fans were of the Sirocco type and made by Messrs Davidson. The fans were 140-inch in diameter and operated at a speed of 180 revs per minute capable of

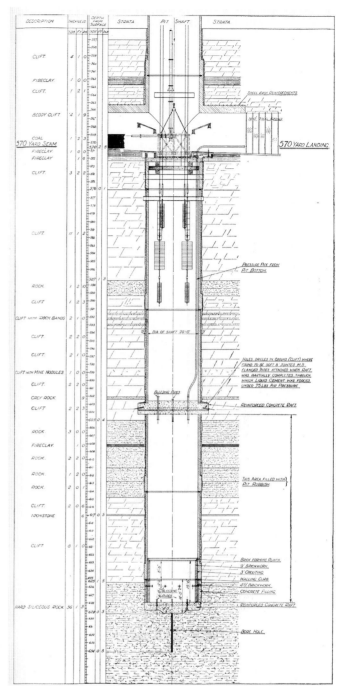

Wyllie Colliery - Civil engineering work at the bottom of South Shaft to provide a 'soakaway'.   *Proceedings, SWIE: 1929, Vol. XLV*

moving 403,000 ft³ of air a minute. As required by the 1911 Coal Mines Act, a fan reversing arrangement was included as a contingency for underground rescue. The South Pit was made the upcast for ventilation by erecting a hollow steel tower within its head-frame. The tower was a part of the air casing needed for efficient ventilating fan operation. Other parts of the air casing comprised boxing and air locks made of reinforced concrete. The steel tower was not fixed to the head-frame so that the motion of air for ventilation did not vibrate the structure.

The colliery's head-frames were each sixty feet high, from the underside of the feet of the main legs to the centre of the sheaves, and were designed by Tredegar Company engineers. The strength and stiffness of the head-frame structure coped with the live load of 19.1 tons and a total dead load of 116.8 ton. 4.65 tons of the live load was attributed to two winding ropes each 1¾ inch diameter and 620 yards long. The balance of the live

Wyllie Colliery – South Pit boxing so that the shaft operated as the 'upcast' for ventilation. *Proceedings, SWIE: 1929, Vol. XLV*

load was due to two cages (9½ tons), four trams, and two loads of coal being raised. Eight cage guide ropes were installed in the shafts. The head-gear sheaves were 16 feet diameter, which with shaft and bearings, each weighed 8 tons. Messrs Rees & Kirby, Morriston, used an estimated 89½ tons of steelwork to fabricate a head-frame. Spinning sheaves proclaimed to spectators on the colliery's surface that either miners or coal were in transit.

On the colliery's surface were: the colliery's offices, a store's building, workshops for smiths, fitters, carpenters, and electricians, and a screening plant.

The colliery's underground featured extensive use of steel arches. Steel arches of twenty-two feet span were incorporated into bricked arches built at each pit bottom. The bricked arches ran a distance of six to seven yards from each pit as a prelude to a constructed extension, sixteen feet in length, of Tredegar pattern straight-sided arches, 'bricked to the quarters and concreted between each arch around the crown'. Such 'very substantial reinforcement' of the pit bottom withstood 'remarkably well' the stresses and strains arising from strata movement. The colliery's 520 yards seam was accessed from South pit bottom and the 570 yards seam from the North pit bottom.

Wyllie Coal

The coal seams found sinking Wyllie Colliery gave the Tredegar Company a puzzle: to match, partly for commercial reasons, the seams found with those met elsewhere in the South Wales Coalfield. There was 'very little doubt' that the Brithdir, otherwise known as No. 2 Rhondda seam, was found at 251 yards. However, two-and-a-half years after sinking ended, the belief was that the seam found at 570 yards was the Nine-feet or Rhas Las whilst the seam at 520 yards was the Six-feet. Headings driven out into the 570 yards seam 'proved the seam [to be] of excellent quality and thickness'. An implication of the believed Rhas Las at Wyllie was if it was like its equivalent in the Aberdare district then there ought to have been 'several seams' under it, but sinking found none. Mining engineers speculated that at Wyllie there was a local thinning of the Lower Coal Measures.

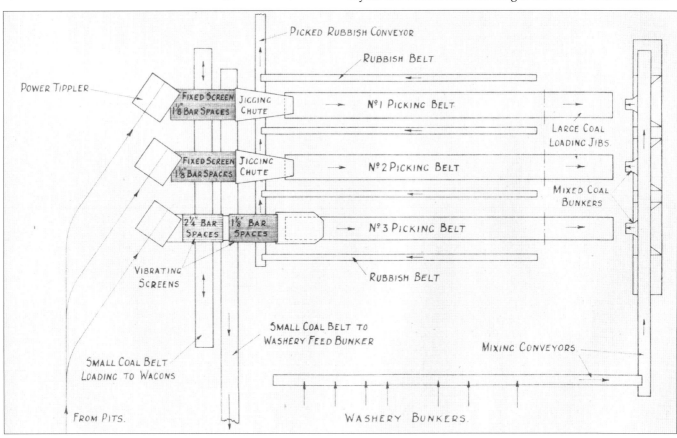

Wyllie Colliery – Screening Plant Coal Flow. *Folio of Technical Information, compiled by Jack Edwards circa 1946. A. J. Edwards collection*

Professor George Knox, principal of the Treforest School of Mines, guided by a stratigraphical study of a colleague at the school, Richard Richards, agreed with the speculation. Regarding the 'coal phase' of the 'Shale Series' in the Lower Coal Measures, Knox observed that it varied in thickness: at Risca it was 30 feet, 50 feet at Wyllie and 150 feet at Penallta Colliery to the north-west of Wyllie Colliery in the Rhymney Valley. He added that the thickness of the coal phase at Llanbradach Colliery, situated to the west of Wyllie, was 80 feet, and 100 feet to the east in the Abercarn District.[50] Professor Knox also suggested that the 'small number of workable seams met with [at Wyllie] might be due to the disturbed nature of the ground.'[51] Moreover, Richard Richards deduced that the seam at the 520 yards level was the Black Vein [a local term] and that the seam at the 570 yards was the Brass Vein of the southern sequence'.[52]

In 1946, the 570 yard level in the North Pit was also known as the Meadow Vein level by the Tredegar Company.[53] The Meadow Vein at 570 yards could also have been called the Yard/Seven-feet but it was not out of place for someone to have called it the Brass Vein.[54]

The geological findings at Wyllie Colliery also enabled the Tredegar Company to learn a lesson. 'The workable seams in their upper [Sirhowy Valley] collieries were very regular and more in number than in the south crop of collieries of Monmouthshire'.[55] The company realised it had taken a greater business risk opening its most southern Sirhowy Valley colliery compared with its earlier colliery investments. Nevertheless, for the Tredegar Company, Wyllie Colliery became a new source of steam coal to sell.[56] The colliery also became one of the two most recent collieries among the 472 collieries operated in the South

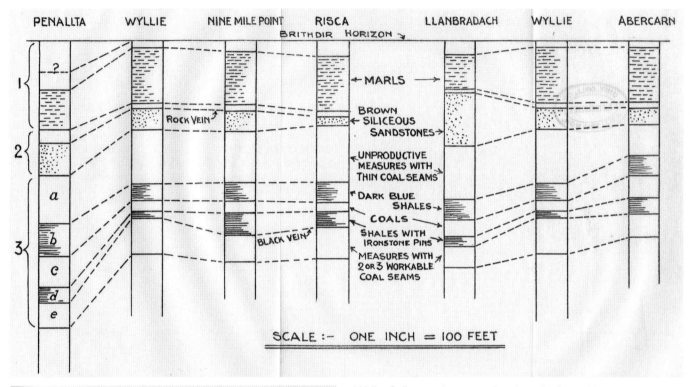

Wyllie Colliery and associated geological information.
Proceedings, SWIE: 1929, Vol. XLV

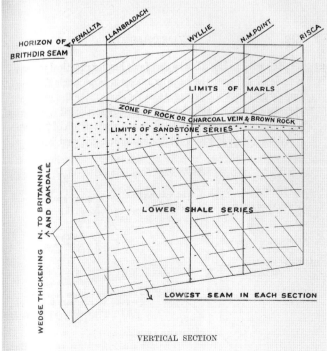

VERTICAL SECTION

Wales Coalfield in 1927.[57] Powell Duffryn's Llantrisant Colliery being the other contemporary of Wyllie Colliery.

In 1929, W. D. Woolley reported that an output of nearly 8,000 tons per week was being raised from the colliery's 570 yards seam. Such an output was achieved employing 1,021 persons overseen by W. H. Warburton, the colliery's first manager.[58] The lamp room was designed for 2,000 lamps. Wyllie Colliery appears to have been engineered to produce more than half-a-million tons of coal a year. A small village, Wyllie, on the doorstep of the colliery, was also planned.

Samuel Commission

The sinking of Wyllie Colliery partly coincided with political unrest in Europe. In early 1923 France dispatched troops to occupy the Ruhr. As an aspect of German resistance to occupation, the output of the Ruhr Coalfield fell. British coals, as a result, experienced a strong demand. Before the middle of 1924, when France evacuated its troops from the Ruhr, German colliery workers began to raise more coal that weakened demand for British coals. The political unrest, accompanied also with foreign exchange instability, made difficulties for selling Tredegar coal abroad.[59]

Wyllie Colliery, Blackwood, Mon.

Wyllie Colliery - sunk for Tredegar (Southern) Collieries Ltd, a subsidiary of the Tredegar Iron & Coal Company, employed 1,400 persons in 1930.
Top: Proceedings, SWIE: 1929, Vol. XLV; Below Pope/Parkhouse Archive

Nevertheless, during that 1923-1924 financial year the company's collieries were said to have 'worked with regularity'. The annual output from its collieries, for the year that ended the 31st March 1924, was 2,946,241 tons, which when compared with the previous year's, was a rise of 28,881 tons. Yet, the output was achieved in spite of an 'unauthorised' strike, the cause not found, in May 1924 at Markham Colliery of fourteen days, followed by further ones of seven day's duration at both Markham and Oakdale collieries. The strikes also kindled sympathy strikes at other company collieries. The human factor that enabled the rise in output during the year was the recruitment of 326 men that raised the total numbers employed by the company to 12,057 men.[60]

However, as a labour-intensive business national wage agreements affected the company's fortunes. A 1924 national wages agreement delighted South Wales Coalfield miners since they obtained an increase of 11 to 12 per cent in their wages. The Tredegar Company's chairman later wrote:

As the coal owners found it impossible to carry on the coal industry under the conditions of this agreement, they gave on the June 30, 1924, the prescribed notice for its termination. On July 30, however, the Government intervened, making new proposals to the owners and miners, including the offer of a subvention [a Government wage subsidy], and these proposals were accepted.

Furthermore, a Royal Commission was appointed to 'inquire into the whole position of the coal-mining industry'.[61] One of the suggestions put forward by the Government's Samuel Commission concerned the rationalisation in ownership rather than coal industry nationalisation.

At the time, the Tredegar Company watched as some coal companies merged or bought other colliery coal companies in the South Wales Coalfield. In Monmouthshire, a move that presaged such rationalisation in the county occurred in 1910 when the Ebbw Vale Steel, Iron, and Coal Company 'handed over the sale agency' for its coal to T. Beynon & Sons. Earlier, in 1873, Thomas Beynon and his brother, Theophilus John Beynon, joined other partners to form the Newport Abercarn Black Vein Steam Coal Company that opened Celynen Colliery, Newbridge.[62] Then in December 1915, Messrs Davis and Sons' stake in John Lancaster and Company was acquired largely by the Ebbw Vale Company and T. Beynon & Sons. The colliery management side of the Lancaster collieries was put under the charge of the Ebbw Vale Company. Such rationalisation was judged to be superior in terms of colliery workers' employment, 20,000 men, than had been achieved by the Cambrian Combine in Glamorgan.[63] Then, in 1920, the Ebbw Vale Company acquired: John Lancaster Company, Newport Abercarn Black Vein Steam Coal Company, and Coalbrookdale collieries, situated around Blaina in the Ebbw Fach Valley.[64] The Tredegar Company's coal property became like an island since not only had colliery company rationalisation occurred east of the Sirhowy Valley but that year Powell Duffryn acquired the Rhymney Iron Company.[65]

The shareholders of the Tredegar Iron & Coal Company may have been content watching other coal companies committing funds to acquisitions. The company reported record levels of profits at £234,022, £249,734, and £187,339 for respectively the years preceding the end of March in 1923, 1924, and 1925.[66] However, later in 1925, the company shareholders became fretful. On the 28th April 1925, Winston Churchill announced, as the Conservative Government's Chancellor of the Exchequer, a return to the Gold Standard, Britain's exchange rate system that once governed other exchange rates in the world, which was suspended during the Great War. The re-introduction of the Gold Standard began with an overvaluation of the price for sterling. Thus, Welsh coal cost more to export. In 1925, the total annual coal output of the South Wales Coalfield fell to 40 million. South Wales' coalowners, with doubts about the viability of their businesses if export earnings fell further in the future, pressed the Samuel Commission for cuts in miners' wages.

The 1926 Strike

The Samuel Commission Report was issued on the 10th March 1926. One of the Report's recommendations was a reduction in miners' wages. Harold Finch of the Tredegar Valley Miners' District judged that the Commission's wage cut was 'not to the extent the owners proposed'. Another recommendation concerned Government ending a coal industry wages' subsidiary introduced as an interim measure at the outset of the Commission's work. Finch related that 'the miners could not accept such recommendations; and wages were once again the main issue around which so much bitterness ensued'.[67] In late April 1926, when asked by a newspaper reporter about 'the prevailing opinion as to the coalowners' terms', one Tredegar collier replied: 'Wicked'. A fellow collier present at the interview added that 'this opinion was generally shared at the pit'.[68] The conversation among Sirhowy Valley miners may have already included a slogan of the general secretary of the Miners' Federation of Great Britain, A. J. Cook: "Not a penny off the pay, not a second of the day."

The publication of the Samuel Commission was followed by a series of events that fostered gravity about a likely national coal strike. The General Council of the Trade Union Congress (TUC) 'took a hand at attempting to negotiate a fair settlement of the miners' claims', but found that the Government 'saw no reasons to consider any concessions'.[69]

The TUC mooted organising a 'General Strike'. The Government proclaimed a State of Emergency with the Emergency Powers Act enforced from the 1st May 1926. A provision in the Act directed that an unauthorised person approaching any public building, mine, shop factory, or even road, 'may be deemed guilty of intent to do injury thereto'. Policemen were instructed to search, or arrest, anyone.[70] Moreover, anticipating civil unrest in the South Wales Coalfield, a troop battalion was ordered to occupy Cardiff barracks.[71] On the 3rd May, a national coal strike, or, as the miners viewed it, a lock-out began. On the 4th May, the miners obtained the support of railwaymen, transport workers, and iron and steel workers, when a General Strike began, but the TUC called it off nine days later. The miners were left alone to fight on for their cause.

The Tredegar Valley Miners' District was arranged as two groupings to organise the strike. Harold Finch 'helped the organisation further down the [Sirhowy] valley. Traffic was stopped and only allowed through if the driver had a permit providing for food and other essential supplies'. Aneurin Bevan 'with active and enthusiastic men around him organised local activities' at Tredegar as the chairman of a Council of Action. As the chairman of the Combined Lodge, he was 'largely responsible for the distribution of strike pay'.[72] Finch recalled, regarding the outset of the strike, Bevan challenging Tredegar miners working at Markham Colliery, who were keen to pick up their pay, to "walk it" as the railwaymen were on strike. 'The Markham men agreed and "walked it"'.[73]

On the 8th May, an Extraordinary Meeting was convened by the Tredegar UDC to meet a Council of Action deputation. The Tredegar Council of Action (C of A) tabled queries and proposed directives about the distribution of Urban District Council stocks of coal. The C of A was 'anxious to maintain peace and harmony in Tredegar' according to one of its representatives at the meeting, E. Moon. On the 10th May, low coal stocks at both Tredegar's Hospital and Workhouse prompted another UDC meeting at which it was relayed that the Tredegar Company thought that locomotive men were not moving coal to distribution points due to 'certain orders' of the C of A. Councillor Bevan heard this, left the meeting to return later with a permit from the C of A authorising the movement of five wagons with fifty tons of coal 'exclusively' for the use by the hospital, the workhouse, a nursing home, maternity home schools, and bakers.[74] Coal was supplied to such 'exclusive' places.

Aneurin Bevan's role as speaker at miners' meetings captivated a former McLaren collier, later a published poet, Idris Davies. Regarding 1926, a verse in an autobiographical poem of his said:

'And there were strikes and lock-outs
And meetings in the Square,
When Cook and Smith and Bevan
Electrified the air.'[75]

One mass meeting of miners held at Waun y Pound, situated mid-way between Tredegar and Ebbw Vale, became part of local folklore. Michael Foot later accused the *Western Mail* of having 'put the coalowners' case more blatantly than any other paper in the country'. According to him, 'Bevan was particularly affronted' when an edition of the newspaper carried an 'obscene attack on A. J. Cook'. The Tredegar strike leader 'organized a huge procession' to Waun y Pound, where 'copies of the *Western Mail* were solemnly burnt and buried, Bevan delivering the funeral oration. He also had the newspaper banned from Tredegar Library'.[76]

Absent in reports by the Monmouthshire press was an item about the attitude of the Tredegar Iron & Coal Company towards the strike. By locking-out its employees it maybe inferred that the company towed the line taken by the Monmouthshire and South Wales Coal Owners' Association.

A situation had also arisen in early 1926 that strained the company-Tredegar UDC relationship. At one meeting in May, held to discuss council water supply to Bedwellty Pits, the company's general manager of collieries, William Woolley, showed 'discourtesy' to the Council's Clerk. After the meeting, Tredegar councillors were told by the Clerk that the 'council regrets that proceedings would be taken against the company'.[77] Woolley's apparent rudeness contrasted with how 'Mr' Tallis had 'courteously' received a Council deputation in 1921 concerning the Pochin landslide.[78] The squabble between the company and the Tredegar Council seemed a trivial aside as the duration of the 1926 Strike lengthened.

Standing Firm

Many failed attempts were made to find a formula to end the stoppage of work in the British coalfields as spring gave way to a hot summer. An uncompromising stance was taken by both sides of the industry. In early June, George Davies, miners' agent in the Tredegar Valley District was quoted as saying: "The miners in the Tredegar Valley are absolutely solid and will stand firmly by the policy of the Federation." An Oakdale miner was also asked how long he thought the strike would last. "I have four more holes in my waist belt to pull up, one for each month. The dispute will go on … until we get our demands," he said.[79]

By July, communal kitchens catered for people in the Sirhowy Valley and at Abertysswg. Late in June, the C of A appealed successfully to the Tredegar Urban District Council for a free supply of ten hundredweight of coke to fuel fires for cooking.[80] For stoking household fires, squads of men picked coal from colliery tips, and mined old levels and opened shallow pits. Fund raising appeals enabled the buying of food supplies for communal kitchens.

In mid-July, Councillor Bevan was granted permission by the council to use Bedwellty Park for a carnival and sports at which a small entry fee was charged.[81] Late in August, the band of the Melingriffth Volunteer and Cadet Corp gave a free concert at Bedwellty Park for the C of A.[82] The Oakdale Male Voice Choir, 'ventured in to the Midlands, often sleeping rough, singing to raise money to send home'.[83]

Harold Finch remembered other aspects of life in the strike numbed Blackwood district. 'The proprietors of the old Palace and Capitol cinemas lent their premises free for concerts by top-ranking artistes, who also gave their services free'. He praised an initiative of a 'well known resident of Blackwood', David

W. Prosser, that led, in conjunction with colliery lodges, to setting up a cash voucher scheme for unmarried miners. At the time, 'single men on strike were not allowed relief'.[84] Harold Finch also became a kind of quartermaster for the distribution of donated clothing. He had to deal with some unpleasant criticism from 'womenfolk' due to, for example, the 'slightest suspicion of unfairness in the distribution of clothing'.[85] The union official was paid no salary during the 1926 Strike since the funds of the union 'were becoming exhausted'. He readily accepted his situation: 'how could we justifiably receive salaries as officials when so many of our members and their families were in acute distress?'[86]

Donations of money were received by the MFGB from trade unions, and from abroad. In late May, the MFGB accepted a donation of around a quarter of a million pounds from communist Russia, the Union of Soviet Socialist Republics (USSR). Received with the USSR offer was a message of fraternal greetings to the MFGB from a meeting of the Congress of Socialist Miners.[87]

One outcome was that when strikers took their 'Federation card to [the] Oakdale Institute', so as to 'get 2s. or 4s., now and then', as strike pay, the recipients called it 'Russian Gold'. Reuben Lucas, of Oakdale, further recollected the 'varied menu' available at the local soup kitchen during the strike. 'One day there would be soup; another day corned beef and mashed potatoes; also suet pudding or something else. On certain days fish was provided for taking home to cook'.[88]

In August, the secretary of the Workers' Union of Ireland, Jim Larkin, spoke at a Tredegar meeting chaired by Aneurin Bevan. The Irish trade unionist defended a charge made at the meeting of him interfering with a Dublin 'collection of funds for the relief of miners' families'. Maybe his observation that the miners' 'struggle could not last much longer' if the flow of foreign coal into Great Britain could be stemmed was politely heard. Coincidentally, 'ever increasing quantities of American coal' were being landed at Newport.[89] The Ruhr Coalfield was booming.

With autumn's arrival, destitution pervaded the lives of Sirhowy Valley and Abertysswg miners' families. In early September, Councillor Bevan declared at a Tredegar UDC meeting that the C of A was 'experiencing great difficulty in obtaining necessary funds to carry on their work and that it was highly essential that the income be augmented in every way possible'. He then appealed to the council for the release of surplus money held in a Tredegar War Memorial Fund.[90] The C of A was granted £12 2s. from the Memorial Fund.[91]

In the month of October 1926, a special conference of the SWMF was held in Cardiff. The conference heard Aneurin Bevan give 'one of the most bitter speeches' in support of the South Wales resolution. The aim of the resolution was 'a last renewed effort to stiffen the struggle', and it was carried at the conference. Early in November, another special conference occurred. 'In Nottinghamshire especially but elsewhere too the threat of starvation was driving men back to work'. Tom Richard MP 'agreed that the position was "crumbling"'. Arthur Horner, a member of the executive of the SWMF, also spoke for 'continued resistance'. Horner was later judged to have been 'by the 1930s, the most prominent communist trade unionist in the country'.[92] Despite the orations of Bevan and Horner, the conference voted against the resolution.

According to Michael Foot, Aneurin Bevan opposed Horner's 'appeal' at another conference in the same month. 'There was nothing to be done but to bow to the inevitable. Bevan once again urged that it should be done speedily before further disruption spread in the district organizations'. His speech, Foot claimed, 'caused a real shock in Tredegar'.[93]

Regardless, during the seven months of the strike, compared with other parts of the South Wales Coalfield, there were no riots and civil strife in the Sirhowy Valley. Riots and 'other forms of civil tumult' at Ammanford, Blaenavon, Bridgend, Brynamawr, Cwmcarn, Cymmer, Fochriw, Pontypool, Pontypridd, Ton

Pentre, and Treorchy were reported in the *Western Mail*.[94] The C of A, in spite of widespread human trauma, maintained 'peace and harmony in Tredegar' as promised at the outset of the strike by one of its representatives, E. Moon.

A settlement was reached between the federation members of the MFGB and coal owners. The terms of the settlement included retaining the pre-strike wage rate until the end of May 1927, an extension in the working hours, and the provision for double coal shift and introduction of machinery. A majority was won in a ballot of the SWMF membership for a return to work. The miners' ballot at Oakdale Colliery was: For 588 votes, Against 63, and at Waterloo Colliery: For 128 votes and Against 65. The numbers voting at each colliery announced a sore fact: prior to the strike 1,500 men worked at Oakdale and 500 men at Waterloo.

Colliery workers may have also greeted with some relief the Government granting permission for the export of South Wales coal 'in cases where it was impossible to find a market for it in this country'.[95] The collieries of South Wales were in 'full swing' by the first week of December 1926.

Reflections

Half a century later, Harold Finch, reflected upon the effect that the 1926 Strike. 'There can be no doubt our men and families were starved into submission. They were bitter and resentful, but the majority remained faithful to the Union despite attempts by some coal owners to encourage the formation of company or what were termed Industrial Unions'.

There were other consequences of the 1926 Strike. The Government placed more limitations upon trade unions by passing into law a 1927 Trade Disputes and Trade Union Act. Support within colliery workers for the South Wales Miners' Federation weakened. The SWMF became fervid opponents of the South Wales Miners' Industrial Union that had a non-political agenda.

The SWMF attempted to counter membership relapses by adopting a practice known as "Show Cards". Harold Finch recalled: 'Every two months the workmen, on entering the colliery premises and before going down the pit, were called on to show their Federation contribution cards to one of the [lodge] committee-men; and, unless had a reasonable excuse for not showing his card, he was sent home by the committee-man'. As a consequence 'there were occasional stoppages of work, the employers resenting such interference with their employees'.

In 1929, the Tredegar Company acted to curtail the practice of "show cards" at Oakdale Colliery and this caused a strike. Aneurin Bevan, as the Tredegar Combine Executive Committee's representative, addressed the strikers. He called for a return to work so that the issue could be raised at a Cardiff SWMF-Coal Owners' meeting. According to Harold Finch, Bevan's speech was 'not well received'. 'After some heated discussions the Oakdale Lodge members agreed to return to work but insisted on taking "show cards" at the pit'.

The strike won keen support among many men at Markham Colliery. In 1927, the Tredegar Company went to court to obtain an injunction to halt a "show cards" event at the colliery, and dismissed Markham Lodge officials.[96]

But for Bevan, Harold Finch later related that 'both at Oakdale and Markham the majority of men were critical of Aneurin's attitude'. Perhaps Bevan's 'brusque tongue', as his future wife, Jennie Lee later described it, featured in his attitude.[97] Grudges were also held by company officials for having been the butt of attacks by Bevan. However, Finch noted that during the Oakdale "show cards" dispute 'he lost favour with the [lodge] committee men …', and it 'took some time for Aneurin to regain the popularity which he later attained by his political activities'.

Aneurin Bevan, though, had begun to ponder that 'with the collapse of the General Strike in 1926, the workers of Britain seemed to have exhausted the possibilities of mass industrial action' as an instrument for change.[98] He later reflected: 'The defeat of the miners [in 1926] ended a phase, and from then on the pendulum swung sharply to political action. It seemed to us that we must try to regain in Parliament what we had lost on the industrial battlefield'.[99] At the 1929 General Election, he stood as the Labour Party's candidate for Ebbw Vale. He won the constituency vote, and almost immediately 'electrified the air' of the floor of the House of Commons.

Although the outcome of the Cardiff meeting about the "show cards" dispute at Oakdale Colliery could not be recalled by Harold Finch, the issue continued to dog Oakdale Colliery's industrial relations. Conflict soured when the 'Oakdale management closed one of the districts underground where some of the more ardent advocates of "show cards" were employed; and they remained out of work for many months'. Harold Finch judged that the Tredegar Company eventually 'realised that their strong attitude was proving futile'. Subsequently, 'the tact and judgement displayed by management and men removed some of the old misunderstandings not only at Oakdale but at the company's other collieries where "show cards" resumed'.[100]

Oakdale Colliery – Underground Developments

After the 1926 Strike, Oakdale Colliery's North and North-East workings thrived and although the original 'South Workings were abandoned' the 'labour force began to increase'. On the North Side of the Main Level the legacy of geological disturbances, locally called the 'Big Fault', created a 'blind patch' that made if difficult to read the line of a coal seam. Time consuming exploratory headings were driven, but 'when the seam was located [it] proved to be as good as before'.

'On the South side a hard heading was driven to the Big Vein seam. It was here that the snaker conveyor was first used as a start to the slow process of mechanisation'. Moreover, a 'hard heading was driven off one of the Rhas Las levels known as "Jonah Prices" to the Yard seam and later it was extended to the Big Vein'.[101]

The Development of Wyllie Village[102]

Amidst the trauma of 1926 the Tredegar Iron & Coal Company developed both Wyllie Colliery and its adjacent village. The village was built under the auspices of the Industrial Housing Association, which Lord Aberconway launched in 1923. The immediate cost to the company was small. The Government advanced a three-quarter share of the money needed with the company's repayment terms being over twenty years at a low rate of interest. Moreover, due to the scheme, after 1923, 100 houses were added at both Oakdale and Markham villages.[103]

By 1927, some of the miners that joined Tredegar (Southern) Collieries Ltd to work at its colliery occupied new houses that marked the birth of Wyllie Village. A. F. Webb planned the village, and in 1929 the company's intention was to build a total of between 200 and 250 houses on land to the north of the colliery.[104] Initially wooden planks served as walkways for the villagers 'since the roads had not been built'. Household furniture was moved by hand to the houses from a removal lorry parked a distance away where the public road ended. Such inconveniences were minor compared with the hardships that some of them had suffered during the previous years.

For example, Wyllie Colliery's opening caused David Edwards to relocate from Brynmawr to the Sirhowy Valley after a lengthy period of unemployment as a miner. "Dai" Edwards prior to 1926 broke a leg in a colliery accident at Stones Pit, Blaina, lost his job, and to 'earn a few pennies extra' to the 'dole' money had 'taken up home cobbling'. In 1927, he was 'taken on' as a Wyllie Colliery collier, and initially took lodgings with his brother, "Fred" Edwards, who had been allocated a house in the village. For a period after joining the colliery, David Edwards's wife, May, remained temporarily at Brynmawr. Every weekend so as to hand his wages to May and 'save 1s. 6d. in bus fare', he walked a round trip of twenty miles from Wyllie.[105]

In late 1927, the Edwards family, that included one adopted son, Albert John, more commonly known as Jack, relocated from Brynmawr to the new Penllyn housing estate, Pontllanfraith. The neighbourhood heard the singing of a fine tenor voice, Dai Edwards's, as he took a bath at home after a day at the pit. He became a founder member of the Wyllie Glee Party in 1931. The family moved into a house in Wyllie in 1937, which was a privilege since only around a half of the number of houses planned by the company for the village were ever built. Due mainly to the rocky nature of the ground only 114 house and two shops were built.

All Wyllie Village's houses were well proportioned and spaced out, and provided with a front and rear garden. House accommodation was made up of: two or three bedrooms, bathroom, toilet, kitchen, living room, and coal house. The village's housing was sited around five roads. First, the top road, Heol y Coed, consisted of four semi-detached house for the most senior colliery officials, namely two under-managers, chief mechanic, and chief electrician. The houses were built on one side of the road with a front and rear garden. Second there was the Avenue, at the centre of the village, that comprised eight semi-detached house each side of the road, and were for the lesser officials such as foremen, deputies, and shot firers. The roads to accommodate colliery workers, comprised: Tir Bach Road, eighteen houses, Penycwarel Road, twenty-six houses; and Glanhowy Road of fifty houses; which were semi-detached and in blocks of four houses. The colliery manager resided at Tyl y Gwyn farm located remote from, and above Heol-y-Coed Road.

In 1931/32 a chapel was built in the village, which was followed in 1934 by the Miners' Institute. A feature of the chapel was that the initials of resident children's names were cut into the brick used to build its front vestibule.

The Miners' Institute was built with South Wales Miners' Federation funds, and was thereafter financed by workers' subscriptions deducted from colliery pay. The ground floor of the building comprised a hall off which were doors leading to: a large meeting hall; an office that also acted as a shop serving sweets and cigarettes during the evenings only; a smaller side room; and a room with two full-sized snooker tables. The ground floor also had toilets and gave access to the building's heating apparatus and fuel store. Stairs from the ground floor led to a storeroom, a committee room, and a reading room and library. Junior children were schooled in a 'temporary' army hut at the centre of the village until they were accommodated in the hall of the institute.

Although two semi-detached shops were built in the village, only one ever traded. The operated shop, a general store, sold foodstuff, newspapers, and other goods, and served as a Post Office. A General Post Office telephone box was located outside the shop.

In accordance with an aim of the Tredegar Company, but attributed to meeting a term of the landowner's lease, no alcohol was sold in the village. However, the Half-Way public house, in nearby Gelligroes, became the regular place to drink for villagers. The landlord was 'Mr Pope' who was viewed as a 'character' by Jack Edwards. He also recalled a custom that the last train from Newport north to Nantybwch junction took a halt outside the Half-Way. Standing ready on the pub's bar were pints of beer for the locomotive's crew.

Concerning the friendliness found at Wyllie Village, Jack Edwards wrote that 'within nine months' of residing at Wyllie he knew everyone who lived in each house, 'starting with Jim Crewe in No. 1 nearest the pit and ending with Tom Davies in No. 50, the first house met entering the village'. After ten years living at Penllwyn he knew just people residing in two dozen households. However, the village never became the home to most of Wyllie Colliery's workers. In 1930, the company employed 1,384 people at the colliery. That year, W. H. Warburton was the manager of the colliery, but in 1932 he was succeeded by A. M. Strang.

A Wyllie Colliery Manager

Archie Strang's entry into mining may have been due to his father, an accountant with the Alexandra Dock Company, knowing senior managers within the Tredegar Company. Archie began work articled to Alfred Tallis. If his entry into the company placed him in a favourable position for future advancement, the nature of his formation as a mining engineer appears to have won the respect of Harold Finch. According to Finch, Archie 'was trained in the hard school of practical experience'. Strang's training began at the Tredegar Works in the foundry and pattern shop, he then did stints of work in mechanical fitting, and the electrical department. Afterwards he became a 'collier's assistant and repairer at Pochin Colliery'. Posted to Oakdale Colliery, he climbed the official's career ladder from fireman to overman, and then under-manager. He possessed resolve to qualify as a mining engineer since he attended technical classes at the Crumlin School of Mines after a working day from 6 a.m. to 5 p.m. He obtained his colliery manager's certificate in 1926. He then qualified, with one of his examiners being Sir Richard Redmayne, as a HM Mines Inspector. Archie Strang's 'hard school' formation and his abilities were valued by the Tredegar Company. He rejoined the company and prior to his appointment as manager of Wyllie Colliery he was manager of Ty Trist and Bedwellty Pits. In 1935, he became the agent for Oakdale and Wyllie collieries, and served in the post for twelve years.[106]

In 1933, Strang reported to Dan Morgan, colliery agent. David Evans, general manager of collieries, and W. D. Woolley Tredegar Company's general manager, held the higher managerial roles. Regarding the founding of Wyllie Colliery, Woolley acknowledged that 'the lay-out and general design of the colliery was carried out under the direction of the late Mr A. S. Tallis'.[107]

Prominent Colliery Owner Passes Away

In September 1927 Alfred Simeon Tallis died aged sixty-four at 'Llwyn Celyn', Caerleon. He had suffered 'declining health for a considerable time'. His wife, Mary Frances, predeceased him by a few years. He was survived by one daughter, and three sons, W. Tallis, the company's chief electrical engineer, Roy Tallis, the manager of McLaren Colliery, and Russell Tallis.

The South Wales Argus praised Tallis as a 'prominent colliery owner'.[108] Although he may have held a number of company shares, he had never been a colliery owner. Such recognition accorded with a common perception of valley people about who controlled the affairs of a coal company.

The newspaper's obituarist registered that the former manager of the Tredegar Company had 'for many years played an important part in the social and industrial life' of Monmouthshire. His career's rise within the Tredegar Iron & Coal Company, a prominent Monmouthshire business, was sketched. His involvement in the affairs of the Monmouthshire and South Wales Coalowners' Association was mentioned. Notably, he was credited for being 'chiefly responsible for the great developments at Abertysswg and the coal areas from Pochin down to Pontllanfraith'. Under Tallis's command, the Tredegar Company opened four collieries, McLaren, Oakdale, Markham, and Wyllie, to win West Monmouthshire deep-mined steam coal.

The obituary offered no appreciation of Tallis's skills and abilities, or gave any insight into the way he managed. His background before joining the Tredegar Company was in colliery management. He never made a contribution to the meetings of the South Wales Institute of Engineers that evokes the thought that he had no desire to excel in technical colliery engineering. Yet, he successfully led the engineering of new collieries, and contributed to the planning of model villages. Tallis's attitude to technical matters might be an explanation for W. Angus Scott's long service to the company as consulting engineer. Through the delegation of duties to initially a colliery agent for the oversight of operational collieries regarding production, industrial relations, and the administration of age old mining leases, he was freed to organise the founding of Oakdale, Markham, and Wyllie collieries. The role he played as the company's managing director warranted a fuller analysis, but alas this was impossible due to a lack of related information.

The South Wales Argus obituarist acknowledged that Tallis showed a 'good deal of interest' in the public life of the town. Indeed, the leadership role he played in the creation of the Tredegar Cottage Hospital was notable. Moreover, as made evident earlier, he had a 'deep personal interest in the Tredegar Company's employees in the Sirhowy and Rhymney Valleys. Oakdale is regarded as a model village—a fact which he was largely, if not mainly responsible'.

His conduct in human affairs also deserved recall. In 1910, Sir Arthur Markham identified 'the tact of Mr Tallis' as an asset for the pursuit of good company industrial relations.[109]

Offered in this work is evidence that he treated people with courteousness. In an industry prone to angry arguments, and deep conflict, a courteous approach contrasted with notions of a hard-hearted coalowner. Nevertheless, workers, whose political views rejected capitalism, would have been ever eager to besmirch his reputation by recalling decisions he made that humiliated the dignity of fellow workers. Enlightened paternalism, which Tallis characterised, attracted critics. That he rose to become managing director under Lord Aberconway, a man who was comfortable about consulting people regardless of rank, encourages a thought that even as the general manager of collieries, he had vital say in the development of the Tredegar Company. That Alfred Simeon Tallis was able to behave in his human dealings in the way that he did was also due in part to the sustained support he received from the Tredegar Company's chairman.

NOTES

1 SWWA, 17 May 1913.

2 Compiled from: 'Surprise Royal Visit. Prince Albert Among the Welsh Colliers', WM, 17 Jan 1920, p.9; 'The Prince's Visit', WM, 17 Jan 1920, p.10; and 'Prince Albert with a Pick', SWWA, 24 Jan 1920.

3 Letter, Prince Albert to Queen Mary, 20 Jan 1920. Royal Archive ref.: RA QM/PRIV/CC11/11. With the permission of Her Majesty Queen Elizabeth II.

4 The general source: The South Wales Coal Annual 1920-21, pp.490-493.

5 Barry Supple, op. cit., p.117.

6 The reduction in the price of domestic coal demanded was 14s. 2d. per ton, and a flat rate wage's increase demanded were: workers aged 18 years and over a rise of 2s. per shift; a rise of 1s. per shift for persons between 16 and 18 years; and 9d. for persons under 16 years.

7 Report of Proceedings, 50th Annual Ordinary General Meeting, TI&C, [hereafter RP 50th AOGM, TI&C], 29 June 1923. p.2. The million tons of coal was estimated based upon comparing the company's annual coal output of 1,835,671 tons, for the financial year that closed at the end of March 1921, with its next twelve month output of 2,917,328 tons. The speculation is based upon the assumption that the numbers of people employed by the company at its collieries were the same for both years, which they were not.

8 TUDC, 3rd May 1921. A35/M/31, Gwent Archives.

9 TUDC, 27th Feb 1923. A35/M/31, Gwent Archives.

10 George Knox, 'Landslides in South Wales Valleys', SWIE, Vol.XLIII (1927/28), pp.250-254. Comment A. J. Edwards to Writer, August 2007: following the Aberfan disaster, Knox's paper became vital reading for National Coal Board engineers.

11 The price paid by the council: large coal was 25s. 6d. per ton, and small coal 22s. 9d. per ton. TUDC, 27th Sept 1921. A35/M/31, Gwent Archives.

12 A. J. Cronin, Adventures in Two Worlds. (1953), p.143. The year when he arrived in Tredegar is not given in the reference, which is an autobiography. However, TUDC notes for 27th April 1922 a payment of £3 15s. to Dr Cronin for providing unspecified services; A35/M/31, Gwent Archives. Moreover, Cronin noted in his autobiography that 'for three years now we lived at Tredegar' (p.169), and this preceded his move to a London practice in around 1924.

13 A. J. Cronin, op. cit., p.159.

14 A. J. Cronin, op. cit., p.161.

15 'Tredegar Invaded', ME, 10 Sept 1921, p.2.

16 Source unless otherwise referenced: Michael Foot, Aneurin Bevan. (1997, Abridged edition, Victor Gollancz), pp.27-37.

17 Harold Finch, born at Barry in 1898, was 'brought up in a very religious atmosphere'. Aged 17, he became secretary of the Barry branch of the Railway Clerk's Association, and later gained a scholarship to the Labour College in London.

18 Harold Finch, Memoirs of a Bedwellty MP. (1979), p.25.

19 'Tredegar Invaded', ME, 10 Sept 1921, p.2.

20 'March of the 8,000', ME, 17 Sept 1921, p.2.

21 'March of the 8,000', ME, 17 Sept 1921, p.2.

22 Michael Foot, op. cit., p.37.

23 Michael Foot, op. cit., p.38.

24 Harold Finch, op. cit., p.43.

25 For example, in April 1925, Councillor Bevan at a Special Meeting of Council 'expressed dissatisfaction' with 'perfunctory answers' received from a Government body regarding a council letter to the body about rules governing unemployment benefit. TUDC, 8 Apr 1925. A35/M/33, Gwent Archives.

26 Michael Foot, op. cit., p.43.

27 Aneurin Bevan, In Place of Fear. (1952), p.44.

28 RP 50th AOGM, TI&C, p.1.

29 RP 50th AOGM, TI&C, p.2.

30 The South Wales Coal Annual for respective years.

31 In 1913 employment figure includes Gwrhay, but for the 1923 employment figures includes also Waterloo Pit and Levels.

32 RP 50th AOGM, TI&C, p.2. The employment figure quoted was found to be higher than that given in The South Wales Coal Annual for 1923 but more or less the same as that given in The South Wales Coal Annual 1924. The South Wales Coal Annual figures have been found by Trevor Boyns to be 'usually two years behind'; comment to Writer, 31 Aug 2015.

33 RP 50th AOGM, TI&C, p.2.

34 Trevor Boyns, 'Of Machines and Men in the 1920s', Llafur, Vol. 5, No. 2, (1989), p.30.

35 Tredegar unemployment, according to the Ministry of Labour, Cardiff, comprised: 74 colliers, 50 underground labourers, 5 hauliers, 17 surface labourers, and 1 coke oven worker: see TUDC, 27 March 1923. A35/M/31, Gwent Archives.

36 The Tredegar Iron & Coal Company Limited 1873-1923. Gwent Archives, Misc Mss 1147. The description of the document being a 'little statement' was taken from RP 50th AOGM, TI&C, p.4.

37 RP 50th AOGM, TI&C, p.4.

38 RP 50th AOGM, TI&C, p.5.

39 Trevor Boyns-Gwent Coal Industry, table 3.3, p.39.

40 RP 50th AOGM, TI&C, p.5.

41 RP 50th AOGM, TI&C, p.4.

42 The following description of the colliery is, unless otherwise referenced, based upon W. D. Woolley, 'Wyllie Colliery', SWIE, Vol. XLV (1929), pp.353-383.

43 OS Ref. No. ST177933.

44 By 1928, the success of the sheep dog trials caused the formation of a local agricultural body with Lord Tredegar as its president. Before the Second World War the body was called The Mynyddiswyn Sheep Dog Trials and Agricultural Show Society. Len Burland, A Historical Tour around Mynyddislwyn Mountain. (Old Bakehouse Publications, 2002), pp.83-84.

45 RP 50th AOGM, TI&C, p.3.

46 Report of Proceedings, 51st Annual Ordinary General Meeting, TI&C, [hereafter RP 51st AOGM, TI&C], 27 June 1924. p.2.

47 RP 50th AOGM, TI&C, p.3.

48 Major E. Ivor David's remark, 'Wyllie Colliery', op. cit., p.396.

49 A Board of Trade Unit (hereafter called 'unit') was equal to one kilowatt-hour, or 3,415 British Thermal Units (Btu).

50 The President's remark, 'Wyllie Colliery', op. cit., p.405.

51 The President's remark, 'Wyllie Colliery', op. cit., p.403.

52 Richard Richards's remark, 'Wyllie Colliery', op. cit., p.410.

53 Folio of Technical Information – Oakdale and Wyllie Collieries, compiled by Jack Edwards circa 1946, p.8 (Wyllie section). From the papers of A. J. Edwards in the keeping of the Writer.

54 Ray Lawrence, op. cit., see pp.22-24, and p.135.

55 W. D. Woolley remark, 'Wyllie Colliery', op. cit., p.414.

56 Wyllie Colliery coal was classified in 1946 as follows: the upper seams were bituminous III (Gas Coals): volatiles 29-36%; carbon ranged from 88.0% to 84%; hydrogen 5.0–5.5%, and calorific value 15,650 to 15,050 Btu/lb; and its lower seams were Bituminous II (Coking Coals): volatiles 22-30% carbon ranged from 91.0–88.0%; hydrogen 4.8–5.3%; and calorific value 15,800 to 15,500 Btu/lb, SWC-RegRpt, pp.20-21.

57 Lord Aberconway, The Basic Industries of Great Britain. (Ernest Benn, 1927), p.255.

58 The South Wales Coal Annual 1929, p.209.

59 RP 51st AOGM, TI&C, 27 June 1924. p.2.

60 RP 51st AOGM, TI&C, pp.2-3.

61 Lord Aberconway, op. cit., p.253.

62 The South Wales Coal Annual 1916, pp.4-5.

63 'South Wales Coal Deal: Messrs Beynon and Co.'s Enterprise'; a cutting dated 14 Dec 1915 taken from an unknown newspaper, and found inside Newport Central Library's copy of The South Wales Coal Annual 1916.

64 Trevor Boyns-Gwent Coal Industry, p.38.

65 Leslie M. Shore, op. cit, pp.170-172.

66 Trevor Boyns-Gwent Coal Industry, p.39.

67 Harold Finch, op. cit. (1979). p.57.

68 'Prince Albert with a Pick', SWWA, 24 Jan 1920.

69 The History of the TUC 1868-1968 a Pictorial Survey of a Social Revolution. (1968, TUC), p.78-79.

70 South Wales Echo, 'The Act Explained', 1 May 1926, p.1.

71 South Wales Echo, 'Troops for Cardiff', 1 May 1926, p.1.

72 Michael Foot, op. cit., p.46.

73 Harold Finch, op. cit., p.57.

74 Tredegar UDC Minute Book [hereafter TUDC], Extraordinary Meetings 8 May 1926, and 10th May. A350/M/34, Gwent Archives.

75 'I was born in Rhymney', The Collected Poems of Idris Davies. (1972, Gomerian), p.129. Herbert Smith was the president of the MFGB.

76 Michael Foot, op. cit., p.45.

77 TUDC, Ordinary Meetings 11 May 1926. A350/M/34, Gwent Archives.

78 TUDC, Ordinary Meetings 3 May 1926. A35/M/31, Gwent Archives.

79 SWWA, 19 June 1926, p.2.
80 TUDC, Ordinary Meetings 22 June 1926. A350/M/34, Gwent Archives.
81 TUDC, Ordinary Meetings 15 July 1926. A350/M/34, Gwent Archives.
82 TUDC, Ordinary Meetings 24 Aug 1926. A350/M/34, Gwent Archives.
83 Ralph Thomas, op. cit., p.64.
84 Harold Finch, op.cit., p.66.
85 Harold Finch, op.cit., p.68.
86 Harold Finch, op.cit., p.67.
87 SWWA, 22 May 1926, p.2.
88 Harold Finch, op.cit., p.66.
89 SWWA, 14 Aug 1926, p.2.
90 TUDC, Ordinary Meetings 14 Sept 1926. A350/M/34, Gwent Archives.
91 TUDC, Ordinary Meetings 21 Sept 1926. A350/M/34, Gwent Archives.
92 Hywel Francis, 'Horner, Arthur Lewis (1894-1968)', *The Oxford Dictionary of National Biography, Vol. 28*, p. 157.
93 Michael Foot, op. cit., pp.48-51.
94 '1926', *Western Mail Centenary Review*, 1 May 1969, p.15.
95 SWWA, 4 Dec 1926, p.2.
96 Ray Lawrence, op. cit., p.65.
97 Aneurin Bevan, *In Place of Fear*. (1952), 'Foreword 1976 edition', p.11.
98 Aneurin Bevan, op. cit., p.45.
99 Aneurin Bevan, op. cit., p.46.
100 Harold Finch, op. cit., pp.30-31.
101 BIDCO, p.15.
102 Source unless otherwise noted: Leslie M. Shore, 'A South Wales Coalfield Engineer': Albert John 'Jack' Edwards (1920-2008). (Unpublished, 2015) [Hereafter 'AJE'], pp.7-10. Compiled from a set of Albert John Edwards's hand written notes of recollections with additions due to conversations with the Writer over a period of years.
103 RP 50th AOGM, TI&C, p.3.
104 W. D. Woolley, 'Wyllie Colliery', SWIE, Vol.XLV (1929), p.383.
105 A note addendum in A. J. Edwards's papers.
106 Harold Finch, op. cit., pp.27-28.
107 W. D. Woolley, 'Wyllie Colliery', SWIE, Vol.XLV (1929), p.383.
108 'Mr A. S. Tallis JP: Prominent Colliery Owner Passes Away', SWA, 10 Sept 1927, p.6.
109 'Eight Hours Bogey', CT, 25 June 1910, p.7.

View of surface of Oakdale Colliery from the top of No. 2 Chimney Stack in 1939. Note the shadows cast by the colliery's two chimney stacks. Looking northwards with the South Pit headgear prominent with the roof of the power-house to its right, and to its left coal screens and washery. Top centre the Tram Shop.

Photograph taken by Jack Edwards. A. J. Edwards collection

Chapter Eight
DEPRESSION & NATIONALISATION

It can be inferred from a read of Tredegar Company annual reports that it was the directors under Lord Aberconway's chairmanship that determined company policy before seeking shareholder approval. Some clues to the complex issues that the directors faced around 1927 are found in a survey Aberconway published that year.[1] He offered a notable historical reflection in the survey: 'the outstanding feature' of the South Wales Coalfield 'is the great foreign trade which has sprung up … bringing prosperity to those supplying the overseas demand'. In 1925, the South Wales Coalfield exported 22,686,691 tons, 'being 44 per cent of the coal exported from the United Kingdom, and 45.2 per cent of South Wales itself'. France bought more Welsh coal than the following, in descending order, Italy, Spain, the Argentine, and Egypt. Although he accepted a reckoning that the South Wales Coalfield had sufficient coal deposits 'to last for considerably over 1,000 years' based upon the current rate of 'consumption', he and fellow directors had grounds to wonder: who would be the future users of Tredegar coal?[2]

Aberconway registered that since the Great War oil-fired boilers had 'become almost universal in ships … in the active service of the Royal Navy'. He detailed that the sale of a 'privileged group' of coals, the Admiralty List's thirty-four coals, had fallen from 1,697,250 tons in 1913 to 273,750 tons in 1926. 'The advent of the internal-combustion engine' had caused nearly the whole of "Admiralty qualities" of coal to be 'thrown' into 'the general market at a price about a shilling higher than second-class coal'. As a man with shipbuilding interests, he further knew that merchant ships under construction were on the whole being equipped with oil-fired boilers. Yet, as a coalowner he clung on to a hope that 'possibly oil fuel may yet become too scarce and expensive to hold its own against coal, which may come into vogue once more'.

Nevertheless, implied from above, McLaren Merthyr coal had been switched to supply the general market. The company had for a long time supplied the general market with Tredegar coal, a second-class steam coal of a bituminous kind that was suitable not only for steam-raising, but gas and manufacturing purposes, and also household use. However, a Government duty of 12½ per cent had 'enabled Germany to get into neutral markets, to the exclusion' of the South Wales Coalfield. He predicted that the saleable value of Welsh coal would fall to a 'figure nearly approaching South Yorkshire', and that German 'hard coal' was a formidable rival to steam coal.

Nevertheless, the 'special quality' of Welsh steam coal appeared to be grounds for him as a director of a South Wales coal company to assert that the 'comparative value' of Welsh coal in 1925 was 'shown by the prices it fetches'. The coal prices quoted by him for 1925 were: large Welsh steam coal 21s. 3d. at the pit, Midland coal around 9s. per ton, and South Yorkshire coal 16s. 6d..

Nonetheless, his admiration for the value of Welsh steam coal was offset by a dour business appraisal. Although the owner of a Welsh colliery 'made a higher price for his output' they 'may make less profit than the owner of a well-equipped colliery in South Yorkshire'. Since Oakdale, Markham, and Wyllie collieries were well-equipped he could have mentioned that the Tredegar Company was the technical equal of Yorkshire competition. But, in his 1927 survey, he asserted that the working costs of 'Welsh mines are at least 1s. per ton in excess of those in other coalfields'. Moreover, Welsh mining lease royalty payments, which he claimed were in 'excess of those in other British coalfields', added to the cost burden borne by coal companies.

Before writing about labour relations in the South Wales Coalfield, he detailed some factors that influenced the 'value of colliery investments'. 'It is the last 50,000 tons of output which, generally speaking, make the colliery profit'. 'Every day's stoppage of a pit means a loss due to standing and other charges, which soon absorb, when prolonged, the dividend which otherwise would be available at the end of the year'. His statement had meaning for shareholders who obtained earnings from the coal industry. Yet, the South Wales miners' union leaders with Left-wing ideals loathed the capitalist system and its drive for profit to pay shareholders a dividend. The vocabulary of Karl Marx can give rise to bemusement, but the use of 'exploitation' in his writings had become part of valley vernacular. Miners contested that they were exploited since they were denied wage rises so that shareholders received dividends as a matter of course.

Moreover, there was a risk that some miners received Lord Aberconway's views about them as condescension. In his survey, he judged that there was 'no better miner than a Welshman'. The Welsh miner was a 'respectable and religious citizen, careful of his appearance', and his 'courage' was 'unbounded'. About a valley miner's reaction to an underground explosion, or another such calamity, he wrote: 'No danger, however menacing, ever deters him; and there are no finer pages in history than those that record the devotion of the Welsh miner to his comrades in the darkness of the mine'. Such fellowship, he registered, had also manifested itself in another way. Due to the miners' 'passion for music' the 'male voice choirs in South Wales are among the best in Great Britain'. However, in expressing his esteem for the character of the Welsh miner, there was chance he could have been labelled a romantic by critics of miners' militancy and the 1926 Strike.

However, the Tredegar Company's chairman further claimed 'it is true' that the Welsh miner is 'hot-headed, impulsive and difficult to lead. Sentiment appeals to him more than reason'. Moreover, he reasoned that such characteristics to 'some extent, accounts for the development of Communistic ideas among his class; he readily falls victim to the subversive doctrines lately imported into this country, which are preached at open-air meetings in the mining villages'. His charge that the miners of the South Wales Coalfield were vulnerable to being duped into believing Communist ideas was untrue. The swing of the miners' parliamentary vote in the coalfield from the Liberal Party to the Labour Party was mainly due to support for electoral candidates who came from a shared background, and were proven, trusted, union leaders. An electoral candidate espousing Communist ideas was unlikely to convince the ordinary miner that a revolution was needed to transform their world. Thus, Aberconways' reading of character may be said to make false any charge that he held a romantic view about the Welsh miner.

Lord Aberconway was on surer ground to rank the Tredegar Iron & Coal Company among a dozen of 'important' South Wales coal companies. In general, he held a dim view about the financial performance of South Wales coal companies. 'The quoted shares of the most South Wales public [coal] companies have never stood on the average at a high market value, nor are their average dividends large, considering the general prosperity of trade in the district'. Mirroring in part the business history of the Tredegar Company he reflected: 'Leading concerns that were floated with inflated capitals more than fifty years ago, have written down their assets and reduced their capital to moderate limits, and steel-and iron making has, in some cases been definitely abandoned, as good profits can be made from coal alone'. 'But', as a rider, he cautioned that 'there are collieries producing first-class coal which rarely, if ever, shown a surplus over their expenses'.

Yet, 'during the last twenty-five years large sums' by some South Wales Coalfield companies, 'provided from revenue', had been spent on 'extensions and improvements which strengthened the financial position of these undertakings and encouraged investors'. He then indicated that 'the Powell Duffryn group, the Tredegar group, and the Ocean group were locally known as "The Big Three"'. And these companies' 'shares are usually quoted at a high premium in the market'. Furthermore, a later study concluded that Powell Duffryn and the Ocean Company were examples in the coalfield of companies whose performances, were shaped by 'long-term, rather than short-run, development'.[3]

But to speak of a 'Big Three' in 1927 was misleading. Aberconway's survey showed that a 'Big Two' had emerged. 'During the last twenty years there has been a striking development in the grouping and amalgamating of colliery undertakings in the South Wales coalfields (sic)'. Rationalisation of ownership within the South Wales Coalfield had seen two bigger companies emerge. By 1923, Guest Keen & Nettlefolds (GKN), having absorbed Viscount Rhondda's Cambrian Combine in 1920, was 'gobbling up Welsh colliery companies'.[4] Powell Duffryn Steam Coal Company not only controlled the Rhymney Iron Company, but had further bought the insolvent Windsor Steam Coal Company whose colliery lay in the Aber Valley, an appendix of the Rhymney Valley, entered into a joint venture with the Ocean Company to sink Taff-Merthyr Colliery, and opened three new collieries: Ogilvie, in the Bargoed Rhymney Valley; and on the South Crop of the coalfield, Llanharan and Llantrisant.

After a lapse of two decades, the opening of Wyllie Colliery was the only strategic measure taken by the Tredegar Iron & Coal Company to sustain itself as a coal company. In so doing, the company had also taken more than likely the last lease available in the Sirhowy Valley to mine untouched steam coal seams. The company needed to take a radical new course for it to survive a thousand years mining coal. Nevertheless, a year after the publication of Lord Aberconway's survey of the basic industries of Great Britain, the Tredegar Company was able to assert that it remained a force in the South Wales Coalfield. Company colliery investments made early in the twentieth century achieved notable results.

A Million Ton a Year Colliery

For the year from the 1st April 1927, to the 31st March 1928, Oakdale Colliery produced 1,004,311 tons of coal, and Markham Colliery 779,186 tons.[5] The respective manning levels at Oakdale and Markham collieries were: 3,154 and 2,502 in 1927; and 3,465 and 2,825 in 1928.[6]

At the time, a colliery breaking the one million ton a year output barrier placed it among an elite number of collieries in the British Coalfield. Within the Tredegar Company there would have been satisfaction about progress since the company's total annual colliery output had only attained such a prized output level a quarter of a century earlier.

The output achievements at Oakdale and Markham collieries also enlivened inter-valley competition. Anecdotal evidence suggests that Rhymney Valley's Bargoed Colliery, not Penallta Colliery, was seen among workers at Oakdale Colliery as its direct rival. In 1925, members of the Institution of Mining Engineers visited Bargoed Colliery and learnt that its annual output was about 750,000 tons.[7] The followers of horse racing at Oakdale Colliery might have imagined in 1928 that they beat their counterparts at Bargoed Colliery by many horse lengths. Followers of the turf at Markham Colliery may have envisaged a horse's head victory over Bargoed Colliery.

For the record, Wyllie Colliery's output for 1928 was 154,157 tons. Using a racing analogy, the colliery had charged out of the starting gate to match the 1889 coal output of Bedwellty Pits. However, and notable, in 1929, Bedwellty Pits' name was no longer listed in *The South Wales Coal Annual*. The coal workings of the pit had been put under the control of Ty Trist seemingly when Archie Strang returned to the company as the colliery's manager.

A falling off in demand

Concerning the period from April 1929 to March 1930, the Tredegar Company experienced a 'falling off of demand' from 'Continental markets, where 'large stocks' of coal had been 'accumulating during the last year'.[8] German and Polish coal exports undersold not least Tredegar coal. Aberconway further confessed that 'when you know that a great amount of [ship] tonnage is lying idle today and remember that great numbers of the newer vessels being built are designed for oil-fuel, you will see that the outlook is by no means rosy'.

Yet, in June 1930, the company's order book was said to be 'well filled'. Lord Aberconway reported that 'the Railway Administrations abroad had a strong preference for Tredegar coal'. A marketing scheme, set up as a result of the 1930 Coal Act, to sell British coal to British railway companies, he thought, 'saved' the coal industry from a 'serious' slump. In the case of the company, inferred from one of his remarks, coal sales to railway companies of South Wales and the Midlands improved. Maybe as a result, the company's general manager, William Woolley, was 'paying closest attention to sizing and grading' of coal to 'produce the qualities … customers require'.

Another feature of the company's performance was that the Oakdale power-house had generated over thirty million units of electricity, which was akin to 'the quantity of current consumed by many towns of considerable size'. The total potential generating capacity of Oakdale's power-house by 1930 was 17,500 kW.[9] In 1931, all the villagers at Oakdale became customers of the 'long-delayed arrival' of electricity.[10] The electrification of Oakdale village was a sign of the company earning some income from domestic users in the Sirhowy Valley.

Maybe it was not surprising that the sales department, under Norman McNeil, was praised by Lord Aberconway for being 'most successful in keeping our collieries in work'. The company's colliery pay roll had by June 1930 grown by 1,200 compared with the previous year to 11,235. The growth in employment was due mainly to jobs being created at Wyllie Colliery that in 1930 saw its manning reach 1,384.[11] Following the illustrious annual colliery output performances reported in 1928 for Oakdale and Markham, in 1930 the total number of men employed at these collieries fell by 1,400.[12] However, in 1930 the company's southern area of the Sirhowy Valley – Markham, Oakdale, and Wyllie collieries – represented in manning terms a fifty-five per cent share of the people employed by the company. The manning of Ty Trist Colliery, the flag bearer for Tredegar as a coal town, at 1,274 persons in 1930, represented just eleven per cent share of the company's total manning.[13] The town of Blackwood's importance in terms of coal mining had flourished as Tredegar's had waned. However, Tredegar still retained a pool of technical skill at the company's works. Skilled engineering labour was further vital if another local technical entrepreneur like L. D. Whitehead could raise capital to grow a manufacturing company in the town.

Regardless, for the year that ended March 1930, the company's miners produced a total output of 3,065,000 tons, which was 180,000 tons higher than the previous year's output. Wyllie Colliery, apparently, had 'rapidly' become a 'profitable and extremely efficient undertaking'.[14]

If the general picture presented by the company in June 1930 was a reassuring one, the company's financial accounts contained an item that illustrated the directors' inclination for caution. In 1930, the general reserve was raised to £100,000 of which a part was invested in British Government securities. The company's chairman hoped that the shareholders would agree that 'when bad times come' that they 'would want' to 'get at' their 'reserves in the form of cash'. However, in 1930 shareholders accepted a company dividend of five per cent. A shareholder, at the company's 1930 meeting, observed 'how delighted every shareholder must be that a South Wales Colliery Company [had] nothing said against it'. Such praise might have been more restrained if the risk to company colliery assets during the last two months of 1929 and in January 1930, due to excessive rainfall in the Sirhowy Valley, had been appreciated.[15]

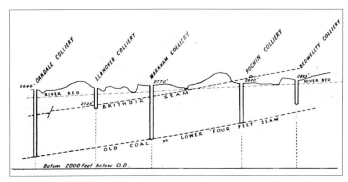

Simplified geological section through northern end of the Sirhowy Valley. *Proceedings, SWIE: 1934, Vol. L*

Curing a Water Problem[16]

In 1929, with the closure of Llanover Colliery certain, the loss of that colliery's pumping operation meant that 'additional water' could 'get through' to Oakdale Colliery. There was a danger also of Markham Colliery being 'drowned out'.

The exhausted Brithdir seam of the territory north of Pochin Colliery and around Markham Colliery, served like a storm water sewer. The working of the seam had 'almost invariably [been] accompanied by a heavy make of water'. The rocks of the Pennant Measures of Sirhowy Valley's mountains was 'full of breaks and joints'. William Woolley observed that 'surface water, therefore quickly and easily' found 'its way into the workings, and as the roads and goafs in this seam do not close up or squeeze so readily as most other seams, water easily' found its 'way from one point to another'.

In July 1929, the Tredegar Company, 'anticipating the trouble', reopened Hollybush Level that lay to the south of Markham Colliery. The level once worked the Brithdir seam. At a distance of 700 yards from the mouth of the level low lift centrifugal pumps were installed, and from around the start of 1930 were removing 25,000 gallons of water per hour.

At Llanover Colliery, in 1910-1912, two Hathorn Davy steam pumps had been installed at pit bottom; one pump had a capacity of 120,000 gallons per hour, and the other 60,000 gallons per hour. However, due to the deluge of water in late 1929, the pumps became 'overloaded' and 'breakdowns occurred and it was [found] impossible to carry out the necessary repairs'. Water rose to 84 feet 4 inches in the colliery's shaft, and an estimated 80,000 to 90,000 gallons of water ran on in the direction of Oakdale Colliery.

The owner of Llanover Colliery, Bargoed Coal Company, employed a diver to repair the pumps. Difficulties were met 'providing air by a hand-operated pump for the diver'. H. J. Rake, Oakdale Colliery's chief mechanical engineer, 'evolved' a 'very ingenious method' that enabled the diver to receive a reliable supply of air.

William Woolley disclosed that the 'period December 1929 to March 1930 was an anxious time' for the Tredegar Company. 'Consultations' occurred between the Tredegar Company and the Bargoed Company. The Tredegar Company decided that 'the only solution was to install an electric [powered] sinking pump'. Llanover Colliery's head-gear could not safely bear the heavy load of the sinking pump. A specially designed, fabricated, gantry was erected on the colliery's top pit to attach winch gear for lowering the sinking pump. The winch, initially steam powered but later electric, was capable of raising a load of eighty tons.

The colliery had no electric power. The Tredegar Company's electric overhead line between Markham Colliery and Oakdale power-house passed near the colliery and was 'tapped'. Installed at Llanover Colliery were switchgear and a 6600/3300 volt transformer. In March 1930, with electricity supplied, a 60,000 gallons per hour Sulzer sinking pump 'was put to work'.

By this time the Tredegar Company had acquired Llanover Colliery from the Bargoed Company. The Tredegar Company contemplated 'various' pumping schemes and decided to 'take out the steam pumps and install Sulzer Deepwell pumps'. Relatively small-sized Deepwell type pumps were used 'extensively' for the supply of water in London and waterworks in the North and in the Midlands. The chief mechanic of Markham Colliery, E. Pearce, 'performed the very difficult task of taking out the big Hathorn Davy pumps', and it was completed 'without accident or delay'.

The Deepwell pumps were specified by W. Angus Scott, the company's consulting engineer, in conjunction with the manufacturer. The key parameters of the final pump specification were:

Quantity ....about 150,000 gals per hr[17]
Total head including all losses ....505 ft
Speed...1,480 rpm
Power absorbed on motor coupling......about 540 h.p.

Each pump was designed for the flow of water to be reduced from 150,000 gallons per hour to 30,000 gallons per hour. The pumps were of the 'extra duty type'.[18] An electric motor to drive a pump was placed on the colliery's surface at the top of a column of pumping system components.[19] The company's electrical engineer responsible for such work was possibly W. W. Hannah.

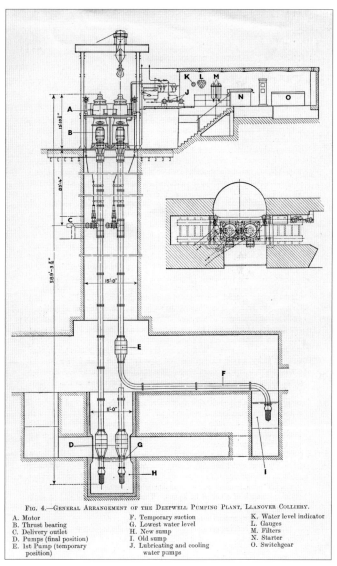

Fig. 4.—General Arrangement of the Deepwell Pumping Plant, Llanover Colliery.

A. Motor
B. Thrust bearing
C. Delivery outlet
D. Pumps (final position)
E. 1st Pump (temporary position)
F. Temporary suction
G. Lowest water level
H. New sump
I. Old sump
J. Lubricating and cooling water pumps
K. Water level indicator
L. Gauges
M. Filters
N. Starter
O. Switchgear

General Arrangement of Deepwell Pumping plant installed in Llanover Colliery by the Tredegar Company circa 1931. The pumps, each capable of raisng a maximum of 150,000 gallons of water per hour, were installed to protect Oakdale Colliery's workings from flooding of a kind experienced in late 1929. *Proceedings, SWIE: 1934, Vol. L*

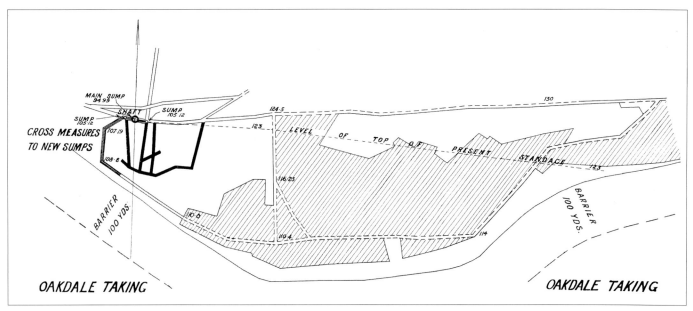

Layout of undergound work done at Llanover Colliery to make fuller use of standage as a water reservoir in the event of flooding.
Proceedings, SWIE: 1934, Vol. L

The electric motor that drove a Deepwell Pump System. The motor was situated on the surface of Llanover Colliery. The pump was claimed to be the 'largest of its type in the world'. *Proceedings, SWIE: 1934, Vol. L*

Looking down the shaft of Llanover Colliery. Viewed are an assembly of pipe and pump drive sections (within the pipe) of a Deepwell Pump system. *Proceedings, SWIE: 1934, Vol. L*

Furthermore, with the first Deepwell pump operating at pit bottom, miners deepened the shaft by twenty-seven feet so as to create a permanent sump for water. In addition, miners excavated connections with 'certain old workings in the Brithdir seam' to increase the water storage capacities of what were termed 'standage roads'. The standage roads were used like a kind of subterranean reservoir with the aim of limiting the quantity of water from rising above pit bottom. A water storage test found that 2,800,000 gallons rose to a level equal to the pit bottom. Moreover, it was calculated that 4,000,000 gallons 'could be stored without interference to the ventilation', which was a small blowing fan on top of the pit.[20] The design of the pumping system further ensured that water rising up the shaft would not interfere in 'any way' with electrical and mechanical operation.

With the pump system commissioned, one man per shift was employed at the surface of Llanover Colliery to attend to the running of the Deepwell pumping system. The intention was to operate the pumps during afternoon and night shifts, and weekends, which were 'periods of light loads' on the Oakdale power-house.

In 1934, it was thought that the only other Deepwell pump installed in the South Wales Coalfield was 'put in by the Ebbw Vale Company at their pumping pit at Sirhowy'. Made by the Harland Engineering Company, the pump was designed for 5,000 gallons per hour with a lift of about 500 feet. Concerning the Llanover Colliery's Deepwell pumping system, the Tredegar Company claimed in 1932 that it represented the 'largest of its type in the world'.[21]

The pumping system eased William Woolley's worries. In 1934, he admitted: 'there was definitely at one time a danger of Oakdale and Markham Collieries being drowned out'. Indeed, around Christmas 1932, underground at Oakdale Colliery, 'water burst through the floor and flooded the workings'. 'The water pressure was so great, the rise so rapid, that there were fears about the possibility of a flood of the South Pit'. The ventilation became blocked so raising the risk of gas accumulation, which was an 'alarming hazard'. A compressed air system was rigged to feed miners with fresh air in order that they could 'frantically' work to 'salvage machinery and install a [battery] of pumps'. One underground section was 'subsequently abandoned'.[22] However, the Tredegar Company could not engineer an escape from the effects of an economic crisis that occurred as the Llanover Colliery work progressed.

Depression

By 1931, a world-wide economic recession had deepened in the wake of the 1929 Wall Street Crash. Although the Depression, as it later became known, reached its nadir in 1931, economic recovery was to prove a long process.

The period from June 1929 to August 1931 saw a Labour Government hold power under Ramsey MacDonald. During MacDonald's political career he 'addressed a meeting at Blackwood under the auspices of the Tredegar Co-operative Society'.[23] Aneurin Bevan judged that 'MacDonald was a pitiful strategist'. In 1930, the two men met for an argument. Bevan had put down a 'resolution for discussion by the Parliamentary Labour Party meeting, calling attention to the impending financial crisis, and asking for a special national conference of the party to be called'. Bevan was asked to 'withdraw the resolution because it was an embarrassment to the party', and told that 'recovery was just around the corner'. Nevertheless, the Tredegar man reckoned that it 'never seemed to occur' to MacDonald 'that it was our business to grapple with the crisis ourselves, and that if Socialism had no remedy for a crisis in capitalism, then [the Labour Party] had no political territory to stand on'. Aneurin Bevan did not withdraw the motion.[24]

At the time a 'little known' Labour Party politician, Clement Attlee, was also 'opposed to a deflationary policy' that the Gold Standard represented, and was to regard as 'political betrayal' a subsequent action of MacDonald's.[25] In August 1931, the Labour Government resigned, and a Coalition Government under Ramsey MacDonald was formed. An early action of the Coalition Government was to abandon the Gold Standard.

The Sirhowy Valley, like elsewhere in the United Kingdom, was severely affected by the Depression. Unemployment in Tredegar in 1927 was measured at 8 per cent, but in 1929 it had leapt to 18.2 per cent. The year 1930 saw a little fall in Tredegar's unemployment, but it worsened to 22.7 per cent in 1931.[26] Speculatively, since relevant data was not found, the rise in unemployment at the head of the Sirhowy Valley was partly due to the closure of the Ebbw Vale steel works in 1929. Some Tredegar district men, particularly those living at Sirhowy, lost their jobs at Ebbw Vale. Much more significantly maybe, since the associated figures were not found, the closure in 1931 of Whitehead Iron & Steel Company's Tredegar Mill caused a rise in local joblessness. Whiteheads cited as a reason for closure the ending of supply of steel billets from the Ebbw Vale works. However, another factor that Whiteheads took into account was that 'the 'purchase of imported steel was found to be more economic, so it was decided to centralise the whole production at Newport with the consequent reduction in transport charges'.[27]

Untenable business economics and pessimism, which trade slumps foster, forcibly re-shaped the geographical location of the South Wales iron and steel industry. A year after the Ebbw Vale steelworks closed, Guest Keen and Nettlefolds (GKN) ended 171 years of ironmaking and seventy-five years of steel manufacture at Dowlais to focus such industry at its Cardiff works. The demise of the 'great' Heads of Valleys ironworks, so labelled by Sir Henry Bessemer at least, seemed complete. The Tredegar Company's good fortune was to have closed its iron and steelmaking operation earlier to focus upon coal mining.

Remarkably it seems, in 1930 the Tredegar Company's collieries operated at 86 per cent of full capacity output.[28] Short-term adjustments in manning at the collieries were made to attune with the tempo of the market. An expedient action, but as far as a colliery worker laid off was concerned, he was the casualty of hard-headedness. A pool of idle, disaffected, miners dwelt in the company's territory. Some of these miners may have once worked at Bedwellty Pits, and so were victims of long-term unemployment. At least some key workers at Whitehead's Tredegar Mill removed to Newport. However, the Tredegar Iron & Coal Company was rooted where it operated, and like a sitting duck had to endure not only the vagaries of the market, but changes in Government policy.

In July 1932, Lord Aberconway's addressed Tredegar Iron & Coal Company shareholders about the 'changed atmosphere' due to the country 'having departed' the Gold Standard. The 'departure had imposed such a heavy charge on our manufacturing costs, meant in theory a heavy bonus in favour of our exports and a similar tariff against our imports'. He further submitted that the Coalition Government's 'adoption of a Protectionist policy was intended to strengthen this position. Most persons thought these changes would have facilitated sales abroad and consumption at home, but actually these changes were largely ineffective, owing to the prompt countervailing measures by other nations'. He elaborated:

As coal is our chief export, obstacles were imposed by France, Belgium, and Germany, and subsidies were put into force by Poland and Germany through the lowering of railways rates for coal which operated against our prices, and in other ways by Holland and Belgium. Italy also levied a surtax on coal imports.[29]

Regardless, in the South Wales valleys, doomsayers of capitalism found reasons to blame the failure of free markets for the Depression. Educational classes had 'convinced' the likes of Harold Finch 'that unemployment was inherent in the capitalist system, with its booms and slumps'.[30] The responses that coalowners made in the South Wales Coalfield for survival, like laying off labour, cut no ice with men who believed that Socialism was an alternative to capitalism.

In reality, the slump in the South Wales Coalfields' coal trade was outwith the control of Britons. For the year ending early April 1932, the production of the South Wales Coalfield 'amounted to only about 38,000,000 tons—the lowest figure recorded (except strike years) since 1897'. 'Our coalfield', the chairman of the Tredegar Company may have sighed, 'owing to its dependence on exports', was 'more seriously affected than other districts'. He illustrated 'the general collapse of world industry' in terms of 'the idleness of merchant shipping, of which 13,000,000 tons' were 'laid up, resulting in a heavy loss' of 'bunker supplies' of coal. He must have felt some humility acknowledging that two 'important factors in the reduction of the South Wales output' was the 'practical substitution' of oil for coal by the Admiralty, and the 'conversion to oil burning by forty-three per cent of world [merchant shipping] tonnage'. The 'reduced [coal] consumption' by the British iron and steel industry was another 'important' factor.

The state of the market forced William Woolley's hand to make 'certain reorganisations' within the company's colliery operation. The cliché, reorganisation, meant layoffs. In July 1932, the company's employment total fell below 10,000 for 'the first time for many years'. Company shareholders heard Woolley's report that the 'large number [of men] mentioned of approximately 4,000 was in order to enable us to rearrange our employ to the best advantage, but the number of notices which will operate immediately if trade does not improve will be under 2,000, and we shall be able to meet any increase in trade that may arise. It is practically reducing two of the collieries from double shift to single shift'. Some of the company's miners, who produced a total output for the year that ended on the 2nd April 1932, of 2,562,375 tons, had already been dismissed since there was a decrease of 169,345 tons in output compared with the previous year.

In 1931, many house-bound miners in the Sirhowy and Rhymney Valleys were among the nearly three million British people unemployed. The woefulness continued into 1932 since unemployment reached 31.7 per cent in Tredegar and 33.6 per cent in Blackwood. It would have been no consolation for Sirhowy Valley people suffering hardship that year to know that unemployment at Blaina stood at 93 per cent, Merthyr Tydfil 61 per cent, Pontlottyn, where idle McLaren Colliery miners registered, 57.4 per cent, Caerphilly 50.8 per cent, Ebbw Vale 38.6 per cent, and Bargoed 37.7 per cent.[31]

The Tredegar Iron & Coal Company's action in 1930 to increase its general reserve fund proved prudent since 'bad times' had not only 'come' but loitered. Thus, in July 1932, Lord Aberconway was in 'a very happy position' to propose a dividend of 5 per cent, which was the same as what the shareholders had received in 1930 and 1931.[32] He further alleged that the Tredegar Company was the only company in the South Wales Coalfield to pay such a rate of dividend. Such a result 'reflects the greatest credit on the officials and those responsible for the conduct of our business'.[33]

Lord Aberconway, a competent judge of colliery company management, ruled that he knew of 'no Company which is more efficiently and intelligently managed' than the Tredegar Iron & Coal Company. However, such a judgment involved some conceit. In 1932 Powell Duffryn had begun to see improved profits due in part to the modernization of at least the former collieries of the Great Western and Lewis Merthyr companies, which it had acquired in 1928.[34]

Yet, maybe due to bluster, Lord Aberconway offered a homily: that 'from the highest to the lowest' in the Tredegar Company 'there is a esprit de corps and good feeling which counts for so much in all businesses especially in a coal business. It is largely due to the wage-earners as well as the shareholders and we have such pleasant relations with our men'. He hoped that such a state of 'relations would continue'. The homily would have been thought absurd by company colliery workers beset by fears of uncertain employment prospects.

Viewed in the wider context of unemployment in the South Wales Coalfield during the 1930s, Oakdale 'village was fortunate in that a certain number were still employed at the colliery, though not in the same number as before'.[35] Yet, Oakdale Colliery workers faced harrowing choices. Two or three-day working weeks became the norm as it did throughout the South Wales Coalfield. In opting to work, a miner forewent unemployment benefit. 'After deductions for rent, coal, etc., many men [at Oakdale] took home so little pay that it was not uncommon for them to seek "relief", or public assistance'. That some colliery workers would have been slightly better off financially by signing on as unemployed was another option. Maybe the most traumatic choice concerned whether, or not, to migrate.

An exodus from Oakdale village was later recognised as an irony by Ralph Thomas. 'Because of many attractions, [that the village] had had new families pouring into fill houses as they were built'. He revealed that many families moved in the 1930s from Oakdale to the Kent Coalfield, and to the Midlands of England, the 'new trading estates at Slough and London'. He attested that 'so common did this emigration become, that one time there were forty empty houses in the village'.[36] However, the company sought to fill the vacant houses by pressing colliery workers, who did not live in the village, that 'to safeguard their employment, they should move to the village'. The implicit 'warning' was heeded and some workers removed to the village.[37]

The Meadow Vein and Coal Cutting Machinery[38]

Around 1933, Oakdale Colliery's underground workers were deployed to open up new seams of coal. A decision to abandon working the Old Coal seam in "John Williams" played some part in shaping such action. Efforts made to work "John Williams" were thwarted by a geological fault. Another district of the Old Coal seam was opened, but an 'out-burst of water occurred'. The pressure of the water 'was so great' that it fractured the 'extremely hard' floor under the seam comprised of white quartz. The floor was broken into 'chunks and boulders' with some the 'size of billiard tables up at the Institute'. The subsequent visit of a HM Mines Inspector led to work continuing to develop the Old Coal seam coal provided that the company met three conditions: the provision of another escape exit, which was speedily effected; keeping a full-time watch on water levels; and regular escape drills for miners in readiness for another out-burst of water.

The company was also forced to open seams due to an embarrassing calamity. The eastern boundary of the Oakdale Company's 'Ted Henry' and 'Parrs' districts of the Rhas Las seam was shared with Partridge, Jones & John Paton Limited's Crumlin Navigation Colliery coal take. However, the surveyors of Partridge, Jones & John Paton discovered that the two Oakdale Company's districts workings had trespassed by 100 yards. 'Ted Henry' and 'Parrs' districts were closed and so previously busy 400 miners were dismissed by the company.

However, it was development of the Meadow Vein during this period in a north-eastern direction that was to 'give the colliery years of production'. 'Gradually the Meadow Vein' succeeded the Rhas Las as the main producing seam at Oakdale Colliery.

Furthermore, around 1933, the Tredegar Company introduced coal cutting machinery. The machinery was first installed at Markham and Oakdale collieries to work thinner seams. Men working the Big Vein at Oakdale Colliery witnessed the arrival of a coal cutter and a face conveyor. The introduction of machinery coincided with the 'pit' returning 'to good production and so unemployed men were reabsorbed'.[39] Moreover, during the 1930s, Tredegar Company miners were issued with equipment that improved safety at work. A new type of headlamp was introduced for use in the steam coal seams. Disregarding objections by miners who preferred 'a skull cap … usually made from a bowler hat' that 'fitted snugly on their heads', the safety helmet was introduced to become a basic piece of safety equipment.[40] As the forgoing developments proceeded Lord Aberconway was troubled by ill health.

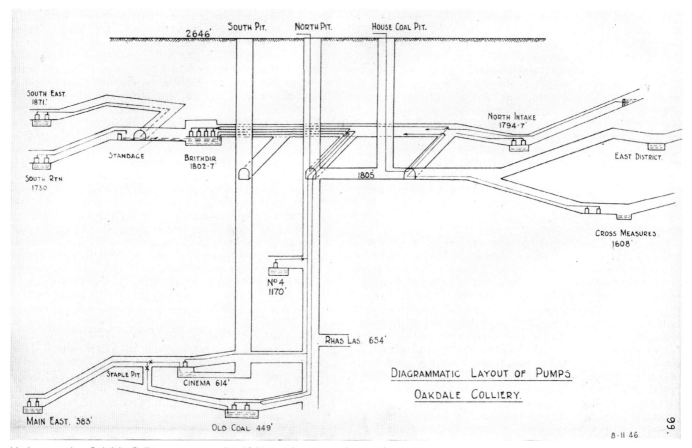

Underground at Oakdale Colliery represented in 1946 as a diagramatic layout of pumps.
Folio of Technical Information – Oakdale and Wyllie Collieries, compiled by Jack Edwards circa 1946. A. J. Edwards Collection

Charles McLaren, 1st Lord Aberconway (1850-1934).
Served as the chairman of Tredegar Iron & Coal Company for four decades.
Photograph taken in 1920 by Bassano Ltd. © National Portrait Gallery

'A man of ability'

On the 23rd January 1934, aged eighty-three, Lord Aberconway died at his London home, 43 Belgrave Square. His wife, Laura, predeceased him. She passed away on the 4th January 1933.

The obituary in *The Times* proclaimed that Lord Aberconway 'was a man of ability who passed from a successful career at the Bar to an equally successful career in industrial development.'[41] The obituarist proposed that Charles McLaren 'found no difficulty in his new career of industrial development' owing to his practice at the Bar being 'chiefly in company and mercantile cases'. His legal work certainly gave him the chance to learn from case studies concerned with the blunders of industrial affairs. Nevertheless, his legal background was not the only factor that enabled him to exchange a barrister's wig for an industrialist's top hat with 'little difficulty'.

It was British industry's good fortune that he married Laura Pochin. Her father, Henry Pochin, gave him the chance to become party to company directors' decision making. As a company director, he was pitched into resolving crises, some unforeseen, in a shorter timescale than that observable in the way that the legal world does its business.

Furthermore, Lord Aberconway's qualities were a boon for an industrialist. The *North Wales Chronicle* recalled that 'his versatility and energy were amazing almost to the end of his long life'.[42] This newspaper's obituarist recognised him as 'one of the busiest men of his generation' who became 'one of Britain's princes of industry, commerce, and finance'. Moreover, the obituarist, it is proposed, advanced an acute appreciation of character that had a bearing upon his subject's success: 'Although a forceful personality in business, Lord Aberconway was kind and gentle to all. Handsome, well-built, affable, he had the characteristics of the fine old Englishman'. The rigour with which he studied philosophy at Edinburgh probably helped make him a convinced Radical Liberal that guided his conduct in business.

The Tredegar Iron & Coal Company was the beneficiary of his leadership. By 1904, some company officials espoused a man-management principle: to hold the 'scales of justice evenly' between the needs of the company and those of workmen. The principle had a legal ring about it that suggests that Charles McLaren may have been its author. During the 1898 Strike he showed an exceptional example of leadership by meeting face-to-face disgruntled company workers. His 1932 company homily may have been a statement of reaffirmation in his life long quest to foster 'a feeling of friendship between master and man'. As a coalowner, contrary to the thoughts of company workers, he made genuine attempts to foster good industrial relations. Moreover, 'the keen interest displayed by Lord Aberconway' for both improving working conditions and the welfare of people living in the communities associated with the company's collieries would be recalled by at least Archie Strang, company agent, into the 1960s.[43]

Lord Aberconway also warrants recognition for the long-term nature of his involvement in the company. Of considerable value was a man having a national reputation with wide connections in business and politics. Securing and retaining shareholder support for a risky coal mining venture, regardless of the market value of South Wales steam coal in its heyday, was not an easy task. His writings on the financial aspects of industry reveal that he was an accomplished practitioner in the field of financial management and it is evident that the Tredegar Company benefitted.[44] The company reports he presented show that under his stewardship disciplined financial management was practiced. The role he played in the Tredegar Company directors' major strategic decision to abandon steelmaking to focus on coal mining was found to be unclear, but an unsatisfactory outcome would more than likely have seen him unseated as chairman. However, during the company's financial crisis of 1899, it seems highly likely that he led the appeal to 2nd Lord Tredegar for help. The manner of his approach won help from the landowner for the company and led to its survival as a business.

Lady Aberconway

Nearly six decades earlier, Laura Pochin cut the turf that marked the start to sinking Pochin Colliery. Her inherited investments were astutely managed by her husband. She died leaving an estate valued at £750,000. Yet, the prevailing attitudes towards women's achievements granted Lady Aberconway CBE scant mention in the press. *The Times* pithily observed that she 'was a zealous and life-long supporter of what used to be called "women's rights", of which, indeed, her mother was a pioneer'. The newspaper understated her talent for horticulture: 'she was an enthusiastic gardener, both at Bodnant, in Denbighshire, and Château de la Garoupe', Antibes, France, where she died.[45] Lady Aberconway was buried in a family mausoleum built in a 'garden that became famous under her inspiration', Bodnant.[46] Lord Aberconway was interred in the same mausoleum.

Successors

In the same year of Lord Aberconway's death, the 2nd Viscount Tredegar also passed away. The close link between the Morgan family of Tredegar House and the Tredegar Company seems to have ended with the death of Godfrey Charles Morgan, 1st Viscount Tredegar. The 'main interests' of his successor, Courtney, were 'gentlemanly pursuits of hunting, shooting, and fishing. He also much enjoyed travelling, and quite often made use of his personal yacht'.[47] He died in 1934. During his years as viscount, the income after tax of the Tredegar Mineral Estate fell gradually from £110,948 in 1914 to £65,362 in 1933, which was the last income figure found.[48]

The 2nd Viscount's son, Evan, was destined to surpass his father's extravagances. As the 3rd Viscount, he 'entertained on a lavish scale' at Tredegar House. 'His wild weekend house parties' were 'attended by a curious mixture of the famous and the entirely unknown, gained local notoriety'. His profligacy, a form of wealth distribution, in the pit of the Depression, belittled

the good that Godfrey Charles Morgan and his ancestors had done in Monmouthshire. Evan, who died in 1949, was the last of the Morgans to live at Tredegar House.[49]

The Hon Henry Duncan McLaren CBE succeeded to the title Aberconway. Aged fifty-five, he was absorbed in the trials besetting British industry. In 1934, he was chairman of Thomas Firth and John Brown Limited, and held directorships in the British Overseas Bank, and Tredegar Iron & Coal Company.[50] By 1935, he was elected chairman of the Tredegar Company in the poorest of times.

Stubborn Unemployment

In June 1935, the new chairman appealed to shareholders not to ask him to 'make any prophecy as to the future'.[51] His appeal was made against a background of poor company performance, but might be considered a declaration of impotence when faced by considerable business uncertainty. The Tredegar Iron & Coal Company announced a profit of just £40,015 for the 1934-35 financial year, which was one of the lowest ever in the company's history. The shareholders accepted a meagre dividend payment of 2½ per cent per annum, free of Income Tax.

In 1935, the company's collieries worked 'below two-thirds capacity'. David Evans, the general colliery manager, who retired

Lady Aberconway (1854-1933).
As Laura Pochin, she was the only daughter of a founder director of Tredegar Iron & Coal Company, Henry Pochin. She performed the Pochin Colliery opening ceremony in 1876. She was a prominent campaigner for women's suffrage. The medals worn by her may have been the CBE and one representing the Dame of Grace of the Venerable Order of Saint John. *Courtesy McLaren Family, Bodnant House*

Henry McLaren, 2nd Lord Aberconway (1879-1953)
Served as the chairman of Tredegar Iron & Coal Company from 1935 until the company ceased trading.

Courtesy McLaren Family, Bodnant House

'owing to age, after fifty-six years of service with the Company', was one official that had experienced the coal industry's booms and troughs. Yet, the performance at Wyllie Colliery caused Lord Aberconway to be protective. The colliery was 'of course, a new concern; it is still developing and cannot be expected to be in full profit-earning condition all at once'. Although the company's annual coal output rose by 238,531 tons compared with the previous year, an 'adequate return on the capital of the Company' was 'not obtainable'. The 'unsettled state of the various foreign currencies and restrictions placed upon the import of coal into practically all European countries' had curbed export business. The stark effect of the company's poor state was suffering and misery within the people living in its associated communities. In 1935, at Blackwood unemployment was measured at 33.2%, Tredegar 29.6%, and 64.9% and 55.3% for the years 1934 and 1935 respectively at Pontlottyn labour exchange.[52] McLaren Colliery's manning level stood at 1,450 in 1932, but had halved by the mid-1930s. Unemployment within the Tredegar Company's territory held at a stubbornly high level.

In the House of Commons in 1935, Aneurin Bevan attacked the Unemployment Assistance Bill. "The House ought to be heartily ashamed, when children are going without boots and clothing and are badly nourished when the local authorities have not the means to provide them with these things," was one of many points he made.[53] He also spoke in a Finance Bill debate about an aspect that had implications for the British steel industry. He brought attention to the long-term unemployed due to the closure of the Ebbw Vale steel works.[54]

In December, the Labour Party called for a national increase in wages for miners. A debate in the House of Commons heard a host of observations that illustrated that the coal industry was in crisis, and that despair and privation pervaded British mining communities. Ebbw Vale's MP raised minor queries during the debate.[55] Yet, in June 1935, a meeting of the Tredegar Company covered items of meaning for coal mining in a part of Aneurin Bevan's constituency.

Amalgamation[56]

The Tredegar Iron & Coal Company's 1935 annual report presented no investment plans, which was a valid strategic option when poor trading conditions prevailed. The annual report, though, portrayed a company that historically had a 'wonderful record'. The chairman's only 'hope' was for an 'improvement in the demand for coal'. However, in April 1935, Powell Duffryn Associated Collieries Ltd (PDAC) was formed due to the merging of Powell Duffryn Steam Coal Company and Welsh Associated Collieries. The new company became Great Britain's 'biggest colliery enterprise'. A few years later, in 1938, PDAC owned fifty collieries and employed 37,607 men, and produced almost twelve million tons of coal a year.[57] But in June 1935, at the Tredegar Company's Annual Ordinary General meeting, a shareholder asked: 'Is there any possibility of amalgamation? We have seen rumours in the newspapers'. Lord Aberconway answered: 'I do not think you can take rumours in the papers as being correct'.

However, the company announced at the 1935 meeting the appointment of two managing directors. Aberconway acknowledged that 'in some concerns the appointment of two managing directors' had 'not been entirely successful'. Nevertheless, he had endorsed such appointments for two reasons. First, he judged that the 'personalities of the two men concerned' would enable 'the most complete and harmonious co-operation between them in the conduct of the Company's affairs'. Adding: 'both Mr Woolley and Mr McNeil' had 'been connected with the Company for a great many years, and we are very fortunate in being able to count upon' them 'to carry out the important and responsible duties entrusted to them'. There appeared to be no change to their duties. He related that 'Mr Woolley is in charge' of the 'production side while Mr McNeil is responsible for sales'. In 1935, the Tredegar Iron & Coal Company's five collieries, three as subsidiary companies, raised around two-and-a-half million tons of coal per annum. Could the company overcome the uncertainties of adverse times?

Nine Mile Point Colliery 'Stay-In' Strike

A likely threat to the company's colliery operation was a simmering, and bitter quarrel between the SWMF and the non-political South Wales Miners' Industrial Union (SWMIU) over membership recruitment. By 1935, under a new president, James Griffiths, the SWMF was 'just beginning to climb out of the sloth of despond after 1926'.[58] In 1933, only forty-four per cent of the miners employed in the South Wales Coalfield were members of the SWMF, but the share rose to fifty-five per cent in 1935.[59] Prior to 1935, the Ocean Company bought Nine Mile Point Colliery that stood to the south of Wyllie Colliery in the Sirhowy Valley. Regarding the 'allocation of working places at the colliery', the SWMF lodge at the colliery complained that the Ocean Company favoured members of SWMIU.[60] In the month of October 1935, as a demonstration of objection, members of the SWMF used a new tactic, a 'stay-in' strike. James Griffiths negotiated an end to the strike of nine days.

Events at Nine Mile Point Colliery caused sympathy strikes at other collieries including Oakdale Colliery. At Oakdale Colliery, 'although relations were strained, at no time did the Tredegar Iron & Coal Company refuse to negotiate with its employees' leaders, and the leaders of the men on picket duty were never refused access to the colliery'.[61]

Pithead Baths

In July 1936, opened at Oakdale Colliery were pithead baths with a canteen. Designed by W. M. Trailor LRIBA, the plan of the building ensured that men in a clean state, whether arriving for work, or dressing after having bathed, were isolated from dirtied miners and soiled clothing. The Ocean Company pioneered pithead baths in the South Wales Coalfield at Deep Navigation Colliery in 1906. Oakdale Colliery set the pithead baths' precedent in the Sirhowy Valley due to the allocation of

Oakdale Navigation Colliery – Pithead Baths. Opened in July 1936.

Photographer Jack Edwards A. J. Edwards collection

money from a Miners Welfare Fund raised from a small levy on the price of coal. The men employed at the colliery contributed weekly 6d. towards the building's upkeep.

Ralph Thomas declared that the Oakdale Colliery pithead baths 'was probably the single greatest advance in the village's amenities'. Villagers' pride was boosted. He recalled: 'Our village was the envy of surrounding pits and villages, and for some weekends after the opening the public from miles around came to inspect this innovation'.[62] In April, 1936, drawing plans for the Markham Colliery's pithead baths were issued by the Miners Welfare Committee, and construction of the building began not long afterwards. Wyllie Colliery's pithead baths opened in the mid-1950s.

One Week's Paid Holiday[63]

In 1937, astute negotiations by Arthur Horner, president SWMF, won for colliery workers one week's paid holiday a year. Previously, workers forfeited pay if they took holidays. Horner's tactic involved offering that SWMF members would forego an agreed wage increase with the coalowners in exchange for one week's paid holiday. Some miners and their families subsequently took holidays that involved seaside bathing for the first time. Many sun bathing miners could be readily identified since their backs were black with ingrained coal dust. Such miners believed that washing their backs made them weaker for toiling at the coal face.[64] Pit ponies were given a week of grazing in fields with colliery hauliers keeping an eye on their animal friends.

A Start in the Coal Mining Industry[65]

A dimension of 1930s unemployment in the South Wales valleys was the lack of job opportunities for school leavers. In July 1936, the plan for Jack Edwards, a pupil at Pontllanfraith Secondary School, was to leave school. His 'misfortune' was 'that no work could be found anywhere – not even delivering newspapers'. He returned to the school for another year.

In 1937, Jack was interviewed by the Wyllie Colliery manager, D. H. Thomas, for a job as a labourer in the washery He accepted the labouring job, and later learnt that he 'filled a dead man's shoes'. His predecessor, Emmanuel Bruges had been killed

'apparently' due to being 'entangled in the drive of the small coal conveyor feeding the washery from the screening plant'. Jack Edwards first task each day at the colliery, which began at 6.30 a.m., 'unbeknown to management', was to start the duff and slurry shaking screens by 7 a.m. He recalled that he had to 'move quickly to fill all the [screen plant's] Stauffer grease cups'. The greaser pondered how to make his work easier. On the washery wall at Wyllie Colliery, Jack 'drew a pictorial sketch in chalk … on how to mount the caps on a steel frame and how to connect them to the bearings with rubber tubes'.

Unbeknown to Jack, J. M. Reynolds, a Member of the Institution of Mechanical Engineers, the group engineer for the Tredegar & Iron Coal Company, saw the sketch. J. M. Reynolds's father, T. Reynolds, had served as Pochin Colliery's manager for twenty years at the start of the century. Thus, J. M. Reynolds became at least the second generation of a family to serve the Tredegar Company in a managerial role. When Jack was told to see the colliery manager urgently he 'thought' he was to be rebuked for 'defacing the brickwork'. He met not only the colliery manager but J. M. Reynolds. The two managers asked him 'a lot of questions; the upshot of it was: would I like to become a draughtsman? And undergo training?' as an apprentice. He 'accepted the proposal conditionally on my parents agreeing'. As a colliery labourer he earned 15s 4d per week, and by working a Sunday, he took home £1 0s 6d. The first year wage of an apprentice was 7s 6d. However, the company eased parental concerns by viewing his year of work as a labourer as part of his apprenticeship, and he was paid a second year apprentice's wage, which was 12s 6d per week.

Jack Edwards joined the small number of staff at Oakdale Colliery engineering offices. His working day began at 8.10 a.m. and ended at 5.00 p.m. on weekdays and at 12.30 p.m. on Saturday. Keith Clancy, the son of Oakdale's chief draughtsman, Clifford Clancy, introduced Jack to his initial duties, and supervised him for the 'couple of weeks he was in the office'. Keith Clancy's apprenticeship terms enabled him to attend a sandwich course at Treforest School of Mines for an external BSc examination.[66] On starting work at Oakdale, Jack Edwards enrolled to study an Ordinary National Certificate in Mechanical Engineering at Crumlin School of Mines.

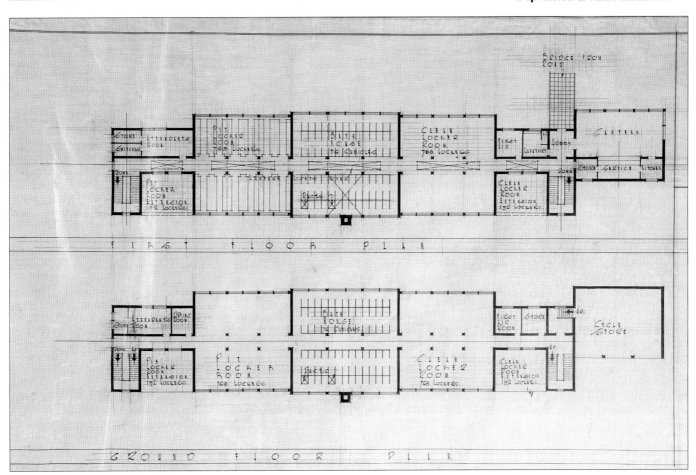

Drawing Plans for Markham Colliery Pithead Baths. Drawn for the Miners Welfare, Romney House, Westminster, London. *Above* is a plan view of Baths. Note the clean locker area to the right of the seventy-six shower (bath) cubicles. On the left of the cubicles is the pit locker room for soiled clothing. Below are the front and side elevations of the baths.

Courtesy of Gwent Archives

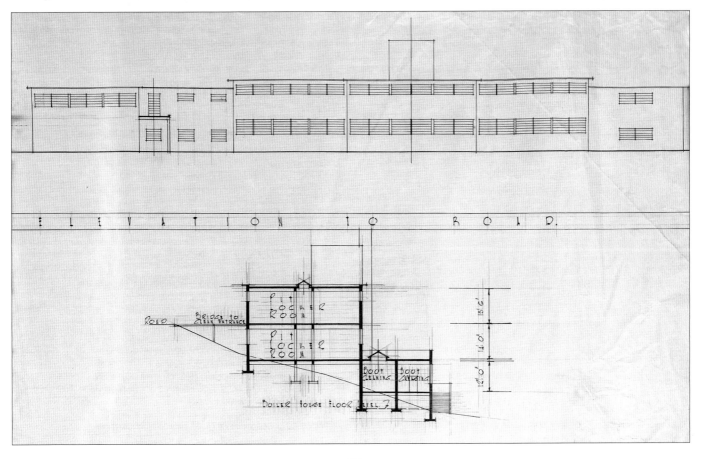

Learning a range of craft skills in the colliery's workshops was another aspect of Jack Edwards's apprenticeship. He found a 'pecking order' among metal shaping machinery craftsmen in the fitting shop.[67] His apprenticeship also enabled him to gain operational experience in at least the colliery's power-house, and coal preparation plant. 'Rarely, did' he go underground. He was at one stage "paired" with a qualified fitter, 'Ron' Morgan.[68] The pair undertook two 'unusual' projects: replacing the sheaves on Oakdale Colliery's South Pit head-frame, and repairing a commutator of a Ward Leonard set at Markham Colliery', which introduced the apprentice to electric winding.

Jack Edwards recalled it was 'noticeable' from when he began his apprenticeship that he 'was treated slightly differently to other workers' of his age. As a staff member of the company he was entitled to two weeks paid holiday each year. It 'seemed', to him, 'that being an apprentice made a person somewhat special and being groomed for higher things'. Early in his apprenticeship, 'Doug' Bosley who 'worked on the telephone switchboard and also issued coal notes', was overheard by 'Mr Reynolds' speaking to 'Jack'. J. M. Reynolds, Jack Edwards recollected, gave Doug Bosley a 'good dressing down' and told him to call the apprentice 'Mr Edwards' thereafter. 'Mr Reynolds' also told 'Mr Edwards' about the reprimand adding: 'that such people [like Doug Bosley] must learn their place in society'. The company thus enforced a deferential code of behaviour within at least its staff. Doug Bosley later represented a Blackwood ward as a Monmouthshire County Councillor.

Around 1938, the Tredegar Iron & Coal Company chose two other young men to become apprentices at Oakdale Colliery. Apprentice 'Alec' Jones was the son of the senior pitman at the colliery, 'Dick' Jones.[69] Jack and Alec were joined by 'Geoff' Richards.[70] For the end of the 1930s, just a tiny number of apprentices met the Blackwood district's main employer's need for sustaining its engineering capability into the future. The number of youths taken on as 'butties' for underground work during this period was not found, but it is surmised that the number was relatively much greater than apprentices recruited. A training centre at Croespenmaen, adjacent to, and to the east of Oakdale, catered for unemployed people, but the numbers under training, and the skills taught were not found.[71] Nonetheless, in summary, the district was bereft of a technical resource that might attract a company to relocate and invest locally in engineering manufacture.

Over the years 1938-39, a No. 2 chimney stack with a base diameter of nearly twenty-two feet was built at Oakdale Colliery to a height above ground level of 216 feet 6 inches by R. Hilton Limited.[72] A draughtsman's duty was to periodically measure the height of the chimney stack as it was being built. 'At first', wrote Jack Edwards, 'Ivor Catleugh would sit on the bosun's chair, and be hoisted through the chimney with the tape measure; but as the chimney grew taller, this privilege fell' on Jack's 'shoulders – being younger and more agile'.

Second World War

On the 3rd September 1939, the United Kingdom declared war on Nazi Germany. Coal reclaimed national strategic importance as in the Great War, hereafter the First World War. The years preceding the outbreak of war had seen the Tredegar Iron & Coal Company achieve improved profits: £102,520 in 1937, £88,467 in 1938, and £83,380 in 1939.[73] On the eve of war, the company produced from eight collieries 2,343,179 tons of coal that represented a 6.14 percentage of the output of the South Wales Coalfield.[74] The company recovered as a business partly due to an improvement in export trade. Before the war 'an understanding was reached with Germany' about Britain's 'relative share of the market' and a similar agreement was reached between the British

A queue of Oakdale Colliery trams on sidings for Tram Shop. Jack Edwards did a stint repairing trams as part of his apprenticeship with the Tredegar Iron & Coal Company.

Photograph taken by Jack Edwards. A. J. Edwards collection

and Polish coal industries. The three nations produced in total 90 per cent of European coal marketed.[75] France received most of the South Wales Coalfield's exports of coal. However when Nazi Germany annexed France in 1940 British producers lost a market of four million tons of coal per annum.

The call to arms saw 'many' local miners join the armed forces, and this 'created an acute labour shortage'. 'Later, conscripts were given the choice of the armed forces or the pits'. A training centre at Oakdale prepared trainees, called 'Bevin Boys', after Earnest Bevin the Government's Minister of Labour and National Service, for underground work. Many of the Bevin Boys, lodged at Oakdale family homes, came from backgrounds unfamiliar with the mining industry and valley life. Ralph Thomas reflected: 'Hopefully, the process of working and living together was both beneficial to Bevin Boys, and their hosts, if only in creating understanding of each others' outlook'.[76]

Across South Wales the Air Raid Precaution (ARP) and the Auxiliary Fire Service (AFS) were expanded, and the Local Defence Volunteers (LDV) was formed that afterwards became known as the Home Guard. The captain in charge of the local 'C' company of the Home Guard, attached to the 5th Monmouthshire Regiment, was Major J. M. Reynolds, the Tredegar Company's chief engineer. In 1917, he was injured in battle serving as a lieutenant with the King's Own Yorkshire Light Infantry.[77] Jack Edwards joined the Home Guard, and his base was Wyllie Colliery where 'all the arms such as rifles, machine guns and ammunition were kept under lock and key in the cellar below the lamproom'. 'Only once were we put on alert, and that was when a bomb was dropped in Cwmfelinfach'. The Wyllie platoon was under the control of Sergeant "Reg" Roberts, and Corporal George Perry. As elsewhere across Great Britain, army drills and field exercises were held at regular intervals 'with lots of excursions to other areas, such as relieving the regular army from guard duty at the various prisoner-of-war camps'.

Jack Edwards, aged nineteen, was not called up to fight due to holding a 'reserved occupation'. He recalled: 'When the Second World War broke out in September 1939, no one in Wyllie village seemed perturbed and life continued as usual, except that some young people were conscripted for the forces, and evacuees arrived' as they did also at Oakdale. Following the evacuation of British forces from Dunkirk in June 1940, the prospect of 'dire consequences' for 'our easy village lifestyle formerly dawned on us with alarm. Winston Churchill became Prime Minister, and all of a sudden we were galvanised into action'. Indeed, 'every man in the village became a member of some organisation and lots of women, particularly the younger ones, enrolled in the munitions factories at Rogerstone, or Caerwent, or Chepstow'.[78] His future wife, Delsie Morgan of Blackwood, became a clerk at the Admiralty, Bath.

During the course of the war a number of Oakdale men were decorated. Sgt 'Tom' Daniels and flight lieutenant 'Bobby' Lewis were recipients of the DFM, lance corporal Brinley Little the MM, and petty officer Francis Hurley the DSM.

Contrasting with men facing the dangers of warfare, Ralph Thomas reflected that in the Sirhowy Valley, 'as a natural result of the war with its rationing of food and clothing, blackout and shortages, life was drab but never dull, there were too many things to be done'.[79]

'The Dust'[80]

The 'acute shortage' of miners to work the Tredegar Company collieries during the Second World War was partly eased by re-employing miners receiving money under a Workmen's Compensation Act scheme. Miners certified for compensation, attributed to silicosis, which was a non-infectious lung disease, had been previously 'suspended' from work in the 'hope that they would be protected from further deterioration'.

Harold Finch dealt with compensations claims. He frankly admitted, regarding 'lung disability', that he could not 'treat the subject without some feeling and some bitterness'. The disability of the dust was 'responsible for much pain, death and tragedy in

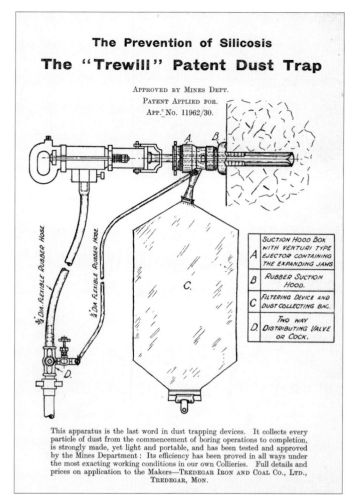

The Prevention of Silicosis

The "Trewill" Patent Dust Trap

APPROVED BY MINES DEPT.
PATENT APPLIED FOR.
APP. No. 11962/30.

A	SUCTION HOOD BOX WITH VENTURI TYPE EJECTOR CONTAINING THE EXPANDING JAWS
B	RUBBER SUCTION HOOD.
C	FILTERING DEVICE AND DUST COLLECTING BAG.
D	TWO WAY DISTRIBUTING VALVE OR COCK.

This apparatus is the last word in dust trapping devices. It collects every particle of dust from the commencement of boring operations to completion, is strongly made, yet light and portable, and has been tested and approved by the Mines Department : Its efficiency has been proved in all ways under the most exacting working conditions in our own Collieries. Full details and prices on application to the Makers—TREDEGAR IRON AND COAL CO., LTD., TREDEGAR, MON.

the mining valleys of South Wales'. He recollected that during his early years at the Tredegar Valley Miners' Blackwood offices, circa 1920, that colliery lodge officers reported that miners 'were unable to work because of chest trouble. They were constantly spitting up coal dust'. Moreover, 'in some fatal cases the post-mortem examination confirmed that death was due to lung coagulation from coal dust'. Evidence collected by the SWMF, raised with the TUC, led in 1921 to work by the Industrial Research Board.

A compensation scheme for men suffering from silicosis, or silicosis accompanied by tuberculosis, was introduced on the 1st January 1929. The case put for the man seeking compensation had to show that he had worked in one of the processes 'involving the handling of silica rock' that 'contained not less than 50% of free silica'. Harold Finch seethed about this criterion: 'It was a battle between geologists on behalf of employers and those for our organisation'.

Drilling rock to place explosives was "one of the processes". By 1930, the Tredegar Company had 'brought out a 'dust trap' to collect 'every particle of dust from commencement of boring operations to completion'.[81] However, once an explosive had fired, 'the dust from the rock, also from the fumes from the shot firing' would be inhaled by miners present in the locality.[82] Moreover, after 1914, ground rock, that more than likely contained silica, was spread underground at the company's collieries with the humane objective of limiting the spread of an explosion. Miners at the company's collieries were exposed to the 'dreaded complaint called silicosis'. However, the danger to miners' health posed by coal dust was viewed as less important than silica dust. Moreover, in the early 1930s, a quandary prevailed about the instances of bronchial troubles among miners of over fifty years of age being 'a disease or an ailment'.[83] Bronchial troubles were further complicated by a range of doctor diagnoses such as asthma, bronchitis, and emphysema. Widespread cigarette

Drilling Rock underground with Dust Trap.

Pope/Parkhouse Archive

smoking among colliery workers was generally discounted as a cause of lung problems. In 1934, the silica criterion that Finch railed against was relaxed.

After 1942, the appointment by the Medical Research Council of Dr D'Arcy Hart, Dr Aslett and other doctors, began a fuller investigation into the silicosis problem in the South Wales Coalfield. The subsequent research considered all 'forms of dust in and about collieries', and recommended a 'wider definition than silicosis'. Consequently, on the 1st July 1943, the Government included a 'condition known as reticulation of the lungs – pneumoconiosis' as a basis for a compensation claim. Also, in May 1943, the Ministry of Fuel and Power set up an Advisory Committee to give advice 'on the measures that should be taken to provide for the medical treatment and rehabilitation … of coalminers in the Wales region suffering from pneumoconiosis'.

Moreover, the Mining Department at the University College of South Wales and Monmouthshire, Cardiff, was also a 'forerunner' in the study of silicosis. The research undertaken by a department lecturer, Charles Webb, made a notable contribution to the study.[84]

Harold Finch was appointed a member of the Advisory Committee. Although he became familiar with the general statistics of men who were granted 'assessments' suffering from 'the dust', in his autobiography he gave no numbers to measure its effect upon Tredegar Company miners. He had, though, 'no doubt that many men were disabled and died from pneumoconiosis prior to the first scheme in 1928 because of the lack of knowledge of the disease; and some men continued to work with serious pulmonary disability which hastened their death'.

A Wartime Oakdale Colliery Investment

The wartime year of 1943 saw an aerial ropeway erected at Oakdale Navigation Colliery.[85] Rubbish was moved by means of around fifty buckets, suspended from the ropeway, to a tipping site to the east of the colliery. The buckets were fed rubbish from a ferro-concrete bunker having a 200 ton capacity. A 'scraper' conveyor transferred rubbish from No.2 Washery and screens to the bunker. Pit rubbish and shale were moved to the bunker from No.1 washery by tram.

The aerial ropeway was erected by Messrs R. White & Sons. The length of the ropeway was 3,720 feet and it moved at 280 feet per minute. A 120 B.h.p electric motor powered the rope drive system. The capacity set for the amount of rubbish handled was 120 tons per hour, which involved 100 loads per hour. A load was defined as 24 hundredweights per bucket. The life of the ropeway was forecasted at 10 years based upon carrying 250,000 tons per annum. The subsequent gathering mound of rubbish would not only become an eyesore but a hazardous playground for children.

The aerial ropeway investment, £28,819, suggested that the company foresaw a post-war coal boom. However, the investment was minor compared with the strategic measures that Powell Duffryn Associated Collieries Ltd had taken the year before. In 1942 Powell Duffryn acquired the collieries of Cory Brothers & Co. Ltd that included Penrikyber Navigation Colliery Co. Ltd, and commissioned a 'Phurnacite' plant in the Cynon Valley to make a fuel product from coal slurries.[86] Powell Duffryn had not curbed its coal business ambitions despite doubts being promoted about the form that the coal industry's ownership would take after the war.

State Control

During the course of the war the Tredegar Iron & Coal Company, like all British coal companies, came to terms with growing State control, while the advocates for industry nationalisation were emboldened. The coalowners must have fumed as a Labour Party and Miners' Federation campaign for nationalisation gathered pace.

In January 1942, coal reserves became the property of the State under the 1938 Coal Act. South Wales Coalfield coal companies compared with elsewhere Britain, paid higher royalties and wayleave charges. During the war, the charges became 'onerous' due to the 'proportion of [coal] output available for disposal commercially' decreasing.[87] Yet, Aneurin Bevan, in a 1937 Parliamentary debate regarded the action 'as largely irrelevant', but ended his speech caustically: 'it leaves the nation in the position of having handed over to an irresponsible and unbusinesslike set of men the control over the primary raw material of the country'.[88] State ownership of coal property could have been said to signify a preliminary step towards industry nationalisation.

In June 1942, in a debate on coal policy, the Ebbw Vale MP claimed that 'in the matter of the mining industry, the House is well behind the country. That has been proved, and we do not need to prove it again. The reason the House is not nationalising the coal industry is that the House is not the servant of the people, but the instrument of vested interests'. Specifically adding later: 'the coalowners were the most powerful vested interests in Great Britain'.[89] He might have captured the mood of the nation, but during his 1937 Coal Bill speech, he contested that 'amalgamations [of coal companies, whether compulsory or voluntary] were stupid'. As a paradox, though, coal industry nationalisation involved coal company amalgamations on a mammoth scale.

By 1943, Government 'machinery for the operational control of the coal mining industry' was being used.[90] An aspect of the machinery became known as 'Dual Control': colliery managers continued to be the 'servants' of the coal owners but subject to removal at the instance of the Controller under the Government minister. Another aspect of the machinery was a novel addition compared with that used in the First World War, a Production Committee. Each colliery was expected to form a Production Committee comprising officials and worker representatives.[91]

During the years 1943 and 1944, a series of lectures by the Fabian Society scoped a post-war 'plan for Britain' along socialist lines. Aneurin Bevan, in his lecture, insisted that the basic industries, he defined as 'light, power, production of steel up to semi-finished forms, shipbuilding, and coal mining', 'must become national property'.[92] A contention of the Tredegar politician was that 'people are appalled at the notion taking complicated industries and putting them under the management and control of a moribund bureaucracy', the Civil Service.[93] In brief, his lecture sought to make political action in Parliament as crucial for the command of State industries.[94] G. D. H. Cole, though, in his lecture, was 'worried about the calibre of Parliament'.[95]

In his lecture, James Griffiths, Labour MP for Llanelli, referred to Dual Control in the coal industry. As a basis for the State control of the industry, he judged that it 'was 'the best structure so far adopted in this country'.[96] However, his ideas about management control in the industry may have been influenced by the thoughts of G. D. H. Cole. In his lecture, G. D. H. Cole observed that 'management has to come to terms with labour as a co-operating partner and not a hostile force'. He asserted 'that the key to [industrial democracy, which he promoted] in the economic sphere lies in a conception of management as fraternal leadership and not as plutocratic delegation'.[97]

The former president of the SWMF proposed that the Production Committee was the forum where partnership could develop between technician and operator as 'the prerequisite of real democratic control of industry'.[98] Griffith's use of the term technician to describe colliery officials seems patronizing. The officials were men trained to various levels as mining engineers, and experienced in the art of man management. Moreover, the group of officials involved a hierarchy whose conduct and

actions, accountable under statute law for overseeing safety, was fundamental to keeping order in the place of work. In the case of Tredegar Company officials, they had for forty years at least been alive to the border line between 'fearlessly protecting the interests' of the company and 'knowingly doing an injustice to the workmen'.

Nevertheless, if industrial democracy successfully succeeded autocracy then it would have been a revelation. James Griffiths tabled some issues: 'can we get the worker to look upon the technician as something other than a "boss's man"? Can we get the technician to think of the operator in terms of a human being and not a robot to obey?' Resolving discord by means of democracy was for him an attractive process, but decision-making would be slower than autocracy and operational accountability for work and safety less clear.

The operation of another institution, the Miners' Federation, the former Welsh miners' leader recognised, had also to adapt to a shift of control to 'the point of production—the single pit'. He presented an issue: 'It is one of the most vital and urgent, problems confronting Trade Unions—the building of a trade-union structure that will enable the unions to take their share of the control of the publicly owned industry of tomorrow'.[99] Furthermore, he was keen to 'free industry from the restrictive control of financiers', to 'remove the dead hand of privilege', and 'sweep away the industrial nepotism that puts the wrong men in charge of the operation'.[100] However, he did not identify where the correct men would come from to run the industry

During the war, miners' leaders appeared less than able to deliver agreements they had entered into. In July 1942, following settling an agreement for an increase in wages, the president of the Mineworkers' Federation, W. Lawther said: "We pledged our word, we expressed faith that the changes we obtained would help to give [the nation] the coal needed day by day."[101] When the year 1943 ended the British Coalfield was plagued by unofficial stoppages and high absenteeism.[102] A surprising finding of a 1943 study into absenteeism in the coal industry was 'that older men' recorded less absenteeism than younger men.[103]

Although James Griffiths was in favour of Dual Control, miners' leaders attacked its operation. However, no evidence was received by Government to prove that 'managerial staffs at the pits failed to carry to carried out Government instructions, or that the owners had attempted to persuade them not to do so'.[104] Another claim by miners' leaders was that the coalowners were working the poorer seams, or districts, so as to preserve the richer ones for after the war. The allegation was not proved by a Government investigation.[105]

Regarding the discipline of financial management of a nationalised industry, Aneurin Bevan's Fabian Society lecture also tackled pricing a 'certain category of products', which included coal. He proposed that the consumption of a product 'cannot' be 'decided only by competition in price'. Moreover, he argued that 'the balance sheets of the [nationalised] industries … can no longer accord with certain capitalist costing' methods.[106] Abandoning orthodox managerial economics and accounting risked hampering Britain's nationalised industries ability to compete in the liberal, capitalist system that operated around the world except the USSR.

National planning, though, was a major topic of the Fabian Society's lectures. Sir William Beveridge viewed Communist Russia as 'impressive proof of the possibility of rapid change by resolute national planning'.[107] G. D. H. Cole, on the other hand, commented upon a 'curious blindness' among 'many of my fellow-Socialists' about the 'problem of democracy' and 'what is happening in the Soviet Union'.[108] Stalin's totalitarianism ruled the USSR.

In September 1944, the Minister of Fuel and Power requested that a survey be made of the British coalfields. In the case of the survey of the South Wales Coalfield the terms of reference were: "to consider the present position and future prospects of the coalfield and to report— (a) what measures (apart from measures of ownership, form of control or financial structure of the industry) should be taken to enable the fullest use to be made of existing and potential resources of the coalfield; and (b) in this connection, what provision of housing and other services will be required for the welfare of the mining community."[109]

William Woolley, deputy chairman and managing director, Tredegar Iron & Coal Company, was a member of the committee tasked with conducting the survey. The committee comprised around twenty men. Chaired by William Jones, the regional controller, Wales Region, Ministry of Fuel and Power, the committee comprised seven executive managers of the coal companies and six miners' leaders from the newly named National Union of Mineworkers (NUM).[110] The survey was conducted as the wars in Europe and the Pacific Ocean entered their concluding phases.

The survey's report, issued in 1946, mentioned that a Coal Commission, reporting in May 1939, had pressed for more *'appropriate extensions'* [source's emphasis] of the four predominating groups in the South Wales Coalfield and observed: 'The natural spheres for this purpose of the Tredegar Iron & Coal Company Ltd and Partridge, Jones & John Paton Ltd, are obvious' implied an amalgamation involving these two companies.[111]

Nevertheless, before the survey began, some coalowners objected publicly to the clamour for nationalisation. In January 1944, A. K. McCosh, chairman of the Scottish Colliery Owners, offered a 'case against nationalisation of the coal mines'. He claimed that its 'advocates are concerned with social change rather than with industrial efficiency'. The Labour Party's "Coal: The Labour Plan", he argued, was 'an elaborate camouflage for the control of the industry for the benefit, not of the public, but of the mine workers'. The plan, he noted, 'specifically' stated that "a proper wage [for the miner] must be taken as a starting point", and that 'in developing a Socialised industry the right to strike be preserved'. He judged that the 'right to define the word' "proper" was 'implicitly reserved for the Mineworkers' Federation'. 'Owing to the industrial and political power' of the Mineworkers' Federation, he predicted that 'the miners' would be continually demanding higher wages, shorter hours and other concessions, irrespective of the economic ability to provide them, and in the firm conviction that something could always be squeezed out of the tax payer'.[112]

McCosh, regarding the USSR offering an alternative model for the British coal industry, judged that it 'was notoriously difficult to get reliable and uncoloured information about industrial conditions in Russia'.[113] Thus: 'Are we being asked today to make this colossal experiment because it will result in the production of more coal – or because the miners' want it?'[114]

Will Lawther, NUM president, in 1945, observed: "The problems that result from hundred years of mismanagement will not melt like magic at the word of nationalisation; but once the word is spoken and once legislation is passed, we shall have the chance to tackle the job we have longed for—to give the nation a mining industry to be proud of."[115]

Bloodless Revolution

On the 26th July 1945, the Labour Party won a 'landslide' majority in the first general election after the war. Clement Atlee formed a Government. Emmanuel Shinwell was appointed Minister of Fuel and Power. Aneurin Bevan was made Minster of Health. 'A steady flow of nationalisation measures followed … A revolution without the usual accompaniments of revolution', like the shedding of human blood, followed.[116] A tribunal was set up to settle compensation for the assets 'transferred to the Board' from coal companies like the Tredegar Iron & Coal Company. In December, 1945, Shinwell presented the Coal Industry (Nationalisation) Bill to the Government's Cabinet.[117]

At the December Cabinet meeting the Minister of Health queried a proposal 'to pay over the Government funds to meet interest and amortisation on stock issued to coal owners as compensation'. Aneurin Bevan contended: 'One of the problems of the industry was to remove the feeling among workers that they were working to make profits for the owners and, while he did not object to the substance of the proposal, he suggested that, for psychological reasons, it was important to avoid any suggestion that under the new dispensation miners would still be working to provide payments to the owners to compensate them for their former profits'. Discussion led to an amendment to the Bill that accommodated the Ebbw Vale Member of Parliament's contention.[118]

The Minister of Health was engaged preparing a Bill that created the National Health Service. In 1953, A. J. Cronin, by then a successful author of novels, wrote:

In actual fact this [Tredegar Medical Aid Society] can definitely be regarded as the foundation of the plan for the socialized medicine eventually adopted in Great Britain. Aneurin Bevan who was mainly responsible for the national project was at one time a miner in Tredegar, and here, under the local aid organization, the value of the prompt and gratuitous treatment for the worker was strongly impressed upon him.[119]

Irksome as it may have been for Aneurin Bevan to have admitted it, the support of the Tredegar Iron & Coal Company had been crucial to setting up the Tredegar Medical Aid Society. The society was founded in 1873, the year the company was formed.

In 1946, the Coal Industry Nationalisation Bill became an Act of Parliament. The National Coal Board (NCB) was formed by the Government. A clause in the Act noted that 'the revenues of the Board shall not be less than sufficient for meeting all their outgoings properly chargeable to revenue account', which implied that the NCB was required by law not to make a financial loss.[120]

The 'Vesting Day' for the NCB to take ownership of the assets of the coal companies was the 1st January 1947.[121] For the year 1938 the eight collieries of the Tredegar Iron & Coal Company, which in total employed 6,524 on the 19th March 1945,[122] produced 2,343,179 tons of coal. For the year ending the 30th March 1946, Oakdale and Wyllie collieries each produced 458,952 tons and 155,444 tons respectively.[123] Nevertheless, the company's total output in 1938 represented just 6.14 per cent of the total amount produced by the South Wales Coalfield's five principal companies. In a list for 1938 of the output rankings of the five principal companies of the South Wales Coalfield the Tredegar Company was placed last. Powell Duffryn ranked first with a coal output of 12,327,210 tons. Partridge, Jones & John Paton Ltd, took second place having produced 4,345,589 tons followed next by Ocean & United National Collieries Ltd due to raising 3,406,091 tons. In fourth position was Amalgamated Anthracite Collieries with an output of 3,777,844 tons.[124]

An item in the *Western Mail* on New Year's Day 1947 reported that the Tredegar Company had given notice to liquidate its debenture stock as a prelude to being wound-up.[125] The company's voluntary liquidation was effected on the 25th June 1953. The holders of 10s. shares were paid 11s. 3.32d., with a balance of £4,299 paid into Companies' Liquidation Account. The company's Final Meeting return was registered on the 16th April 1957.[126] The process of dissolving the Tredegar Iron & Coal Company was a sideshow as far as its former employees were concerned. The Socialists' clamour, not least among West Monmouthshire miners, for industrial change, achieved an apogee.

NOTES

1   Lord Aberconway, *The Basic Industries of Great Britain–Coal: Iron: Steel: Ships*. (Ernest Benn, 1927), pp.248-262.

2   His reckoning was based upon an estimate of the South Wales Coalfield's coal reserves made by Sir William T. Lewis for the Royal Commission on Coal Supplies, 1904.

3   Trevor Boyns, 'Growth in the Coal Industry: the Cases of Powell Duffryn and the Ocean Coal Company', ed. Colin Baber and L. J. Williams, *Modern South Wales: Essays in Economic History*. (University of Wales Press, 1986), p.169.

4   Andrew Lorenz, *GKN – The Making of a Business*. (Wiley, 2009), p.68-69. See also Leslie M. Shore, op. cit, pp.211-217.

5   W. D. Woolley, 'Wyllie Colliery', SWIE, Vol.XLV (1929), p.356.

6   The 1927 and 1928 editions of *The South Wales Coal Annual*. 1927 edition: p.231 (Markham), and p.233 (Oakdale); and respectively the same pages in the 1928 edition.

7   *The Powell Duffryn Steam Coal Company, Limited: Visit of the Institution of Mining Engineers to Bargoed Colliery*. (Business Statistics Company, Cardiff, 1925).

8   Report of Proceedings, 57th Annual Ordinary General Meeting. (T&IC, 27 June 1930), in what immediately follows, from various pages unless otherwise referenced.

9   *Oakdale Colliery*. (The Tredegar Iron and Coal Company, Limited, 1930). p.2.

10   Ralph Thomas, op. cit., p.93.

11   *The South Wales Coal Annual* 1930, p.201.

12   *The South Wales Coal Annual* 1930. Manning of Oakdale Colliery (2,830 persons) p.197, Markham Colliery (2,020), p.195.

13   *The South Wales Coal Annual* 1930, p.201.

14   Report of Proceedings, 57th Annual Ordinary General Meeting. (T&IC, 27 June 1930), p.2.

15   A total rainfall of 46.13 inches was recorded at Tredegar for 1929's November and December, and January 1930. The average for the previous ten years was 57 inches per annum. Ibid, p.161.

16   W. D. Woolley, 'A Water problem in the Sirhowy Valley', an excerpt from SWIE, Vol.L (1934), pp.159-175.

17   In a test of the pumps, 16 May 1934, a water flow of 163,000 gals/hr was measured for No.1 Pump, and 159,000 gals/hr for Pump No.2. A pencil note by Jack Edwards on his copy of W. D. Woolley, 'A Water problem in the Sirhowy Valley', op. cit.

18   Each pump was provided with three double-inlet self balancing impellers working in series. Special bronze was used to make the impellers and guide passages. Cast iron of high tensile was used for the 'overflow pieces containing the passages for moving the water'. The top and bottom covers were of cast steel and the shaft of special steel'. The two pump bearings were of lignum vitae and lubricated with filtered water.

19   The motor was a vertical machine of the slip-ring type built by Brown Boveri for an output of 700 B.h.p. at 1,480 rpm, and powered by a 6,000 V, 3-phase, 50 Hz circuit. The motor was mounted on top of a bracket that held the thrust bearing. The main components in the column of the pumping system were: a 16 inch diameter water delivery pipe, which hung down the length of the shaft, and a pump's driving shaft that was placed in the vertical axis of the pipe. There were 'sixty-seven pipe and shaft sections all made to one standard length of about 8 feet 21/2 inches'.

20   2,003,500 gallons and 3,815,500 gallons respectively according to a pencil note by Jack Edwards on his copy of W. D. Woolley, 'A Water problem in the Sirhowy Valley', op. cit.

21   Report of Proceedings, 59th Annual Ordinary General Meeting. (T&IC, 1 July 1932).

22   BIDCO, p.17.

23   Harold Finch, op. cit., p.55.

24   Aneurin Bevan, op. cit., pp.47-48.

25   Neville Penry Thomas, op. cit., p.114.

26   Steven Thompson, *Unemployment, Poverty, and Health in Interwar South Wales*. (University of Wales Press, 2006), p.252. His source was Ministry of Labour, Local Unemployment Index (1927-39).

27   *The Whitehead Iron & Steel Company 50 Years of Progress*. (Whitehead Iron & Steel Company, 1953), p.4. A copy of the company's document is in the keeping of Newport City Libraries.

28   The company reported in 1930 that its collieries were operating at 500,000 tons less than capacity of output. Report of Proceedings, 57th Annual Ordinary General Meeting. (T&IC, 27 June 1930).

29   Report of Proceedings, 59th Annual Ordinary General Meeting. (T&IC, 1 July 1932), p.1.

30   Harold Finch, op. cit., p.61.

31   Steven Thompson, op. cit, pp.250-252.

32   TI&C1934.

33   Report of Proceedings, 59th Annual Ordinary General Meeting. (T&IC, 1 July 1932). Regarding the comments attributed to Lord Aberconway and William Woolley.

34   See Leslie M. Shore, op. cit, pp.192-194, and p.206.

35   Ralph Thomas, op. cit., p.76.

36   Ralph Thomas, op. cit., p.76.

37   BIDCO, p.16.

38   BIDCO, pp.18-19.

39   BIDCO, pp.18-19.

40   BIDCO, p.20.

41   'Lord Aberconway', *The Times*, 26 Jan 1934, p.12.

42   'Lord Aberconway', *North Wales Chronicle*, 26 Jan 1934, p.5.

43   Harold Finch, op. cit., p.28.

44   For example, he authored a series of articles on 'The Financial Aspects of Engineering and some Allied Industries' for an Engineering Supplement of *The Times*. *The Times*, 26 Jan 1934, p.12.

45   Furthermore, at her 'instance', her husband introduced nine Parliamentary Bills, 'which together were described as a women's charter. One of these measures provided that a husband must pay his wife a salary for her services as a housekeeper'. 'Lady Aberconway', The Times, 5 Jan 1933, p.12.

46   'The late Lady Aberconway', *North Wales Chronicle*, 13 Jan 1933, p.9.

47   David Freeman, op. cit., p.10.

48   William Smith, op. cit., p.113.

49   The 3rd Viscount's estate passed to Frederick George Morgan who sold Tredegar House in 1951, and retired to Monte Carlo, a tax haven. Frederick George Morgan died in 1962 by which time the Morgan estates in Wales, Scotland, and England had been sold. David Freeman, op. cit., pp.10-11.

50   'Lord Aberconway', The Times, 26 Jan 1934, p.12.

51   Proceedings, Sixty-Second Annual Ordinary General Meeting. T&IC, 28 June 1935.

52   Steven Thompson, op. cit, p.251 for Pontlottyn, and p.252 for Blackwood and Tredegar.

53   'Unemployment Assistance (Temporary Provisions) (No.2)', *House of Commons Debates*, Vol.301, cc 1198 & cc 1202, 9 May 1935.

54   He judged that there was 'no prospect' of workpeople made idle by the closure of the Ebbw Vale steel works 'ever getting into employment there again'. "There are men and women who had grown up in Ebbw Vale, Dowlais, and Blaenavon who, with their fathers before them, have established the foundations of Great Britain. I said, all the fortunes because steel is the basis of all fortunes." 'Clause 24 – Deductions from profits of contributions paid to rationalise industry', *House of Commons Debates*, Vol.303, cc 462-463, 19 June 1935.

55   He queried a comment made by a MP that power stations could use diesel engines to generate electricity. 'Mining Industry', *House of Commons Debates*, Vol.307, cc 1935, 11 Dec 1935.

56   Proceedings, Sixty-Second Annual Ordinary General Meeting. T&IC, 28 June 1935.

57   Leslie M. Shore, op. cit, pp.211-221.

58   James Griffiths, *Pages From Memory*. (Dent, 1969), p.141.

59   Chris Williams, *Capitalism, Community and Conflict*. (University of Wales Press, 1998), p.89. A table of 'Unionization of South Wales miners, 1898-1947' from the 'Digest of Welsh Historical Statistics', Public Record Office.

60   James Griffiths, op. cit., p.37.

61   Ralph Thomas, op. cit., p.82.

62   Ralph Thomas, op. cit., p.82.

63   BIDCO, p.23.

64   Telephone Conversation, the late Arthur Lewis and Writer, 21 Feb 2016. William Arthur Lewis (1922- 2016) OBE, BSc, MIMinE. He

entered the mining industry at fourteen years of age and for ten years was employed variously as a coal hewer, packer and timberman. In 1950 he graduated with a degree in mining engineering after part-time study at University College of South Wales and Monmouthshire, Cardiff. Following a period as a management trainee, he 'worked his way up' to serve as manager of Six Bells Colliery from 1966 to 1973. In 1975, he was appointed Senior Lecturer in the Mining & Mine Survey Department, Polytechnic of Wales.

65 Source unless otherwise noted in what immediately follows: AJE, p.7 and pp.10-12.

66 During the Second World War, Keith Clancy served in the RAF, flew Spitfires, and was demobbed as a Squadron Leader. He joined the Mines Inspectorate, and retired as Chief Inspector, Mechanical Division.

67 Craft skills learnt included fitting, welding, carpentry, and machining. The Oakdale fitting shop contained five main groups of machines 'that were constantly in operation' seven days per week. Full-time turners operated two lathes, a 'Dean, Swift & Grace' for fine machine work, and a 'Laing' for 'repetitive and rough work'. The turners let no other man work these two lathes.

68 After the nationalisation of the coal industry, Ron Morgan became the Unit Mechanical Engineer at Markham Colliery. In the late 1970s, he was member of the NCB's Plant Team, Ystrad Fawr.

69 Alec Jones later joined PDAC and later became Divisional Chief Draughtsman with National Coal Board. He later became an 'engineering curator' with the National Museum of Wales.

70 In circa 1946, Geoff Richards joined British Nylon Spinners, Mamilhad, Pontypool. In the 1950s, the BNS plant was claimed to be the 'greatest single industrial development of Monmouthshire and the largest nylon spinning undertaking in the country', C. J. O. Evan, *Monmouthshire*. (William Lewis, 1953), p.399. After working with a Chepstow shipbuilding company that provided steelwork for the construction of the first Seven Suspension Bridge, he removed to South Africa.

71 Ralph Thomas, op. cit., p.100.

72 *Folio of Technical Information – Oakdale and Wyllie Collieries*, compiled by Jack Edwards circa 1946, p.9. From the papers of A. J. Edwards in the keeping of the Writer.

73 'Trevor Boyns-Gwent Coal Industry', table 3.3, p.39.

74 SWC-RegRpt, Table LXVIII, p.144.

75 A. K. McCosh, *The Case Against Nationalisation of the Coal Mines*. (Scottish Colliery Owners, 1944), p.22.

76 Ralph Thomas, op. cit., pp.100-10. Ralph Thomas and Jack Edwards were contemporaries at Pontllanfraith Secondary School, see *Pontllanfraith Secondary School Magazine*. (1937) p.29. The scool was later made a grammar school.

77 *Monmouth Guardian*, 1 June 1917.

78 AJE, pp.14-15.

79 Ralph Thomas, op. cit., p.104.

80 Unless otherwise referenced source: Harold Finch, op. cit., pp.173-178.

81 The date for the availability of the Tredegar Company dust trap was taken from *Transactions-Institution of Mining Engineers*, Vol. LXXX (1930-1931), pp.428-429. The company marketed, at one stage, two types: the 'Trewill' Patent Dust Trap, and the 'Hay' Dust Trapping Apparatus, see: Tredegar Iron & Coal Limited, Tredegar, Mon.: Catalogue of Steel Arches, Rails and Colliery Requisites. (Printed by *Western Mail & Echo*, date not stated), pp.38-39.

82 The observation of an Oakdale villager who had worked at Oakdale Colliery for 50 years. Ralph Thomas, op. cit., p.80.

83 Transactions-Institution of Mining Engineers, Vol. LXXX (1930-1931), p.428.

84 Letter, Arthur Lewis OBE to Writer, 11 April 2016.

85 *Folio of Technical Information – Oakdale and Wyllie Collieries*, compiled by Jack Edwards circa 1946, pp.97-98. From the papers of A. J. Edwards in the keeping of the Writer.

86 Leslie M. Shore, op. cit., pp.224-225.

87 SWC-RegRpt, with also Table LXVII, p.141.

88 'Coal Bill', *House of Commons Debates*, Vol. 329, cc 1129, 23 Nov 1937.

89 'Coal Policy', *House of Commons Debates*, Vol. 380, cc 1296, 11 Jun 1942.

90 'War Cabinet - Coal', 16th February, 1944, WP (44), p.1. The National Archives, Catalogue Reference: CAB/66/47/15, Image Reference: 0001.

91 G. D. H. Cole et al., *Plan for Britain*. (George Routledge, 1943), pp.62-63.

92 G. D. H. Cole et al., op. cit., p.38.

93 G. D. H. Cole et al., op. cit., p.38.

94 G. D. H. Cole et al., op. cit., pp.41-42.

95 G. D. H. Cole et al., op. cit., p.23.

96 G. D. H. Cole et al., op. cit., pp.62-64.

97 G. D. H. Cole et al., op. cit., pp.30-31.

98 G. D. H. Cole et al., op. cit., p.63.

99 G. D. H. Cole et al., op. cit., p.64.

100 G. D. H. Cole et al., op. cit., p.65.

101 A. K. McCosh, op. cit., p.4.

102 A. K. McCosh, op. cit., p.21. In 1940, the absenteeism of all persons at the coal-face was recorded at 10.34 per cent, but in 1943 (40 weeks to 9th October provisional) had risen to 14.81 per cent; A. K. McCosh, op. cit., p.24.

103 On 30th October, 1943, the average percentage of voluntary absenteeism (excluding time lost due to sickness and accidents) among coal workers was 10.06 per cent for men up to an including 30 years of age, but just 5. 95 per cent for men over 30 years of age. A. K. McCosh, op. cit., p.5.

104 'War Cabinet - Coal', 16th February, 1944, WP (44), p.2. The National Archives, Catalogue Reference: CAB/66/47/15, Image Reference: 0001.

105 A. K. McCosh, op. cit., pp.7-8.

106 G. D. H. Cole et al., op. cit., pp.44-45.

107 G. D. H. Cole et al., op. cit., pp.89-90.

108 G. D. H. Cole et al., op. cit., p.31.

109 SWC-RegRpt, p.1.

110 SWC-RegRpt, op. cit., p.ii.

111 SWC-RegRpt, p.143.

112 A. K. McCosh, op. cit., p.17.

113 McCosh cited a report by J. A. Hall, president of the Yorkshire Miners' Association in 1944, after a British mineworkers' delegation visit to the USSR. Hall appraised that Russian mines were not as 'efficiently managed as ours', and that the 'Russians do not attach the same importance as we do to safety'. A. K. McCosh, op. cit., p.10.

114 A. K. McCosh, op. cit., p.15.

115 'Coal troubles will prolong food shortages ', SWWA, 25 June 1945, p.4.

116 Neville Penry Thomas, op. cit., p.162.

117 'Conclusions of a Meeting of Cabinet', 13th December, 1945, Cabinet 62 (45), p.313. The National Archives, Catalogue Reference: CAB/128/2, Image Reference: 0015.

118 'Conclusions of a Meeting of Cabinet', 13th December, 1945, Cabinet 62 (45), p.314.

119 A. J. Cronin, op. cit., p.159. A J Cronin, MB in 1919, MD in 1925, and from 1924 to 1926 served as a Medical Inspector for Mines, retired as a doctor in 1930 to write fiction, and one of his books, *The Citadel*, has associations with Tredegar.

120 Section 1 para 4c, *Coal Industry Nationalisation Act*, 1946, p.2C1.

121 A term having some of its origins in Section 8 'Vesting of rights to use of certain property', *Coal Industry Nationalisation Act*, 1946.

122 Appendix VII Part C, SWC-RegRpt, p.216.

123 *Folio of Technical Information – Oakdale and Wyllie Collieries*, compiled by Jack Edwards circa 1946, p.18. From the papers of A. J. Edwards in the keeping of the Writer.

124 Table LXVIII, SWC-RegRpt, p.144.

125 WM, 1 Jan 1947, p.3.

126 *Register of Defunct Companies*. (Macmillan, 1990), p.498

THIS COLLIERY IS NOW
MANAGED BY THE
NATIONAL
COAL BOARD
ON BEHALF OF THE PEOPLE
JANUARY 1ˢᵗ 1947

MINES ORDER

Ty Trist Colliery – The notice board makes a statement about ownership following the nationalisation of the Coal Industry's Vesting Day in 1947.
Courtesy of Amgueddfa Cymru National Museum Wales

Chapter Nine
CLOSURE

Most of the miners of the South Wales Coalfield acclaimed the dawning of the nationalisation of their industry. Press coverage of Vesting Day, Wednesday, the 1st January 1947, in the eastern part of the South Wales Coalfield reported colliery ceremonies led by General Reade Godwin-Austen, chairman of the NCB's South Western Division.[1] No ceremony of the general's occurred at a former Tredegar Iron & Coal Company colliery.

Jack Edwards later recalled the start to nationalisation at Oakdale Colliery. 'In the week prior' to the Wednesday, 'a notice board about 8ft square' was 'attached to the external wall of the North Pit house for information' about pending change. On New Year's Eve, J. M. Reynolds read to senior members of his staff a copy of a telegram addressed to William Woolley from Lord Hyndley, the Chairman of the NCB. The telegram 'informed' that 'Mr Woolley' was to be employed by the NCB as a Unit Director 'on a temporary basis until such time that a new organisation was formed'. After Vesting day: 'It was amusing; that when Mr Strang (Agent) and Mr Reynolds walked from their homes to the office, they both wore cloth caps instead of their normal trilbies'.[2] Although Jack Edwards might have viewed the switch of hat styles as a symbol of change from autocracy to egalitarianism, the weather may have caused his superiors' actions.

Intense cold struck the nation during January 1947, and there were acute coal shortages. In the first week of January, the GWR and the L&NER were forced to withdraw 150 trains due to low stocks of coal for locomotive fuel.[3] Snow also fell in parts of Great Britain that hampered coal distribution. Manufacturing industry was hit by the lack of fuel and some workers became unemployed as a result. Such troubles did not affect the outlook of the Minister of Fuel and Power, Emmanuel Shinwell foreseeing 'big coal exports by the year end'.[4] In 1947, as the demand for coal grew at home, the NCB was engrossed organising itself.

Area No. 6 (Monmouth)

Compared with a private coal company's few tiers of organisation, the Ministry of Fuel and Power instituted a tall organisational structure to manage the NCB. The Board's headquarters, Hobart House, Grosvenor Place, London, was where the corporation was managed by Lord Hyndley as full-time Chairman with eight full-time members responsible for particular functions, such as production, finance, and industrial relations. At Hobart House, each full-time member was supported by staff with function competency. The separate coalfields were organised into divisions. The NCB's South-Western Division comprised the South Wales Coalfield, and the coalfields of the Forest of Dean, and Somerset. Each division had a chairman and a board. Collieries of a division were grouped in areas. The NCB's South-Western Division's Area No. 6 contained nearly thirty collieries organised into the following groups of collieries: Abercarn, Abertillery, Blaenavon, Crumlin, and Tredegar. The NCB Tredegar group of collieries comprised: Markham, Oakdale Navigation Steam, Pochin, Ty Trist, and Waterloo Pit. McLaren Colliery was assigned to Group Number 2 of Area No. 5 (Rhymney [Valley]). Wyllie Colliery was also placed in Area No. 5, Group No. 4, with Nine Mile Point and Risca collieries. Mainly hereafter, Area No. 6 receives attention.

A less than adequate idea of the coal reserves of the NCB Tredegar group of collieries can be sourced from the Ministry of Fuel and Power's 1946 survey of the South Wales Coalfield. In the survey, the Sirhowy Valley was combined with the Afon Lwyd, and Ebbw Valleys for data purposes. Regarding the Big Vein Group of seams that included the Yard and Three Quarter, an estimated workable reserves of 185 million tons lay under these Monmouthshire valleys. Of interest with respect to Markham, Oakdale, and Wyllie collieries, the survey noted that there were 'large unworked areas in the centre and south' of these valleys. The Rhas Las, called the Black Vein around Risca and Crumlin-Newbridge, was described as 'nearing exhaustion in some localities', but was estimated to have reserves of 90 million tons.[5] The estimated workable coal reserve of the Afon Lwyd, Ebbw, and Sirhowy valleys was 685.3 million tons. In 1938, the total output from the collieries of these Monmouthshire valleys was 9.021 million tons.[6] A share of the county's coal had been exploited by the Tredegar Iron & Coal Company for seventy-three years. In theory, if Monmouthshire miners continued to raise nine million tons a year they looked set to be employed by the NCB for a similar period of time that is until the year 2013.

A Colliery Manager's Anxieties

Anxieties about nationalisation troubled at least one colliery manager, Philip Weekes. He was in charge of Wyllie Colliery on Vesting Day. Weekes joined the Tredegar Company from Tredegar Grammar School in the late 1930s, became a junior company official in 1939, then studied for an honours degree at the University College of South Wales and Monmouthshire, today Cardiff University. After serving in the RAF between the years 1942 and 1944 he rejoined the company. At twenty-five years of age Weekes was appointed the manager of Wyllie Colliery in 1946. He greeted nationalisation with a 'mixture of hope and confusion':

'Hope in as much as I could see many errors … committed in the coal industry being put right; but apprehension in as much as I had read G. D. H. Cole many years before and had not understood what the hell it was all about and I was convinced on January 1st 1947 I wouldn't really be a colliery manager and I'd have a revolutionary committee running the pit and I'd be a sort of professional advisor … I wanted change desperately, felt it was right but feared for my own position in the set-up. I didn't want a complete revolution. I hadn't thought things through very clearly, but on balance I thought it was good'.[7]

Socialists advocated that miners ran the point of production, the colliery. The NCB retained the services of colliery managers.

Philip Weekes was further troubled by both the extent of control in, and attitudes of, previous Powell Duffryn officials in the NCB's South Western Division. Knowing that Powell Duffryn Associated Collieries Limited had been by far the largest operator in the South Wales Coalfield before nationalisation he anticipated that PD men would come 'out on top' to control the Division He believed that his former boss in the Tredegar Company, W. D. Woolley, was 'too much of a gent to tangle with the Hanns or the rough and tumble boys of Powell Duffryn'.

During the first week of 1947 Mr H. McVicar was appointed the Area No. 6 (Monmouth) General Manager. Hubert McVicar had served as general manager of PD's Rhondda Area for at least seven years.[8] Among McVicar's early tasks was to choose 'the best place to locate a central office' for Area No. 6, and to appoint key Area personnel. Abercarn, in the Ebbw Vale, was chosen as the location for the central office, which became known as the 'Prince of Wales Colliery Buildings'. Regarding some of McVicar's key appointments they were, according to Jack Edwards: A. M. Strang – Deputy Underground Planning, J. M. Reynolds – Area Mechanical Engineer, Mr Hannah– Area Electrical Engineer, and Mr Rees – Administrative Officer. Moreover, another crucial appointments was Arthur Hiscox who became 'the driving force behind the mechanisation of Area 6 coal mines'.[9] The Tredegar Company's works at Tredegar became the central workshops for the Area, where also the area's veterinary surgeon was based. Oakdale Colliery became the location for the Area's safety officer, mechanisation engineer, and roof control engineer before 1958.[10]

As colliery manager, Philip Weekes reported to the manager of the NCB Tredegar group of collieries, whose name was not found, who reported to Mr H. McVicar. Although a relative newcomer to colliery management, Weekes showed early that he had the guile to deal with ex-PD men when the need arose. Just after taking up his post at Wyllie Colliery he learnt that Powell Duffryn had commissioned the first A-B Mecco-Moore power loader[11] in the South Wales Coalfield at Penallta Colliery. He received a 'blank refusal' from the company to his request to view the loader. The rebuff was a sign to him of the 'secrecy' and 'bitchiness' prevailing at the time between rival coal companies. He pursued his interest by posing as a Bevin boy. Carrying a 'bloody big hand-lamp' he 'went to Penallta Colliery with the Bevin boys in the forlorn hope that I would be taken to see the Meco Moore, and they wouldn't know I was a Tredegar Company bloke'.[12] However, after Vesting Day, the NCB stood to benefit from Powell Duffryn former managers possessed of a drive for efficient coal production.

Colliery Performance

Analyses of output per manshift, coal waste, the number of 'men on the books', and absenteeism figures gave clues to where colliery efficiency could be improved, and accounting knowledge was vital for management decision making. The uses made of production and accounting figures have long been a cause of unbridled dread among workers. Livelihoods are at risk of being lost when adverse figures arise. Nationalisation may have ushered in a belief among some miners that managerial power over their work had been tipped in their favour, but the NCB did not heed workers' views about production and accounting measurement.

Indeed, the point of production, the colliery, came under scrutiny in a way that Philip Weekes had not experienced as the manager of Wyllie Colliery when under private control. In 1946, he 'did not know whether' or not the colliery was 'making a profit or a loss'. He claimed that his Tredegar Iron & Coal Company superiors 'didn't want people to know detailed costs because their competitors would get it …. So, there was a great resistance, even with the manager having costs …It wasn't until after nationalisation … that I really had a profit and loss …. A tremendous improvement because it began to make you more cost conscious'.[13]

The practice of managers knowing their colliery profit and loss accounts became routine in the NCB South Western Division by 1950.[14] However, it seems that a 'statistical digest' of colliery production and manpower was made available to colliery managers in the South Western Division before December 1948. Regarding absenteeism figures these were issued per Area, and in the case of Area 6 for 1948 for men at the coal-face it was just over 10 per cent. Area 6's absenteeism for face workers was not only better than the 15.6 per cent average measured in the South Wales Coalfield for 1944, but in 1948 returned the coalfield's best performance for an Area.[15] Concerning manpower, and 'pithead output' per NCB colliery a sample of such data, for the week that ended the 11th December 1948, grants a rough appreciation of the manning and performance of former Tredegar Company collieries at the outset to nationalisation:[16]

Such a sample of data may give a false impression about the performances of the collieries in the context of the previous year's period. Nevertheless, according to the data, the set of collieries employed 6,323 people, which indicated a fall of only 201 since the 19th March 1945. Moreover, the data presents Pochin Colliery as the poorest performer of former Tredegar Company Sirhowy Valley collieries. Yet, at a time of coal shortages, output may have had a higher priority than efficiency. Again speculatively, the week's production at Oakdale Navigation Steam Colliery can be used to estimate that its annual output was just over half a million tons, from which it can be inferred that its heyday may have passed. However, a glance at the same week's data for former Powell Duffryn collieries in the Rhymney Valley, where output per manshift ranged between 27.14 cwts (Penallta Colliery) to 44.20 cwts (Elliot Colliery), suggests scope for efficiency improvements at Oakdale Colliery.

The degree of mechanisation at Tredegar Company collieries lagged well behind the Rhymney Valley collieries of Powell Duffryn. However, in 1948 the NCB announced underground mechanisation plans for Oakdale Colliery.[17] The introduction of modern belt conveyors caused the 'disappearance of horses' with 'one happy result': 'a fall in the rat population'.[18] The next year saw stall work ended in favour of conveyor faces. Then, in 1950, further coal-face mechanisation occurred at the colliery.[19]

During the mid-Fifties the NCB Area 6's Arthur Hiscox set up a mechanisation team of mining engineers. The team's first members were Arthur Lewis and Keith Jones. The team members, each assigned to work with a colliery manager, successfully introduced underground Armoured Face Conveyors (AVCs), friction props, hydraulic props, cantilever bars, and 'eventually Disc Shearers (DS) that became universally adopted'.[20]

Oakdale Colliery's former surface granary was used to develop a large training centre for introducing West Monmouthshire youths also to the new mechanised world of mining.[21]

Other Investment at Oakdale Colliery

In January 1950, Jack Edwards was made the senior draughtsman at Oakdale. For him, the period from the start of nationalisation to May 1953 was the 'New Oakdale Group' era. One of his first responsibilities was engineering a Baum Froth Flotation plant at Oakdale that served both Oakdale Navigation and Markham collieries. As a coal washing process, the Baum process involved separating coal dust from a tank of liquid for transformation into a dried cake called 'fines' that became a fuel stock. The liquid in the tank comprised coal dust, water, and a tiny amount of oil. The air bubbles that arose from stirring the liquid attached themselves to the coal dust and floated to the liquid's surface as a froth that was collected by mechanical skimming. The plant, made by Unifloc, was commissioned at Oakdale in 1952. Of worth to Oakdale and Markham collieries, the Baum Froth Flotation plant enabled coal previously wasted to become a saleable fuel product and so of benefit to colliery profit and loss accounts.[22]

Jack Edwards also engineered at Oakdale Colliery 'man riding lifts' that sped up the movement of workers from the pit top to the pithead baths. The lifts were installed '1952/53'.[23]

The end of the 'New Oakdale Group' occurred when its draughtsmen were removed to the Area's Abercarn

Colliery	Manpower (on Colliery Books)				Pithead Output (Tons)	Pithead Output per Manshift (cwts)
	At the Face	Underground	Surface	Total		
McLaren	369	225	133	727	4,528	22.00
Pochin	345	356	154	855	3,316	16.12
Ty Trist	241	166	135	542	2,645	19.84
Wyllie	285	387	127	799	4,391	21.82
Markham	686	457	190	1,333	6,160	18.52
Oakdale	845	708	339	1,892	11, 443	23.13
Waterloo	73	76	26	175	1,139	22.94

Horses ceased to be used for hauling work at Oakdale Navigation Colliery around the mid-1950s due to coal-face mechanisation. However, horses were still used underground for work until the late-1950s in at least McLaren and Ty Trist (*shown above*) collieries.

Courtesy of Amgueddfa Cymru National Museum Wales

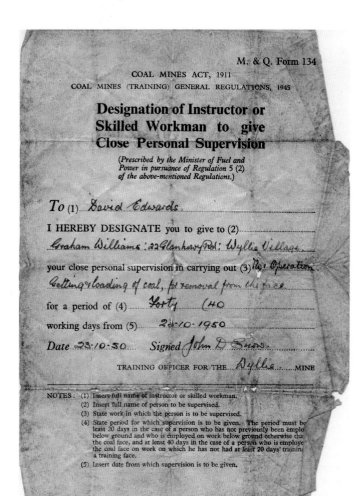

Left: Documentation that authorises the collier and 'butty' system used in 1950. *A. J. Edwards collection*

Philip Hadfield Photography
A. J. Edwards collection

engineering offices. Jack Edwards's project work at Oakdale Colliery continued with three compressors being installed at Oakdale's power-house (commissioned October 1953) and the colliery's Old Coal pumps (1954/55) upgraded.[24] For colliery coal production, the Old Coal and Yard seams had begun to take on increasing importance with the Meadow Vein. However, perhaps his most notable work for Area 6 concerned engineering electric winding.

During the Second World War Jack Edwards was employed as a fuel efficiency officer by the Tredegar Iron & Coal Company. He 'gathered all relative data from the company's various log books, and equated this information with the generated power and coal burnt at Oakdale'. He portrayed this information 'in the form of a family tree and showed quite clearly how all the power generated at Oakdale was distributed' to the company's collieries and workshops. Reports he wrote afterwards for his superiors 'highlighted the fact that an efficient steam colliery such as Oakdale consumed between 7.09% and 7.42% of its output, whereas the all-electric collieries such as Markham

Wyllie Colliery Officials visiting Cheddar Caves in 1955. *Left to Right:* David Edwards (also founder member of Wyllie Glee Party in 1931), David Minton, John Fox (manager) [he also served three periods as manager of Oakdale Colliery], Dai Davies, Jack Prescott, Bill Bennett, Ernie Price, Tom Brazier, Jim Pritchard, Cliff Evans, Jack Edwards (Senior Draughtsman, NCB South Western Division, Area No. 6), Jim Meredith, Reg Hunt, Unknown, Edgar Blakeman, Charles Hughes, Bill Read.
A. J. Edwards collection

and Wyllie used between 4.6% and 5.23% of their outputs'. He reasoned that by replacing steam winders with electric winders at Oakdale Colliery would yield a 5% saving in coal. Thus his reports offered the Tredegar Iron & Coal Company a way to improve its financial performance, which would have been a large return on their fuel efficiency officer's annual salary of £270. Nevertheless, his recommendations were not acted upon by the company.[25]

However, one of the reports he wrote for the Tredegar Iron & Coal Company was heeded in at least the No. 6 Area. A man inclined to self-effacement later observed:

'I flatter myself that this report had been seen by more than one person, and my findings were acted upon after the nationalisation of the industry. Tremendous attention was given to replacing all steam plant by electricity machines and with all the electricity boards being absorbed by the National Grid Network provision was thereby achieved for the sudden surges of power (such as 2,000 h.p. for a winder) coming on line.'

Significantly Jack Edwards concluded: 'To me, this was the end of the Steam Era!'

At Abercarn offices Jack Edwards was tasked with substituting some of the Area 6's steam winders with electric winders. Moreover, evidence suggests a fellow draughtsman of his at Oakdale, Ivor Catleugh, was also involved in the Area's conversion of colliery winders. Tredegar Company technical know was applied for the benefit of Area No. 6 (Monmouth).[26] Although one nationalised industry was investing in coal mining in the Sirhowy Valley another, British Railways, had ended coal traffic at the northern end of the valley.

Last train Merthyr Tydfil to Abergavenny

The coal traffic, by way of the Merthyr Tydfil to Abergavenny railway, ended in 1954. On the 5th September 1958, a crowd of people, among them members of the Stephenson Locomotive Society, met at Nantybwch Station. The crowd watched the last public passenger train steam across the Head of the Valleys. An aspect of the line's past importance to Britain was recalled in a press report. During the First World War, vast stocks of coal had been moved along the line to fuel the ships of His Majesty's navy.[27] Some Monmouthshire miners, who had served in the forces during the Second World War, might have wondered about their value to the NCB.

Disillusionment

Between 1948 and the end of the 1950s around sixteen collieries closed in Monmouthshire.[28] Among the closures were McLaren and Ty Trist. McLaren Colliery was closed on the 18th July 1958, due to the exhaustion of its coal reserves. The date of closure coincided with the Empire Games at Cardiff that captured newspaper interest whereas McLaren Colliery's demise did not. The colliery's underground workings were linked to Ogilvie Colliery to the west. For a period afterwards winding continued at McLaren Colliery to give local men access to Ogilvie Colliery's workings.[29] The colliery's last manager was R. Elliot.[30]

Ty Trist Colliery was closed on the 31st January 1959. The day before was called 'Black Friday' by miners at five other collieries who were informed about the closures of their place of work by the NCB South Western Division. Steps had been taken at Ty Trist to arrange for a bus to take forty-seven workers to Marine Colliery, Cwm, in the Ebbw Vale, for job interviews. A 'fear' about being offered 'the lowest labouring jobs' at Marine Colliery, even among mechanical tradesmen, discouraged interest in the

Philip Hadfield Photography
A. J. Edwards collection

because they had no other work and families to keep'. The NCB spokesman, questioned about the matter, acknowledged that a 'lot of points arise that can only be resolved by negotiation' with the union.[31] What part the colliery's last manager, A. F. Williams, played in any negotiations is unknown.[32]

The trauma of colliery closure felt by workers at Ty Trist may have soured any feeling they had for the history of their former place of work. The colliery had operated for one hundred and twenty-five years and was believed in Monmouthshire to have been the oldest British colliery in operation at the start of nationalisation. Somerset's New Rock Colliery, sunk in 1819, closed in 1968, was one colliery that operated for a longer period than Ty Trist.[33] Uneconomic working of the Garw seam appears to have been the last straw that decided Ty Trist's fate.[34]

Nevertheless, the transfer of Ty Trist workers to Marine Colliery suggests that the NCB strived for security of employment. On the other hand, with 1958's unemployment rate in Wales being just three per cent, there were rival opportunities to attract colliery workers away from the industry.[35] Mining communities, though, had not forgotten the ills of mass unemployment.

By the year 1948, alleged the *Western Mail*, the 'mild intoxication of vesting day and a brief honeymoon with the Labour Government' was spent. The newspaper asserted that 'the miners of South Wales now considered that they had one enemy, the NCB, instead of five, Powell Duffryn Ltd., Partridge, Jones and John Paton Ltd., Ocean and United Collieries Ltd, Tredegar Iron & Coal Co. Ltd', and Amalgamated Anthracite Collieries'.[36] That the *Western Mail* was open about its criticism of the Atlee Government, and persisting to 'pursue Mr Bevan', its observations might be considered as scaremongering.[37] Yet, colliery closures based on 'uneconomic' grounds were grounds for miners to think that the NCB was acting like a coal business before nationalisation.[38]

journey. Thirteen of the forty-seven men had decided to 'send in their notices … although they had no other work to go to'.

The fifty year old Tom White, father of two children, was in charge of the Ty Trist bus party. It had taken him thirty-six years to attain 'the top paid surface job', winding-engine man. Some administrator had classed him as a belt repairer and assigned him for work as a labourer at Marine Colliery. 'It looks as if they have just put their hand in the hat, and picked out the jobs,'he said: 'Obviously, the men already at Marine cannot be expected to suffer, but all we ask for is reasonable consideration. The arrangements just don't make sense. Some men have been injured in the mines and had light labouring jobs. Now we are all expected to rough it.'

Tom White reckoned that Ty Trist workers stood to lose between £1 10s. and £2 12s. a week by taking jobs at Marine Colliery. His take-home pay from his prospective job at Marine Colliery was £7 14s. per week. Moreover, a penalty for refusing to move to Marine Colliery was the loss of a work guarantee. Thus the guarantee was viewed by some men as a 'force to go

Miners making their way home from a shift at Ty Trist Colliery on the 6th June 1956. Over a period of a hundred and twenty-five years generations of such men worked undergound at the colliery. Over the period 1902 and 1912 the colliery regularly employed over 1,000 miners annually. The year 1904 saw the peak in employment of miners at the colliery at 1,311.
Derek Harding LRPS Courtesy of Amgueddfa Cymru National Museum Wales

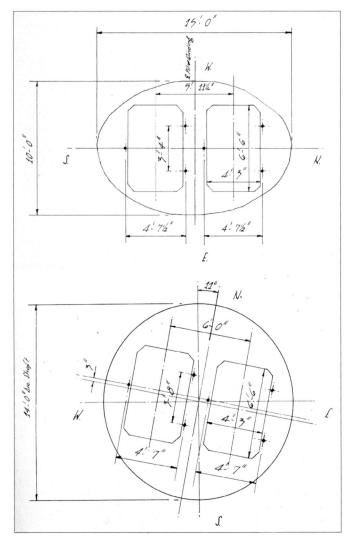

The final record of Ty Trist Colliery's shafts held by the National Coal Board, South Western Division, No. 6 Area. Dated 24-10-1962 with a handwritten notes that No. I Pit had been filled in with the Fan Pit retained for pumping. The oval shape of No. I Pit recalls that balance-winding was abandoned at the colliery circa 1870. At closure the colliery's other shaft was known as Fan Pit and was 14ft in diameter and was thus the upcast. The date when the fan was introduced, and thus furnace ventilation superseded at the colliery has not be found. For furnace ventilation a fire, itself a great hazard, was placed near the foot of the shaft allowing the hot air thus generated to create an upcast flow of air and to thus draw air through the rest of the workings, fresh air being drawn down the other shaft.   *A. J. Edwards collection*

There was another seed for propagating disillusionment among miners about nationalisation. Some workers contended that the management power of the 'old Gang', the managers and officials of the coal companies, lived on after Vesting Day. The claim was not entirely true since there was a small exchange of senior managers between the coalfields of Great Britain. J. R. Tallis, as an example, moved to become the group manager of production in the NCB's Forest of Dean Group by 1957.[39] Nevertheless, Oakdale Colliery's Dan Canniff, interviewed sometime before 1992 regarding nationalisation, was exasperated: 'We felt … it was the same people in different jerseys. And we were up against the same old situation … with regard to negotiation and everything else'. He had entered the coal industry in 1940 as a collier with the Tredegar Company and at twenty-eight years of age, in 1953, was elected a lodge officer at the colliery. In 1964 he was elected chairman of the lodge and served in the office until 1985. He earned the respect of at least two colliery managers. Arthur Lewis, for a

period manager of Six Bells Colliery, judged 'Danny' Caniff to be a 'sensible, considerate person'.[40] Des Caddy, Oakdale Colliery manager, considered him to be a 'gentleman'.[41] Dan Canniff's hopes pre-Vesting Day had been: 'if you talk of nationalisation … you should have control. … All we could do now was suggest on the way to run the pit. We couldn't do anything like insist'.[42]

Oakdale Colliery – Electric Winding

The time taken for the NCB to approve colliery engineering projects frustrated engineers. Regarding Oakdale Colliery, Jack Edwards recalled that a submission for an electrification project was made September 1957 to the NCB London headquarters. The project had previously been reviewed by the NCB's Area No. 6 management and the South Western Division before it was put in a stack of other British coalfield colliery projects on a desk in the Production Department, Hobart House. The Ministry of Fuel and Power might also been involved in the review of the submission prior to Board approval. Indeed, the course for the evaluation of projects in London was a mystery for the likes of Jack Edwards. Only two stages were involved approving developments at a colliery of the Tredegar Iron & Coal Company. A. S. Tallis supervised colliery design-development work and cost estimates, and the directors gave final approval for work to proceed.

The electrification of winding at Oakdale Colliery caused the abandoning of 'internal generation [to] take in power from the South Wales Electricity Board'. The turbo generators and boiler plant within the Oakdale power-house were also in a 'poor condition'.[43] At Oakdale Colliery, Waterloo Shaft was where electric winding was introduced in 1960, followed by the North Pit in 1962. Electric winding was installed at the South Pit in 1963 with its head-frame replaced in 1964. In October 1959, Jack Edwards became chief draughtsman of Area No. 6 and took overall charge of the engineering of the Oakdale winding electrification project.[44] Without giving further details, he noted that the project was 'never completed in its entirety'.

Decline and performances

During the Fifties many miners associated with the former collieries of the Tredegar Company clung on to a belief that coal mining was crucial to their being. Zweig observed in 1952 that miners 'love and hate their jobs, and the pit often has a fascination for them, especially if they are 'born and bred' to the mines'. He prefaced this statement by writing that a characteristic of the miner was a 'quest for justice and fair play, his strong class consciousness, his strong sense of solidarity, his long memory, his proneness to grievances, his great generosity and eagerness to help, his interest in rescue work, his great sense of independence, a suspicion against men on the top who want to get something for nothing'.[45] Although studies of human nature have limitations, Zweig's description of a British miner may be claimed to enhance Lord Aberconway's views a quarter of a century earlier.

At the February 1950 General Election, Harold Finch, the Labour Party candidate, won the vote of the Bedwellty Constituency. He succeeded Sir Charles Edwards, who had held the seat for the Labour Party for forty years. Finch held the seat at the October 1951 General Election but it was a Conservative Government that took office. 'The human suffering and loss of manpower due to pneumoconiosis' was the central theme of the fifty-one year old Harold Finch's maiden speech in March 1950.[46] During the 1950s he argued in the House of Commons for a better deal for sufferers of pneumoconiosis and silicosis and industrial injury compensation. He was prominent also in debates on the coal industry. In 1957, he urged Government to 'take steps at least to start a campaign to get rid of the rubbish tips in the Welsh coalfields'. "It is not only a question of marring landscape. These heaps are dangerous to health, for the airborne dust blows across towns and villages in Wales, with all the evil that accompanies it," Finch maintained.[47]

Sir Harold Finch (1898-1979)
Born in Barry, Glamorgan. In 1918 he was employed as a clerk by the Tredegar Valley Miners' District of the SWMF and rose to become a miners' agent. As a Labour Party member he served as chairman of the Mynyddislwyn UDC and as a Member of Parliament for the Bedwellty Constituency from 1950 to 1970. He won a reputation in the House of Commons as a campaigner for improved compensation for workers suffering from industrial lung diseases.
Walter Bird, taken in 1965. © National Portrait Gallery

Regardless, in 1960 the death of Aneurin Bevan left Harold Finch with private memories of the time they worked together for the Tredegar Valley Miners' District. In 1952, Aneurin Bevan appraised that he led a 'somewhat busy and contentious public life'.[48] A later biographer of Bevan, the forty-seven year old Michael Foot, retained the Ebbw Vale Constituency for the Labour Party at a by-election. Partly through sounding the opinions of Tredegar District miners, like those employed at Pochin Colliery, and maybe Markham Colliery, Michael Foot learned the sentiments, hopes and fear of such constituents. Workers at the Ebbw Vale steelworks, restored to full operation by the late 1930s, and miners of nearby Marine Colliery, Cwm, also had the ear of Michael Foot. Harold Finch had entered the Commons with intimate knowledge of the Sirhowy Valley coal industry and was aware of his constituency's industrial decline.

In 1957, the NCB employed a total of 5,187 men at former Sirhowy Valley collieries of the Tredegar Company, which represented half the number of people working for the company in 1923.[49] In 1957, manager and employment figures, underground and surface for former company collieries were:

Markham Colliery:	L. Pearce, 959 and 229.
Oakdale:	J. H. Fox, 1,548 and 299.
Pochin Colliery:	H. J. Williams, 511 and 132.
Ty Trist:	A. F. Williams, 275 and 80.
Waterloo Pit:	T. H. Wallace, 249 and 42.
Wyllie:	D. C. Kinnair, 723 and 140.[50]

Around 1957, an expenditure of £ 2 million was authorized in – principle – for modernizing Markham Colliery.[51]

The figures of the 'Profit and Loss Account' for collieries gave Hobart House its picture of mining in the Sirhowy Valley. In 1957 Oakdale Navigation Steam Colliery produced 529,138 tons of saleable coal and made a 'cumulative' profit, rated on an 'inland basis', of £543.3K. No comparable profit/loss figures were found for other former Tredegar Company collieries. Nevertheless, the performance of Oakdale Colliery for the years 1958 to 1961 varied little from that achieved in 1957. In 1962 the colliery distinguished itself by making a profit of £673K having produced 499,992 tons of saleable coal.[52] During 1963 South Pit winding halted to allow engineering work and this would have affected the colliery's performance.

The Coal Market

By the end of the 1950s the demand for coal in Britain was falling by tens of millions of tons a year. In 1959, Alfred Robens MP (Labour, Blyth) observed in the House of Commons 'there is a world glut of fuel, both of coal and oil', and identified 'intensified oil competition' as a 'serious' threat to coal.[53] In February 1961, Robens was appointed chairman of the NCB, and later that year was made a life peer.[54] He later reflected that 'all through the war, and for twelve years afterwards, coal was 'allocated', and selling in the true sense of the word did not arise'. Towards the end of the Fifties 'vast undistributed stocks of coal (about 37½ million tons) were lying on the ground' due in part to the operation of new oil refineries. Under his leadership, the NCB began to market coal. Electricity generation was identified by the NCB as a 'growth market'.[55]

Sirhowy Valley people holidaying in Pembrokeshire in the mid-Sixties would have seen a sight that illustrated the expansion of oil. 100,000 ton crude oil tankers queued to berth at terminals in Milford Haven. The landed oil was processed by Esso at its Milford Haven refinery, and by BP at Llandarcy refinery, east of Swansea. The specific effect that oil had upon coal mining in the Sirhowy Valley is unknown, but one industrial development in Monmouthshire was beneficial.

In 1962, Richard Thomas & Baldwins Ltd began operating its £140 million Spencer Works, sited east of Newport. Oakdale Navigation Colliery's Nine-Feet seam (the Rhas Las) was classed as a type 301A Prime Coking Coal. The properties of the Nine-Feet included low ash content, in a range 5% to 9%, and low sulphur, ranging from 0.6% to 1.5%. Some miners at the colliery believed that they cut the 'best coking coal in the World'.[56] From the perspective of modern steel making the choice of coal for coke for use in blast furnaces is a complex subject. However, today's steel makers might consider Oakdale's coal's sulphur content high but view the low ash content as good. Such an appraisal might win for the coal favour internationally for being 'good'.[57] Regardless, Spencer Works became a customer for Oakdale's coal.

Arthur Lewis later recalled a downside for the coal industry concerning new industrial developments in South Wales after the Second World War. 'A lot of coalminers and pit craftsmen were lost to factories and steelworks'. At a meeting with the NCB's chairman, Alfred Robens, he raised the issue. "But Arthur, we are training craftsmen for the country," was Robens's reply.[58]

Employment Prospects

During the 1960s the type of employment opportunities available for young people of South Wales became another issue. In 1962 the share of Welsh youths entering an engineering apprenticeship was twenty-eight per cent compared with the United Kingdom's average of thirty-eight per cent.[59] Seventy-years earlier James Colquhoun had remarked upon the 'long practical training' followed by men employed in shipbuilding, and this was true also for areas where engineering manufacturing thrived. However, since Colquhoun's time, the coal industry needed fewer apprentices compared with other industrial areas of Britain since it employed a smaller number of engineers and craftsmen.

Philip Hadfield Photography
A. J. Edwards collection

finding employment only nineteen, thus seventeen per cent, had been recruited as apprentices. As an aside, he remarked that Johnston & Johnston, the American health care products company, had 'begun to employ people' at its new modern factory north of the Bryn, Pontllanfraith. Although he observed that the dearth of vacancies for young people was due to a 'lack of labouring jobs' he added that 'young people are unhappy at taking employment below their abilities'.[63] Discerning standards about job choices by school leavers of the Swinging Sixties had superseded ones that their parents had accepted in the Depression of the Thirties.

Nevertheless, during the 1950s, at Pontllanfraith, a South Wales Switchgear factory operated a scheme to train local youths for the electrical engineering industry. The company's recruiting ground for apprentices were local grammar and technical schools. By the early 1960s, around five hundred apprentices were employed at the Pontllanfraith factory. Also in the 1960s, the NCB No. 6 Area (Monmouth) advertised to attract school leavers for work as miners and craftsmen.[60] There appeared to be a lot of job opportunities for young men in the Sirhowy Valley.

The closure of collieries, though, compromised claims about a future for young men in Sirhowy Valley mining. Pochin Colliery was closed on the 25th July 1964.[61] The colliery had operated for just over eight decades in a kind of blind spot between the towns of Blackwood and Tredegar. Since no large community ever grew up near the colliery maybe only meagre local folklore kept alive the memory of sixteen men killed underground there in the 1884 explosion. Although no press account was found regarding the closure, exhaustion of coal reserves was probably the cause. The colliery's last manager was H. J. Williams.[62]

In early 1968, the youth employment officer for the Rhymney and Tredegar Valleys, Denzil Cole, reported that there was 'little work for boys in the valleys'. He detailed that of the 109 boys

East Area's Profitable Performance

In 1967 the NCB's South Western Division was superseded. The NCB South Wales Area came into being arranged as East and West areas. The Areas No. 4 (Aberdare), No. 5 (Rhymney) and Area No. 6 (Monmouth) were united to create East Area in which around 30 collieries operated. 'Ystrad Fawr', Ystrad Mynach, Glamorgan, previously the central office for Area No. 5 (Rhymney), became the headquarters for East Area. 'Ystrad Fawr', a mansion complete with a cricket field, was once the home of Col. Morgan Lindsay the son of a sister of 1st Viscount Tredegar.[64] Area No. 6's Abercarn office was closed.

The dawning of the East and West areas coincided with the NCB's introduction of a 'new technique' of management by objectives. Lord Robens, the chairman of the NCB, judged that the technique was 'comprehensive and sensible'. Area Directors were held responsible to the 'Board for achievement of annual objectives set out for them in terms of output, sales and profitability, after full discussion with them'. 'Consultation' followed afterwards with colliery management to agree colliery objectives, and to draw up a programme of action to achieve the objectives. However, he later conceded that 'early forecasts proved highly optimistic'.[65]

Concerning colliery closures, it might be inferred from Lord Robens's memoir as chairman of the NCB, they did not adversely affect industrial relations in the South Wales Coalfield as did wage issues. He gave much credit to Will Paytner (1903-

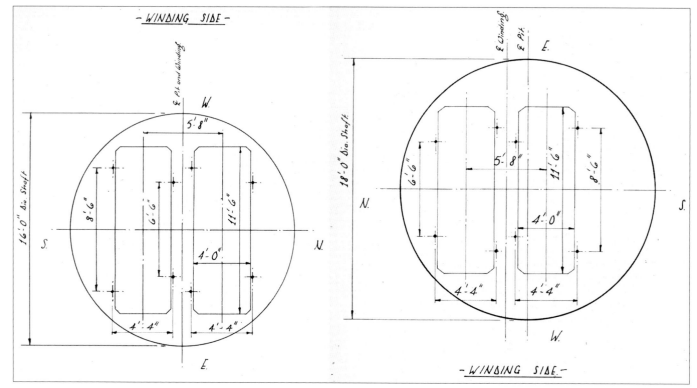

The final record of Pochin Colliery's shafts , No. 1 left and No. 2 right, held by the National Coal Board, South Western Division, No. 6 Area. Dated 19-10-1962 but has a handwritten note indicating the shafts being filled. No. 2 Pit served as the colliery's downcast. *A. J. Edwards Collection*

1984), the National Union of Miners' (NUM) general secretary, a Communist, for persuading its members in the coalfield to abandon piece-rate based wages for national day rates. Moreover, although he recognised that Communists 'dominated' the Scottish and South Wales Areas an implication from his memoir is that the Communists in the Yorkshire Area were much more forceful as 'trouble-makers' and in promoting militant activity.[66]

However, the change to national day rates by the NCB was brief. Arthur Lewis recalled that 'it soon became evident' that 'poor standards of work by unskilled road work rippings men and erection of steel arches' occurred due to there being no incentive for skilled workmen to do such work. Piece-rate based wages were re-introduced.[67]

Nevertheless, the end of Area No. 6 (Monmouth) was marked with Oakdale Colliery returning a profit for the 1966-1967 year of £774K due mainly to an output of 461,948 saleable tons of coal.[68]

In March 1968 the East Area held the bragging rights for colliery profitability in the British Coalfields for the half a year that began on the 28th September 1967. A profit of £1,607,000 was reported for the half year by East Area. The collieries of the former Area No. 6 topped the NCB's profit performance list. East Area was just one of four such NCB areas in Britain to show a profit. For the half year period the NCB reported a loss of £19,800,000.[69]

Any East Area boast would have been scorned by the 650 miners employed at Wyllie Colliery. Earlier, on the 9th January 1968, a 'NCB spokesman' disclosed that the colliery's 'closure was under consideration by the management of East Wales Area'. The colliery was producing a modest 3,250 tons a week. The spokesman tried to comfort anxious men. 'We hope to be in a position to offer every person employed at Wyllie a suitable job in a neighbouring colliery' with Britannia, in the Rhymney Valley, Markham, and Oakdale cited as their possible future workplaces.[70]

The NCB was also in the throes of following its Colliery Review Procedure[71] with regard to Ynyscedwin and Cefn Coed collieries in the western part of the South Wales Coalfield. Harold Wilson, the Labour Government's Prime Minister, made a tour of the area where these collieries lay. On the eve of the tour, the Minister of Power claimed that the Board had not 'followed the proper procedure and therefore had been wrong' to close the two collieries. Harold Wilson 'backed up the Minister's statement'. Lord Robens was emphatic that the NCB had 'consulted the NUM on both pits, each of which had been given a trial period'. Moreover he later claimed that the 'NUM leaders in South Wales were not taken in by the prime minister's window-dressing'. At the time he 'railed against the Wilson Government's determination that he should speed up pit closures in the face of competition from oil and nuclear power'.[72] He attacked the 'Government [for] spending enormous sums on nuclear power stations', and later observed that between 1965/66 and 1968/69 the NCB closed 204 collieries. Lord Robens charged Labour Governments with shutting collieries at a 'faster rate than when the Conservatives were in office'.[73]

As a high-level Government-NCB quarrel raged, Wyllie Colliery closed on the 28th March 1968, with its last manager being H. Beddoe.[74] The colliery was notable for being among the last three collieries sunk in the South Wales Coalfield. Wyllie Colliery had a longer independent operational life than one of the three, Powell Duffryn's Llantrisant Colliery, whose geological puzzle of workings had been assigned to Llanharan Colliery to solve.[75] Nevertheless, with the demise of Wyllie Colliery, the Sirhowy Valley's future as a mining area relied upon the fortunes of just Markham, Oakdale and Waterloo collieries.[76]

In October 1967 Jack Edwards submitted a new Oakdale washery project for approval. A senior project manager in the Area's Engineering Section, he held the post of Assistant to the Chief Engineer, William Humphreys. The Oakdale Colliery washery was built 1969/70. Then in 1971 he led work for the 'first extension' of the colliery's Froth Plant.[77] In 1972, the throughput of Oakdale Colliery's coal preparation plant, at a nominal capacity of 400 tons per hour, was only surpassed in

Philip Hadfield Photography
A. J. Edwards collection

the South Wales Coalfield by plant at Mardy Colliery, Rhondda Fach Valley, which had a throughput of 440 tons per hour.[78] The goals for NCB colliery plant projects were to spend within an approved budget and to achieve an incremental rise in a colliery's profit performance.

The coal output per miner was constantly scrutinized by the NCB. In March 1970, Oakdale and Abertillery collieries were 'leading' the 'productivity drive' in Monmouthshire. The average produced per manshift of the 1,200 employed at Oakdale was 33 hundredweights whereas at Abertillery, an average of 38 hundredweights of useable coal was cut per manshift.[79] The performance of Monmouthshire miners featured on the front page of a local newspaper with the reports of rugby and soccer competitions on the back page.[80]

The foregoing *South Wales Argus* good story about miners' performance also hinted at an imminent sad one for 170 Sirhowy Valley miners. On the 28th March 1970, Waterloo Colliery was closed since its coal reserves were exhausted.[81]

The 1972 Strike

In late 1971, the National Union of Miners, led by Joe Gormley as president, submitted a demand to the NCB for a pay rise for its members, which was rejected. A national strike began on the 8th January 1972. Earlier, in anticipation, Michael Foot MP called for the Labour movement to 'support the strike to the hilt'.[82] In the House of Commons, Edward Heath's Conservative Government was called to account by the Labour Party.

In mid-January, based upon a claim that British Leyland car workers earned £42 a week, Lawrence Daly, NUM secretary, contested that 'miners think they are worth that kind of money'. The day on which Daly's remark was reported South Wales Coalfield miners picketed 'Ystrad Fawr', NCB's East Wales office, and power stations.[83]

In early February the *South Wales Argus* observed:

The miners are obviously not going to yield easily and if they do yield it will only be after a protracted fight which can have the gravest effect on the national economy.[84]

Colliery lodge meetings, unlike in the 1926 Strike for instance, could discuss almost instantly the current state of national level dealings. Television and radio interviews with NUM leaders, NCB spokesmen, Government ministers, and Labour Party politicians gave miners a direct, if not complete, insight.

In the middle of February electricity power cuts made evident that the nation was subsumed by crisis. After the NUM rejected a number of NCB wage rise offers, the Government set up the Wilberforce Enquiry. The enquiry recommended that underground face workers be £34.50 per week.[85] The NCB put the Wilberforce Enquiry's recommendation to the NUM executive and it was accepted subject to a national ballot. In the South Wales Coalfield, with 22,232 votes of miners for, with 1,078 against, the NCB's offer was accepted.

Britain's miners returned to work on the 28th February elated that they were as capable as militant industrial workers at forcing their employer to concede pay rises. In 1972, on the South Wales 'colliery books', after nearly a quarter of a century of the NCB, were roughly a quarter of the 105,693 men employed in December 1948.[86] The number of miners of the South Wales Coalfield may have fallen markedly, but a generation of miners had re-discovered the bond that in the 1926 Strike had helped make their predecessors stubborn adversaries of coal owners.

Sirhowy Valley Collieries – South Wales Area

In 1979, the retired Member of Parliament Sir Harold Finch offered a reflection about the coal industry in the Sirhowy Valley with respect to 1971.[87] He was complementary about the 'able guidance' of Lister Walker, the director of the NCB East Area. The NCB had been 'very enterprising' at Markham and Oakdale collieries, and other collieries in Monmouthshire. Sir Harold wrote: 'He and his local management officials have maintained employment for a considerable number of men, and it is hoped that these pits will remain in production for some years to come'.

Both Oakdale and Markham collieries, he observed, had been profitable, in the case of the former since nationalisation, and regarding the later for the previous fifteen years. He described that at Oakdale Colliery four power-loaded faces, three of which were equipped with self advancing supports, enabled the colliery's 1,275 workers to produce a saleable output of 389,220 tons. At Markham Colliery, 722 men produced a saleable output of 222,283 tons by working 'by hand' at two coal faces whilst the only other face worked was equipped with power-loading and self advancing supports. Moreover, there were plans to fully mechanise the colliery. He noted that both collieries served the domestic and coking markets.[88] In 1969/70 a 'Roomheat' smokeless fuel plant was built and commissioned at Markham Colliery.[89]

In 1973 the NCB made the South Wales Area a unitary body. The area operated around fifty collieries that made it, in terms of collieries, the equivalent of one-and-a half times Area No. 6 (Monmouth) a quarter of a century earlier. Appointed as the Area's director was Philip Weekes. Regarding another former Tredegar Company staff member, on the 1st July 1973, Jack Edwards became assistant to the Area's mechanical engineer. 'Ystrad Fawr' offices became the centre for the operational management of the South Wales Coalfield

1974 Miners' Strike

In November 1973, a NUM overtime ban began. In January 1974, if a strike followed, the future of Oakdale Colliery was claimed by the NCB to be in jeopardy due to a threat of flooding.[90] An NUM national strike for wage increases began on the 10th February 1974, which occurred in the wake of the 1973 world oil crisis. By March 1974, there was a fourfold leap in the price of crude oil per barrel to $12 over a period of months. The coal miners' strike further disrupted the nation's economy. The NUM campaign encouraged an idea that miners were 'a special case'.

On the eve of the strike, Prime Minister Edward Heath called a General Election for February. An issue raised by the Conservative Party's campaign concerned trade unions challenging the authority of government. The General Election returned a minority Labour Government led by Harold Wilson, and the strike ended on the 10th March due to the NUM being awarded wage rises.

The Tredegar born twenty-eight years old Neil Kinnock, who had succeeded Harold Finch as Member of Parliament for Bedwellty at the 1970 General Election, spoke in the Queen's Speech debate in the House of Commons on the 12th March 1974. He opened by registering a belief that it 'was the first occasion on which a Member of Parliament for Bedwellty had been called upon to second' the motion of such a debate. During his speech he offered a picture of his constituency:

Bedwellty is not Welsh by language, although Welsh by character and temperament. We have all the essentials of Welsh valley life – clubs and choirs and chapels, and a 22,000 Labour majority. We are also situated in the Bible belt of rugby football. In the 15 towns and villages that make up the constituency there is also a unique quality of life in South Wales, and that is a competitive self-sufficiency ...

Adding: 'Among the 3,000 coal miners in my constituency, their wives, disabled comrades and former workmates who have left the industry to seek health and reasonable pay, there has been great rejoicing at the dawn of justice that broke for the miners of Britain as recently as last week'.

Regarding the Labour Government's plans he pledged that they had 'been presented' as 'a blueprint for democratic Socialism'.[91] Miners in the South Wales Coalfield might have expected that the blueprint included keeping pits open in the 'national interest'. If crude oil prices continued to rise then coal made the United Kingdom less vulnerable to the power and politics exerted by OPEC (Organization Petroleum Exporting Countries). Michael Foot spoke for keeping pits open in the national interest in the House of Commons when the 1974 strike was at its pitch with employed people experiencing 'three day weeks'. Moreover, he also argued a case for employing more miners. Used as an illustration for proposing such a policy, Foot referred to Ogilvie Colliery. 'Many' of his constituents living at Abertysswg worked at the colliery.[92] Concerning recruiting more miners he thought that there was a lack of understanding that they 'must come from overwhelmingly .... villages such as Abertysswg'.

A year later, on the 11th February 1975, Margaret Thatcher succeeded Edward Heath as the leader of the Conservative Party. Heath's Government had failed to cure widespread industrial unrest in Britain with the 1971 Industrial Relations Act. Trade unions had proved hostile towards any legislation aimed at reforming the way they conducted industrial relations. After the 1974 miners' strike a question lingered: who governed the United Kingdom?

The Celynen North-Markham-Oakdale Mining Complex

Remote from Westminster politics, the South Wales Area decided upon its priorities for meeting business goals set by the NCB in keeping with the 'Plan for Coal' of 1973/74. Thus, in 1975, the South Wales Area closed three collieries, one of which was Ogilvie Colliery.[93]

The 'Plan for Coal' gave a boost to the industry in the Sirhowy Valley and the Ebbw Vale. Prior to February 1975, Jack Edwards was party to preparing a project for merging the colliery operations of Markham, Celynen North, situated near Newbridge in the Ebbw Vale, with Oakdale. In 1913, what was to become a shaft for Celynen North Colliery was sunk by Newport Abercarn Black Vein Steam Coal Company and linked for ventilation with Celynen Colliery, a peer of Pochin Colliery. Around 1924, the sinking of another shaft created Celynen North Colliery. Celynen Colliery was thereafter called Celynen South. Hereafter, Celynen North and South collieries are included in this history since Hobart House approved merging Celynen North-Markham-Oakdale collieries.

The Celynen North-Markham-Oakdale mining complex project appears to have been approved with some speed since much work was completed over the period of years 1977/78. A goal of the project was to produce 11.2 million tons of coking coal aided by computer control.[94] Other important aspects of the project were 'improvements in haulage and transport with endless haulage and man riding facilities'. At Oakdale Colliery a second extension was made to the Froth Plant, a conveyor for rubbish at the North Pit installed, and erected were house coal yard bunkers with conveyors, and rapid loading facilities for British Rail.[95] The investment sustained both the operation of the three collieries and a part of the coal industry in the county of Gwent, formed in 1974, as a successor to the county of Monmouthshire.

Celynen North Colliery was sunk by the Newport Abercarn Black Vein Coal Company in 1913 to complement Cleynen Colliery, whose two shafts became known as Celynen South thereafter. At the time of nationalisation 1,208 workers were employed underground at Celynen North. During the 1950s the colliery's annual production was on average nearly 250,000 tons of coal.   *Pope/Parkhouse Archive*

Yesterday's Men

Jack Edwards's last major piece of work concerned the Celynen North-Markham-Oakdale project. He retired in 1981 after forty-four years of employment in the coal industry.[96] He became a founder member of 'Yesterday's' Men', a group of around twelve fellow coal industry engineers. The group met regularly, once a month, throughout the year at Aberdare for lunch. In subsequent years, its numbers more than doubled.

The group flourished due to the decline in engineers, draughtsmen, and unit engineers responsible for colliery maintenance, employed by the NCB in the South Wales Coalfield. A group belief, or assumption, was if the industry was not investing in itself then it was heading towards death. Even as experienced men with rich knowledge about the South Wales coal industry their views did not attract the attention of the media. Such men would have greeted with laughter any accusation that they were doomsayers.

Prior to their retirement from the NCB, some of the men had given safety cover at collieries during the 1972 and 1974 NUM strikes. In retirement, many of these men may have reminisced about providing safety cover, but the task had not been taken on gleefully. Some assigned tasks were viewed as boring.[97]

Left to Right: David Morgan, NCB mechanical engineer; Jack Farr, unit mechanical engineer, Celynen South Colliery; and Jack Edwards. Photograph taken in June 1981 to record Jack Edward's retirement after 44 years service as a coal industry engineer. He began his career with the Tredegar Iron & Coal Company. He was Chief Draughtsman, Area No. 6, South Western Division, NCB, from around 1960 until the end of 1966. He retired as a NCB senior projects manager.

An unknown NCB Photographer. A. J. Edwards Collection

A prelude for a Strike

The talk among miners at Celynen, Markham, and Oakdale collieries, at the start of the Eighties, included exchanges of opinion about three national leadership changes. In 1981, Arthur Scargill, a militant leader of the Yorkshire NUM, was elected president of the NUM. He had been 'briefly a Communist when young', and Terry Thomas, executive member of the NUM South Wales, was to observe later that 'he always seemed to want to appear further left than anyone else'.[98] In September 1983, Ian MacGregor, a Scottish born successful American industrialist, was appointed the chairman of the NCB. In October 1983, the Labour Party elected the local Member of Parliament, Neil Kinnock, as its leader.

On joining the NCB Ian MacGregor read a report of the Monopolies and Mergers Commission. The report told him that during 1981-1982, the Conservative Government gave the NCB £575 million of which £428 million covered losses. The report identified, in MacGregor's assessment, the 'nub of the problem: over-capacity and high-cost pits'. He accepted that he was 'expected to put things right'.[99] One stance of the president of the NUM was resolute opposition to colliery closures, which was a bar to the elimination of over-capacity.

After the demise of the Heath Government, a Conservative Party policy group produced a report that forecast, in the event of a Thatcher Government, that coal was 'the most likely battleground'. 'Building up a stock of coal stocks, particularly at power stations', was first in the report's six point plan. In 1985, *The Times*, reflected: 'There was always the prospect of a full-scale conflict between the miners under Arthur Scargill, and Mrs Margaret Thatcher's confident second-term administration'. The first Margaret Thatcher Government implemented measures that built stocks of coal. By 1984, 'coal stocks at power stations, and at the pit heads, were practically tripled from 1972 levels to 57 millions tonnes, half the annual output of the industry'.[100]

Moreover, by 1983, nuclear power generation had increased. The electric generating capacity of England's Hartlepool nuclear power station was added to others like Trawsfynydd and Wyllfa in Wales.[101] Furthermore, oil-fired power station electricity output was boosted by some engineering modifications. Nonetheless, 'electricity generated from coal accounted for 80 per cent of the Central Energy Generating Board (CEGB) output'. Significantly also, the biggest customer for the NCB was the CEGB that took 'three-quarters of the coal mined in the UK at well above the world market price'.[102]

In October 1983, without a members' ballot, the NUM began an overtime ban as a protest against colliery closures but with an aim to reduce the size of coal stocks. Stocks were little affected due to mild winter weather. On the 1st March 1984, the area director for South Yorkshire revealed his 'intention to close Cortonwood pit as soon as possible'.[103] Four days later, a strike occurred in Yorkshire over Cortonwood Colliery. On the 6th March, the NCB announced plans to cut four millions tonnes of coal capacity. The executive of the NUM reacted and avoided a national ballot by promoting use of the union's Rule 41. The rule allowed colliery lodges to ballot a proposal for a strike that upon winning support needed national level approval before taking action. In early 1984, it was taken for granted that the NUM executive, bent on a national strike, would endorse a lodge's vote for a strike.

A sketch of the 1984-85 Miners' Strike

Hereafter, a sketch is offered about the 1984-85 miners' strike with respect to the miners at Celynen, Markham, and Oakdale collieries. Initially, eighteen of the twenty-eight colliery lodges in the South Wales Coalfield voted no to a motion for a strike.[104] 880 miners at Oakdale Colliery voted to strike. At Celynen South, the vote was 'overwhelmingly against striking'. Ray Lawrence, lodge secretary Celynen South, explained: 'Basically the main issue is not having a [national ballot] vote.'[105] Miners on strike at nearby collieries acted swiftly to form picket lines. As the week of the 12th March began non-striking miners at Celynen North, Celynen South and Markham collieries were 'turned back by "flying pickets."'[106] Ron Stone, lodge secretary at Penallta Colliery, later recalled picketing by Penallta miners at Celynen South. 'It got quite nasty over there. There was a lot of arguing and shouting because they wanted to return to work, and we did not want them to.'[107]

The strike became "solid" across the South Wales Coalfield. Late in March, a number of Markham and North Celynen miners picketed Littleton Colliery, Staffordshire.[108]

At the end of March, a 'smoke filled, hard-floored transit van' carried a number of Celynen South miners to picket Coventry Colliery, Kersely, near Coventry. Warnings had been issued by the NCB that unless new workings were found at Celynen South then the colliery would be closed. Mike Rees, a twenty-two year old faceworker, with a wife expecting their third child, had a 'serious desire to see the coal industry survive'. "They just can't continue closing pits on what they claim are economic reasons but if we don't stop them now we never will and thousands more people in mining areas will find themselves on the dole," he was reported as saying. His view was endorsed next day by fellow worker John Harrison, forty-six years of age, who had made the trip with his work mate, Mark, his twenty-three year old son.

A brief, sleepless, overnight stay at a 'small wooden hut with about seventy fellow flying pickets' was the prelude to the Celynen South men gathering at Coventry Colliery's gates at 4 30 a.m.. A 'handful of policemen' stood guard. Around 5 a.m. local miners arrived for work in cars. Some cars turned around, but 'car after car crossed' the picket line. A Kent miner was left shaken, but uninjured, after being knocked down by a car. After the incident, the 250-plus pickets, which had gathered, 'impressed [witness Colin Clark of the *South Wales Argus*] by their restraint'. Nevertheless, 'tension mounted and, and there was a brief flare-up at 6 15 a.m.' 'Scuffles broke out and as more police rushed on the scene … But as quickly as they exploded, tempers subsided and the pickets, resigned to the fact that they were not going to stop production that day, began to move away at 6 30 a.m.'

The Celynen South men drove back to Crumlin in the transit van. 'Spirits continued to run high'. Yet, Colin Clark was 'convinced that these men were not the intimidatory thugs they were so often labelled'. He held: 'They are genuinely concerned about the future for themselves, their families and their communities, all of which are greatly affected by the coal industry'.[109]

By the end of April the *South Wales Argus* noted that 'Gwent's miners are all in the same boat – on strike and rapidly running out of cash'. The 'luxuries of life – drinking, cigarettes and videos – are the first to go as mining families strip their spending down'. Local branches of building societies and banks were reported making arrangement to enable miners reduce, or even suspend their house mortgage repayments.[110] A food collection scheme had already been organised by workers at local factories to help Oakdale miners and their families.[111]

Outwith South Wales, in late May, the supply of coke to Scunthorpe steelworks from Orgreave coke works, which used South Yorkshire coal, began to be heavily picketed. On the 18th June, the police and pickets clashed on a scale that earned the event recognition as the 'Battle of Orgreave'. The event was viewed by not only critics of the NUM as a battle lost by the miners. A hitch followed. The South Wales NUM was 'fined £50,000 and funds sequested for picketing contempt'.[112]

Early in September, men providing safety cover at Oakdale and Celynen South collieries withdrew their services. The men's action was a protest at being requested by the NUM to pay a levy of £3 to a food fund out of their wages earned at £15 per shift. Kim Howells, research officer, NUM South Wales, argued that the men were only being asked to 'donate one-fifth' of their shift rate 'to feed the people of their own area'. If the men held to their position then he warned that 'we will just have to find workers who will' provide the cover.[113] The next day saw flooding 'averted' at Oakdale Colliery due to the measures taken by two winding-engine men.[114]

As September ended, the strike's duration of seven months equalled the 1926 Strike. As in 1926, severe hardship and suffering was being borne by miners' families.

For at least the miners at Oakdale Colliery, picketing the BSC (British Steel Corporation) Llanwern steelworks put at risk their employment prospects. The workers at Llanwern steelworks also had fears about their futures in part due to a fall in trade, but also the threat of closure in favour of Ravenscraig steelworks in Scotland. Late in September, the South Wales Area's director, Philip Weekes, issued a 'strong warning' of a 'big cut back in the 4,000 jobs that depend on Llanwern steelworks'. He foresaw future unsuccessful coal supply contract negotiations with the BSC if imported coal was used at the steelworks.[115] Imported coal was delivered to the steelworks to keep it operational. Moreover, the Iron and Steel Trades Confederation, although the union gave money to local strike committees, refused to call its members out on strike in support of the NUM.[116] In October, agitation by leaders of the National Association of Colliery Overmen, Deputies and Shotfirers (NACODs) alarmed the Government. The future operation of all collieries would be jeopardised by a NACODs strike. On the 25th October, NACODs withdrew their threat of a strike.

'Stop the back-to-work movement'

In November, to encourage a return to work, the NCB offered miners a Christmas bonus. On the 12th November, 'violent scenes' marred a 'stop the back-to-work movement' response that saw a number of men start work at Celynen South. Ray Lawrence, the colliery's lodge secretary, asserted: 'They are putting the pit in great danger by their actions and I am bitterly disappointed at them. They will probably be expelled from the union tomorrow, but we might not have a pit by then.'[117] Complaints were also lodged by pickets about police behaviour. Later in the month, at the colliery, six policemen were stoned, and two miners were remanded. PC Walter Ludlow and PC Timothy Davies entered the Royal Gwent Hospital, Newport, for treatment for cuts and bruises.[118]

On the 30th November the death of a taxi driver, David Wilkie, was reported. He was killed by a three-foot concrete post dropped on to his car by men standing on a Heads of Valleys' road bridge. David Wilkie's customer was a miner who was being driven to work at Merthyr Vale Colliery. Philip Weekes thought it an 'appalling tragedy'. Neil Kinnock MP, the leader of the Opposition, 'urged the person who did it to come forward'.[119] Two men were later remanded for the killing of David Wilkie, aged thirty-five, and later sentenced to imprisonment for manslaughter.

The role that Neil Kinnock played nationally is a subject that lays outwith this sketch. Maybe Beckett and Hencke's observation that 'Kinnock had to walk a delicate line between splitting his party irrevocably by failing to support the NUM, and committing electoral suicide by failing to support the police', offers an interim idea about the role he had to play.[120]

Perhaps the following gives some appreciation of his constituency work during the strike. From the strike's outset, Neil Kinnock and 'his wife Glenys … sent cheques to support Welsh miners' families'. Concerning the community associated with the Celynen collieries, Dot Phillips of the Newbridge Women's Support Group was full of praise for him as her Member of Parliament.[121] However, in December, Kinnock was 'quizzed' with 'tough questions' by members of the Oakdale Colliery lodge about the stance he had taken during the strike. Allan Baker, the colliery's lodge secretary, reflected, 'The invitation to attend this meeting was made to Mr Kinnock after he said he wouldn't be going to any miners' rallies.'…'Since then, however, he has shared a platform with Arthur Scargill which proved his support for the NUM and dispelled some doubts that striking miners had about him.'[122]

At the Oakdale Colliery lodge meeting, Neil Kinnock made a promise to join a picket line. Just after New Year's Day 1985, he joined pickets at Celynen South. Dr Kim Howells observed, "His appearance will have given a great boost of encouragement to all the area's striking miners."[123]

Neil Kinnock, MP for Islwyn, leader of the Labour Party and the Government's Opposition from 1983 to 1992, meets striking miners at Celynen South Colliery in January 1985.
South Wales Argus. Supplied by Llyfrgell Gendlaethol Cymru/ The National Library of Wales

Some local miners, though, pressed for a return to work. Early in December, twenty-five miners at Markham Colliery 'petitioned' their lodge to call a general meeting to hold a secret ballot after hearing a case 'for staying out longer'. One of the petitioners was quoted as saying, "Worst of all, the leadership is desperately out of touch with the feelings of the men. Here in South Wales, where we have been more loyal to the cause than anywhere else, people are suffering real hardship and all to no purpose."[124] Moreover, in contrast with Dr Howells's hope, on the occasion of Neil Kinnock's visit to Celynen South, thirty-three men had reported for work at the colliery. Even more astonishing perhaps, the day after, a colliery lodge committee member for twenty-one years, Des Williams, contested, "The men have been let down by their union and most of all by Arthur Scargill and I think should show their anger by breaking the strike," which is what he had done.[125]

At Oakdale Colliery in mid-February, the NUM refused to give safety cover due to four miners returning to work. The pit bottom became submerged. One coal face was lost.[126]

Back to Work

On St. David's Day, South Wales NUM delegates met in conference at Porthcawl. At the end of February, the NCB reckoned that 50.75 per cent of British miners were back working.[127] Attempts made by the NCB, in and after October 1984, to try to negotiate a settlement with the NUM always foundered. An intrusion by the Government and the TUC to find a basis for settlement also failed. By February 1985 at the latest, Ian MacGregor presumed to think 'it was clear to everyone that Scargill had no intention of settling'.[128] At Porthcawl, a decision was made by NUM South Wales to 'push for a return without a settlement'.[129]

At a NUM national executive meeting held at Congress House, London, on the 3rd March, South Wales NUM put the motion to end the strike. 'The hard left argued that there should be no return to work until all the dismissed men had been reinstated; Welsh miners, who still form the most solid strike area, and their allies on the soft left insisted that there should be an immediate march back, with negotiations thereafter'. By a 'narrow vote' the decision was made to end the longest strike in the history of the British coal industry.[130]

Dr Kim Howells promptly dismissed charges that the South Wales leadership had 'betrayed and "sold out" the union'. "If we had stood by and watched the blood of the union dying away it would have been a betrayal of everything everyone had fought for." Alan Baker, Oakdale lodge secretary, felt that 'the decision was the right one' and was hopeful that the 'majority' of the men sacked would get their jobs back. Ray Lawrence, South Celynen lodge secretary, said: "It's a decision that we first proposed in area conference. It's an inevitable decision although I can't say I'm pleased about it."[131]

On Monday, the 4th March 1985, South Wales Coalfield miners marched back to work. The miners and their families were saddled with much financial debt. In communities where grudges can particularly be long remembered there were many targets for rage like a scapegoat – the 'scab', the police, Ian MacGregor, Margaret Thatcher, and Arthur Scargill.[132] Ian MacGregor afterwards made plain in his book about the strike that one of his missions had been to regain for the NCB 'the power to manage', which for miners opposed to being bossed about was antagonistic.

How Margaret Thatcher dealt with the NCB and Government ministers regarding the strike, and to obtain some idea about her doubts and resolve, has been described by Charles Moore.[133] The Prime Minister's phrase 'the enemies within', said at a meeting of the Conservative Party's 1922 Committee, directed at the miners' leaders, was resented by all striking miners and their families.[134] That the outcome of the strike enhanced her reputation, and ushered in the privatisation of nationalised industries further perpetuated enduring hatred against her in Labour Party strongholds, former mining communities.

Up until at least the year 2009, Scargill has appeared reticent to reply to accusations made against him about his motives for, and his direction of the strike.[135] At the strike's end, he refused to 'concede defeat' on the grounds that the NCB had no 'signed agreement' with the NUM 'that pit closures could be made on economic grounds'.[136] Yet, success eluded the national strike he had led. Indeed, shortly after work resumed, six Gwent collieries closed. Of particular interest in 1985, the closures were announced of: Celynen North Colliery, on the 31st March; Celynen South Colliery on the 5th September; and of Markham Colliery on the 20th September.[137]

Closures

Depending upon viewpoints, a series of underground rockfalls at Celynen South Colliery early in September 1985 were irrelevant, or an aside, or a set back, regarding the future employment of its miners. After around 110 years of operation the colliery's coal workings neared exhaustion and this might have had a bearing upon its grim status. For the year 1983-4, the colliery produced around just 80,000 tonnes that yielded a loss per tonne of £59.5, which placed it at the foot of the Gwent collieries' business economic league.[138] On the 5th September, Carl Browning, lodge chairman, spoke for the colliery's 350 miners: "It was [due to] Welsh pride more than anything else. Rather than the coal board coming to us in six weeks to close the pit we can say we have made the decision to close at South

Celynen'.[139] Celynen South men would have viewed as trivial being told that their colliery had outlived its peer at birth, Pochin Colliery, by twenty-one years.

For the year 1983-4, when 570 miners were employed, Celynen North Colliery produced around 150,000 tonnes of coal but at a loss per tonne of £24.2.[140] By October 1985, according to Ernie Way, lodge chairman, the colliery's 470 miners faced 'Blackmail', owing to the threat of the loss of benefits so as to force the colliery's closure.[141] The lodge had voted to fight against this, nevertheless, Ernie Way watched 'miners surrender to closure plans'. One hundred of the last miners to cut coal at the colliery took voluntary redundancy payments. Neil Kinnock MP commented: 'Miners were under terrible pressure' because of the regulations concerned with redundancy payments and unemployment benefits.[142]

The end of Markham Colliery appeared not to win any notice in local newspapers. The colliery's last manager was Steve Williams.[143] For the year 1983-4 the colliery's 595 miners produced around 230,000 tonnes of coal. All things being equal, a loss per tonne of a mere £3.9 suggested there was a chance that the colliery could become profitable.[144] Yet, after the strike ended, 'adverse conditions' met working the colliery's OC (Old Coal) 7 face thwarted efforts made to attain production targets.[145] In September 1985, after around seventy years of operation, the practice of the colliery's 569 miners standing as shift groups on pit top to be lowered by an electric winder in a cage for work at the coal-face ended.[146] Just one former Tredegar Company colliery survived, Oakdale, that employed 867 people in 1983-84 and produced just over 300,000 tonnes of coal at a loss per tonne of £7.5. Moreover, a managerial link with the Tredegar Iron & Coal Company was broken in 1985 when Philip Weekes retired from the NCB.

New Production Targets

In September 1985 Maes Manor Hotel, located at a secluded spot north of Blackwood, hosted an NCB manager's conference. If the former mansion's walls had ears and were able to speak they could have recalled earlier talk about coal mining. The building, as Maesrhuddud House, was built for Edward Williams, a coal owner, who moved into the house around 1901.[147] Cliff Davies, Philip Weekes's successor as director of the NCB South Wales Area offered the conference a kind of statement that Edward

Williams might have said in similar circumstances. "If South Wales didn't get its prices down it risked losing key customers like power stations and steelworks."

The conference also heard that millions of pounds had been spent at Oakdale Colliery on 'hitech' equipment. The quid pro quo for the investment would have found favour during the time of the Tredegar Company: the setting of new production targets.[148]

At the end of the month, the director of the NCB South Wales Area publically praised the performance of the miners at Oakdale Colliery. The miners set 'an all time productivity record' for the South Wales Coalfield, 2.73 tonnes [54 cwts]. The record was a sign that the £22 million investment was returning value to the NCB. His message of praise though appeared to contain a contradiction. He acknowledged that, 'Oakdale was one of the best collieries in the coalfield,' but was also quoted as saying, 'The sleeping giant of Oakdale has woken up.'[149]

On the 1st January 1987, the National Coal Board became British Coal Corporation. Two years later, during the financial year April 1988 – April 1989, the Oakdale 'complex' produced 850,000 tons of coal won from the Old Coal (OC) seam. Des Caddy later reflected that this output was 'just 150,000 tons short of the majestic 1,000,000 tons which no other mine could produce'. However, 'unfortunately a fall occurred on the OC 10 face at the end of March 1989 which prevented us achieving such a goal!' Although the OC 10 face 'had been a considerable success major "geological conditions" at the Celynen North Section of the mine' caused the closure of Oakdale Colliery.[150]

Gwent's Last Pit

In August 1989, a management-lodge officials meeting was held to conclude the closure consultation process for Oakdale Colliery. The Oakdale lodge members present at the meeting included Colin Trapper, the lodge Secretary, Simon James, Ken Sullivan, and Gareth Woods. Des Caddy, the colliery's manager, was to retain the 'greatest respect' for Colin Trapper as a 'gentleman'.[151] Present also at the meeting was Terry Wheatley, British Coal's director for South Wales Area. He became the target for defamatory language voiced by some of the lodge officials. The press judged that the language demonstrated worker bitterness. 'British Coal complained it was a personal attack'. Terry Wheatley's recourse was to withdraw from the meeting. At the meeting, 'lodge officials spoke with one voice, claiming they had been blackmailed into closure by British Coal's deadline of August the 26th for redundancy payments'.[152] British Coal had 'announced overnight that no more coal would be raised and that interviews would be held for those wishing to transfer to other pits'.[153] Oakdale Colliery's miners voted 435 in favour of closure with 376 against.[154]

Oakdale Colliery closed on 24th October, 1989. The colliery produced 1,004,311 tons during a year that ended 31st March, 1928. The three men shown represent just over 800 miners who manned Gwent's last deep-mine. The colliery's annual output record set in 1928 was nearly equalled during the year that ended in April 1989.

South Wales Argus. *Supplied by Llyfrgell Gendlaethol Cymru/ The National Library of Wales*

Phillip Higgins's last day of employment at Oakdale Colliery. Ten weeks earlier he had moved for work to the colliery due to the closure of Marine Colliery, Cwm, Ebbw Vale.

South Wales Argus. *Supplied by Llyfrgell Gendlaethol Cymru/ The National Library of Wales*

On the 24th October 1989, miners walked around the surface of Oakdale Colliery 'looking bewildered, not quite believing that their pit—the last in Gwent—had finally been condemned to closure in the name of profitability'.[155] Maybe forgotten by miners was that since the 1946 Coal Industry Nationalisation Act the 'body corporate', initially the NCB, had been required not to make a loss.[156] However, a consequence of not enabling British Coal to meet such a requirement was that 850 men at Oakdale Colliery, with an average age of about thirty, were made redundant.

A confession by Alan Matthews, the last miner to be wound up from underground at Oakdale Colliery, that five generations of his family had 'gone underground at the colliery' could serve as fitting summary for the history of the colliery. Yet, he and his son, also an Oakdale miner, faced a bleak future. "Where can I get a job? Where can I get employment at 49?" he asked. His prediction was that his twenty-five years old son 'will be paying for his mortgage from his dole money'.

An opinion exchanged among the men was that there was 'no point in moving on' to another colliery. Just a few collieries operated in the South Wales Coalfield. Years earlier, Gwent miners had transferred from Blaenserchan, Six Bells, and Marine collieries to Oakdale Colliery. Ten weeks earlier, Philip Higgins moved from Marine Colliery, closed on the 10th March, for work at Oakdale. That many Oakdale's miners uttered that they 'had enough' was a frank admission of desolation.

Colliery officials and maintenance men had also to bear anxieties having lost their occupations. Three-quarters-of-a-century of employment for the colliery's overmen, firemen, deputies, shot firers, colliery engineers, blacksmiths, electricians, mechanics and welders had also ended.

The colliery's workers, generally averse to management, were not inclined to reflect like one former chairman of the National Coal Board did about the onerous duties borne by their manager. Lord Robens observed that 'managing a colliery is not the easiest way of earning a living'. Robens revealed that 'only a small fraction of their day's work was spent doing the job for which they had been required by law to qualify over a long period – mining engineering'. A colliery manager's time was largely taken up dealing with industrial relations issues. He paid tribute: 'It is a hard life but it breeds an exceptional kind of men'.[157] Put in charge of Oakdale Colliery, succeeding Tredegar Company men also of such quality, with tentative dates of appointments, were: David H. Thomas (1947-1948); Philip G. Weekes (1948-1953);[158] W. B. Cleaver – known as 'Billy Kick' Cleaver for his defining rugby union skill,[159] John Fox (served three periods: 1948, 1954-1964, and 1969-1970)[160]; R. John Williamson (1965-1968); W. John Watkins (1980-1982); K. A. Morris (1983-1986) , W. G. Cecil (1983-1985) and Des Caddy (1985-1989).[161] It fell to Des Caddy, as the colliery's last manager, who held the 'greatest respect for' its 'entire workforce', to oversee decommissioning work.[162] On a bleak day in his life, like the men under his charge, he would not have viewed it as an honour to have qualified to enter the pages of industrial history.

A Summary Chronicle – Tredegar Coal & Iron

John Evans proposed that the firing of the Sirhowy Furnace in 1778 marked 'the beginning of the industrialization of the Monmouthshire valleys on a scale never before imagined'. The development of industry in the Sirhowy Valley supports his proposal. Thomas Atkinson and William Barrow are to be credited for opening Sirhowy Furnace. By 1794, the market for pig iron and the advance in canal and tramway communications, made Richard Forthergill and Matthew Monkhouse keen to operate a bigger iron works than their Sirhowy Furnace. In conjunction with the landowner, Sir Charles Gould Morgan of Tredegar House, and Penydarren's Samuel Homfray, ambitions were realised. Shortly after 1800, blast furnaces were lit at the Tredegar Ironworks built at Uwchlaw y Coed. With the opening of the ironworks, the Tredegar Estates' immense natural resources of coal and clay-ironstone under the north-west area of Monmouthshire were destined to be exploited to near exhaustion.

The novel sight in Wales of commercial steam locomotion traffic in the Sirhowy Valley had at least one local consequence. Under Samuel Homfray Junior, from the 1830s onwards, the ironworks rolled rail to meet a market created by the Railway Age. By 1850, the 'great' works had not only become the source of the name used for a fledgling town, but 'Tredegar' was bandied around the globe by railway men thinking about buying rail.

The scraping away of ground by miners to unearth coal at the head of the Sirhowy Valley before 1768 was a primitive start for an industry that was to flourish on a great scale. The realisation of Samuel Homfray Junior's orders to sink pits caused the scenery to take on a monochrome blackness that would spread down the valley. Arguably the opening of Evan Davies' Pit in 1829, featuring a novel balance-winder, announced the start to deep-mined coal in the Sirhowy Valley.[163]

Praise in 1841 by Captain Hosken, master of the *Great Western*, for 'Tredegar coal' anticipated a clamour from around the world for the supply of such steam coal. During and after the 1840s 'Tredegar coal' bunkered merchant steam ships, and fired also railway locomotives. Local job opportunities multiplied and drew hosts of migrants to the area such that in 1850 a London newspaper reporter registered that the town of Tredegar was one 'of rising importance'.

Around the cusp of the 1870s, the Tredegar Company experienced uncertain times commercially and in 1873 was beset by a miners' strike. Nonetheless, in 1873, a body of investors, proven industrialists, acquired the assets of the company to form the Tredegar Iron & Coal Company. The ethos of many of the investors aligned with that of the Liberal Party and this was to have an effect upon the way in which the company was managed. With the appointment of James Colquhoun, the company's first general manager, there was an immediate sign of the company's willingness to support an idea of its workforce. In 1873, a workers' delegation obtained his support for what eventually became known as the Tredegar Workmen's Medical Aid, notably a forerunner of the National Health Service.

Under James Colquhoun, the company swiftly began to extend the exploitation of the company's coal property, and entered steel making. Whitworth Colliery and Pochin Colliery were sunk in 1875 and 1876 respectively. 'Blows' issuing from steel making Bessemer converters lit the sky above Tredegar. Yet, the rolling of steel rail after 1882 lasted for only two decades.

After the directors elected in 1894 Charles McLaren, later 1st Lord Aberconway, as chairman, the Tredegar Iron & Coal Company solely focused upon producing and selling coal. A 'man of ability', Aberconway served as chairman with considerable effect for nearly forty years. His character, rounded practical knowledge of industry, commerce, and finance was of benefit to the company. Regardless of scepticism among working people about the motives of industrial leaders he made genuine efforts to nurture good industrial relations. Under his leadership, the living conditions and the welfare of people living in the communities associated with the company's collieries improved.

In 1898, McLaren Merthyr Colliery opened, but the related financial strain, without generous concessions made by the landowner, Godfrey Charles Morgan, 1st Viscount Tredegar, could have bankrupted the company. A boom for Welsh steam coal, as the 20th century began, was another godsend. McLaren Merthyr coal fuelled the boilers of naval ships.

A. S. Tallis, a man of 'tact', appointed agent and manager of the company's collieries in 1899, further expanded the colliery operation. He appears to have applied lessons learnt from the 1902 McLaren Merthyr Colliery explosion. The subsequent collieries he was responsible for opening, Oakdale, Markham, and Wyllie, were not only well engineered for producing coal but saw attention paid to safety like copious underground ventilation. Moreover, under Tallis, electricity for the powering of colliery plant and machinery was introduced in the South Wales Coalfield, and steel arch roof supports for underground use was pioneered in the British coalfields. Just one fatal colliery explosion occurred after 1902, at Markham Colliery in 1912, which marked William Woolley's heroic entry into company management.

The company's directors also learnt a lesson from the McLaren Merthyr Colliery funding crisis. Oakdale, Markham, and Wyllie collieries were set up as subsidiary coal companies as a safeguard against the risk of mining failure. Furthermore, a company director, Sir Arthur Markham, was a notable influence for good not only in terms of business initiatives but mines safety for the nation during the first decade and a half of the 20th century. In addition, he fully supported Tallis's lasting legacy, the building of four model villages, Abertysswg, Oakdale, Markham, and Wyllie.

From around 1910 onwards the Tredegar Iron & Coal Company was beset by troubles, many outwith its control. In 1911, the founding of a Tredegar branch of the Independent Labour Party announced a new political force in the Sirhowy Valley. During the 1910s, a generation of local union leaders who embraced Socialist ideals were less accommodating than their predecessors when negotiating with the company. The lucrative profits made by the coal companies during the First World War was a gift to Left-wing agitators crusading for radical change regarding the ownership of the industry. In the 1920s, the premier status of South Wales Coalfield in Great Britain waned due to the substitution of steam coal with oil to power ships. The nation's return to the Gold Standard in 1925 made Welsh coal more expensive to sell in export markets. Competition from Germany and Poland became acute, and protectionism distorted trade.

The company, though, possessed a resolve to survive as a business. Even during the highly competitive market of the 1920s the company continued to win coal orders. The company's generally good record of profitability continued to capture City investor interest, which was a feat. During the early years of the 1920s, the company produced nearly 3 million tons of coal annually, employed around 12,000 people, and paid a regular dividend 12½ per cent to its shareholders. Worthily, if only momentarily, the company was regarded as one of "The Big Three" of the South Wales Coalfield. The company's strategic caution, though, was a bar to pursuing an amalgamation policy like Powell Duffryn's. But the company's practice in financial discipline kept it afloat in troubled times. Mass unemployment of the 1920s, the ill-fated 1926 Strike, and the Depression of the 1930s bred considerable discontent, and dire poverty in valley communities. The advocacy of fraternal dealings in industrial relations by the company's directors was subverted. The hope

grew among ordinary miners and their families that there was a better alternative to the way that capitalists managed the coal industry, and that Parliamentary reform could bring it about.

The 1945 Labour Government's response to the hopes of miners and their families was the 1946 Coal Industry Nationalisation Act. The Tredegar Iron & Coal Company was voluntarily liquidated. By 1948, the company's last managing director, William Woolley, resided at St. Mellons, Cardiff, but removed later to Bournemouth, and died in 1970 aged eighty-five. The company's last chairman was Harold Duncan McLaren, 2nd Baron Aberconway, who died at seventy-four years in 1953.

Through the vesting of rights, six former company collieries became a tiny part of the operation of the National Coal Board. The demand for coal at home boomed during the Fifties. However, the exhaustion of coal reserves made some colliery closures certain: in 1958, McLaren; and Ty Trist in 1959. Moreover, oil refinery investments in Britain after the war weakened the demand for coal now reliant upon home markets. Pochin Colliery closed in 1964. After Wyllie Colliery closed in 1968 a leap in oil prices seemed to enhance coal's prospects during the Seventies. However, the coal industry's largest customer, the Central Generating Electricity Board, was building nuclear power stations. The national miners' strikes of 1972 and 1974 made energy industry policy makers acutely aware that the supply of coal was ever vulnerable to industrial strife. The impact of the 1984-85 national strike will long be debated, but the demise of Markham Colliery was one result. A casualty of the decline of the coal industry was the Tredegar works that was closed in 1990. However, constant NCB investment in Oakdale Colliery sustained one of the best collieries to have ever operated in the South Wales Coalfield.

Yet, contrary to some miners' beliefs the financial policy set for the National Coal Board by Government required that a colliery at worst break even. The national budget could be more wisely spent on other functions and services of Government than

Filling in North Pit, Oakdale Colliery. On the left is Alan Matthews who was the last miner to be raised from undergound at the colliery. On the right is his son, David.

Courtesy of the Alan Matthews collection

wasted on uneconomic collieries. Oakdale Colliery's officials and miners valiantly responded after the 1984-85 national strike to try to stem closure, but ultimately the profit and loss account did not count in favour of their efforts.

Monuments and Memories

Notably then, the 24th October 1989, marked the end of one of natures' and the Industrial Revolution's greatest gifts to Gwent: a deep-mined coal industry. By 1989, the Sirhowy Valley's iron industry was a distant memory. The valley's coal industry could suffer a similar fate.

Such a fate depends partly upon how dearly the descendants of miners and iron workers treasure the past. The men who peeled off for the final time soiled, faded orange coloured, overalls at Oakdale Colliery might not take kindly to being identified as the last miners of their kind in Gwent. Moreover, redundant miners might also view as a trifle a reflection that on removing for the last time electric head lamps from white helmets a local link was broken with an initiative of a Tredegar Company coalowner, Sir Arthur Markham.

Generations of miners, though, had long tolerated filthy work and danger to life and limb underground. Surprisingly, though, a 1995 *South Wales Echo* 'roll of honour' of miners who lost their lives in pursuit of their work in the South Wales Coalfield listed only six men employed at Tredegar Company collieries, one at Markham, one at Pochin, and the others at Oakdale. Some relatives were moved to remember miners who had lost their lives due to accidents, or the 'dust'.[164]

The once commonplace sights of the coal industry in the Sirhowy Valley and Abertysswg vanished as if a magician's wand had been waved. All the Tredegar Company collieries have been razed, and generally all the associated grounds and coal tips landscaped. Only photographs remain to convey some idea about the company's capital investment of billions of pounds, in today's value, in buildings having functional architecture, and structures, plant and equipment designed by engineers. Such investment, on the whole, gave steady employment for tens of thousands of workers and hundreds of officials, over many decades.

A legacy of the Tredegar Company's expansion was the birth and growth of a number of towns and villages in Gwent. Tredegar and Blackwood became towns of importance due to their local industries. The villages of Abertysswg, Markham, Oakdale and Wyllie owe their existence to coal mining. The strength of neighbourliness found within such communities today has rich roots due in part due to the camaraderie engendered by men pursuing a physically tough and potentially dangerous shift of work.

Maybe only railway enthusiasts have the knowledge to imagine the scale of the civil engineering and the money spent by railway companies to move Tredegar coal and iron rail. The railway on the west side of the Sirhowy Valley ceased operation in 1960 with an exception being a stage northwards from Wyllie to Penar Junction, which was closed in 1970 after Wyllie Colliery's closure. In 1979, the railway from Oakdale Halt to Markham was closed. With the end of coal traffic from Oakdale Colliery, the

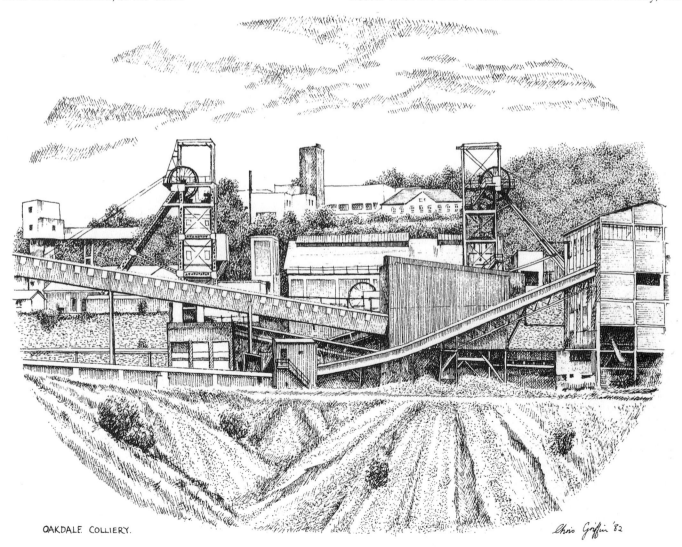

OAKDALE COLLIERY.

Chris Griffin '82

Chris Griffin's water colour presentation of this sketch provided for many former workers at the colliery a special momento of their former place of work.

Courtesy of the Artist

Penar branch days ended in 1989. A stage of the Penar branch was afterwards used to lay a road that has at its northern end the fine, Arup designed, cable stayed, Chartist Bridge, which was opened in 2005.

For motor car visitors to the valley, travelling up from the south, maybe it will be the Chartist sculpture on the eastern side of the Chartist Bridge that first captures interest. Caerphilly County Borough Council commissioned Sebastion Boyesen to design the sculpture that was unveiled in 2008. The sculpture represents a chartist and recalls the cohorts of Sirhowy Valley men who marched on Newport in November 1839. Perhaps the sculpture can also serve to recall that workers of the valley were drawn to radical political ideas in the hope that their realisation would better their lot in life.

Vitally, tribute has been made to colliery workers. A memorial for Oakdale Colliery's workers was erected to the north-east of the Chartist's Bridge aside 'Coal Yard Rise' road.[165] The design of the memorial incorporates three semi-circle structures to represent sheaves that once spun above the three shafts sunk at the colliery. The miners of McLaren Colliery are also recalled with a monument at Abertysswg erected by the 'Communities First Partnership' – a Welsh Assembly initiative, and unveiled in 2008.[166]

Equally notable at Abertysswg are buildings associated with the management and supervision of a colliery. McLaren House and McLaren Cottages stand as a statement of the accommodation for respectively a colliery manager and his officials. The Miners' Institute, McLaren Hotel and cottage hospital have all been razed.

In Blackwood stands a Miners' Institute with an impressive façade whereas Oakdale's Institute was removed to St. Fagans National History Museum. The institutes recall initiatives taken by colliery workers to provide education and recreational facilities that catered for their needs. Rebuilt, the Oakdale

Institute was opened in 1995 for the public to inspect by Neil Kinnock MP who had resigned as leader of the Labour Party three years earlier. In 1930, the Oakdale Colliery manager, David Evans, told HRH Prince Albert on an inspection of a room at the institute that: 'It's here in this room, that all the village's conspiracies are hatched.'[167] During its last years as an Oakdale building, the institute no longer served as it did in its early decades as the centre for entertainment, recreation, gossip and scheming. People sought out alternative venues to the institute to satisfy their needs.

Maybe Oakdale Hospital will survive as a village building, and so serve as a reminder of workers' initiatives that established hospital care with Tredegar Company support. The pioneering cottage hospital at Tredegar remains but no longer provides a medical service.

Perhaps some inkling about deep-mining can be obtained by standing by the side of the A4048 near the former site of Pochin Colliery.[168] The colliery's former surface is roughly level with the soles of a person's shoes. At around 500 feet above can be seen on the western hillside the Darren Dhu escarpment with its Rocking Stone. The depths of the shafts at Pochin Colliery were roughly two times the vertical drop from the escarpment to the road, with Oakdale Colliery's steam coal shafts being four times. A safe shaft journey by cage relied upon the strength and condition of a steel rope having a diameter of roughly the length of a thumb. The crush of rock strata below ground level has squeezed the sites of work at the coal-face into oblivion. However, a visit underground at Big Pit National Museum, Blaenafon, offers people a means to perceive why mothers once felt anxiety when their sons were away from home toiling at the coal-face.

An excursion north-east on the A4047 from Tredegar leads to a monument that celebrates the life of Aneurin Bevan.[169] A large, shaped, block of rock, with a plaque, is said to be placed on the

The landscaped site of Pochin Colliery taken from near the Rocking Stone, Darren Ddu, Sirhowy Valley.   *Photograph by writer in September 1989*

spot of bleak Waun y Pound where he burnt a copy of the *Western Mail* as a show of defiance against the newspaper's attack on the miners' leadership of the 1926 strike. The one time Ty Trist collier, chairman of Pochin Colliery lodge, holds an exclusive place in both the history of the Labour movement and in the House of Commons for his oratory and as the founder of the National Health Service. A statue of Aneurin Bevan in the prime shopping centre of Cardiff, Queen Street, presents him striding resolutely westwards. In the National Portrait Gallery, London, a bust of the Tredegar man's head stands on a plinth between portraits of Clem Atlee and Ernest Bevin. It is proposed that such an arrangement of art works can give the impression that these were the three major politicians in the 1945 Labour Government. Hopefully electors in Bevan's Ebbw Vale constituency can take kindly to a thought that the Waun y Pound monument sustains another memory: the many union meetings held by workers to debate taking action against the Tredegar Company, and later the National Coal Board, regarding matters of dispute.

Nothing remains of the Tredegar Ironworks, but at the heart of the town of Tredegar stands the sturdily built Bedwellty House.[170] The monolith of coal that was not shown at the 1851 Great Exhibition can be viewed in surrounding parkland. The house has connections with the management of the Tredegar Company since it served as Samuel Homfray Junior's residence, and for a period was used by the Tredegar Iron & Coal Company. In situ also is the meeting chamber of the extinct Tredegar Urban District Council where, as elected councillors, a few Tredegar Company officials and Labour Party representatives debated.

On a wall of a large room in Bedwellty House hangs a portrait of Godfrey Charles Morgan, 1st Viscount Tredegar. Perhaps local people have reached some accommodation with a man who earned great wealth from the Tredegar Estate. A bust of Aneurin Bevan is also placed in the room. References to Bevan's scorn for the Lords of Tredegar are perpetuated.[171] However, the constructive contributions that Godfrey Morgan and his predecessors made to encourage the industrialization of the Sirhowy Valley and Cwm Tysswg cannot be denied.

This work offers a case for linking Bedwellty House with two other great houses of Wales. The link with Morgans' home of Tredegar House is a firm one. The tie with the privately owned Bodnant House, near Conwy, is due to it having been the home to former Tredegar Iron & Coal Company chairmen, Henry Pochin and two Lords Aberconway. A 'man of ability', the 1st Lord Aberconway led the Tredegar Company with considerable effect. Due to the vision of Henry Pochin and his inheritors the 'delights' of Bodnant Garden are open to the public.[172] The garden was nurtured, if only to a tiny extent, by family income from Tredegar Company dividends.

A short walk up into town from the gates to Bedwellty House stands the Victorian clock tower of Tredegar. The clock tower, for as long as it survives weathering and structural deterioration, can serve as a totem for the Industrial Revolution. For around 150 years, entrepreneurship demonstrated by the Tredegar Company in its various forms, considerable capital investment, management skill, technical knowhow, and human labour united to make wealth from supplying steam coal and iron rail to the world.

This view taken towards the end of the working life of Markham Colliery. It makes an interesting contrast with that reproduced on page 6.
courtesy Bob Marrows

NOTES

1 General Reade Godwin-Austen was commissioned as a South Wales Borderers officer in 1909.

2 AJE, p.19.

3 'Coal Shortage Cuts Trains', WM, 4 Jan 1947, p.1.

4 'Big Coal Exports', WM, 11 Jan 1947, p.1.

5 Appendix I, SWC-RegRpt, pp.173-174.

6 Table LV, SWC-RegRpt, p.99.

7 South Wales Miners Library Interview with Phil Weekes, 26 Aug 1981. From Hywel Francis and Kim Howells, 'The Politics of Coal in South Wales 1945-48', Llafur, vol.3, no.3, (1988), p.80.

8 Colliery Year Book & Coal Trades Directory. Years 1940 and 1947.

9 Letter, Arthur Lewis OBE to Writer, 11 April 2016.

10 Details regarding the formation of No. 6 Area: AJE, p.19.

11 The two main components of an A-B Meco-Moore machine, a cutter and loader, were coupled so that the machine could ride floor undulations. Two 60 h.p. electric motors powered the cutter.

12 South Wales Miners Library Interview with Phil Weekes, 26 Aug 1981, op. cit., p.80.

13 Interview with Phil Weekes (South Wales Miners Library), pp.19-20. Extract from Ina Zweiniger-Bargielowska, 'Colliery Managers and Nationalisation: The Experience in South Wales', Business History, Vol. 34, No. 4, (1992), pp.69-70.

14 Ina Zweiniger-Bargielowska, 'Colliery Managers and Nationalisation: The Experience in South Wales', op. cit., p.70.

15 'Statistical Digest for South Western Division National Coal Board', Reference STAT/K/7, 20 Dec 1948. Section C, p.3, presented the absenteeism and reported figures for 'week ended' 27 March, 26 June, 25 Sept, and 25 Sept. Absenteeism for 1944: SWC-RegRpt, table XLVI, p.86.

16 'Manpower (on Colliery Books), Pithead Output and Pithead O. M. S. [Output per Manshift] Each NCB Mine', Reference STAT/K/7/App.II, 11 Dec 1948, pages not numbered. South Western Division, National Coal Board. Data for McLaren Colliery Area 5 and other collieries Area 6.

17 Trevor Boyns-Gwent Coal Industry, p.51. From NCB Report and Accounts, 1949, vol.1, p.36.

18 Horse feed attracted rats. Thus, 'a rat catcher' had been 'employed who killed 100 rats per shift' yet 'it was still a losing battle'. BIDCO, p.23.

19 Trevor Boyns-Gwent Coal Industry, p.51. From NCB Report and Accounts, 1950, vol.1, p.71.

20 The adoption of Disc Shearers was due to their 'ease of turn around at Mechanised face ends'. On colliery surfaces, Shunt Backs, and/or Turntables were also introduced. After their period of service with the mechanisation team both Arthur Lewis and Keith Jones were appointed colliery under-managers. Arthur Lewis was made under-manager at Graig Fawr, which was the household pit for Celynen North Colliery. He later served from 1966 to 1973 as manager of Six Bells Colliery, situated south of the town of Abertillery. Keith Jones later became manager of Cynheidre Colliery, Gwendraeth Valley, Carmarthenshire, for a period. Letter, Arthur Lewis OBE to Writer, 11 April 2016.

21 BIDCO, p.23.

22 AJE, p.20. also Collieries of Wales: Engineering and Architecture, op. cit., p.115, and 'Coal Preparation Plants – East Wales Area', NCB, 'A. J. Edwards' signature dated 'June 1972'.

23 AJE, p.15.

24 AJE, p.20.

25 AJE, pp.17-18.

26 Jack Edwards's notes indicate that he was involved with the introduction of electric winders at Llanhilleth Colliery, one in 1956 and the other in 1963, and Six Bells Colliery No. 4 and No. 5 pits in 1959 and 1957 respectively. AJE, p.21.

27 ME, 11 Jan 1958, p. 1 & p.11.

28 'South Wales Coalfield Pit Closures: Post-Nationalisation (1947)'. (British Coal, 1986 with an update to 25 May 1990). Trevor Boyns-Gwent Coal Industry, table 3.11, p.50.

29 The Writer's father, William (Bill) Shore, as an engineer at McLaren Colliery was among men transferred to Ogilvie Colliery. Living at New Tredegar, he used local bus transport.

30 Guide to the Coalfields 1959. (The Colliery Guardian), p.415.

31 The collieries were: in the Forest of Dean Coalfield, Cinderford and Eastern United; Mount Colliery, Ammanford; Steer Colliery, Gwaun Cae Gurwen; Pentre (including Aberbaiden), Kenfig Hill; and Tydraw, Treherbert. 'Wreath of Red Roses foe Shut Down Pit', and regarding Ty Trist 'New Job Offers Anger 50 Men'. WM, 31 Jan 1959, p.7.

32 Colliery Year Book & Coal Trades Directory 1959, 1960-1962 (as "spare manager" Ty Trist).

33 'South Wales Coalfield Pit Closures: Post-Nationalisation (1947)'. (British Coal, 1986 with an update to 25 May 1990).

34 Regarding 'reason for closures' of McLaren and Ty Trist: Trevor Boyns-Gwent Coal Industry, table 3.11, p.50.

35 Centenary Review. (WM, 1 May 1969), p. 18.

36 Centenary Review. (WM, 1 May 1969), p. 18.

37 Centenary Review. (WM, 1 May 1969), p. 8.

38 During the 1950s 'uneconomic' was cited as the reason for the closure of half of around 16 collieries closed in Monmouthshire. Trevor Boyns-Gwent Coal Industry, table 3.11, p.50.

39 Guide to the Coalfields 1959. (The Colliery Guardian), p.415.

40 Letter, Arthur Lewis OBE to Writer, 11 April 2016.

41 Letter, Des Caddy to Writer, 10 April 2016.

42 Ina Zweiniger-Bargielowska, 'South Wales miners' attitudes towards nationalization: an essay in oral history ', Llafur, vol.6, no.3, (1992), pp.77-78, and p.80 for details about Dan Canniff.

43 'Oakdale Colliery 12th August, 1957'. A page only that was probably the first page of the electrification project's submission. From the papers of A. J. Edwards in the keeping of the writer.

44 Also delivered as part of the project were: an extension to the pithead baths (1963), and boiler plant and two chimney stacks were demolished (1965). AJE, p.21.

45 Ferdynand Zweig, The British Worker. (Pelican, 1952), p.34.

46 'Debate on the Address', House of Commons Debates, Vol. 472, cc676-678, 10 March 1950.

47 'Colliery Spoil Heaps', House of Commons Debates, Vol. 570, cc1566, 23 May 1957.

48 G. D. H. Cole et al., Plan for Britain. (George Routledge, 1943), p.34.

49 See earlier: 31 March 1923 the Tredegar Company employed 11,731 people in total. The calculation of decline for Sirhowy Valley collieries was made after deducting an estimated 1,400 McLaren Colliery people from the 11,731. The nearest employment figure found for the year 1922 for McLaren Colliery, 1419, was for 1923.

50 Guide to the Coalfields 1959. (The Colliery Guardian), p.406 and p.408.

51 Trevor Boyns-Gwent Coal Industry, p.52.

52 Oakdale Colliery: 'Profit and Loss Account- Collieries. (National Coal Board, South Western Division, various years from 1947 to 1966/67).

53 'Coal Industry', House of Commons Debates, Vol. 609, cc143, 23 July 1959.

54 Lord Robens of Woldingham (1910-99). Lord Robens, Ten Year Stint. (Cassell, 1972), p.124.

55 Lord Robens, Ten Year Stint. (Cassell, 1972), pp.58-59.

56 Ray Lawrence, op. cit., p.73.

57 Email, Philip Hayman to Writer, 27 Nov 2011. Prof. Philip Hayman, with international knowledge and experience of the steel industry during a forty year career, was formerly head of the Heavy Industry group WS Atkins plc.

58 Letter, Arthur Lewis OBE to Writer, 11 April 2016.

59 'Wales and Monmouthshire (Report)', House of Commons Debates, Vol. 664, cc864, 2 Aug 1962.

60 For example see SWA, 23 July 1964, p.9.

61 'South Wales Coalfield Pit Closures: Post-Nationalisation (1947)'. (British Coal, 1986 with an update to 25 May 1990).

62 Colliery Year Book & Coal Trades Directory 1964.

63 SWA, 23 Feb 1968, p.5.

64 'Lord Tredegar's Sister', WM, 20 May 1912, p.3. Morgan Lindsay (1857-1935) served as an officer with the Corps of the Royal Engineers. He played in the first FA Cup in 1872 for the Corps who lost to the Wanderers. He also played cricket for Glamorgan County Cricket Club, and trained winners of the Welsh Grand National in 1926 and 1928. Press release, ECB, 9 July 2014. A team of NCB staff used the field to play home fixtures in the Caerphilly & District 20 over competition. Letter, Roy Pickford to Writer, 23 Jan 2016.

65 Lord Robens, op. cit., pp.124-125.

66 Lord Robens, op. cit., pp.19-33.

67 Letter, Arthur Lewis OBE to Writer, 11 April 2016.

68 Concerning profit reporting, Robens was imputed to have shown a 'talent for creative accounting, relying on the concept of "operating profit", under which pits were shown to be making money so long as the capital investment was discounted'. Obit. Lord Robens of Woldingham, *The Daily Telegraph*, 28 June 1990, p.23.

69 'Gwent Collieries top NCB List of Profit Makers', SWA, 7 March 1968, p.1.

70 'Wyllie Colliery May Close', SWA, 9 Jan 1968, p.1.

71 For an explanation of the Colliery Review Procedure see Ian MacGregor with Rodney Tyler, *The Enemies Within: the Story of the Miners' Strike, 1984-5.* (Collins, 1986), pp.292-293.

72 Obit. Lord Robens of Woldingham, *The Daily Telegraph*, 28 June 1990, p.23.

73 Lord Robens, op. cit., pp.166-171, with also regard to nuclear power see pp.178-205.

74 'South Wales Coalfield Pit Closures: Post-Nationalisation (1947)'. (British Coal, 1986 with an update to 25 May 1990). Regarding H. Beddoe Colliery Year Book & Coal Trades Directory 1968.

75 See Leslie M. Shore, op. cit., pp.178-179.

76 Sirhowy Valley collieries closed earlier by the NCB were: Nine Mile Point (25 July 1964), and Risca (9 July 1966). 'South Wales Coalfield Pit Closures: Post-Nationalisation (1947)'. (British Coal, 1986 with an update to 25 May 1990).

77 AJE, p.20.

78 'Coal Preparation Plants – East Wales Area', NCB, with 'A. J. Edwards' signature dated 'June 1972'.

79 For the year 1970/71, the NCB's national average output per manshift (cwts) was 44.2. See 'Statistical Summary 1960-1970/71', Lord Robens, op. cit., p.325.

80 The Abertillery Colliery reported is believed to have been Abertillery New Mine where 1,300 miners were employed. 'Gwent Pits Leading Productivity Drive', SWA, 25 March 1970, p.1.

81 'South Wales Coalfield Pit Closures: Post-Nationalisation (1947)'. (British Coal, 1986 with an update to 25 May 1990).

82 SWA, 4 Jan 1971, p.1.

83 SWA, 15 Jan 1971, p.1.

84 SWA, 7 Feb 1972.

85 SWA, 18 Feb 1972, p.1.

86 'Statistical Digest for South Western Division National Coal Board', Reference STAT/K/7, 20 Dec 1948. Summation of Area's 1 to 6 'total manpower'.

87 Harold Finch was knighted in 1976 for services to politics and the trade union movement. He served as Under-Secretary of State at the Welsh Office between 1964 and 1966. Fellow MPs recognised him as 'a great expert on [industrial injury] compensation', John Morris, Fifty Years in Politics. (University of Wales Press, 2011), p.59. He died in 1979, and a monument to his memory was erected in Pontllanfraith a number of years later.

88 Harold Finch, op. cit., pp.32-33.

89 Trevor Boyns-Gwent Coal Industry, p.52.

90 SWA, 16 Jan 1974, p.3.

91 'Debate on the Address', *House of Commons Debates*, Vol. 870, cc 52, 12 March 1974.

92 'The Divided nation', *House of Commons Debates*, Vol. 867, cc 1208, 21 Jan 1974.

93 The other collieries closed in 1975 were: Beynon Colliery, Blaina; and Glyntillery Colliery (also known as Hafodrynys Colliery), that lay east of Crumlin. 'South Wales Coalfield Pit Closures: Post-Nationalisation (1947)'. (British Coal, 1986 with an update to 25 May 1990).

94 Trevor Boyns-Gwent Coal Industry, p.52.

95 AJE, p.23.

96 Albert John (Jack) Edwards died in 2008 aged 87. The Writer dedicated *Vickers' Master Shipbuilder: Sir Leonard Redshaw*, (Black Dwarf, 2011), to his memory.

97 Roy Pickford (1933 – 2016), NCB engineer based at 'Ystrad Fawr', became a pumpsman in the 1984 strike. 'Nothing happened during my 11 months. Never be a pumpsman – boring'. Letter, Roy Pickford to Writer, 23 Jan 2016.

98 Francis Beckett and David Hencke, *Marching to the Fault Line: The 1984 Miners' Strike and the Death of Industrial Britain.* (Constable, 2009), p.1.

99 Ian MacGregor with Rodney Tyler, *The Enemies Within: the Story of the Miners' Strike, 1984-5.* (Collins, 1986), pp.133-135.

100 'How the Tories executed long-term campaign to curb unions', *The Times*, 4 March 1985, p.2.

101 Lord Robens, chairman of the NCB from 1960 to 1971, claimed before the decision was made in 1968 by Roy Mason, Labour Government Minister of Power, to build a nuclear power station at Hartlepool that 10,000 mining jobs 'would be lost in Durham [Coalfield]'. Lord Robens, *Ten Year Stint.* (Cassell, 1972), p.198.

102 Ian MacGregor, op. cit., p.154.

103 Ian MacGregor, op. cit., p.164.

104 Hywel Francis, *History on our Side.* (ICONAU, 2009), p.24

105 'Gwent Miners Reject Strike', SWA, 12 March 1984, p.1.

106 'Gwent Miners' Revolt Over', SWA, 13 March 1984, p.1.

107 Gareth Salway, *Penallta: A Pit and its People.* (Old Bakehouse Productions, 2008), p.64.

108 'Oakdale Miners Picket', SWA, 21 March 1984, p.1.

109 'Night Ride with Gwent's flying pickets', SWA, 26 March 1984, p.6.

110 'Getting back to basics', SWA, 27 April 1984, p.14.

111 'Miners' leaders slam hypocrisy', SWA, 17 April 1984, p.1.

112 'Events that led NUM from strike decision to vote', *The Times*, 4 March 1985, p.2.

113 'Pit Safety hit in food levy', SWA, 3 Sept 1984, p.1.

114 'Urgent meeting held on Pit Safety'. SWA, 4 Sept 1984, p.1.

115 'Pits in Danger – it's Official', SWA, 29 September 1984, p.1.

116 Roy Evans obit., *The Daily Telegraph*, 20 Dec 2015, p.35.

117 'Battle Scenes at Gwent Pit'. SWA, 13 Nov 1984, p.1.

118 'Police Injured in Picket Clash'. SWA, 28 Nov 1984, p.1.

119 'Taxi Driver Killed on Pit Run'. SWA, 30 Nov 1984, p.1.

120 Francis Beckett and David Hencke, op. cit., p.134.

121 Francis Beckett and David Hencke, op. cit., pp.166-167.

122 'Kinnock Quizzed by Gwent Miners', SWA, 7 Dec 1984, p.1.

123 'Kinnock Keeps Picket Line Pledge', SWA, 3 Jan 1985, p.1.

124 'Miners at Gwent Pit Want to End Strike', SWA, 6 Dec 1985, p.1.

125 'NUM Official Breaks Strike', SWA, 4 Jan 1985, p.1.

126 'Switch in the campaign', SWA, 4 March 1985, p.1.

127 Ian MacGregor, op. cit., p.164.

128 Ian MacGregor, op. cit., p.357.

129 'Switch in the campaign', SWA, 4 March 1985, p.1.

130 'Strike ends but Scargill defiant', *The Times*, 4 March 1985, p.1.

131 'Plea for calm on eve of pits return', SWA, 4 March 1985, p.3.

132 Concerning bitterness towards 'scabs' and the police see 'Strike legacy of bitterness', SWA, 6 Sept 1985, p.3.

133 Charles Moore, *Margaret Thatcher, The Authorized Biography, Vol. 2: Everything She Wants.* (Allen Lane, 2015), pp.136-182.

134 Charles Moore, op. cit., pp.162-164.

135 Prior to 2009 attempts made by Francis Beckett to interview Arthur Scargill were 'turned' down. Francis Beckett and David Hencke, op. cit., ppxii-p.xiii.

136 'Strike ends but Scargill defiant', The Times, 4 March 1985, p.2.

137 The other Gwent collieries closed in 1985 were: Blaenserchan, near Pontypool; Bedwas, near Caerphilly; and Abertillery (Rose Heyworth) Colliery. 'South Wales Coalfield Pit Closures: Post-Nationalisation (1947)'. (British Coal, 1986, updated 25 May 1990).

138 Trevor Boyns-Gwent *Coal Industry*, table 3.12, p.55. The table was compiled from: Andrew Glyn, 'The economic case against pit closures', in David Cooper and Trevor Hopper (eds.), *Debating Coal Closures: Economic Calculation in the Coal Dispute, 1984-85.* (Cambridge, 1988), pp.57-94, and pp.80-87.

139 'Welsh pride shuts pit', SWA, 6 Sept 1985, p.1.

140 Trevor Boyns-Gwent Coal Industry, table 3.12, p.55.

141 'Miners panic at pit closure', SWA, 8 Oct 1985, p.3.

142 'Crisis talks as coalfield panic grows', SWA, 10 Oct 1985, p.1, and also SWA, 11 Oct 1985, p.1.

143 *Colliery Year Book & Coal Trades Directory 1984*, and *1986*.

144 Trevor Boyns-Gwent Coal Industry, table 3.12, p.55.

145 Ray Lawrence, op. cit., p.66.

146 Regarding number of miners: 'S. Wales press for pit return', SWA, 28 Feb 1985, p.1.

147 Ewart Smith, *Blackwood Yesterday Book 4*. (Old Bakehouse Publications, 2001), p.29.

148 'New production targets – Oakdale ', SWA, 5 Sept 1985, p.3.

149 'Coal board boss praises miners at record pit', SWA, 20 Sept 1985, p.3.

150 Letter, Des Caddy to Writer, 10 April 2016.

151 Letter, Des Caddy to Writer, 10 April 2016.

152 'Bitterness at doomed collieries', SWA, 25 Aug 1989, p.3.

153 'Chaos at closed pit', SWA, 25 Aug 1989, p.1.

154 'Bitterness at doomed collieries', SWA, 25 Aug 1989, p.3.

155 Unless otherwise referenced the main source for what follows: Mike Parker, Industry Reporter, 'Working pit becomes a 'ghost' —in just 2 days', SWA, 26 Sept 1989, p.2.

156 Section 1 para 4c, *Coal Industry Nationalisation Act, 1946*, p.2C1.

157 Lord Robens, op. cit., p.287.

158 After retirement, Philip Weekes became the chairman of a coal company formed due to a worker buy-out of Tower Colliery sited at the head of the Cynon Valley. On 25th January, 2008, Tower Colliery was closed and can be said to represent the death of South Wales's once great industry. Philip Weekes CBE (1993), OBE (1977) died June 2003.

159 William Cleaver (1921-2003) won 14 caps for Wales as outside-half and full back between 1947 and 1950 and toured Australia and New Zealand with the 1950 British Isles tourists – today called the British and Irish Lions. In 1950 he retired from rugby to focus upon his mining career. His first colliery manager appointment was at Celynen North Colliery He retired as Deputy Director, South Wales Area in 1985. Obit, *Independent*, 5 Oct 2003. In terms of international rugby and the colliery, Percy Jones, in 1937 colliery surface foreman, was awarded 8 caps by Wales between 1912-14 and was a member of a pack of forwards called the 'Terrible Eight'.

160 John Fox enjoyed poetry and could recite many poems from memory. He would give recitations at colliery meetings that sometimes amazed his listeners. Telephone Conversation, Arthur Lewis OBE and Writer, 21 Feb 2016.

161 Compiled in February 2015 by Robert Protheroe Jones, Amgueddfa Cymru – National Museum of Wales, from a search of annuals of the *Colliery Year Book and Coal Trades Directory*. Also Letter, Des Caddy to Writer, 10 April 2016.

162 Letter, Des Caddy to Writer, 10 April 2016.

163 The sinking of Tredegar's Bryn Bach Pit in 1818 could be viewed as a humble predecessor.

164 The Oakdale Colliery fatalities: nominated by Gwyneth Gibbons, Tongwynlais, were David Morgan, killed in 1946; Jocky Simms, 1929; and Joseph Webb, 1929. Rufus Seer, killed at the colliery in 1944 was nominated by his widow Mrs M, Vranch, Blackwood. Concerning Leslie James's fatality at Markham Colliery its year was omitted but his name had been nominated by his sister, Ann Morgan, Blackwood. Regarding a fatality at Pochin Colliery, nominated by R. P. Muir, Ely, Cardiff, was James Griffiths of Victoria Tce., Georgetown, Tredegar, who died in 1929. 'Heroes of Coal', a 'Roll of Honour' supplement, *South Wale Echo*, 27 March 1995, p.27, p.30, & p.31.

165 OS Ref No. ST 184 988.

166 The memorial cost £57,000 and was unveiled Friday, 27th June, 2008. OS Ref No. SO 132054.

167 'Prince Albert with a Pick', SWWA, 24 Jan 1920.

168 OS Ref No. S0 163 044.

169 OS Ref No. S0 152 106.

170 Some features of the Sirhowy Ironworks have survived.

171 For example see Francis Beckett and David Hencke, op. cit., pp.4-5. Perhaps Beckett and Hencke are not at fault for the error that associated the 'mine owner' rather than the landowner with the sale of a house to the Bevans.

172 *2016 Handbook*. (National Trust), pp.360-361.

Celynen North Colliery's redundant sheaves.

Photograph by writer October 1995

BEDWELLTY COLLIERIES. Nr TREDEGAR. 10

The engineering of Bedwellty Pits at the start of the 1850s was a notable milestone in the history of deep mine collieries that thrived later in the Sirhowy Valley under the control of the Tredegar Iron & Coal Company. As a capital investment the colliery announced that that the Tredegar Iron Company was intent upon supplying steam coal in bulk to power merchant ships, which was a new market. Only during the 1840s did the British shipbuilding industry expand the construction of steam powered ships.

Pope/Parkhouse Archive

Appendix One
A SELECT BIBLIOGRAPHY

The newspaper and journal sources included:
Cardiff Times; The Colliery Guardian; The Iron & Coal Trades Review; The Merthyr Express; Monmouth Guardian (Rhymney) and Bargoed and Caerphilly Observer; Monmouthshire Merlin; Llais Llafur; South Wales Argus; South Wales Weekly Argus; The Times; Western Mail; The Journal of the Iron and Steel Institute, Proceedings; Railway Archive (Lightmoor Press), *South Wales Institute of Engineers; Transactions – Institution of Mining Engineers.*

Unpublished sources:
'Background Information to the Development of the Colliery [Oakdale]' (1960s)
George Greeve, 'McLaren Colliery Explosion' (circa 1960)
Fred Hopkins, *Sixty Years at Oakdale Colliery*
The papers of A. J. Edwards: File 82: Electric Winders No. 6 Area. (NCB); 'South Wales Area (Eastern), Chart Showing Shaft Capacities'. (NCB); Winding Engine Data-A. J. Edwards. (NCB); 'Coal Preparation Plants - East Wales Area', (NCB); Folio of Technical Information – Oakdale and Wyllie Collierie, compiled by Jack Edwards circa 1946
Leslie M. Shore, *A South Wales Coalfield Engineer: Albert John 'Jack' Edwards (1920-2008).* 2015

Published papers and reports:
M. Atkinson and T. Boyns, 'Haematite Mining in Glamorgan in the Nineteenth Century', *Glamorgan Historian*, Vol. 12 (1981)
Trevor Boyns, 'Growth in the Coal Industry: the Cases of Powell Duffryn and the Ocean Coal Company', ed. Colin Baber and L. J. Williams, *Modern South Wales: Essays in Economic History.* (University of Wales Press, 1986)
Trevor Boyns, 'Of Machines and Men in the 1920s', *Llafur*, Vol. 5, No. 2, (1989)
M. J. Dowden, 'Land and Industry: Sir Charles Morgan, Samuel Homfray and the Tredegar Lease of 1800', *Cylchgrawn Llyfrgell Genedlaethol The National Library of Wales Journal*, Vol. XXVII (1993)
Hywel Francis and Kim Howells, 'The Politics of Coal in South Wales 1945-48', *Llafur*, Vol. 3, No. 3, (1988)
John B. Hilling, 'The Development of Tredegar 1800-1820', *Gwent Local History, Journal of the Gwent Local History Council*, No. 94 (2003)
John B. Hilling, 'The Migration of People into Tredegar during the Nineteenth Century', *Gwent Local History, Journal of the Gwent Local History Council*, No. 100 (2005)
Reports to His Majesty's Secretary of State for the Home Department on the Circumstances attending an Explosion which occurred at McLaren Colliery (No. 1 Pit), Abertysswg, on the 3rd September, 1902
Reports of Proceedings, Annual Ordinary General Meeting, Tredegar Iron & Coal Company
'Some South Wales Collieries: No. 2 The Tredegar Iron and Coal Company Limited', *The Welsh Coalfields*, reprinted from 'The Syren and Shipping' (1906)
Tredegar UDC Minute Books (Gwent Archives)
G. W. J. Lowering, 'Herbert Francis Mackworth and the Coal Industry in Monmouthshire', *Gwent Local History, Journal of the Gwent Local History Council*, No. 80 (1996)
W. D. Rubenstein, 'The Anti-Jewish Riots of 1911 in South Wales: a Re-examination', *Welsh History Review*, Vol. 18, 2 (1997)
Ina Zweiniger-Bargielowska, 'Colliery Managers and Nationalisation: The Experience in South Wales', *Business History*, Vol. 34, No. 4, (1992)
Ina Zweiniger-Bargielowska, 'South Wales miners' attitudes towards nationalization: an essay in oral history ', *Llafur*, Vol. 6, No. 3, (1992)

Published works included:
Lord Aberconway, *The Basic Industries of Great Britain.* (Ernest Benn, 1927)
R. Page Arnot, *The Miners: A History of the Miners' Federation of Great Britain 1889-1910.* (George Allen & Unwin, 1949)
Michael Atkinson and Colin Baber, *The Growth and Decline of the South Wales Iron Industry 1760-1880.* (University of Wales, 1987)
Trevor Boyns, 'McLaren, Charles Benjamin Bright, first Baron Aberconway', *The Oxford Dictionary of National Biography.*
K. C. Barraclough, *Steelmaking: 1850-1900.* (The Institute of Metals, 1990)
D. S. M. Barrie, *A Regional History of the Railways of Britain, 12: South Wales.* (Inverness, 1994)
Francis Beckett and David Hencke, *Marching to the Fault Line: The 1984 Miners' Strike and the Death of Industrial Britain.* (Constable, 2009)
Aneurin Bevan, *In Place of Fear.* (1952)
Trevor Boyns, 'Communications and Commerce', in *The Gwent County History*, Vol. 4, *Industrial Monmouthshire, 1870-1914*, ed. Chris Williams, Ralph A. Griffiths, and Sian Rhiannon Williams. (University of Wales Press, 2011)
Trevor Boyns, 'The Coal Industry', in The *Gwent County History, The Twentieth Century, Vol. 5*, ed. Chris Williams, Andy Croll, and Ralph A. Griffiths. (University of Wales Press, 2013)
J. C. Carr and W. Taplin, *History of the British Steel Industry.* (Basil Blackwell, 1962)
Coal Industry Nationalisation Act, 1946
G. D. H. Cole *et al., Plan for Britain.* (George Routledge, 1943)
Colliery Year Book & Coal Trades Directory
R. A. Cooke, *Western Valleys.* (Black Dwarf Lightmoor)
A. J. Cronin, *Adventures in Two Worlds.* (1953)
W. G. Dalziel, *Records of the Several Coal Owner's Association of South Wales, 1864 to 1895*
E. E. Edwards, *Echoes of Rhymney.* (Starling Press, 1974)
John Evans, 'Early Industrial Development', in *The Gwent County History, Vol. 3, The Making of Monmouthshire, 1736-1780*, ed. Madeleine Gray and Prys Morgan. (University of Wales Press, 2009)
The Efficient Use of Fuel. (HMSO, 1944)
David Freeman, *Tredegar House.* (Newport Borough Council, 1989)
Michael Foot, *Aneurin Bevan.* (1997, Abridged edition, Victor Gollancz)
Geological Excursions in South Wales & the Forest of Dean, Edited by Douglas A. Basset & Michael G. Bassett. (Geologists' Association South Wales Group, 1971)
Guide to the Coalfields 1959. (Colliery Guardian)
Harold Finch, *Memoirs of a Bedwellty MP.* (1979)
Arthur Gray-Jones, *A History of Ebbw Vale.* (Gwent Count Council, 1970)
Roy Gregory, *The Miners and British Politics 1906-1914.* (Oxford University Press, 1968)
James Griffiths, *Pages From Memory.* (Dent, 1969)
G. M. Harvey, *Colliery Electrical Engineering.* (Sir Isaac Pitman & Sons, 1924)
House of Commons Debates
Stephen Hughes *et al., Collieries of Wales: Engineering and Architecture.* (Royal Commission on the Ancient and Historical Monuments of Wales)
Laurence Ince, *The South Wales Iron Industry 1750-1885.* (Ferric, 1993)
Bill Jones, 'The Coal Industry', in *The Gwent County History, Vol.4, Industrial Monmouthshire, 1870-1914*, ed. Chris Williams, Ralph A. Griffiths, and Sian Rhiannon Williams. (University of Wales Press, 2011)

Edgar Jones, *A History of GKN Volume One: Innovation & Enterprise 1759-1918.* (Macmillan, 1987)

Neville Penry Thomas, *A History of British Politics from the Year 1900.* (Herbert Jenkins, 1956)

Oliver Jones, *The Early Days of Sirhowy and Tredegar.* (Tredegar Historical Society, 1969)

R. W. Kidner, *The Rhymney Railway.* (Oakwood Press, 1995)

Jeremy K. Knight, *Blaenavon Ironworks.* (Cadw, Revised edition 1992)

Ray Lawrence, *The Coal Workings of the Caerphilly County Area*

John Lloyd, *Early History of the Old South Wales Iron Work 1760-1840.* (1906)

Ian MacGregor with Rodney Tyler, *The Enemies Within: the Story of the Miners' Strike, 1984-5.* (Collins, 1986)

A. K. McCosh, *The Case Against Nationalisation of the Coal Mines.* (Scottish Colliery Owners, 1944)

Violet Markham, *Friendship's Harvest.* (Max Reinhart, 1956)

Charles Moore, *Margaret Thatcher, The Authorized Biography, Vol. 2: Everything She Wants.* (Allen Lane, 2015)

J. H. Morris and L. J. Williams, *The South Wales Coal Industry 1841-1871.* (University of Wales Press, 1958)

Oakdale Colliery. (The Tredegar Iron & Coal Company, Limited, 1930)

Evan Powell, *History of Tredegar.*(1884)

Robert Protheroe-Jones, *Welsh Steel.* (Amgueddfeydd Ac Orielau Cenedlaethol Cymru, National Museum & Galleries of Wales, 1995)

Sir R. A. Redmayne, *The British Coal-Mining Industry During the War.* (Clarendon Press, 1923)

Lord Robens, *Ten Year Stint.* (Cassell, 1972)

Rayner Rosser, *Collieries of the Sirhowy Valley.* (Old Bakehouse Publications, 1996)

Rules and Regulations of The Tredegar Iron Company's Collieries and Mine Works. (1865)

Gareth Salway, *Penallta: A Pit and its People.* (Old Bakehouse Productions, 2008)

W. Scandrett, *Old Tredegar Vol. 1.* (Starling Press, 1990)

Leslie M. Shore, *Peerless Powell Duffryn of the South Wales Coalfield.* (Lightmoor, 2012)

Ewart Smith, *Blackwood Yesterday Book 1.* (Old Bakehouse Publications, 1991)

Ewart Smith, *Blackwood Yesterday Book 4.* (Old Bakehouse Publications, 2001)

The South Wales Coal Annual

William Smith, *The History of the Tredegar Mineral Estate.* (Park Mile, 2013)

South Wales Coalfield (Including Pembrokeshire) Regional Survey Report. (HMSO, 1946)

Barry Supple, *The History of the British Coal Industry Vol. 4: 1913-1946 The Political Economy of Decline.* (Clarendon Press, 1987)

W. W. Tasker, *Mid Valley Nostalgia: Hollybush, Markham Village, Argoed, Blackwood.* (D. Brown & Sons Limited, 1990)

Ralph Thomas, *Oakdale: The Model Village.* (1986, Village Publishing)

Steven Thompson, *Unemployment, Poverty, and Health in Interwar South Wales.* (University of Wales Press, 2006)

The Tredegar Iron and Coal Company Limited 1873-1923

Tredegar Iron & Coal Limited, Tredegar, Mon.: Catalogue of Steel Arches, Rails and Colliery Requisites. (Printed by *Western Mail & Echo*)

William Truran, *The Iron Manufacture of Great Britain.* (1855)

R. H. Walters, *The Economic and Business History of the South Wales Steam Coal Industry, 1840-1914,* (PhD thesis, Oxford University, 1975)

George Watkins, *Stationary Steam Engines of Great Britain, The National Photographic Collection, Volume 4: Wales, Cheshire & Shropshire.* (Landmark, 1993)

Charles Wilkins, *The South Wales Coalfield Coal Trade and its Allied Industries.* (1888)

Charles Wilkins, *The History of the Iron, Steel, Tinplate and other Trades of Wales.* (1903)

Chris Williams, *Capitalism, Community and Conflict.* (University of Wales Press, 1998)

The Whitehead Iron & Steel Company 50 Years of Progress. (Whitehead Iron & Steel Company, 1953)

Appendix Two
WEIGHTS & MEASURES

Imperial and metric units

Length
1 inch (in.) = 25.400 millimetres (mm)
12 inches = 1 foot (ft) = .305 metre (m)
3 feet = 1 yard = 0.914 metre
1,760 yards = 1 mile = 1.609 kilometre (km)

Liquid
1 gallon = 4.546 litre

Weight
1 ton = 20 hundred weight (cwt.) = 2,240 pounds (lb.) = 1,016 kilogram
1 Tonne (metric) = 2,205 pounds = 1,000 kilograms

Pressure
1 pound per square inch = 0.07 bar

Currency
1 Pound (£) = 20 shillings (s) = 240 pennies (d)
1 shilling = 5 new pence (post 1971)

INDEX

POCHIN COLLIERIES Nr.TREDEGAR. 3.

Although the operational life of Pochin Colliery at ninety years was greater than the Tredegar Iron & Coal Company's at seventy-four years the colliery's name recalled an eminent industrialist, Henry Davis Pochin (1824-1895). This founder director of the Tredegar Iron & Coal Company's lasting memorial is Bodant Garden, Tal-y-Cafn, near Colwyn Bay, Conwy.

Pope/Parkhouse Archive